INTRODUCTION TO
# MODERN BIOCHEMISTRY

# INTRODUCTION TO
# MODERN BIOCHEMISTRY

## ——SECOND EDITION——————

### by

## P. KARLSON, *1918 –*

*Institute of Physiological Chemistry*
*University of Marburg*
*Marburg/Lahn, Germany*

### translated by

## Charles H. Doering

*John Collins Warren Laboratories*
  *of the Huntington Memorial Hospital*
  *of Harvard University at the*
*Massachusetts General Hospital*
*Boston, Massachusetts*

## ACADEMIC PRESS
## New York and London

First published in the German language under the title
*Kurzes Lehrbuch der Biochemie für Mediziner und Naturwissenschaftler*
and copyrighted in 1964 by GEORG THIEME VERLAG,
Stuttgart, Germany

ACADEMIC PRESS INC.
111 Fifth Avenue, New York, New York 10003

*United Kingdom Edition published by*
ACADEMIC PRESS INC. (LONDON) LTD.
Berkeley Square House, London W.1

LIBRARY OF CONGRESS CARD NUMBER: 65–15772

PRINTED IN THE UNITED STATES OF AMERICA

# FOREWORD TO THE FIRST EDITION

Biochemistry is growing rapidly. No other branch of science has so deepened our grasp of fundamental life processes and so directly influenced the thinking and practice of physicians in recent decades. Its triumphal success with the chemistry of vitamins and hormones has been followed by an experimental attack on the constitution and mechanism of action of enzymes. Basic insight has been gained into the dynamic events of metabolism, so characteristic of every living cell. Understanding has also been gained regarding the production, conversion, and utilization of energy and of the ways in which cellular material is built up and broken down. We in our times have been permitted the first glimpses of the structure and mode of action of hereditary factors, which predetermine the biologic fate of cells.

This brief textbook of biochemistry by Peter Karlson, Professor of Physiological Chemistry at the University of Munich, attempts to organize the vast material according to the new viewpoints and with particular regard for current problems. For the students of medicine or natural science this textbook attempts to supplement the introductory courses in biochemistry and to close a gap existing in our biochemical literature. This book has evolved through our joint effort, over the years, to teach physiological chemistry, first in Tübingen, and now in Munich. I have the impression this book will fulfill its purpose, and with the author I hope that it may prove to arouse interest in the problems and importance of biochemistry and to motivate a deeper study of it.

ADOLF BUTENANDT

# PREFACE TO THE SECOND EDITION

Less than two years have elapsed since the first English edition was published. Evidently the volume has been favorably accepted. The second edition gives a welcome opportunity to eliminate some errors and to include in the English version the revisions made in the fourth German edition (1964). The chapter on nucleic acids has been largely reorganized; in addition, newer developments have been included wherever possible. It is hoped that this new edition will fulfill its purpose: to provide an understanding of the chemical phenomena of life.

*Marburg*                                                            PETER KARLSON

*January 1965*

# PREFACE TO THE FIRST EDITION

Modern biology has extended its analysis of life into molecular dimensions. In this region, the borderlines between the classical disciplines of morphology, physiology, and biochemistry are fading. Morphology is becoming the chemistry of structural elements—large molecules are now visible in the electron microscope; physiology is turning into the study of changes in the structural elements, which is also biochemistry; and "molecular biology," a new discipline, originates to a great extent in biochemistry.

There seemed to be a need for a concise book giving an introduction to biochemistry and a survey of the main facts and ideas. It is hoped that the American edition, translated from the third German edition (1962), will be favorably received and will fulfill its purpose, i.e., to provide a better understanding of the chemical background of biologic phenomena.

The material has been arranged according to didactic needs. Though many textbooks begin with carbohydrates, this seemed to be inappropriate, since the chemistry as well as the biochemistry of carbohydrates is rather complicated. Therefore we begin with simple compounds like amino acids (the introductory chapter on organic chemistry is mainly a short compendium of some relevant facts), and then turn to proteins and to enzyme proteins, leaving the carbohydrates for a later chapter. No distinction has been made between "descriptive biochemistry," the chemistry of natural products, and "dynamic biochemistry" or metabolism. On the contrary, in some chapters the chemical structures of the natural compounds have been deduced from the description of their biosyntheses.

In the selection of the material, biochemistry has been regarded as part of the science of life. Concepts of general importance, such as the generation and utilization of free energy, the role of genes in protein and enzyme synthesis, and the importance of the submicroscopic structure of the cell in biochemical reactions, have been emphasized in various places. Clinical problems have been treated only insofar as they have contributed to the knowledge of normal biochemistry; for a detailed discussion of pathologic biochemistry, the reader should refer to other textbooks.

It was impossible to include, in a short book, all the experimental proofs for the facts to be described. Also, no attempt was made to cover the methodology of biochemistry; only some newer methods have been mentioned, just to show, in a few examples, how the results have been obtained.

The numerous figures and formulas skillfully drawn by Josef Paland for the German edition are reproduced here also. My thanks are due to several colleagues for electron micrographs, to Dr. C. H. Doering for the translation of the text, and to Academic Press for the production of the volume.

*Munich*                                                    PETER KARLSON
*March 1963*

# CONTENTS

Foreword to the First Edition ................................................ v
Preface to the Second Edition.............................................. vii
Preface to the First Edition................................................ ix
Introduction.............................................................. xvii

## I

## Organic Chemistry and Biochemistry

1. Hydrocarbons as Parent Substances............................... 1
2. Functional Groups............................................... 4
3. Polymeric Compounds............................................ 13
4. Isomerisms..................................................... 13
5. Reactions with Biochemical Significance......................... 18
   Bibliography.................................................... 19

## II

## Amino Acids

1. Chemical Properties............................................ 20
2. Individual Amino Acids......................................... 24
3. Separation of Amino Acids...................................... 30
   Bibliography.................................................... 33

## III

## Peptides

1. Structure and Nomenclature..................................... 34
2. Determination of Amino Acid Sequence in Peptides............... 35
3. Naturally Occurring Peptides................................... 37
   Bibliography.................................................... 41

# IV

## Proteins

1. Structure of Proteins...................................................... 42
2. Primary Structure........................................................ 43
3. Secondary Structure...................................................... 45
4. Tertiary Structure and Denaturation...................................... 50
5. Molecular Weights of Proteins............................................ 54
6. Colloidal Nature of Proteins............................................. 56
7. Purification and Check of Purity......................................... 58
8. Classification of Globular Proteins...................................... 60
9. Plasma Proteins.......................................................... 61
   Bibliography............................................................. 67

# V

## Enzymes and Biocatalysis

1. Chemical Nature of Enzymes.............................................. 68
2. Chemical Equilibria and Chemical Energetics............................. 69
3. Catalysts and Enzymes................................................... 72
4. Dynamic Equilibrium and the Steady State............................... 73
5. Energetic Coupling and Energy-Rich Compounds........................... 74
6. Specificity of Enzyme Catalysis......................................... 77
7. Michaelis' Theory....................................................... 79
8. The Mechanism of Enzyme Catalysis....................................... 81
9. Conditions for Enzyme Activity.......................................... 84
10. Classification and Nomenclature of Enzymes............................. 85
    Bibliography............................................................ 89

# VI

## Coenzymes

1. Coenzymes and Prosthetic Groups......................................... 90
2. Coenzymes and Vitamins.................................................. 92
3. Structure and Classification of Coenzymes.............................. 92
4. Coenzymes of the Oxidoreductases....................................... 94
5. Group-Transferring Coenzymes........................................... 100
6. Coenzymes of Lyases, Isomerases, and Ligases.......................... 113
   Bibliography............................................................ 114

# VII

## Nucleic Acids and Protein Biosynthesis

1. Bases, Nucleosides, and Nucleotides............................................ 116
2. Biosynthesis and Degradation of Nucleotides................................... 119
3. Structure of Nucleic Acids..................................................... 123
4. Deoxyribonucleic Acid as Carrier of Genetic Information....................... 127
5. The Transfer of Information: Biosynthesis of DNA and RNA...................... 129
6. Protein Biosynthesis........................................................... 132
7. Mode of Action of Genes........................................................ 135
8. Biochemistry of Viruses........................................................ 138
9. Nucleic Acid-Cleaving Enzymes and Phosphatases................................ 142
   Bibliography................................................................... 145

# VIII

## Metabolism of Proteins

1. Proteolytic Enzymes............................................................ 146
2. Endopeptidases................................................................. 148
3. Exopeptidases and Dipeptidases................................................. 151
4. Outline of the Metabolism of Amino Acids....................................... 152
5. Decarboxylation of Amino Acids................................................. 154
6. Transamination................................................................. 155
7. Oxidative Deamination.......................................................... 156
8. Urea Cycle..................................................................... 157
9. Fate of the Carbon Skeleton of Amino Acids..................................... 159
10. Degradation to Activated Fatty Acids: Oxidative Decarboxylation................ 159
11. Metabolism of Aromatic Amino Acids............................................. 161
12. Amino Acids Supplying $C_1$ Fragments.......................................... 165
13. Ketoglutaric Acid or $C_4$-Dicarboxylic-Acid-Supplying Amino Acids............. 167
    Bibliography................................................................... 172

# IX

## Porphyrins and Hemins

1. Biosynthesis of the Porphyrin System .......................................... 173
2. Chemical Constitution of Heme.................................................. 178
3. Multiplicity of Porphyrin Catalysis............................................ 179
4. The Significance and Reactions of Blood Pigment................................ 180
5. Degradation of the Blood Pigment............................................... 182
6. Cytochromes, Catalases, and Peroxidases. Chlorophyll........................... 184
   Bibliography................................................................... 186

# X

## Biologic Oxidation—Metabolism of Oxygen

1. Combustion and Biologic Oxidation . . . . . 187
2. Oxidation as a Loss of Electrons . . . . . 188
3. The Redox Potential . . . . . 190
4. The Respiratory Chain . . . . . 192
5. The Electron-Transport Particles . . . . . 198
6. Oxidative Phosphorylation (Respiratory Chain Phosphorylation) . . . . . 199
7. Other Oxygen-Activating Enzymes . . . . . 201
   Bibliography . . . . . 204

# XI

## Carbon Dioxide Formation in the Citrate Cycle

1. Significance of the Citrate Cycle . . . . . 205
2. The Individual Steps . . . . . 207
3. Energy Yield of the Citrate Cycle . . . . . 209
4. Relations to Synthetic Tasks. Glyoxylate Cycle . . . . . 210
   Bibliography . . . . . 211

# XII

## Fats and Fat Metabolism

1. Chemical Composition of Fats . . . . . 212
2. Fats as Depot Material . . . . . 215
3. $\beta$-Oxidation of Fatty Acids . . . . . 216
4. Formation of Acetoacetate—"Ketogenesis" . . . . . 219
5. Metabolism of Branched-Chain Fatty Acids . . . . . 220
6. Biosynthesis of Fatty Acids . . . . . 222
   Bibliography . . . . . 224

# XIII

## Phosphatides, Cerebrosides, Gangliosides

1. Occurrence and Classification . . . . . 225
2. Glycerophosphatides . . . . . 226
3. Biosynthesis and Degradation of Glycerophosphatides . . . . . 229
4. Sphingolipids . . . . . 231
   Bibliography . . . . . 234

# XIV

## Isoprenoid Lipids: Steroids and Carotenoids

1. Biosynthesis of Cholesterol.................................................... 235
2. Nomenclature and Stereochemistry of the Steroids............................. 238
3. Sterols and Plant Steroids.................................................... 241
4. Vitamin D.................................................................... 242
5. Bile Acids................................................................... 244
6. Steroid Hormones............................................................ 244
7. Carotenoids.................................................................. 249
8. Vitamin A and Visual Purple.................................................. 251
9. Tocopherol, Phylloquinone, Ubiquinone, and Plastoquinone...................... 252
   Bibliography................................................................ 255

# XV

## Simple Sugars, Monosaccharides

1. Nomenclature and Definitions................................................. 256
2. Hemiacetal Formulas......................................................... 259
3. General Reactions of Monosaccharides........................................ 261
4. The Individual Sugars........................................................ 264
5. Interconversion of Sugars.................................................... 268
6. Glucose Oxidation Through the Pentose Phosphate Cycle........................ 271
7. Glycolysis and Alcoholic Fermentation........................................ 273
8. The Metabolism of Fructose.................................................. 279
9. Aerobic Carbohydrate Breakdown............................................. 280
10. Resynthesis of Glucose: Gluconeogenesis..................................... 281
   Bibliography................................................................ 283

# XVI

## Photosynthesis

1. Importance of Photosynthesis................................................. 284
2. Photophosphorylation........................................................ 285
3. Photolysis of Water.......................................................... 286
4. Binding of $CO_2$ and Reduction to Carbohydrate.............................. 288
5. Further Synthetic Activities of Plants........................................ 290
   Bibliography................................................................ 293

# XVII

## Glycosides, Oligosaccharides, Polysaccharides

1. The Glycoside Bond............................................................. 294
2. Disaccharides.................................................................. 296
3. Enzymic Cleavage of Oligosaccharides.......................................... 298
4. Biosynthesis of Glycosides and Oligosaccharides............................... 299
5. Polysaccharides: Homoglycanes................................................. 303
6. Enzymic Breakdown of Polysaccharides.......................................... 306
7. Mucopolysaccharides........................................................... 311
   Bibliography.................................................................. 314

# XVIII

## Correlations in Intermediary Metabolism

1. Metabolism of Carbohydrates................................................... 315
2. Metabolism of Fatty Acids.................................................... 317
3. Citrate Cycle and Respiratory Chain.......................................... 318
4. Metabolism of Proteins....................................................... 320
5. The Common Pool of Intermediary Metabolism................................... 321
   Bibliography.................................................................. 322

# XIX

## Topochemistry of the Cell

1. The Nucleus of the Cell....................................................... 323
2. The Endoplasmic Reticulum.................................................... 324
3. Mitochondria................................................................. 328
4. The Cytoplasm................................................................ 330
5. Significance of the Compartments............................................. 331
   Bibliography.................................................................. 331

# XX

## Hormones

1. Principle of Hormonal Regulation............................................. 332
2. Adrenocortical Hormones...................................................... 335
3. Gonadal Hormones............................................................. 338
4. Thyroid Hormones............................................................. 340
5. Hormones of the Adrenal Medulla.............................................. 343
6. The Hormone of the Pineal Gland.............................................. 344

7. The Parathyroid Hormone.... 344
8. The Pancreatic Hormones.... 345
9. Hypophyseal Hormones.... 346
10. Hormonal Regulation of Blood Glucose.... 350
11. Hormonal Control of the Menstrual Cycle.... 353
12. Tissue Hormones.... 355
13. Hormones of Invertebrates.... 357
14. Pheromones.... 358
15. Growth Substances of Plants.... 358
Bibliography.... 359

# XXI

## Mineral Metabolism

1. Water Balance.... 360
2. Water as Solvent.... 362
3. Active Transport.... 367
4. Acid-Base Equilibrium.... 368
5. Metabolism of Alkali and of Chloride.... 370
6. Calcium and Phosphate Metabolism.... 371
7. Iron and Zinc.... 372
Bibliography.... 373

# XXII

## Nutrition and Vitamins

1. Caloric Value and ATP Yield.... 374
2. Essential Food Components.... 376
3. Vitamins.... 377
4. Fat-Soluble Vitamins.... 378
5. Water-Soluble Vitamins.... 381
Bibliography.... 383

# XXIII

## Special Biochemical Functions of Certain Organs

1. The Digestive Tract.... 384
2. The Liver.... 385
3. Blood.... 386
4. Kidney and Urine.... 387
5. Other Excretion Products.... 389

6. Biochemistry of Muscles................................................. 390
7. Biochemistry of Nerve Conduction..................................... 393
8. Summary................................................................. 395
   Bibliography............................................................. 396


Appendix................................................................. 397

Index.................................................................... 403

# INTRODUCTION

Biochemistry is one of the life sciences. Its object is to study the phenomena of life by chemical methods.

The first requirement for this study is a knowledge of the chemical nature of cell components, an area commonly called "descriptive biochemistry"; it coincides in great part with the "chemistry of natural products." Organic chemistry nowadays is synonymous with the chemistry of carbon compounds, but in its beginning it was the chemistry of natural products; the purification and investigation of naturally occurring substances was its domain, whereas synthetic organic chemistry has developed since Wöhler's synthesis of urea, at first slowly, and then explosively, at times to the extent of repressing interest in natural products. In recent decades, interest has turned more and more toward high molecular weight natural products. The determination of the constitution of proteins and nucleic acids is at present the most important problem of descriptive biochemistry.

The pure description of chemical substances can, however, offer only a static picture, a snapshot of the living cell (or of a living organism), and cannot cope with the problem of investigating the *phenomena of life*. The fascinating dynamic activities of the living cell, its unceasing changes, are the proper characteristics of life, and the study of the chemical conversions constantly occurring there is the subject of "dynamic biochemistry." We know today that almost all substances built up by the cell are always in a state of turnover. Life is characterized by chemical motion, and what in the past appeared to be a static framework has now become part of its chemical activity.

Modern biochemistry, therefore, is primarily dynamic biochemistry. This includes first of all the various features of metabolism, namely, conversion and degradation of foodstuffs to gain chemical energy and to synthesize endogenous material. All these reactions are catalyzed by particular enzymes, whose study quite naturally occupies a large area in biochemistry.

The second aspect of dynamic biochemistry is chemical regulation. This may be achieved by certain metabolic products; often it is accomplished by special substances called hormones which are produced in endocrine glands.

Third, dynamic biochemistry is concerned with all those chemical processes that take place on the structural elements and that represent their real function. At this point there are close ties to physiology, another one of the "life sciences." Since structures are chemical entities, changes of structure are biochemical reactions. Thus biochemistry is prepared to provide explanations for physiological processes. Indeed, the analytical approach to biochemistry penetrates far more effectively than the physiological approach. Starling has said that every physiological problem ultimately is reducible to a biochemical one.

The chemical methodology employed by biochemistry has already provided significant insight into the true nature of cellular activity. But, on the other hand, this approach does have definite limitations. When we use chemical methods we expect answers only from the field of chemical knowledge and experience. Phenomena of life belonging to other areas of science, as for example bioelectric properties, reaction to stimuli, and behavior cannot be effectively approached by chemical methods; more suitable research methods are needed. Some phenomena, like man's consciousness, do not lend themselves to analysis by the usual scientific techniques.

Just as biochemistry approaches problems in a variety of ways, so have its answers found application in a number of allied sciences. As far as medicine is concerned, many diseases are now recognized to be metabolic disturbances or biochemical anomalies, and obviously every drug, being a chemical substance, affects biochemical systems. To the student of medicine in particular, therefore, biochemical knowledge is simply indispensable.

# CHAPTER I

# Organic Chemistry

# and Biochemistry

Biochemistry concerns carbon compounds and their reactions as they occur in organisms. Organic chemistry, or the chemistry of carbon compounds, therefore, is basic to biochemistry. The chemistry of natural products and that of biochemistry overlap extensively and lack a clearly defined border. Numerous compounds which have only recently been identified as intermediates of metabolism had long been known in organic chemistry.

A good knowledge of organic chemistry, in particular a thorough appreciation of structural formulas, therefore, is a prerequisite for an intelligent study of biochemistry. The following brief outline is not intended to replace a course in organic chemistry, but rather to serve as a handy reference for selected compounds and for reactions of special significance in biochemistry.

## 1. Hydrocarbons as Parent Substances

The great variety of organic compounds may be explained by the ease with which carbon atoms can attach to each other. Since carbon is tetravalent, a great many possibilities for branching arise, leading to a staggering number of carbon skeletons. If the remaining valence bonds are filled with hydrogen, then we speak of the result as a hydrocarbon. From a systematic viewpoint, hydrocarbons are the parent substances of all organic compounds; in practice, however, they are very rarely used to prepare other classes of compounds.

The molecular formulas of all saturated open-chain hydrocarbons are represented by the general formula $C_nH_{2n+2}$. Every time an open chain closes to a ring, irrespective of size of the ring, two hydrogen atoms are lost with a corresponding change in the general formula. Thus it becomes possible to deduce from the molecular formula of a saturated hydrocarbon such as cholestane, $C_{27}H_{48}$ (parent substance of cholesterol), that there must be four rings in its carbon skeleton.

Saturated or alicyclic ring systems actually are of equal if not greater importance in biochemistry than aromatic compounds derived from benzene, which dominate

1

such a large segment of classical organic chemistry. It is well known that the aromatic ring is a resonating system which may be represented only imperfectly by the traditional hexagon and the three double bonds. Yet we shall consistently adopt this symbol to distinguish aromatic compounds from the saturated ring systems, which, in turn, will be represented by simple pentagons and hexagons. The most important ring compounds are listed with their formulas in Table I.

Besides the all-carbon rings, we will frequently come across heterocyclic compounds, in which one (or more) carbon atom is exchanged for one of nitrogen, oxygen, or sulfur. Ring systems of this type, also listed in Table I, have usually received trivial names. Heterocyclic compounds possess chemical properties quite different from analogous strictly carbocyclic compounds; nitrogen, for example, usually imparts basic properties (but occasionally is acidic). This point applies especially to heterocyclic compounds.

Most saturated hydrocarbons are rather inert. By contrast, unsaturated compounds, designated by

$$\underset{/}{\overset{\backslash}{C}} = \underset{\backslash}{\overset{/}{C}} \quad \text{(double bond)}$$

or by

$$-C \equiv C- \quad \text{(triple bond)},$$

are more reactive. They may easily add other atoms or groups of atoms, such as hydrogen or the elements of water:

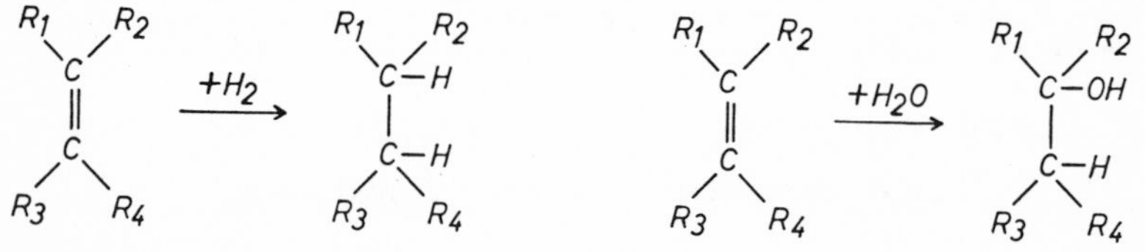

Unsaturated compounds can be cleaved by oxidation at their double bonds. For further addition reactions, the reader should consult textbooks of organic chemistry.

**Explanation of Formulas.**  Strictly speaking, every valence bond in a formula should be represented by a dash, the symbol for an electron pair. For convenience, however, groups saturated with hydrogen are usually written as $-CH_3$ or $-CH_2-$ instead of the cumbersome

$$\overset{H}{\underset{H}{-\overset{|}{\underset{|}{C}}-H}} \quad \text{or} \quad \overset{H}{\underset{H}{-\overset{|}{\underset{|}{C}}-}}.$$

We will simplify further in many cases and let a system of lines represent a hydrocarbon chain in which each corner or kink indicates a $CH_2$ group. The same holds for ring compounds where the abbreviated form is more common. Double bonds

TABLE I

RING SYSTEMS

| Number of atoms in ring | Carbocyclic rings | | Heterocyclic rings | | | | |
|---|---|---|---|---|---|---|---|
| | Saturated | Unsaturated (aromatic) | N-containing | | | O-containing | |
| 5 | Cyclopentane | Cyclopentadiene | Pyrrolidine | Pyrrole | Imidazole | Tetrahydrofuran | Furan |
| 6 | Cyclohexane | Benzene | Piperidine | Pyridine | Pyrimidine | Tetrahydropyran | Pyran |
| 6 + 5 | Hydrindane | Indene | Indole | Purine | | | |
| 6 + 6 | Decalin | Naphthalene | Quinoline | Pteridine | | Chroman | |
| Higher systems | Phenanthrene | | Alloxazine | | | | |
| | Sterane | | | | | | |

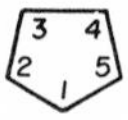

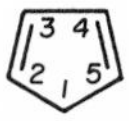

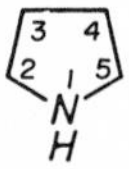

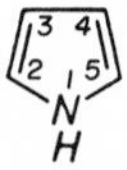

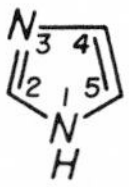

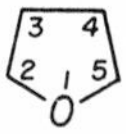

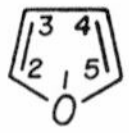

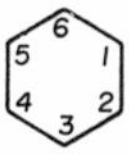

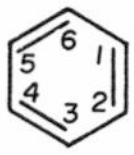

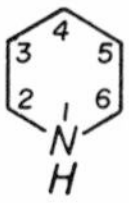

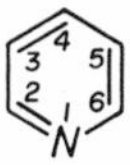

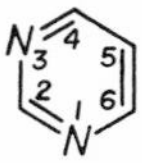

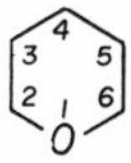

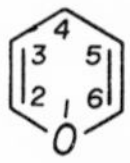

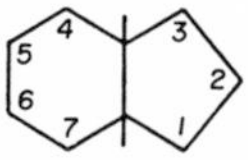

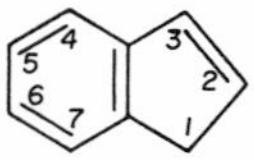

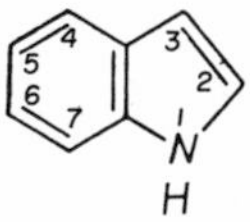

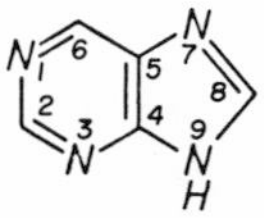

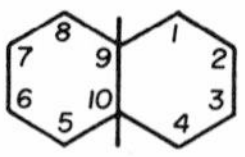

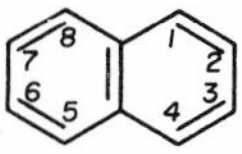

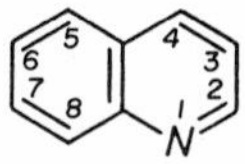

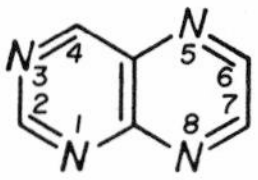

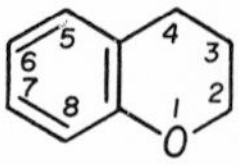

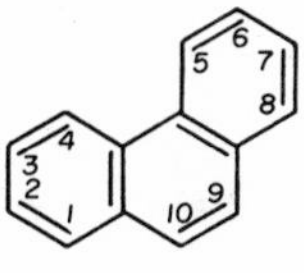

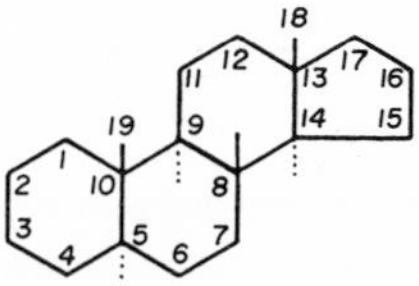

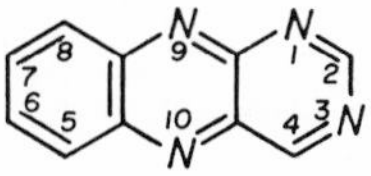

are always shown by a double line; a hexagon with single lines hence means a cyclohexane ring, i.e. a saturated compound and not a benzene ring.

Groups regarded as unimportant in any particular instance, or repeated several times, usually are designated simply by R (= radical). Often R is used at a position where different groups may be substituted.

## 2. Functional Groups

A further reason for the great variability of organic compounds is found in the presence of functional groups. It should be understood that this is a strictly formal derivation that is seldom feasible experimentally. Depending on the number of hydrogen atoms replaced, we distinguish between

monovalent functional group:  —OH (hydroxyl group),   —NH₂ (amino group)
divalent functional group:  =O (carbonyl group),   =NH (imino group)
trivalent functional group:  ≡O (carboxyl group),   ≡N (nitrile)
                                        \
                                         OH

Chemical reactions of the different classes of substances ordinarily are reactions of functional groups; the latters' name derives from this fact.

**Hydroxyl Groups.** Compounds with a hydroxyl group are called alcohols after the best known representative, namely ordinary or ethyl alcohol. In systematic organic chemistry we distinguish

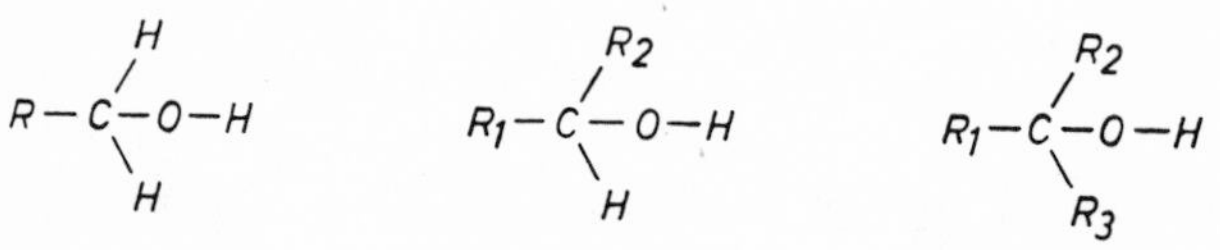

Primary alcohols        Secondary alcohols        Tertiary alcohols

Alcohols form a number of derivatives, of which the esters with organic acids and phosphoric acid interest us most:

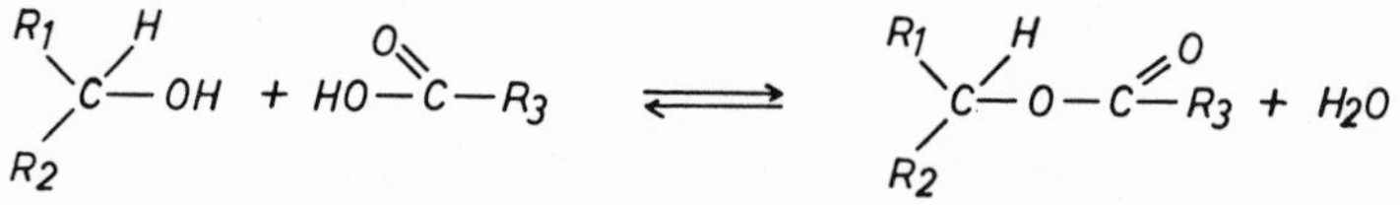

Alcohol    +    Carboxylic acid          ⇌          Ester    +    Water

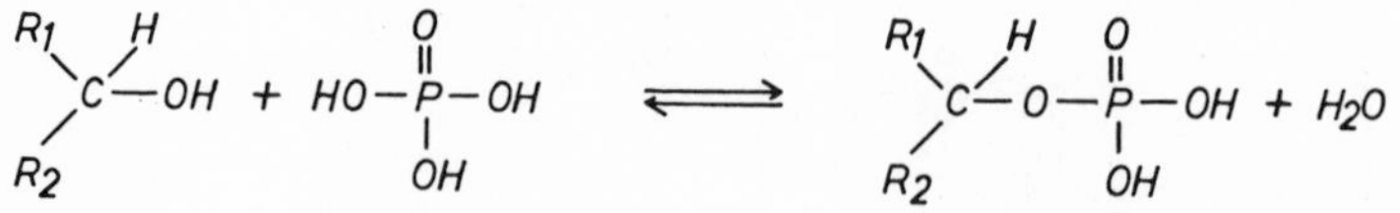

Alcohol        Phosphoric acid                    Ester of phosphoric acid
                                                              or
                                                  alcohol phosphate

The formation of esters is a reversible reaction. The final equilibrium may be approached from either side of the equation (cf. Chapt. V–2).

The removal of one molecule of water from two alcohol molecules produces an ether:

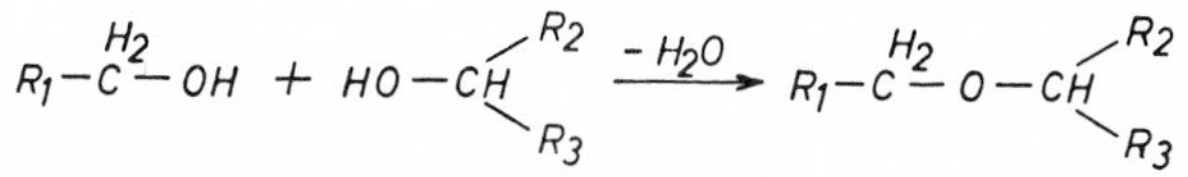

$$R_1-\overset{H_2}{\underset{}{C}}-OH \;+\; HO-\overset{R_2}{\underset{R_3}{CH}} \quad \xrightarrow{-H_2O} \quad R_1-\overset{H_2}{\underset{}{C}}-O-\overset{R_2}{\underset{R_3}{CH}}$$

Many natural products contain ether groups.

One more example of the reactions of the alcohol group is the dehydrogenation to the carbonyl group:

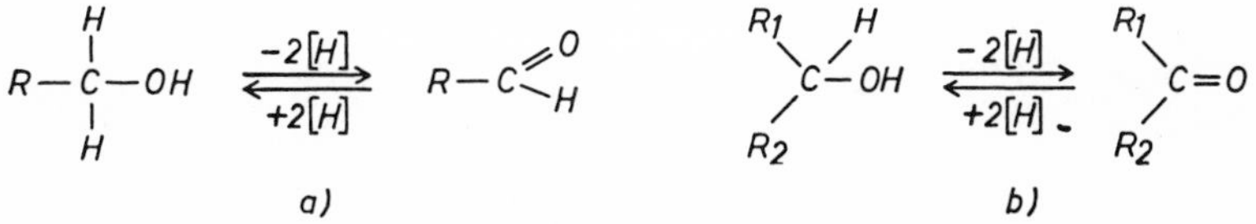

$$R-\overset{H}{\underset{H}{C}}-OH \;\underset{+2[H]}{\overset{-2[H]}{\rightleftarrows}}\; R-C\overset{O}{\underset{H}{\diagdown}} \qquad\qquad \overset{R_1}{\underset{R_2}{\diagup}}C\overset{H}{\underset{}{\diagdown}}OH \;\underset{+2[H]}{\overset{-2[H]}{\rightleftarrows}}\; \overset{R_1}{\underset{R_2}{\diagup}}C=O$$

a)                                             b)

According to reaction a, a primary alcohol yields an aldehyde; according to b, a secondary alcohol yields a ketone. Tertiary alcohols cannot be dehydrogenated without destroying the carbon skeleton. Instead, they split off one molecule of water rather easily to form the unsaturated compound. The other alcohols may be dehydrated, too.

**Amines.** In former days (of "type theories" in organic chemistry), alcohols had been conceived of as mono-alkylated water, and amines as alkylated ammonia. Many properties of these two classes of compounds can indeed be explained that way.

The nomenclature of amines differs from that of the alcohols. The designations *primary, secondary,* and *tertiary* refer to the number of substituents on the ammonia nitrogen:

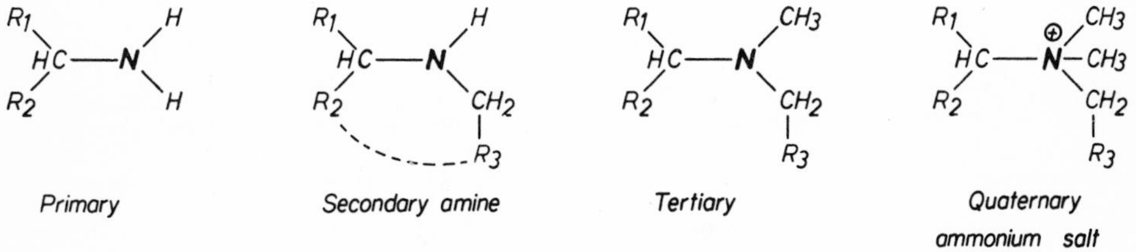

$$\overset{R_1}{\underset{R_2}{\diagup}}HC-N\overset{H}{\underset{H}{\diagdown}} \qquad \overset{R_1}{\underset{R_2}{\diagup}}HC-N\overset{H}{\underset{CH_2}{\diagdown}}{\underset{|}{R_3}} \qquad \overset{R_1}{\underset{R_2}{\diagup}}HC-N\overset{CH_3}{\underset{CH_2}{\diagdown}}{\underset{|}{R_3}} \qquad \overset{R_1}{\underset{R_2}{\diagup}}HC-\overset{\oplus}{N}\overset{CH_3}{\underset{}{\diagdown}}-CH_3{\underset{\underset{R_3}{|}}{CH_2}}$$

Primary            Secondary amine          Tertiary            Quaternary ammonium salt

The fourth formula shows a quaternary ammonium salt, derived formally by replacing all four hydrogen atoms of the salt $NH_4Cl$ with organic radicals. The "free bases," the hydroxides of the quaternary ammonium ion, exist in addition to the neutral salts.

The nitrogen compounds of this series are organic bases. Salt formation, written analogously to ammonium ion formation, is the most important functional reaction of amino compounds (cf. also Chapt. II–1).

$$NH_3 + H^+ \rightarrow NH_4^+; \qquad R\text{—}NH_2 + H^+ \rightarrow R\text{—}NH_3^+$$

Cyclic bases actually are secondary or tertiary amines. The $R_2$ and $R_3$ groups have joined to close a ring. Examples for this are in Table I. Several of the cyclic bases (pyridine, imidazole, etc.) have a double bond between a C and an N atom (aromatic systems).

Another reaction of amines, comparable to ester formation of alcohols, is the formation of amides. Some detours are required, however, in order to accomplish the preparation of amides in practice.

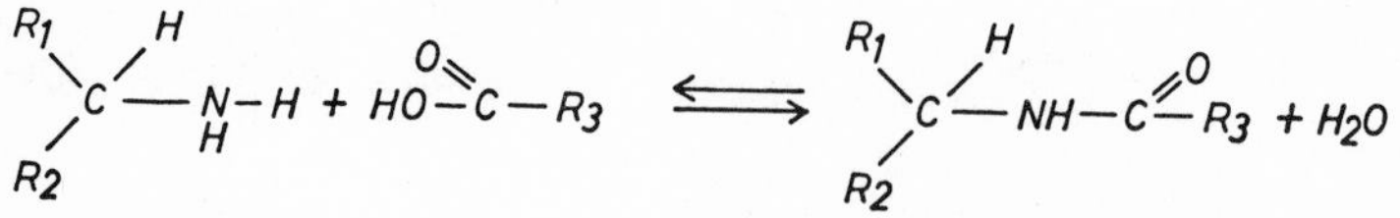

Dehydrogenation of primary amino groups introduces, again in analogy to alcohols, a

$$\diagdown \atop C=NH \text{ double bond,} \atop \diagup$$

changing it to an imino group. Imines are unstable and are hydrolyzed to ketones (or aldehydes, if $R_1$ = H) and ammonia:

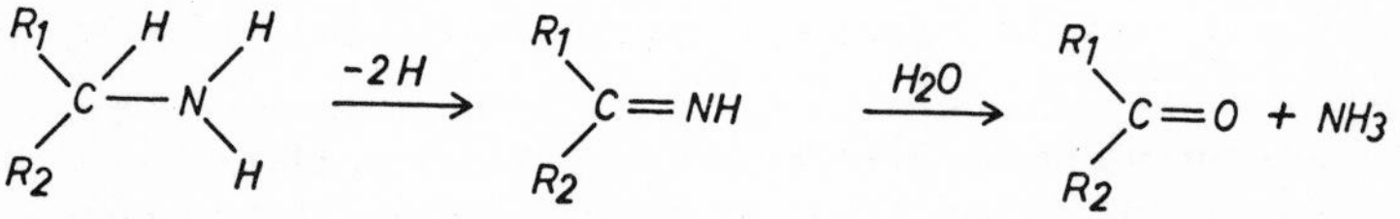

Amine                          Imine                          Ketone

**Carbonyl Compounds: Aldehydes and Ketones.**   Their general formulas are:

Aldehyde                       Ketone

Common to both is the carbonyl group,

which undergoes certain reactions. By reduction (hydrogenation), i.e. addition of hydrogen to the

$$\overset{\diagdown}{\underset{\diagup}{C}}=O \text{ double bond,}$$

alcohols are formed. The reaction is reversible: Primary or secondary alcohols may be dehydrogenated to yield carbonyl compounds, as indicated in the discussion on alcohols. This reversible reaction is particularly important in biochemistry.

Another addition reaction is the introduction of a molecule of water. The resulting hydrates are quite unstable but may serve as intermediates. Addition of alcohols, by extension, gives rise to the analogous hemiacetals. By further reaction with alcohol and removal of water, acetals are formed. The name acetal applies only to derivatives of aldehydes; ketones form ketals.

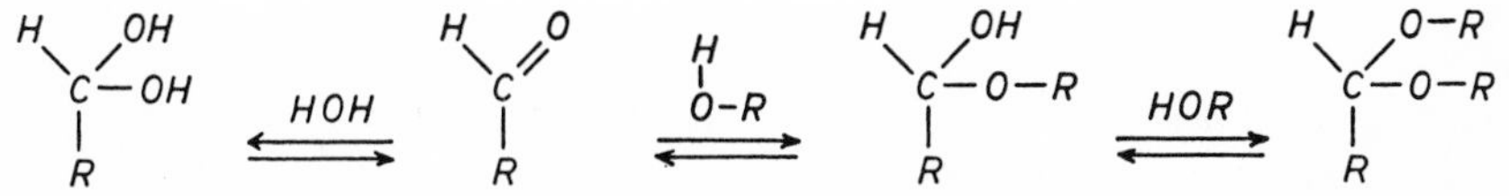

| Aldehyde hydrate | | Aldehyde | | Hemiacetal | | (Full)-Acetal |
|---|---|---|---|---|---|---|

Acetal formation is greatly facilitated by reagents that bind the released water; acetals are also easily hydrolyzed.

Simple dehydrogenation of an aldehyde hydrate produces a carboxylic acid:

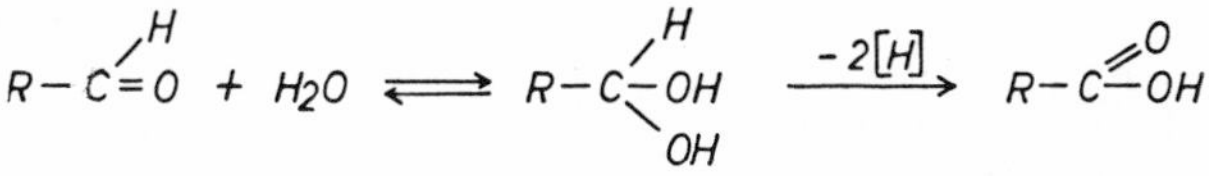

$$R-C\overset{H}{=}O + H_2O \rightleftharpoons R-C\overset{H}{\underset{OH}{-}}OH \xrightarrow{-2[H]} R-C\overset{O}{\underset{}{=}}OH$$

This reaction was the starting point for H. Wieland's "dehydrogenation theory" of biologic oxidation, the subject of bitter controversy in the 1920's. The dispute over "activation of hydrogen" (dehydrogenation) and O. Warburg's "activation of oxygen" (oxidation) seems meaningless today. Now we are able to cite numerous examples of both types of reactions, and cell respiration employs both types.

For the purpose of chemical identification its reaction with derivatives of hydrazine is often used. The example chosen here is the reaction with phenylhydrazine:

| Ketone | Phenylhydrazine | | Phenylhydrazone of the ketone |
|---|---|---|---|

The hydrazone formed in this reaction usually crystallizes easily and is only sparingly soluble. A variation of this reaction is used in the chemistry of sugars. Oximes are formed analogously with hydroxylamine.

Carbonyl compounds react not only with $H_2N$ groups but with reactive $H_2C$ groups as well. In the aldol condensation there is first an addition to the

$$\diagdown C{=}O \text{ double bond,}$$

and subsequently water is split off. In the living cell, these steps are taken separately (examples in Chapt. VI–5 and XV–5):

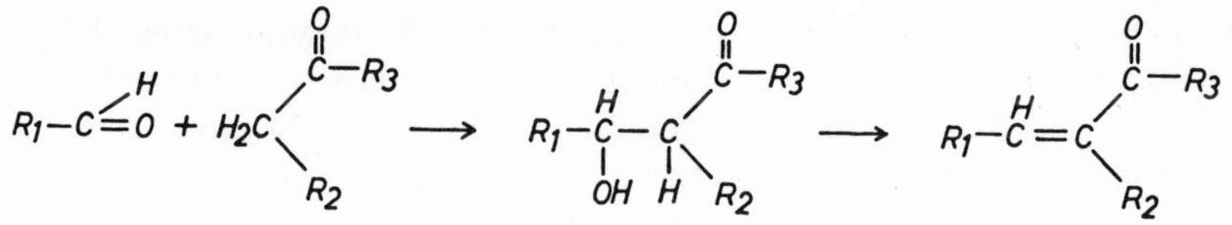

Aldehydes and ketones may change to their *enol forms*; a hydrogen atom wanders to the oxygen atom and the double bond shifts:

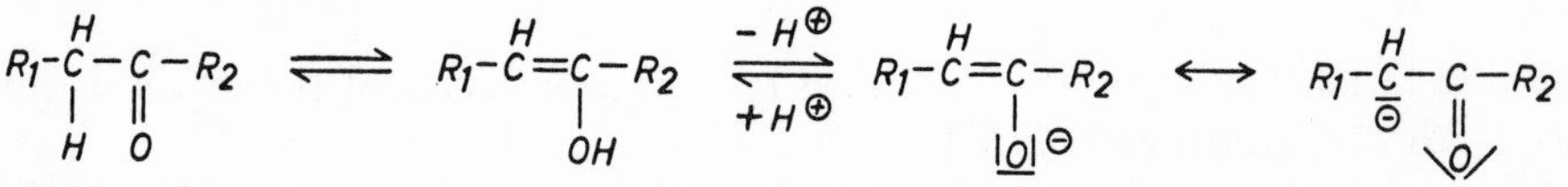

Ketone                    Enol                         Enolate ion
                                          (Limit structures contributing to resonance)

The name "enol" is derived from "en" for double bond and "ol" for alcohol group. The transition from carbonyl to enol is called "tautomerism"; it occurs especially easily whenever other unsaturated groups are in a potentially conjugated position nearby. As seen above, an enol can readily donate a proton, because the resulting enolate ion is stabilized by resonance.

Phenols. The phenols are closely related to the enols and are characterized by a hydroxyl group attached directly to an aromatic nucleus. The phenolic OH group is always next to a double bond which is part of the aromatic system. Many structures contributing to the resonance can be written for the phenolate ion; phenols, for this reason, are weak acids and the simplest representative, phenol itself, originally was called "carbolic acid." Nevertheless, the phenolic OH group can form ethers and esters and in these properties more nearly resembles the alcohols.

Phenol                          Phenolate ion

**Imines.** These are substances with a C=N double bond. They hydrolyze easily and are stable only in special combinations. Ring compounds and the guanidino group

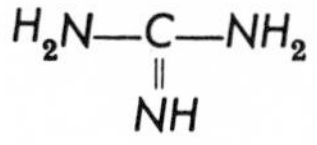

$$H_2N—C—NH_2$$
$$\overset{\displaystyle \|}{NH}$$

are among such combinations (see Chapt. I–1 and VII–1). Guanidine is stable in water.

The older chemical nomenclature also calls secondary amines, R—NH—R′, "imines." In some instances such naming has survived stubbornly. We will avoid it whenever possible and call them "secondary amines."

**Carboxylic Acids.** These contain the carboxyl group —COOH; three valence bonds of the carbon atom have been replaced by oxygen. The name indicates their acidic nature. Carboxylic acids dissociate in water to give one proton (more properly a hydronium ion, $H_3O^+$) and the negatively charged anion

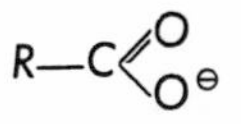

$$R—C\overset{\displaystyle O}{\underset{\displaystyle O^{\ominus}}{\Big\langle}}$$

The negative charge, however, is not localized on one oxygen atom. Both oxygens share this charge by resonance. Nevertheless we will continue to represent the carboxylate anion in this manner for convenience.

**Salts.** At physiological pH most of the organic acids exist in their anionic form, i.e. in their salt form. Acids occurring frequently in biochemistry are listed with their formulas in Table II.

For preparation and purification of organic acids their salts are occasionally used. The silver salts, for example, of most organic acids are only slightly soluble.

**Dissociation of Carboxylic Acids.** Within cells and in other body fluids the carboxylic acids exist almost entirely in their dissociated form; only an infinitesimal fraction retains the group COOH. We may represent the dissociation, somewhat simplified, by the equation

$$R—COOH \rightleftharpoons R—COO^- + H^+ \tag{1}$$

and apply it to the law of mass action. The law states that the ratio of the concentrations is a constant:

$$\frac{[R—COO^-] \cdot [H^+]}{[R—COOH]} = K \tag{2}$$

Conventionally, the brackets signify *concentration* of the individual substances (either molecules or ions). For simplicity we write $[H^+]$ in these equations, although the ion is $[H_3O^+]$ in reality.

TABLE II

IMPORTANT ACIDS

| Monocarboxylic acids | Dicarboxylic acids | Hydroxy or Keto acids |
|---|---|---|
| $HCOOH$ <br><br> Formic acid | $HOOC-COOH$ <br><br> Oxalic acid | $H_3C-\overset{\overset{H}{\mid}}{\underset{\underset{OH}{\mid}}{C}}-COOH$ <br><br> Lactic acid |
| $H_3C-COOH$ <br><br> Acetic acid | $HOOC-CH_2-COOH$ <br><br> Malonic acid | $H_3C-\overset{}{\underset{\underset{O}{\parallel}}{C}}-COOH$ <br><br> Pyruvic acid |
| $H_3C-CH_2-COOH$ <br><br> Propionic acid | $\underset{\underset{COOH}{\mid}}{H_2C}-\underset{\underset{COOH}{\mid}}{CH_2}$ <br><br> Succinic acid | $\underset{\underset{OH}{\mid}}{H_2C}-\overset{\overset{H}{\mid}}{\underset{\underset{OH}{\mid}}{C}}-COOH$ <br><br> Glyceric acid |
| $H_3C-CH_2-CH_2-COOH$ <br><br> Butyric acid | $\underset{HOOC}{\overset{H}{\diagdown}}C=C\underset{\diagdown H}{\overset{\diagup COOH}{}}$ <br><br> Fumaric acid | $\underset{\underset{COOH}{\mid}}{H_2C}-\overset{\overset{H}{\mid}}{\underset{\underset{COOH}{\mid}}{C}}-OH$ <br><br> Malic acid |
| $\underset{H_3C}{\overset{H_3C}{\diagdown}}C\overset{\diagup H}{\underset{}{}}-CH_2-COOH$ <br><br> Isovaleric acid | $\underset{\underset{COOH}{\mid}}{H_2C}-CH_2-\underset{\underset{COOH}{\mid}}{CH_2}$ <br><br> Glutaric acid | $HO-\overset{\overset{H}{\mid}}{\underset{\underset{COOH}{\mid}}{C}}-\overset{\overset{H}{\mid}}{\underset{\underset{COOH}{\mid}}{C}}-OH$ <br><br> Tartaric acid |

With more concentrated solutions, furthermore, the simple stoichiometric concentrations should be replaced by "activities." The interaction among ions seems to lower their effective concentration, i.e., their activity. This phenomenon is expressed by the activity coefficient $f$ (which is always less than unity and is used as a factor for concentrations). For the physiological NaCl solution, for example, $f = 0.76$.

Sörenson has introduced the pH of a solution as a scale for the concentration (or rather activity) of $H^+$ ions appearing in equation (2). The pH is defined as the negative common logarithm (base of 10) of the $H^+$ concentration, or

$$pH = -\log [H^+] \tag{3}$$

Because of the dissociation to $H^+$ and $OH^-$, even pure water has a $H^+$ ion concentration of $10^{-7}$ $M$, or a pH of 7; this is also the neutral pH. The concept of the pH is very important in practical biochemistry, because most cellular processes depend strongly on the $H^+$ ion concentration, i.e. the pH.

The use of pH values follows, of course, the rules of logarithmic calculations: Every change of the pH by one unit corresponds to a change in $H^+$ ion concentration by the factor of 10. For example, the $H^+$ ion concentration of $2 \times 10^{-5}$ $M$ can be expressed as a pH of

$$-\log(2 \times 10^{-5}) = -(\log 2 + \log 10^{-5}) = -(0.3 - 5.0) = 4.7.$$

Let us return once more to the law of mass action. We may rewrite equation (2) in the following way:

$$\frac{[A^-]}{[HA]} \cdot [H^+] = K \qquad (4)$$

$(A^- = $ anion, $HA = $ undissociated acid$)$

If the fraction equals unity, i.e. the amount of undissociated acid equals the amount of anion, then the $H^+$ ion concentration becomes the dissociation constant of the acid. If $[H^+]$ is expressed as the pH, it is expedient to express also the dissociation constant as the negative logarithm. This value is then called the pK: $pK = -\log K$.

The conversion of equation (4) into its logarithmic form yields:

$$\log\frac{[A^-]}{[HA]} + \log [H^+] = \log K$$

$$\log\frac{[A^-]}{[HA]} - \log K \quad = -\log [H^+]$$

$$\log\frac{[A^-]}{[HA]} + pK \quad = pH$$

This last equation, generally known as the Henderson-Hasselbalch equation, is useful particularly for the calculation of pH values arising from mixtures of salts and acids. Mixtures of this kind are called buffer solutions.

**Buffers** are capable of absorbing $H^+$ ions (and $OH^-$ ions) and in this way can resist changes of pH which would otherwise occur with the additions of acids (or bases). This phenomenon can be explained again by the law of mass action. If acid is added to the equilibrium mixture represented by equation (4), the $[H^+]$ will rise. But in order to reach equilibrium again, $[HA]$ must also rise; the latter can be achieved only by the recombination of $H^+$ and $A^-$ to form HA. This reaction consumes nearly all of the added $H^+$ ions, and the consequent change in pH is negligible. All this presupposes, of course, that not too many $H^+$ ions, or not too much acid, have been added. The capacity of the buffer is limited by the number of $A^-$ ions available to trap $H^+$ ions.

Weak acids or weak bases in combination with their salts are, in general, adaptable for setting up buffers; their greatest capacity to buffer is around their pK value. Buffers are indispensable in most biochemical work. Commonly used are buffers of phosphate, citrate, glycine and NaOH or HCl, and more recently tris(hydroxymethyl)aminomethane (or simply "tris buffer"). The exact compositions of different buffer mixtures are listed in biochemical handbooks.

**Esters.** Further functional derivatives of the acids may be derived formally from the acyl residue. (The group R—CO— is called the acyl residue.) Esters, as the first example, are formed from acids and alcohols by an equilibrium reaction:

$$R_1-C{\overset{O}{\Big\backslash}}OH \;+\; HO-C{\overset{R_2}{\underset{R_3}{\Big\backslash}}}H \;\rightleftharpoons\; R_1-C{\overset{O}{\Big\backslash}}O-C{\overset{R_2}{\underset{R_3}{\Big\backslash}}}H \;+\; H_2O$$

In chemical preparative work, conditions can be chosen to obtain the ester in nearly quantitative yields. Under physiological conditions—i.e., in aqueous medium at neutral pH—the equilibrium favors the reactants, acid and alcohol. Yet many esters are found in cells. For biological ester formation and cleavage, see Chapt. VI-5 and XII-6.

**Amides.** Acid amides also play an important role in biochemistry. They are compounds in which the hydroxyl group of an acid has been replaced with —NH₂ or —NH—R. In contrast to esters, amides cannot be prepared from acid and ammonia (or amine), but rather have to be made *via* reactive or "activated" derivatives of the acids. They are very stable in aqueous solution, despite the fact that the reaction equilibrium of hydrolysis is far on the side of cleavage:

$$R-CO-NH_2 + H_2O \rightleftharpoons R-COO^- + NH_4^+$$

**"Activated" Acid Derivatives.** These are very reactive and interact with other substances exergonically (Chapt. V–2). Even esters belong to this class, because they undergo many reactions that are impossible for free acids. In organic chemistry, acid chlorides and acid anhydrides are preferred.

Acid anhydride          Acid chloride          Thioester

When acid chlorides react with other substances, the chloride is released as HCl (in the case of acid anhydrides, the acyl group is released as the free acid). Thus esters, amides, etc. are prepared conveniently. Such "activated" acids are also known in biochemistry. Activated acids are of the anhydride type and some of the thioester type. Thioesters differ from simple esters in that the alcohol component R—OH is replaced by an R—SH compound. They are highly reactive (cf. also group transfer, Chapt. VI–5).

## 3. Polymeric Compounds

Many different compounds can combine to form larger molecules which are susceptible to hydrolysis. They contain C—O—C or C—N—C bonds which may be thought to have arisen by condensation of two parent molecules with loss of one water molecule. Their hydrolysis, therefore, appears to be a reversal of their formation. The list of such polymeric compounds is headed by the acid derivatives, esters and amides. Ethers and acetals also belong to this group.

Nearly all macromolecular natural products are combinations of smaller compounds.[1] Molecular weights of monomeric compounds rarely exceed 600. Polysaccharides (starch, cellulose) are linked by hemiacetal bonds; proteins, by acid-amide bonds, also called peptide bonds (see Table III). Ester linkages are found in fats and lipids (not of very high molecular weights) as well as in the macromolecular nucleic acids, which are phosphoric acid esters.

TABLE III

MACROMOLECULAR NATURAL PRODUCTS

| Type of Linkage | Natural Product | See Chapter |
|---|---|---|
| Polyacetals | Cellulose, starch, etc. | XVII |
| Polyamides | Proteins, polypeptides | III, IV |
| Polyesters | Nucleic acids (phosphate esters) | VII |
|  | Fats (carboxylate esters) | XII |

Macromolecules usually consist of subunits with two functional groups, both of which contribute to the linking; in the case of proteins, they are the amino and carboxyl group. Biosynthesis, however, does not occur simply by splitting out water between components.

## 4. Isomerisms

Another phenomenon contributing to the great variability of organic compounds is isomerism. Isomers are compounds that have exactly the same molecular formula but differ in at least one of their chemical or physical properties.

---

[1] An exception is made by natural rubber which is a polymer of isoprene units with C—C linkages only. The molecular weights may range as high as 350,000. Highly polymerized synthetic products frequently follow the same pattern of composition, although synthetic products of the polyamide (Perlon, nylon) and polyurethane type have gained great importance.

The difference in properties may stem from differing functional groups. Both lactic acid and dihydroxyacetone have the same molecular formula, $C_3H_6O_3$; the former has a carboxyl and a hydroxyl group, the latter has two hydroxyl and one carbonyl group and is not an acid:

$$
\begin{array}{cccc}
\underset{\displaystyle \underset{\displaystyle \underset{\displaystyle CH_3}{|}}{H-C-OH}}{C\overset{\displaystyle O}{\diagup}OH} &
\underset{\displaystyle \underset{\displaystyle \underset{\displaystyle CH_2OH}{|}}{C=O}}{CH_2OH} &
\underset{\displaystyle \underset{\displaystyle \underset{\displaystyle CH_2OH}{|}}{H-C-OH}}{\overset{H}{\underset{C}{\diagup}}\overset{O}{\diagup}} &
\underset{\displaystyle \underset{\displaystyle \underset{\displaystyle CH_2OH}{|}}{HO-C-H}}{\overset{H}{\underset{C}{\diagup}}\overset{O}{\diagup}}
\end{array}
$$

|             |                   |              |        |
|-------------|-------------------|--------------|--------|
| Lactic acid | Dihydroxyacetone  | Glyceraldehyde: |      |
|             |                   | D - Form     | L-Form |

Such differences are rather obvious. For such compounds to have identical molecular formulas appears to be merely an accident. The difference is smaller between dihydroxyacetone and glyceraldehyde (second and third formula, respectively); the carbonyl and the hydroxyl groups have simply been exchanged. In the case of the D and L forms of glyceraldehyde, only the hydroxyl group and the H atom on the middle carbon have changed places, which results in mirror-image isomerism (see below).

**Positional Isomerism** occurs when one or more groups assume different positions on a carbon skeleton, as with dihydroxyacetone and glyceraldehyde in the above series of formulas. Further examples are methylmalonic acid and succinic acid as well as citric acid ánd isocitric acid:

|                 |               |             |               |
|-----------------|---------------|-------------|---------------|
| Methylmalonic acid | Succinic acid | Citric acid | Isocitric acid |

The structural differences are evident without further explanation. The properties of positional isomers generally differ more than those of homologs. A homolog is a compound whose carbon chain has been extended by one extra $CH_2$ group.

**Geometrical Isomerism,** or *cis-trans*-isomerism, requires that an imaginary plane be drawn through a molecule. In the four-membered ring, for example, all four C atoms lie in one plane. Two COOH groups at positions 1 and 3 may either both be on the same side of the plane (*cis*-compound) or be on opposite sides (*trans*-compound).

The drawing clearly shows the difference between the two model molecules.

This difference is reflected in some of their physical properties, as for example their melting points:

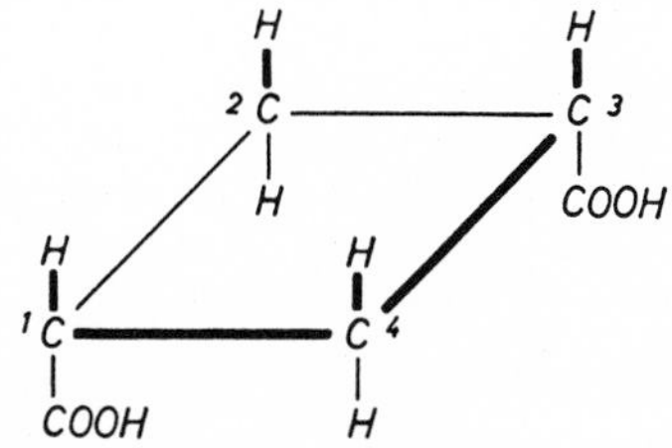

M.p. 131°          M.p. 190°
cis-                trans-
Cyclobutane dicarboxylic acid

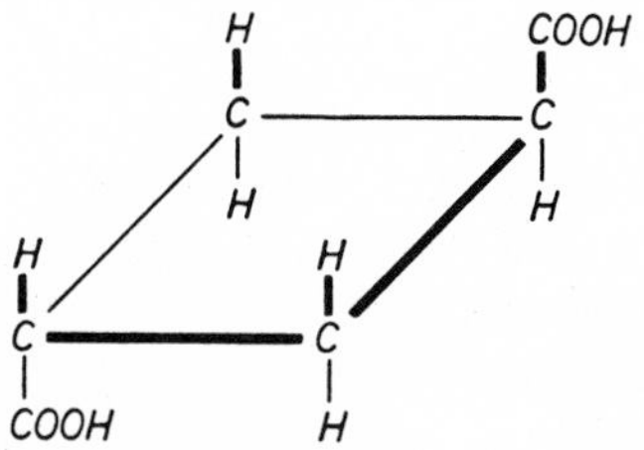

A double bond, in a sense a two-membered ring, presents the simplest case of geometrical isomerism. Here a plane may be imagined to run through the two C atoms perpendicular to the surface of the paper. A well-known pair of isomers is maleic acid and fumaric acid. Stable isomers of this type are not possible with single bonds because of the unhindered rotation around the C—C axis. The two formulas of succinic acid to the right are just two equivalent modes of presenting the same substance.

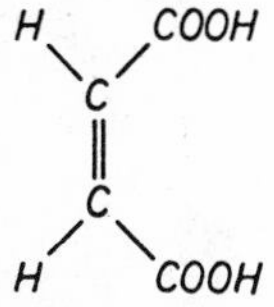

Maleic acid          Fumaric acid          Succinic acid

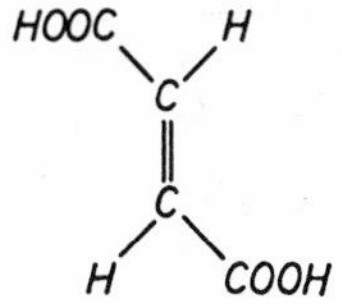

( cis-compound)      (trans-compound)      (Only two manners of presentation, no
                                            isomerism)

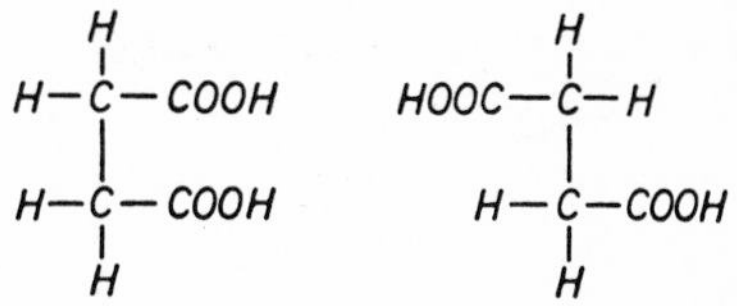

Geometric isomerism with respect to the plane of the ring is also of considerable importance with five- and six-membered ring compounds. In many cases it has been convenient to let the designations *cis* and *trans* refer to one particular substituent rather than indicate relative positions of two groups. According to the conventions of steroid chemistry (cf. Chapt. XIV–2), *trans* in the expression "3-*trans*-hydroxy" establishes the orientation of the hydroxyl group at C atom 3 with respect to the methyl group at C atom 10.

**Mirror-Image Isomerism** appears in asymmetric molecules, of which the simplest member is a C atom with four different substituents. The C atom thus substituted is usually—but somewhat incorrectly—called the asymmetric C atom. Two substances related by this mirror-image isomerism are called enantiomers. They possess the same chemical[2] and physical properties (melting point, boiling point, solubility, etc.), the only difference being in the direction of optical rotation, whence the term "optical antipodes" is derived.

Solutions of such isomers rotate the plane of plane-polarized light. The direction of rotation is indicated by + (dextrorotatory) and − (levorotatory). The degree of rotation listed in tables is based on a light path of 10 cm through a solution of the substance with a concentration of 1 g per 1 ml. Some comprehensive tables of specific rotation also specify wave length and temperature. Experimental determinations on far less concentrated solutions may be converted to specific rotation, since the rotation is proportional to concentration.

It is possible to represent mirror-image isomerism in the plane of the paper through a perspective drawing (Fig. 1). Clearer, however, is E. Fischer's projection formula now widely used in print.

The following conventions apply to the planar projection of a three-dimensional model: If a plane is imagined to pass through the asymmetric carbon atom, then all other carbon atoms of the carbon chain (in vertical position) must lie behind that plane and the other substituents of the asymmetric carbon atom must appear in front of the plane. The arrangement is then projected onto the plane as shown in Fig. 2.

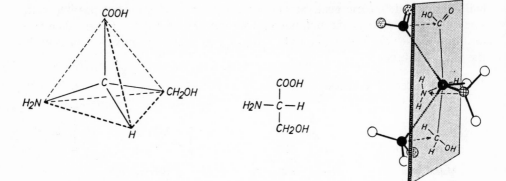

FIG. 1. Tetrahedral structure and projection formula          FIG. 2. Projection of three-dimensional model on a plane

The compound shown in the planar projection formula is L-serine. All amino acids of the L-series have their $NH_2$ groups to the left (if the —COOH is on top) when represented by projection formulas. The mirror-image forms (D-series) have their $NH_2$ groups pointed to the right. The same conventions hold for sugars whose simplest member is glyceraldehyde. The projection formulas given above under Positional Isomerism show both the dextrorotatory D-glyceraldehyde,[3] $\alpha_D = +14°$, and the levorotatory L-glyceraldehyde, $\alpha_D = -14°$.

When projection formulas are used, it should be remembered that they must not be moved out of the plane, nor must they be inverted in somersault fashion (which would result in the enantio-

---

[2] The only exception occurs when they react with other mirror-image isomers (see end of this section).

[3] The arbitrarily adopted convention to represent dextrorotatory glyceraldehyde in the manner indicated has now been substantiated by the determination of its absolute configuration.

meric forms). Within the plane, however, they may be pushed or turned about freely. Normally the formulas are written such that the carbon atom in the highest oxidation state stands on top; D-glyceraldehyde, in that case, has its OH group pointing to the right.

Only very laborious conversions and comparisons can establish whether a compound belongs to the D- or the L-series. The assignment of configuration unfortunately is not related to the direction of rotation of a compound, which may easily be determined experimentally. One example: D-glyceraldehyde is dextrorotatory by definition; oxidation affords D(−)-glyceric acid, which is levorotatory. By reduction of the $CH_2OH$ group to the $CH_3$ group, levorotatory D(−)-lactic acid is obtained, whose ester is again dextrorotatory:

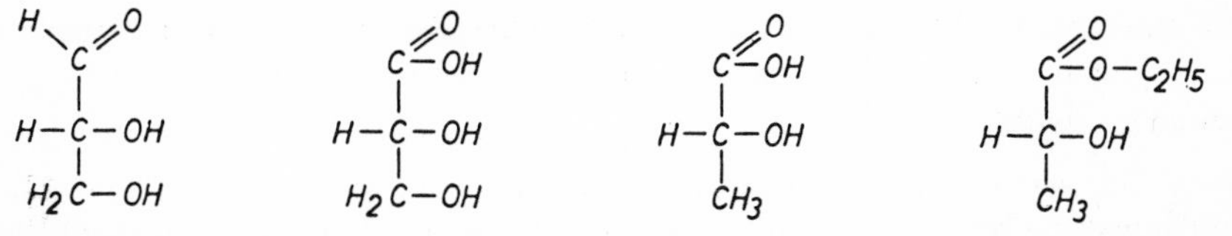

| D-Glyceraldehyde | D-Glyceric acid | D-Lactic acid | D-Lactic ethyl ester (D-ethyl lactate) |
|---|---|---|---|
| $\alpha_D = +14°$ | $\alpha_D = -2°$ | $\alpha_D = -3.8°$ | $\alpha_D = +11.5°$ |

During all these reactions, the configuration at the asymmetric center has remained unchanged.

If a molecule possesses two (generally, $n$) different asymmetric C atoms, then there must be four (generally, $2^n$) different forms. The number of isomers (always a multiple of 2) is grouped into pairs of *enantiomers* (mirror-image isomers), which agree in their melting points, solubility, etc. These physical properties distinguish one enantiomeric pair from another. An illustration can be found in threonine and allothreonine.

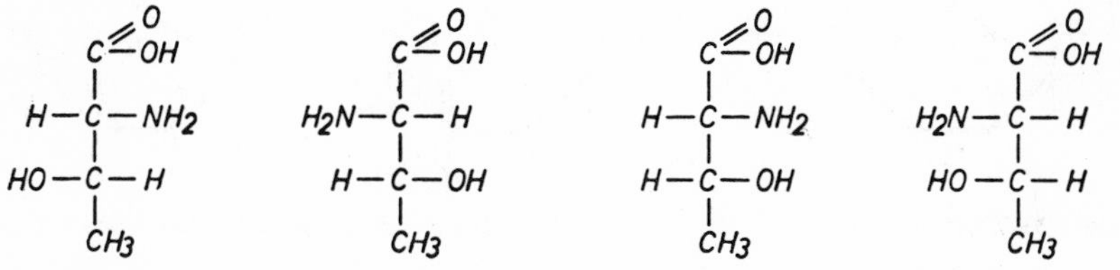

| D-Threonine | L-Threonine | D-Allothreonine | L-Allothreonine |
|---|---|---|---|
| M.p. 253° | M.p. 253° | M.p. 272° | M.p. 272° |

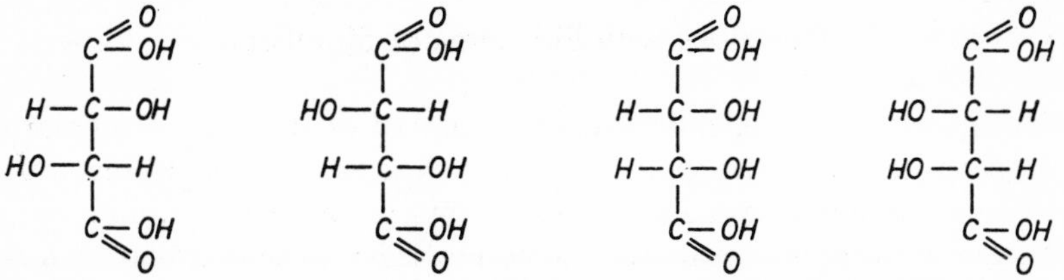

| L(+)-Tartaric acid | D(−)-Tartaric acid | meso-Tartaric acid |
|---|---|---|
| | | (Identical with its mirror image.) |

With two identical asymmetric centers (e.g., as in tartaric acid), one of the two forms is constructed symmetrically, i.e. its mirror images can be superimposed perfectly. Such compounds are optically inactive and are called *meso*-forms.

During chemical synthesis inactive (symmetrical) substances yield a mixture of equal amounts of both enantiomers. A molecular complex often formed from equal parts of the L- and D-isomer is called a *racemate*. Methods are available to prepare the pure optical antipodes from racemates.

The D- and L-forms may be distinguished by their chemical reactions only when they react with other optically active substances. Since all enzymes are optically active, the D- and L-forms react at dissimilar rates (frequently one form reacts immeasurably slowly).

With more complicated molecules, particularly with ring compounds, it is often difficult to predict whether a compound will be optically active. One reliable rule states that any molecular structure will exist in two optical antipodes if it cannot be superimposed completely with its mirror image. This decision can be reached most easily by means of models. In general, it is true that the various stereochemical relations can be appreciated fully only if one constructs models of the molecules, which may be achieved with rather simple means. For example, corks and pins, or soft wax and sections of wire, may help to improvise models adequate for many considerations.

Geometrical and mirror-image isomerism frequently appear together. Thus, 1,3-dihydroxycyclopentane exists both in a *cis*- and a *trans*-form; the *cis*-compound is a *meso*-form, i.e. possesses symmetry; the *trans*-compound, on the other hand, cannot be brought to complete superimposition with its mirror image and, hence, displays two optical antipodes:

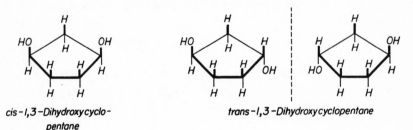

cis-1,3-Dihydroxycyclo-
pentane                              trans-1,3-Dihydroxycyclopentane

(cf. also *myo*-inositol, Chapt. XIII–2).

## 5. Reactions with Biochemical Significance

The living cell utilizes a much smaller number of different reactions than a synthetic chemist does. One very prominent type of reaction is the transfer of groups: Certain groups, e.g. an acetyl or methyl group or even an entire glucose molecule, are transferred to another molecule. The various group transfers are discussed in Chapt. VI–3 (Table X). Similarly, hydrogen may be transferred, very often reversibly.

The following reactions are of great importance in the organism:

1. *Formation and Cleavage of Macromolecules.* Cleavage is mostly hydrolytic (occasionally phosphorolytic). Synthesis, however, employs group transfer.
2. *Dehydrogenation and Hydrogenation,* either of special redox systems (see respiratory chain, Chapt. X–4), where, in effect, oxygen is reduced (hydrogenated) to water, or of any intermediate product of metabolism:

   a. alcohols to carbonyl groups (reversible),
   b. saturated to unsaturated compounds (reversible),
   c. aldehydes to carboxylic acids (not readily reversible),
   d. amines to imines, which in turn are hydrolyzed to carbonyl compounds (reversible only over detours).

3. *Formation and Cleavage of C—C Bonds:*

   a. by decarboxylation of keto acids or, in reverse, by carboxylation of ketones and acids (to malonic acid derivatives),
   b. by condensation of activated carboxylic acids to β-keto esters and its reverse, according to the principle of ester condensation,
   c. by reactions analogous to aldol condensations (Chapt. XV–5) or condensations of ketones with activated $CH_2$ groups (frequently reversible),
   d. by addition to double bonds (establishing a C—C bond).

4. *Loss of Water* (or ammonia) leaving a double bond and *Addition of Water* to a double bond.

The number of reaction types in cells evidently is low. Specificity, on the other hand, is extraordinarily high. From the multitude of potential reactants present in the cell, usually one particular substance is chosen and its specific reaction guided in a definite way. Maybe one of the most striking examples is the direct introduction of oxygen into the steroid molecule by an enzyme which permits the insertion of a hydroxyl group at one and only one position and with a certain steric orientation. Many more examples for specific reactions will be seen later.

BIBLIOGRAPHY

L. and M. Fieser, "Organic Chemistry," 3rd ed., Reinhold, New York, 1956.
P. Karrer, "Organic Chemistry," 4th ed., Elsevier, Amsterdam, 1950 (translated from the 11th German ed.).
E. M. Kosower, "Molecular Biochemistry," McGraw-Hill, New York, 1962.
J. Packer and J. Vaughan, "A Modern Approach to Organic Chemistry," Oxford Univ. Press, London and New York, 1958.
E. H. Rodd (editor), "Chemistry of Carbon Compounds," 5 vols., Elsevier, Amsterdam, 1951–1960.
E. E. Royals, "Advanced Organic Chemistry," Prentice-Hall, Englewood Cliffs, New Jersey, 1954.

# CHAPTER II

# Amino Acids

Proteins are essential components of all living cells. During hydrolysis proteins break down to amino acids, while in the organism they are built up from amino acids. The significance of amino acids, however, is not limited to their being components of proteins. In metabolism amino acids are subjected to many other reactions and supply precursors for other endogenous substances (e.g. hemoglobin of blood).

The chemical properties of amino acids, chiefly of those contained in proteins, will be discussed first. The metabolism of amino acids is discussed in Chapt. VIII along with that of proteins.

## 1. Chemical Properties

Their name indicates that amino acids possess two characteristic functional groups: the amino group, —NH₂, and the carboxyl group, —COOH. All amino acids that occur as components of proteins have their amino group in α-position to the carboxyl group. A list of the 20 amino acids found regularly in proteins is presented in Table IV. They have trivial names which are abbreviated to the first three letters, with a few exceptions.

The simplest amino acid is glycine, H₂N—CH₂—COOH. Glycine is the only amino acid without a carbon-containing substituent, R, on the α-carbon. The substituent R may carry further functional groups. The general formula of amino acids is:

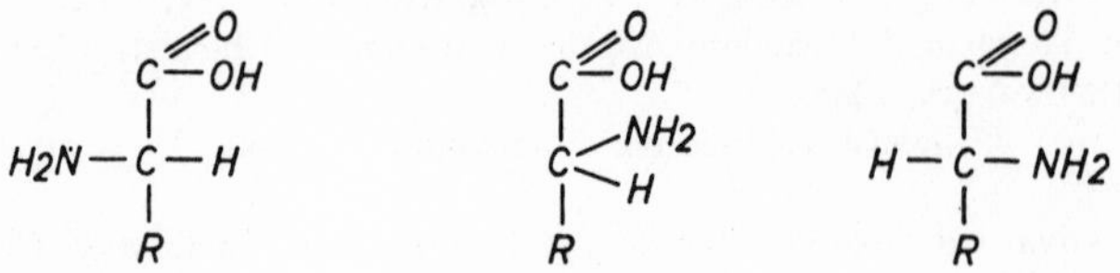

L-Amino acid        General formula        D-Amino acid

20

TABLE IV

IMPORTANT AMINO ACIDS

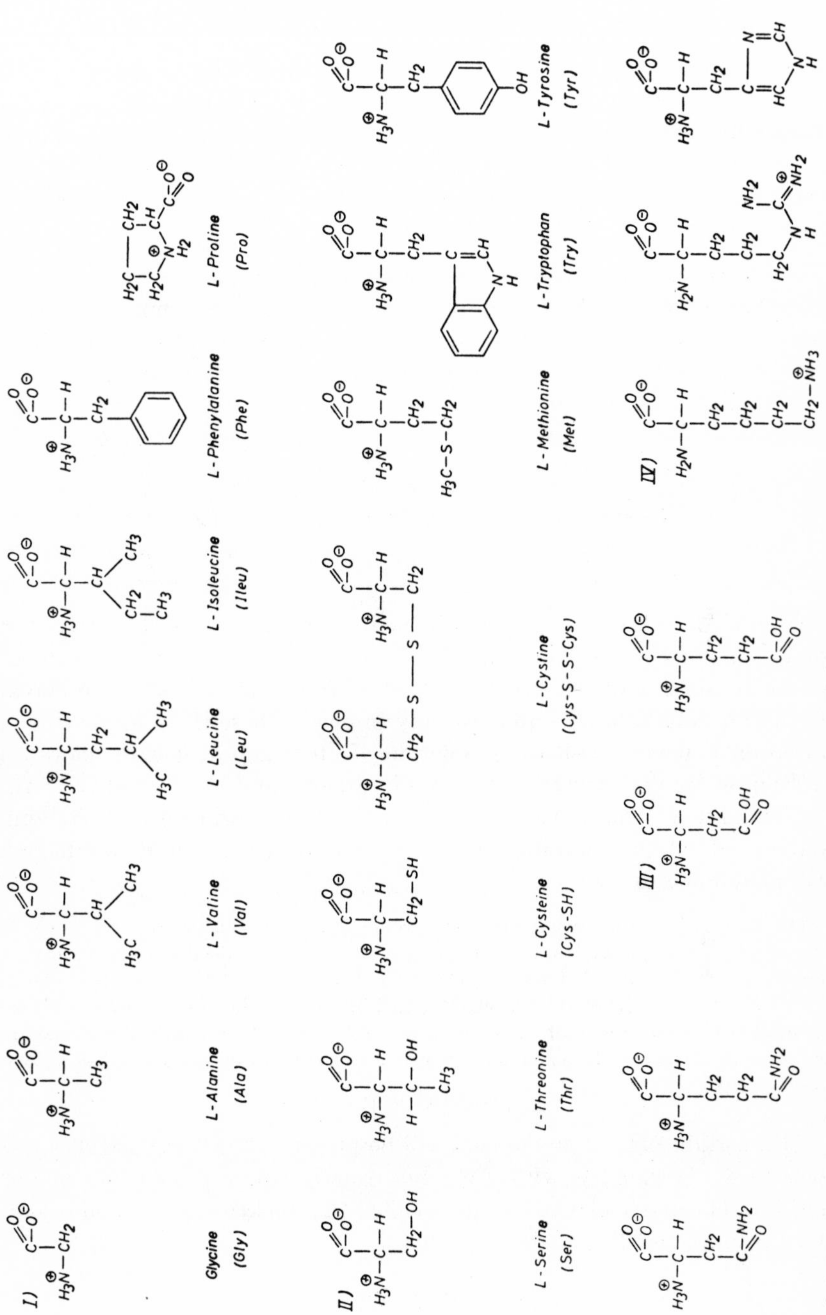

In all cases following the above formula, except when R = H, the α-carbon is substituted asymmetrically. As a result, optical activity appears, since the model cannot be superimposed on its mirror image (cf. Chapt. I–4). We recognize two steric configurations, the D- and the L-series. The amino acids appearing in proteins are members of the L-series. Their α-carbons are substituted just as in L-alanine and L-serine (R = $CH_3$ and $CH_2OH$ respectively). The direction of optical rotation is independent of the configuration.

**Zwitterions.** The carboxyl group, being acidic, can lose a $H^+$ by dissociation. The basic amino group can pick up a proton, in analogy to ammonia: $NH_3 + H^+ \rightarrow NH_4^+$. If both groups are ionized, the result is the so-called zwitterion (German, "ion of both kinds"; amphoteric ion) shown in Formula I. Amino acids in aqueous solution are in zwitterionic form:

$$
\begin{array}{ccc}
\overset{\displaystyle C\overset{O}{\diagup}\!\!\diagdown OH}{|} & \overset{\displaystyle C\overset{O}{\diagup}\!\!\diagdown O^{\ominus}}{|} & \overset{\displaystyle C\overset{O}{\diagup}\!\!\diagdown O^{\ominus}}{|} \\
\overset{\oplus}{H_3N}\!-\!C\!-\!H & \overset{\oplus}{H_3N}\!-\!C\!-\!H & H_2N\!-\!C\!-\!H \\
| & | & | \\
R & R & R \\
\mathrm{II} & \mathrm{I} & \mathrm{III}
\end{array}
$$

The addition of $H^+$ ions (acid) will neutralize the negatively charged groups, as shown in Formula II. Addition of $OH^-$ ions (base) will remove protons attached to the amino groups (cf. Formula III) and form water. A single amino acid molecule in aqueous solution can exist only in one of these three forms (the uncharged variation is never possible). A solution of an amino acid with many quintillions ($10^{18}$) of molecules adjusts itself to a mixture of I and II or I and III with one form predominating. The dissociation constants of the carboxyl and the amino group and the pH of the solution, i.e. the $H^+$ ion concentration, determine which form will predominate.

The dissociation of the acidic and basic groups of amino acids is governed by the law of mass action as with all weak acids and bases. To each group is ascribed a dissociation constant, $K$, whose negative logarithm is called the pK value (cf. Chapt. I-2, Dissociation of Carboxylic Acids). The pK of the carboxyl group is around 2.0 to 2.5; evidently in amino acids the carboxyl group is dissociated to a much greater extent than in acetic acid (pK = 4.65). The amino group, which may also be considered to be an acid according to the following equation, has a pK ranging between 9.0 and 9.5:

$$R—NH_3^+ = R—NH_2 + H^+$$

At a certain pH, an amino acid will be present almost exclusively in its zwitterionic form (Formula I) with little, but exactly equal, proportions of Formulas II and III. This particular pH value is called the *isoelectric point*, and it can be calculated from the acidic and basic groups:

$$\frac{pK_1 + pK_2}{2} = \text{I.P.}$$

The amino acid appears to be without charge, although each molecule carries one positive and one negative charge.

**General Reactions.** The usual derivatives can be prepared from the two functional groups of amino acids (cf. Chapt. I–2).

Salt formation of the carboxyl group has already been discussed in principle; Formula III depicts the anion of a salt.

The carboxyl group can be esterified:

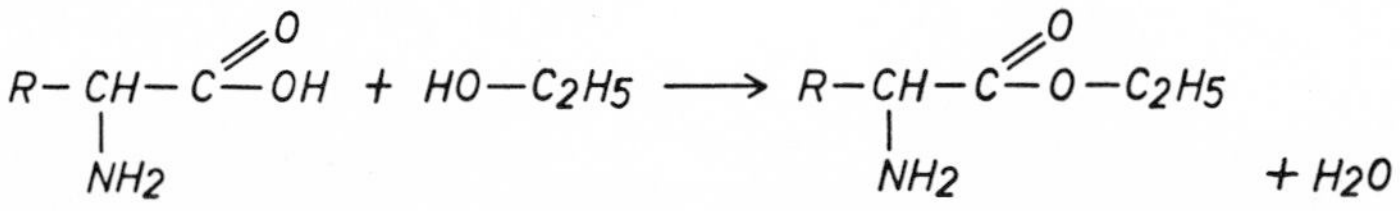

$$R-CH-C{\overset{O}{\diagup}}OH + HO-C_2H_5 \longrightarrow R-CH-C{\overset{O}{\diagup}}O-C_2H_5$$
$$\quad\ \ |\qquad\qquad\qquad\qquad\qquad\qquad |$$
$$\quad\ \ NH_2\qquad\qquad\qquad\qquad\qquad\ NH_2 \qquad\quad + H_2O$$

Furthermore, acid chlorides, hydrazides, anhydrides, etc., may be prepared; they are important in chemical syntheses.

Of biochemical significance is the formation of amides. Ammonia affords unsubstituted amides

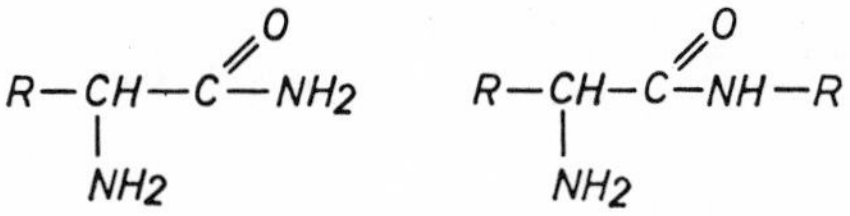

$$R-CH-C{\overset{O}{\diagup}}NH_2 \qquad R-CH-C{\overset{O}{\diagup}}NH-R$$
$$\quad\ \ |\qquad\qquad\qquad\qquad\quad |$$
$$\quad\ \ NH_2\qquad\qquad\qquad\qquad NH_2$$

while amines produce substituted amides, better known as peptides (cf. Chapt. III).

Salt formation, again, is also one of the reactions of the amino group. As with ammonia, it consists of an addition of a proton from another acid:

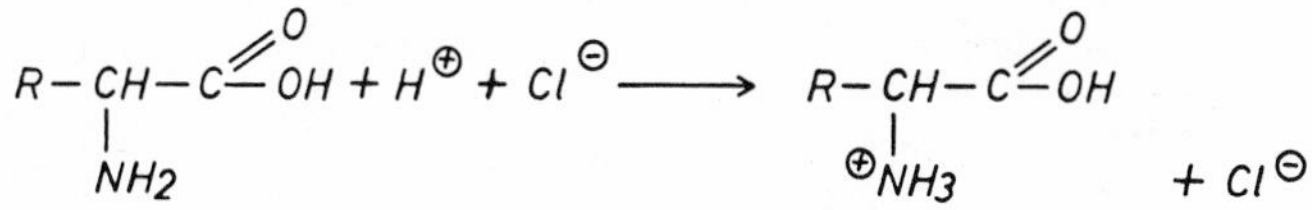

$$R-CH-C{\overset{O}{\diagup}}OH + H^{\oplus} + Cl^{\ominus} \longrightarrow R-CH-C{\overset{O}{\diagup}}OH$$
$$\quad\ \ |\qquad\qquad\qquad\qquad\qquad\qquad\qquad |$$
$$\quad\ \ NH_2\qquad\qquad\qquad\qquad\qquad\quad {}^{\oplus}NH_3 \qquad + Cl^{\ominus}$$

Another important reaction is acylation, which yields again acid amides. The acetyl and benzoyl derivatives of glycine (the latter is called hippuric acid) occur naturally, in addition to a few other compounds of similar composition. If the acylating agent is another amino acid, the result is a peptide.

Carbobenzoxy derivatives play an eminent role in synthetic chemistry, because they can be cleaved by catalytic hydrogenation. Hydrogenolytic cleavage leaves intact bonds which are quite sensitive toward hydrolysis, e.g., peptide bonds (for the reactions involved cf. Chapt. III-1).

Amino groups may also be alkylated, e.g. with methyl groups. Methyl derivatives of glycine play a physiological role.

Reaction with nitrous acid yields hydroxy acids involving the unstable diazo intermediates:

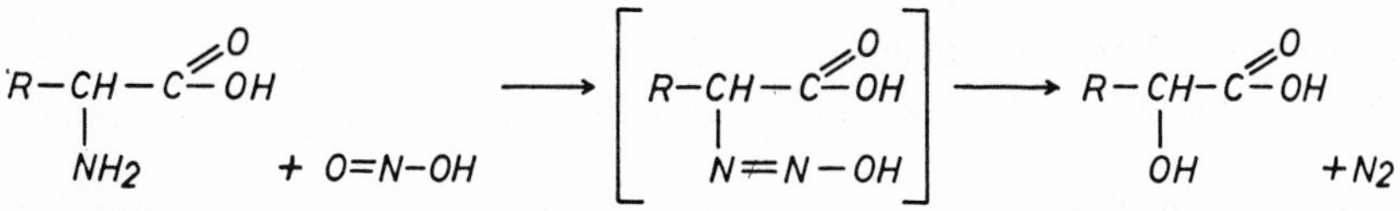

$$R-CH-C{\overset{O}{\diagup}}OH \longrightarrow \left[ R-CH-C{\overset{O}{\diagup}}OH \right] \longrightarrow R-CH-C{\overset{O}{\diagup}}OH$$
$$\quad\ \ |\qquad\qquad\qquad\qquad\quad |\qquad\qquad\qquad\qquad\quad |$$
$$\quad\ \ NH_2 \quad + O{=}N{-}OH \qquad N{=}N{-}OH \qquad\qquad\quad OH \qquad +N_2$$

This reaction has been employed by Van Slyke for the determination of amino acids and amino groups in large molecular combinations.

One important color reaction of amino acids is the reaction with ninhydrin. It is the most widely used method for detecting and determining amino acids and follows the scheme shown here:

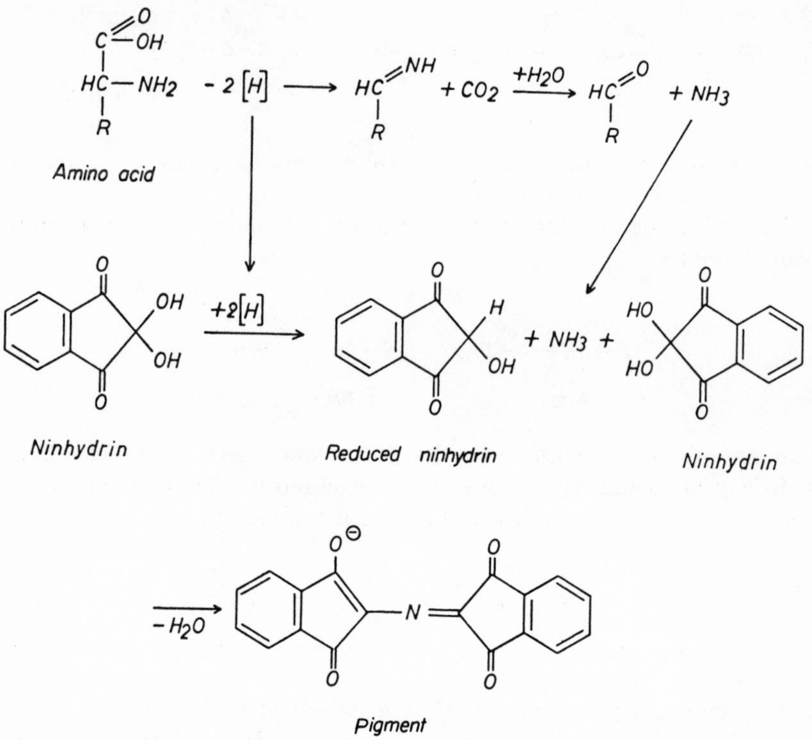

The amino acid is degraded to the next lower aldehyde and $CO_2$. The reagent combines with the ammonia liberated and produces a blue color.

## 2. Individual Amino Acids

Twenty different amino acids regularly appear in proteins. As is evident from the general formula (cf. Chapt. II–1), they differ only in the substituent R. The formulas of these amino acids are found in Table IV. One system of classification groups the amino acids into four divisions:

I. Amino acids with a nonpolar R, i.e. with an unsubstituted hydrocarbon side chain: glycine, alanine, valine, leucine, isoleucine, proline,[1] and phenylalanine.

---

[1] The amino acid proline does not follow the general formula given at the beginning of this chapter, but possesses a secondary amino group. Yet, we classify it as one with a nonpolar R.

II. Amino acids with un-ionized, but polar substituents, such as —OH, —SH, —CO·NH₂, and a few heterocyclic ones: tyrosine, tryptophan, serine, threonine, cysteine, cystine, and methionine. To this group belong also asparagine and glutamine, the acid amides of the acidic amino acids (Group III). The acidic properties of the carboxyl group are lost through amide formation.

III. Acidic amino acids, or monoamino, dicarboxylic acids, containing an additional carboxyl group: glutamic acid and aspartic acid.

IV. Basic amino acids, or diamino, monocarboxylic acids, containing an additional amino group: lysine, arginine, histidine.

V. Less common amino acids.

The organism of man and most animals cannot synthesize every amino acid. Some must be supplied in the diet, and consequently they are known as essential amino acids (see the list in Chapt. VIII–6).

**Group I, Nonpolar Side Chains.** *Glycine* (aminoacetic acid) is the simplest amino acid and the only one lacking an asymmetric C atom.

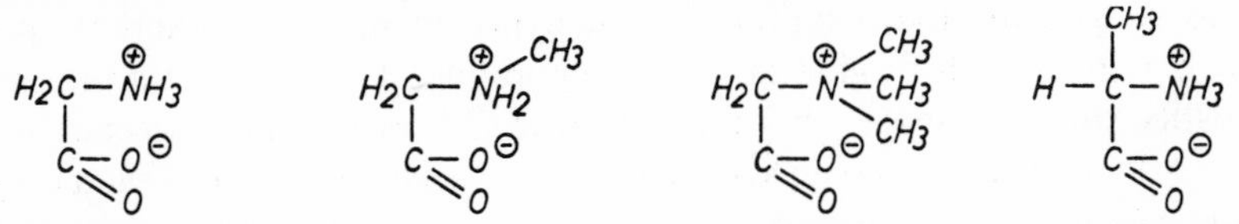

Glycine    Sarcosine    Betaine    L-Alanine

Glycine is present abundantly in scleroproteins (fibrous protein; cf. Chapt. IV–3). Methylation yields sarcosine, which occurs in several peptides. Further methylation yields betain. This substance exists exclusively in the zwitterionic or salt form (zwitterionic formulas sometimes are called betain structures).

The glycine conjugates, acetylglycine and benzoylglycine (hippuric acid) have already been mentioned. Bile acids form similar derivatives (conjugates) with glycine (cf. Chapt. XIV–5).

*Alanine* (α-aminopropionic acid). All amino acids, except glycine, may be regarded as derivatives of alanine; by replacement of one or two H atoms of the methyl group, all the other amino acids can be constructed.

*Valine* (α-aminoisovaleric acid), *leucine* (α-aminoisocaproic acid), and *isoleucine* (α-amino-β-methylvaleric acid) each possess a branched carbon chain. Chemically they are quite alike. Leucine and isoleucine, in particular, provide enough difficulty in separation so that they are usually determined together. Most animals cannot synthesize the branched carbon chain. These amino acids, therefore, are indispensable or essential in the diet (cf. list in Chapt. VIII–6).

*Proline* (2-pyrrolidinecarboxylic acid), frequently found in protein hydrolyzates, is a cyclic amino acid. The amino group in α-position has become part of the ring and consequently is a secondary amino group instead of being the usual primary.

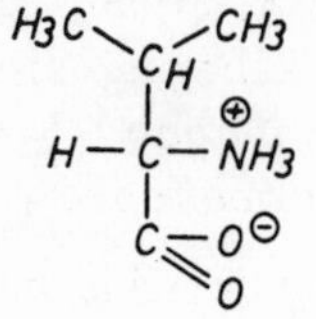

L - Valine 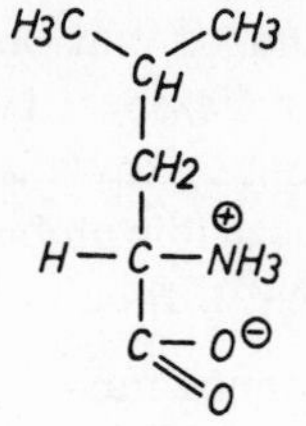          L - Leucine 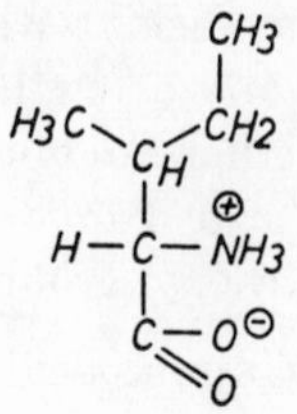          L - Isoleucine

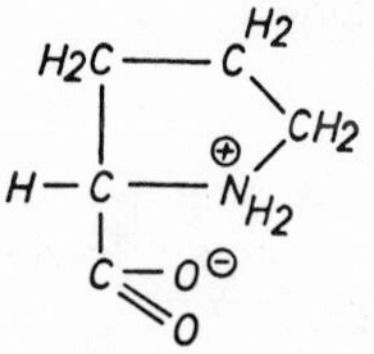

L - Proline 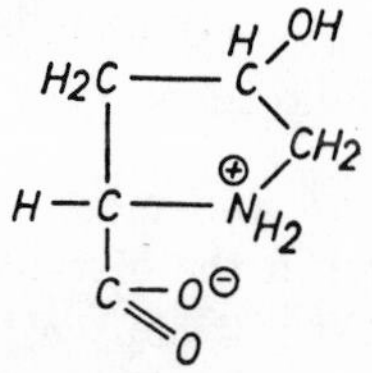          L - Hydroxyproline

The same is true for hydroxyproline, which occurs only in structural proteins. Collagen is rich in both proline and hydroxyproline. The hydroxy group actually would justify the inclusion of this amino acid in Group II. These secondary amino acids are still called "imino acids" after some archaic chemical nomenclature. Compounds containing the group

$$\begin{array}{c} C \\ \diagdown \\ NH \\ \diagup \\ C \end{array}$$

and formerly called "imines" must not be confused with the true imines, which contain the imino group,

$$\diagdown C{=}NH.$$

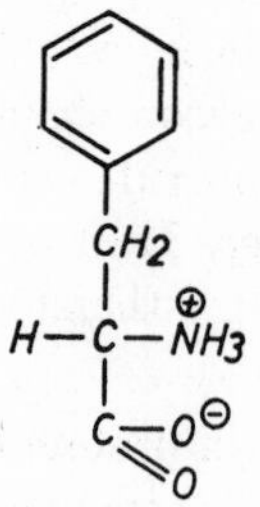

L -Phenylalanine 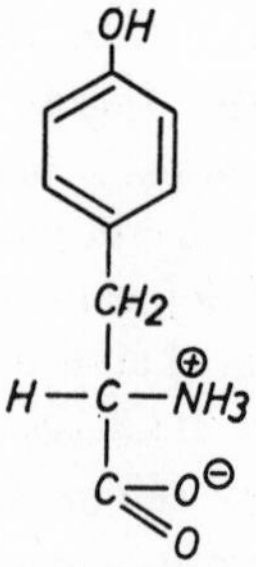          L -Tyrosine 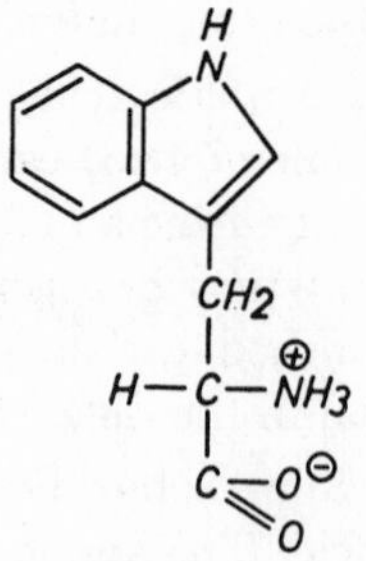          L -Tryptophan

*Phenylalanine* (α-amino-β-phenylpropionic acid) cannot be formed in the animal organism because of its aromatic ring. It is closely related to tyrosine which belongs to Group II with its phenolic —OH group.

**Group II, Un-ionized Polar Acids.** *Tyrosine* (α-amino-β-(*p*-hydroxyphenyl) alanine). The phenolic group of tyrosine is weakly acidic and loses its proton at a pH above 9.

*Tryptophan* (α-amino-β-3-indolepropionic acid) is a heterocyclic amino acid, being a derivative of indole (with one N atom).

The three amino acids phenylalanine, tyrosine, and tryptophan may be grouped together on the basis of their aromatic substituents.

*Serine* (α-amino-β-hydroxypropionic acid) contains an alcoholic hydroxyl group which may engage in the usual reactions, such as ester formation. Esters with phosphoric acid have physiological significance as components of nucleotides and some proteins. The unesterified serine residue appears to possess special functions in several enzymes.

*Threonine* (α-amino-β-hydroxybutyric acid) is the next higher homolog to serine. Its name points to the relationship with the sugar threose. Threonine has two asymmetric centers (cf. Chapt. I–4) manifested by four stereoisomeric forms of which two are always mirror images of the other two; namely D- and L-threonine and D- and L-allothreonine. Threonine was discovered in an interesting manner: it was identified as a necessary supplementary factor of a synthetic diet mixture (Rose 1935) and thus became the first amino acid to be recognized as indispensable.

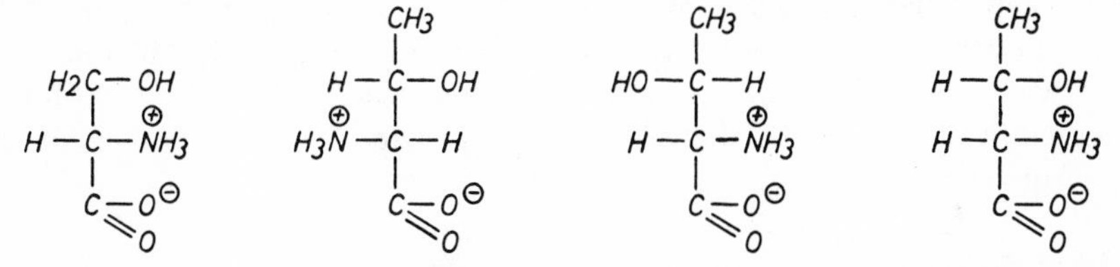

L-Serine        D-Threonine        L-Threonine        L-Allothreonine

*Cysteine* (α-amino-β-mercaptopropionic acid) contains sulfur. The SH group is quite reactive and especially easily dehydrogenated (even while part of a peptide chain). When it is dehydrogenated (i.e. oxidized), two molecules will join to form the amino acid cystine (compare with reaction of glutathione, cf. Chapt. III–3).

*Cystine* (di-[α-amino-β-mercaptopropionic acid]). Being a diamino-dicarboxylic acid, cystine may be attached to two different peptide chains at the same time, or to the same chain at widely separated places; such S—S linkages occur in many proteins.

*Methionine* (α-amino-γ-methylmercaptobutyric acid) may be looked upon as a methylation product of homocysteine. Aside from its role as a protein constituent and as an essential amino acid, methionine is also important as a donor of active methyl groups.

L-Cysteine          L-Cystine               L-Homocysteine    L-Methionine

*Asparagine* and *glutamine*, the amides of the "acidic amino acids," are grouped here. The amide group bestows hydrophilic properties to these two amino acids. Acid or alkaline hydrolysis of proteins also splits amide groups, and ammonia and aspartic or glutamic acid are released.

L-Asparagine    L-Glutamine                pH 3            pH 7              L-Glutamate
                                              L-Aspartate

**Group III, Monoamino, Dicarboxylic Acids.** *Aspartic* (aminosuccinic) and *glutamic* (α-aminoglutaric) acids. Both are monoamino, dicarboxylic acids; their side chain, in other words, contains an extra carboxyl group with a dissociable proton. The resulting additional negative charge is very important for the electrochemical behavior of proteins.

**Group IV, Diamino, Monocarboxylic Acids.** *Lysine* (α,ε-diaminocaproic acid) is distinguished by the extra amino group in its side chain which imparts basic properties to it. Depending on the pH of the solution, lysine may bear various charges. Furthermore, *hydroxylysine* has been discovered in collagen.

pH 9            pH 5              L-Hydroxylysine    L-Arginine        L-Histidine
      L-Lysine

*Arginine* (α-amino-δ-guanidinovaleric acid) is another basic amino acid. Due to the guanidino group, arginine is more strongly basic than lysine.

*Histidine* (α-amino-β-imidazolepropionic acid), the last entry in this list, contains the only weakly basic imidazole system (pK = 6.1). In many enzyme proteins it functions as a proton donor or acceptor.

**Group V, Less Common Amino Acids.** Besides the 20 amino acids regularly present in proteins, several others occur in natural material. Some are found free in plant or animal tissue; some are bound to simple peptides and more rarely to special proteins; others function as intermediates in metabolism. From the great number of possible examples only a few have been selected.

Both *hydroxyproline* and *hydroxylysine* mentioned above have been found only in protein of connective tissue. In protein from corn, *α-aminoadipic acid* (one $CH_2$ group more than glutamic acid) was detected, and in bacterial protein, *α,ε-diaminopimelic acid*:

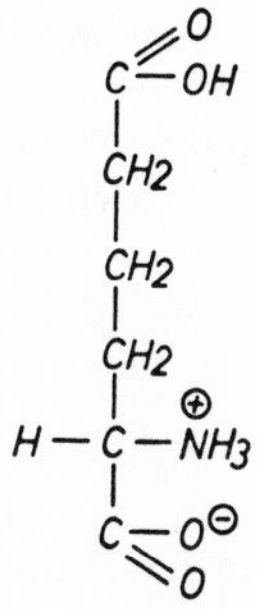

L-α-Amino-adipic acid 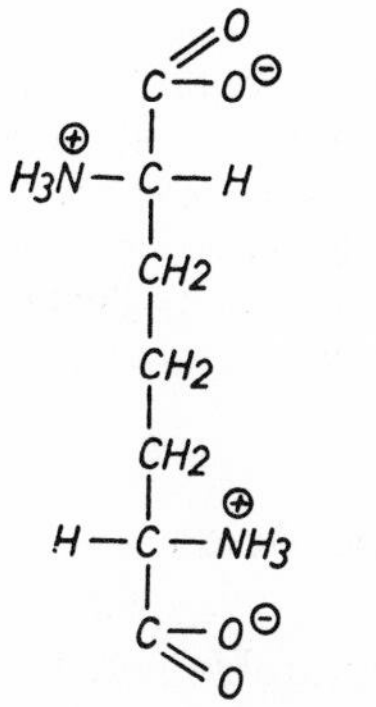     L,L-α,ε-Diamino-pimelic acid 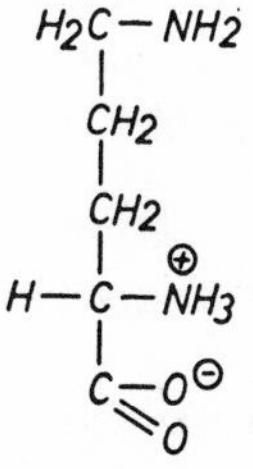     L-Ornithine 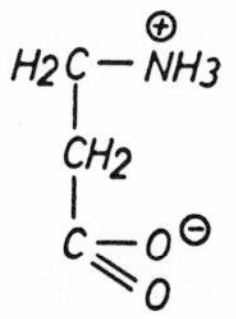     β-Alanine 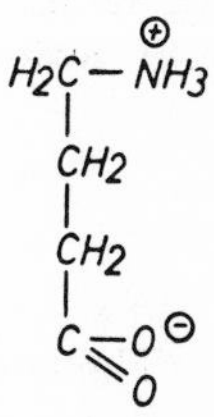     γ-Amino-butyric acid

There are some amino acids that occur in several peptides, but not in proteins. They arise by ordinary metabolic processes from the common amino acids. Examples are *ornithine* (from arginine, cf. Chapt. VIII–8); *β-alanine* (from aspartic acid, cf. Chapt. VIII–5), a component, among other things, of the vitamin pantothenic acid (cf. Chapt. VI–5); and lastly, *γ-aminobutyric acid* in free form in the brain.

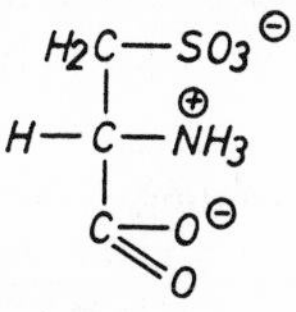

L-Cysteic acid 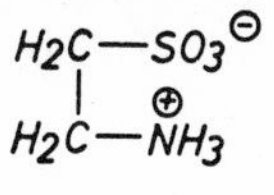     Taurine 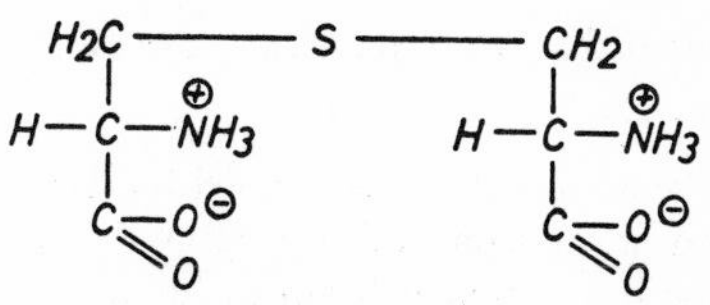     L-Lanthionine

Sulfur-containing amino acids related to cysteine and methionine are *cysteic acid* and its decarboxylation product *taurine*. *Lanthionine*, with one sulfur atom less than cystine, has been isolated from wool hydrolyzates. *Homocysteine* is the de-methylation product of methionine.

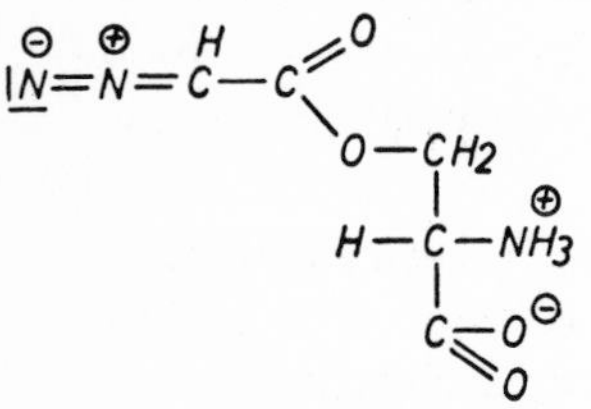

| Azaserine | Cycloserine | L-Phenylserine | D-Chloramphenicol |

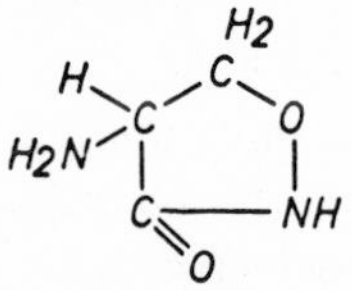

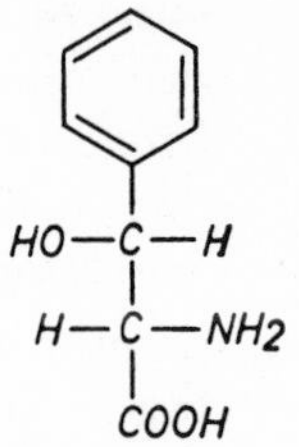

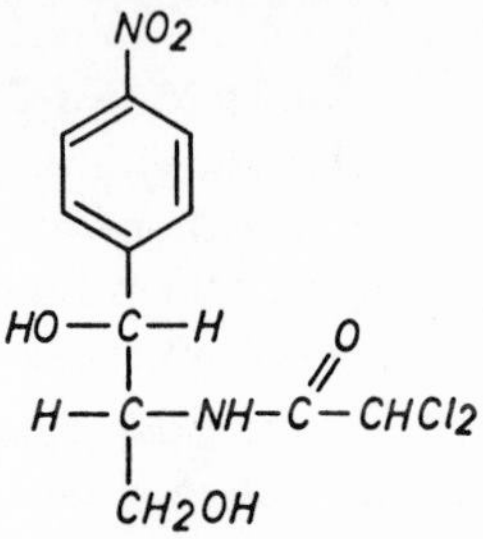

Two derivatives of serine produced by streptomyces have become recognized as antibiotics: *azaserine* with an unusual diazoacetyl group and *cycloserine*. Further, *chloramphenicol* (chloromyce-tin) should be mentioned, because it is structurally similar to *phenylserine* and is applied thera-peutically as an antibiotic. With the last few examples, it should be noted that apparently micro-organisms readily synthesize functional groups that seem entirely "unphysiological" such as nitro, hydroxylamino, dichloroacetyl, and diazoacetyl groups.

## 3. Separation of Amino Acids

The components of proteins may be freed by hydrolysis. After protein has been boiled in 6 $N$ hydrochloric acid for some time, a mixture of amino acids is obtained. The first step in the analysis of proteins is to determine the content of amino acids both qualitatively and quantitatively. This approach has met with great difficulty, since amino acids are chemically rather similar and often have identical functional groups. Progress had been held up for decades because of these analytical problems. Two methods have been developed since 1940, with outstanding results: paper chromatography[2] and ion-exchange chromatography.

**Paper Chromatography.** Its primary purpose is the identification of amino acids (or other substances); very small amounts (5 $\mu$g and less) may be detected. The technique is simple. The material is applied to filter paper and allowed to come into equilibrium with the vapors of a solvent. The paper is then dipped into the

---

[2] Chromatography was defined by Tswett (1906) as a procedure for separating dyes based on repeated adsorption and desorption in successive layers of some absorption medium. Later the term has been applied to all techniques of separation in which a selective process is repeated a great number of times on carrier material. Minute differences in properties are thus magnified for effective separation.

organic solvent system which is drawn up by capillary action and carries the mixture of substances with it part of the way. Easily soluble substances are carried farther than less soluble ones. Substances are separated according to their relative solubilities in water and in the organic solvent. The distance traveled by a substance relative to the distance the solvent rises is called the $R_f$ value (cf. Fig. 3).

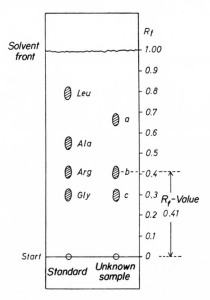

FIG. 3. Separation of amino acids by paper chromatography. Substance a is unknown; b is identical with arginine, c with glycine.

With minimal technical effort, paper chromatography provides excellent separation not only of amino acids but also of many other substances, as long as the correct solvent system is chosen. Particularly, its use for qualitative fractionation and identification has become valuable. Monographs should be consulted for the various applications and modifications of the method.

**Ion-Exchange Chromatography.** For the quantitative separation and determination of amino acids from hydrolyzates the preferred method is now ion-exchange chromatography. Ion-exchange resins are synthetic polymers with many acidic or basic groups. Each of the acidic groups (—$SO_3H$ or —COOH) can dissociate one proton which, however, for electrostatic reasons, remains in the vicinity. The proton may move away only when another positively charged ion (cation) takes its place. This is the mechanism of ion exchange. For example, $Na^+$ or $NH_4^+$ in solution are loosely bound to the resin and $H^+$ ions are released in exchange into solution until equilibrium concentrations are re-established. Analogously, the $OH^-$ of resin —$NH_3^+OH^-$ may exchange for $Cl^-$ or R—$COO^-$.

In practice, a "column" is prepared by filling a glass tube with resin in its $Na^+$ form. The solution of amino acids is allowed to seep into the top layer of resin and

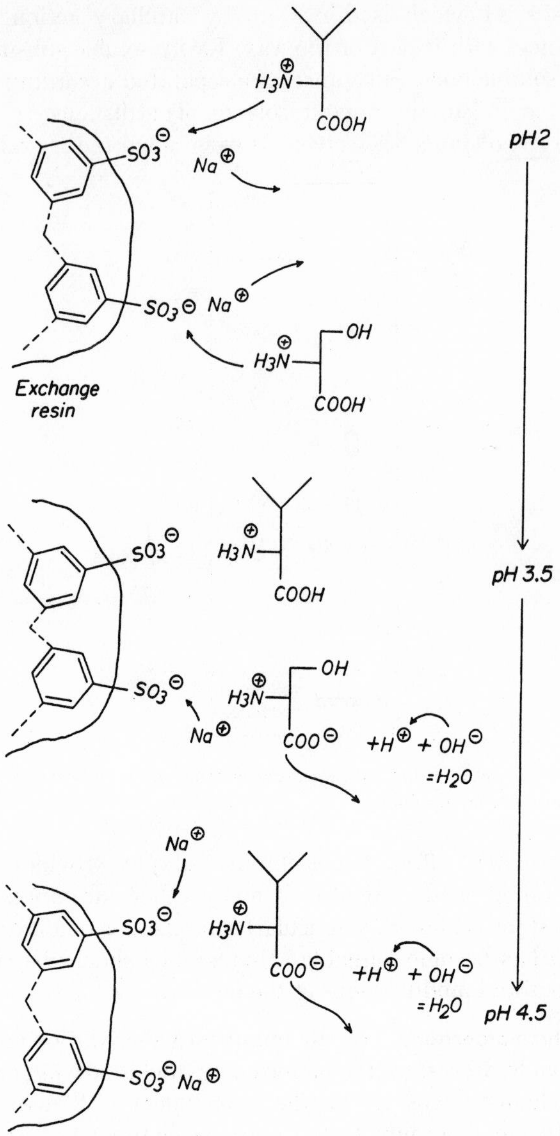

FIG. 4. Mechanism of ion-exchange chromatography of amino acids.

then is eluted slowly with a buffer to hold the H⁺ concentration approximately constant. At first the amino acid cation is bound, but later it is released in exchange for a Na⁺ of the buffer when it converts to zwitterionic form (cf. Fig. 4). This exchange process is repeated layer after layer until the amino acid leaves the column in the eluate where it may be determined quantitatively by the ninhydrin reaction. Curves can be drawn as shown in Fig. 5.

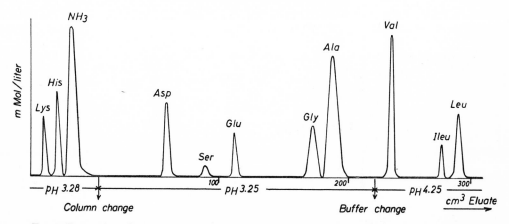

FIG. 5. Separation of amino acids by ion-exchange chromatography (partial diagram). Abscissa: volume of eluant; ordinate : concentration of amino acid in eluate (= intensity of ninhydrin color).

To what extent an amino acid is bound by exchange resins is, of course, a function of the degree of ionization of the amino acid, i.e., of the dissociation constant $K$ of the individual groups and the pH of the elutant. In other words, this method of fractionation utilizes the rather small differences of ionization of amino or carboxyl groups. Fully automatic but rather intricate apparatuses have been developed that carry out the chromatography and the measurement of ninhydrin color in the eluates, and plot the result as a curve.

BIBLIOGRAPHY

R. J. Block (editor), "Amino Acid Handbook," C. C Thomas, Springfield, Illinois, 1956.
G. Braunitzer, Fully automatic amino acid separation, *Angew. Chem.* **72**, 485 (1960).
J. P. Greenstein and M. Winitz, "Chemistry of the Amino Acids," 3 Vols., Wiley, New York, 1961.
A. Meister, "Biochemistry of the Amino Acids," 2nd ed., 2 Vols. Academic Press, New York, 1965.

# CHAPTER III

# Peptides

## 1. Structure and Nomenclature

Chemically peptides are acid amides. According to the definition in Chapt. I–3, they are combinations of compounds and may be decomposed by hydrolysis to amino acids:

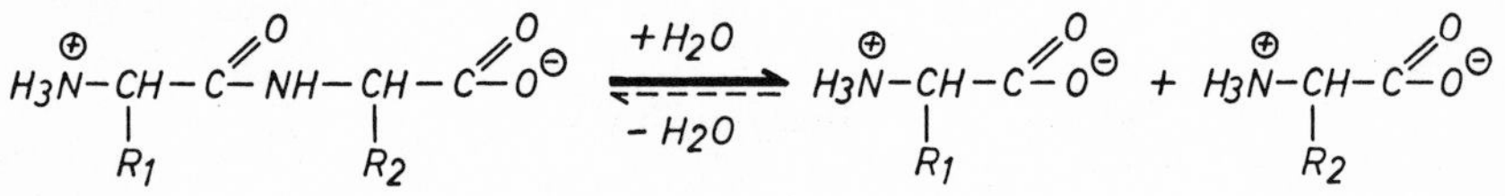

$$\overset{\oplus}{H_3N}-CH-\overset{O}{\underset{R_1}{C}}-NH-CH-\overset{O}{\underset{R_2}{C}}-O^{\ominus} \underset{-H_2O}{\overset{+H_2O}{\rightleftharpoons}} \overset{\oplus}{H_3N}-CH-\overset{O}{\underset{R_1}{C}}-O^{\ominus} + \overset{\oplus}{H_3N}-CH-\overset{O}{\underset{R_2}{C}}-O^{\ominus}$$

The above reaction comes to equilibrium, as every chemical reaction does, but strongly favors the direction of hydrolysis. The major reason is that peptide links arise only from the un-ionized nonpolar forms of amino acids, which in practice do not exist in aqueous solution.

The bond

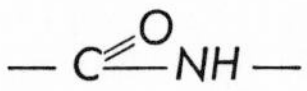

$$-C\overset{O}{\nearrow}NH-$$

is called the peptide bond. In a typical peptide both components are amino acids. However, in some substances, only the amine component is an amino acid. Although such substances should more properly be called acyl amino acids, occasionally they are included among the peptides.

Two amino acids form a dipeptide, three a tripeptide, eight an octapeptide, etc. If a peptide is made up of not more than ten amino acids it is called an oligopeptide; beyond that it is a polypeptide. Polypeptides become proteins when they are made up of over a hundred amino acids; sometimes they are also called "macropeptides." Since in systematic nomenclature peptides are acyl amino acids, the specific name for peptides is derived by attaching the ending -yl to that amino acid whose carboxyl group has undergone reaction; e.g. glycylalanine and alanylleucyltyrosine.

Complete knowledge of peptides is not satisfied by merely knowing the kind or number of the component amino acids; it must include the sequence in which they are linked. Notice that even the dipeptide glycylalanine is not the same as alanylglycine.

To avoid lengthy names a suggestion by Brand and Edsall will be followed here. Amino acid residues are abbreviated by the first three letters of the name of the amino acid. Therefore, Ala stands for the alanyl-, Glu for the glutamyl-, His for the histidyl residue, etc. (summarized in Table IV). The amide group (as in glutamine) and the cystine link are expressed especially by adding —NH₂ and —S—S; end groups are indicated by —H and —OH. The accompanying figure

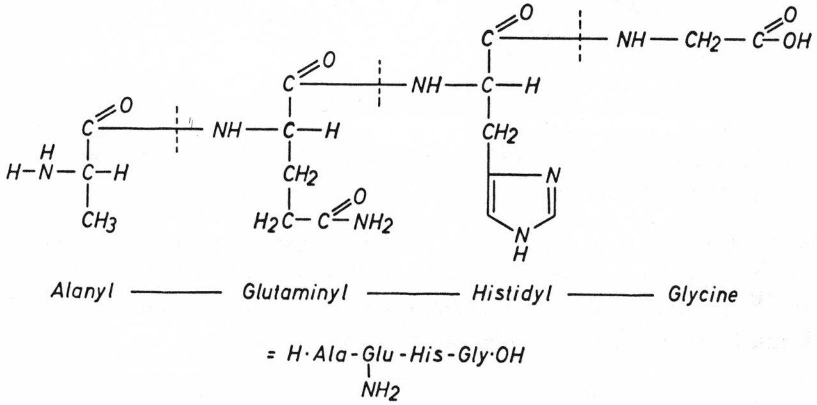

Alanyl ———— Glutaminyl ———— Histidyl ———— Glycine

$$= H \cdot Ala - Glu - His - Gly \cdot OH$$
$$NH_2$$

compares a structural formula with the systematic name and its abbreviated form. In writing the formulas of peptides, by convention, the terminal amino group is always written to the left. If this proves impractical, then an arrow indicates the direction: CO → NH. We will frequently use these conventions, since they are used widely in describing sequences of amino acids.

## 2. Determination of Amino Acid Sequence in Peptides

It is of equal importance to ascertain the sequence of amino acids in naturally occurring peptides as in peptides found in protein hydrolyzates (cf. Chapt. IV–2). The methods can be indicated only briefly. Terminal amino groups are allowed to react with fluorodinitrobenzene. Hydrolysis frees the characteristically yellow dinitrophenylamino compounds (Sanger).

The labeling group is retained during hydrolysis. Along with all the other amino acids *one* dinitrophenylamino acid is obtained which, of course, originally was the one with a free amino group, i.e. the N-terminal amino acid It is. identified easily.

The Edman degradation permits one to remove the N-terminal amino acid in the form of a hydantoin derivative; the procedure may then be repeated on the remaining peptide, which is thus degraded stepwise.

Other methods have been developed for the identification of carboxyl-terminal (C-terminal) amino acids.

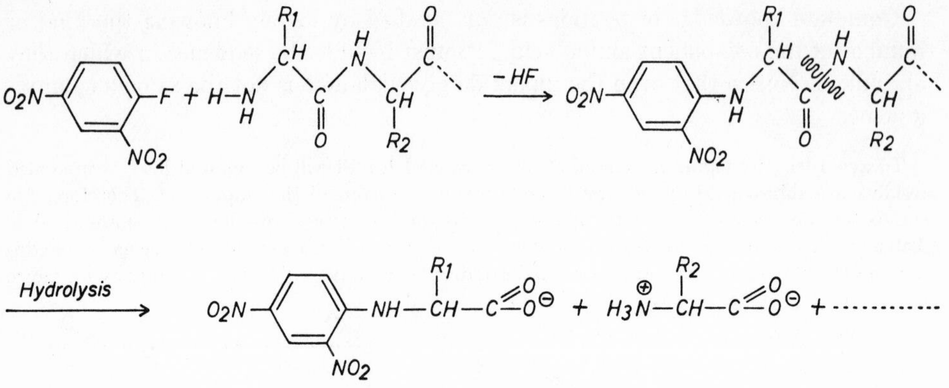

Finally, enzymic methods are available for the cleavage of larger peptides and for the identification of terminal groups (cf. Chapt. VIII–3). Long sequences have been established in this way.

**Peptide Synthesis.** Any synthesis of peptides must resort to some activation (cf. Chapt. I–2) of the carboxyl or the amino group. One of the oldest methods of organic chemistry involves acid chlorides. In that case, the amino group of amino acids must be protected, e.g. by a carbobenzoxy residue:

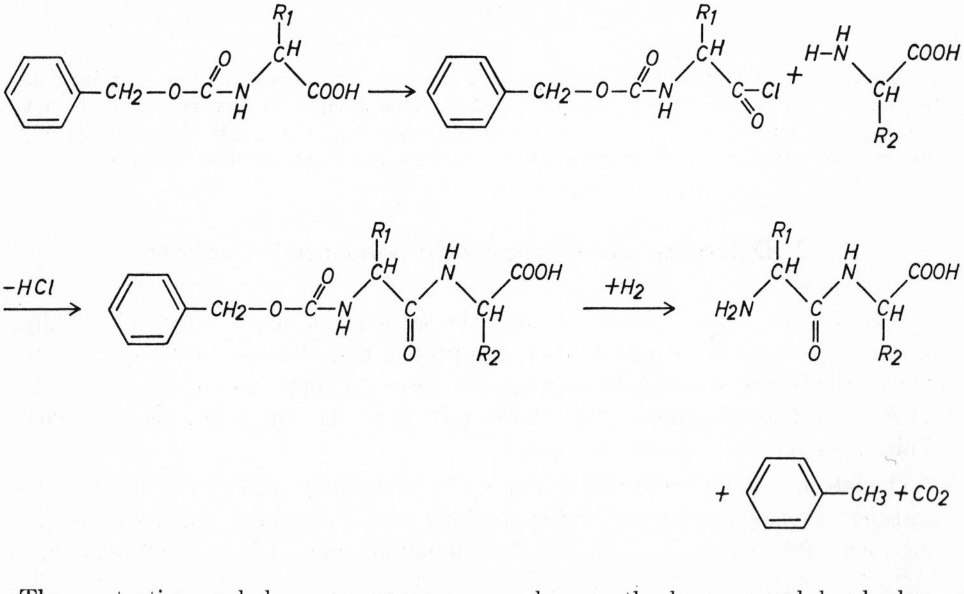

The protective carbobenzoxy group may subsequently be removed by hydrogenolysis (cleavage by catalytically activated hydrogen).

Chemical synthesis of peptides has been important for the development of peptide chemistry. We cannot describe all the newer methods which employ various other derivatives for activation.

One important feature has been the prevention of racemization of amino acids. Numerous longer peptides, including peptide hormones, have recently been synthesized. Some synthetic peptides, being well-defined substrates, have served in the study of proteinases and peptidases.

## 3. Naturally Occurring Peptides

*Glutathione* ($\gamma$-glutamylcysteylglycine) is a natural and widely distributed peptide.

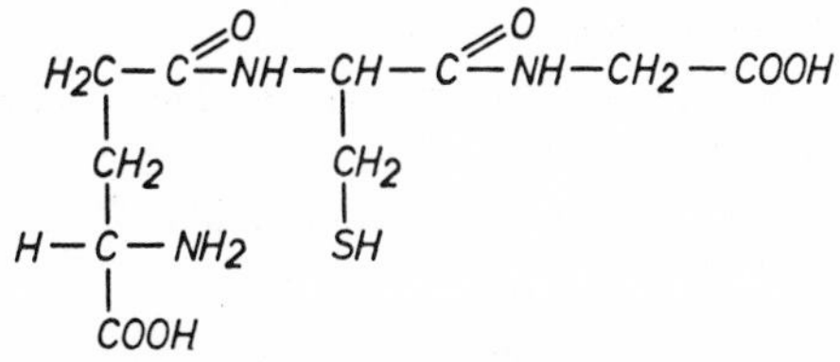

*Glutathione*

Note that here, in contrast to most peptides and proteins, the $\gamma$-carboxyl group of glutamic acid has entered the peptide bond. Glutathione is easily dehydrogenated and converted to the disulfide form. The reaction can be taken as an oxidation if the ionic form of glutathione is assumed to lose one electron pair (SH groups are weakly acidic since they derive from hydrogen sulfide):

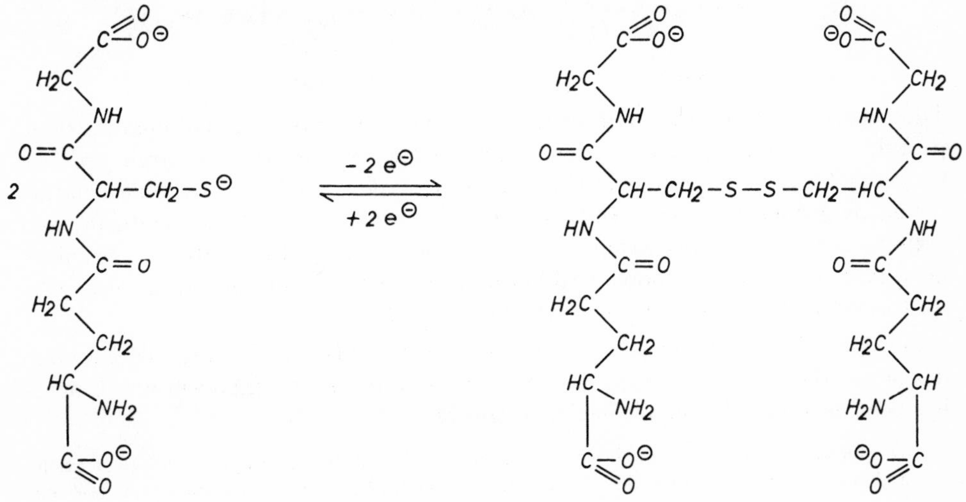

The reaction is reversible and glutathione hence is considered to be a biologic redox system. It is the coenzyme to glyoxalase.

Carnosine and anserine are found in muscle; both are dipeptides of $\beta$-alanine and histidine. Their biologic role is still unknown (cf. pantothenic acid, Chapt. VI–5).

$$H_3\overset{\oplus}{N} - CH_2 - CH_2 - C\overset{O}{\underset{}{}}NH - \underset{\underset{}{CH}}{\overset{C\overset{O}{\diagdown}O^{\ominus}}{}}$$

Carnosine

$$H_3\overset{\oplus}{N} - CH_2 - CH_2 - C\overset{O}{\underset{}{}}NH - \underset{\underset{}{CH}}{\overset{C\overset{O}{\diagdown}O^{\ominus}}{}}$$

Anserine

**Protamines** are highly basic polypeptides of molecular weights between 1000 and 5000. They are isolated from fish sperm where they occur together with nucleic acids. Their arginine content is very high; clupein, e.g., consists of 22 moles of arginine and only 11 moles of all other amino acids (K. Felix). Nothing is known about their biologic function.

**Peptide Hormones.** Several hormones of the pituitary gland and the pancreas are peptides. First we mention *ocytocin*[1] and *vasopressin*:

```
H·Cys ──→ Tyr                 H·Cys ──→ Tyr
  |        ↓                     |        ↓
  S       Ileu                   S       Phe
  |        ↓                     |        ↓
  S      Glu (NH2)               S      Glu (NH2)
  |        ↓                     |        ↓
 Cys ←── Asp(NH2)               Cys ←── Asp(NH2)
  ↓                              ↓
 Pro ──→ Leu ──→ Gly-NH2        Pro ──→ Lys ──→ Gly-NH2
                                         (Arg)

      Ocytocin                       Vasopressin
```

The occurrence of cystine, one of whose amino groups is terminal, enables these peptides to assume a ring structure. Lysine may be replaced by arginine. The C-terminal glycine is present in the form of its amide. *Vasotocin* is the designation for an analogous hormone, which has isoleucine in position 3 (as ocytocin) and arginine in position 8 (as vasopressin). First produced synthetically, it was subsequently identified as a hypophyseal hormone of frogs. The physiological roles differ for these chemically similar hormones (cf. Chap. XX).

*Corticotropin*, or adrenocorticotropic *hormone* (ACTH), of the pituitary anterior lobe is a rather complicated peptide. The sequence of its 39 component amino acids has been established. The molecular weight is 4500.

It is interesting to observe that in corticotropins of different animal origin (sheep, pigs, cattle) minor changes occur in positions 30–33. The same is true for the melanocyte-stimulating hormone (MSH), or *melanotropin*, of the intermediate lobe of the pituitary gland. In this case, species specificity is also reflected in the length of the peptide chain. The sequence of melanotropin is the same as that of corticotropin for some distance. These sequences and the species-dependent variations are gathered on the reverse side of the foldout chart in the back of the book.

---

[1] Often called oxytocin. We prefer ocytocin, since the name derives from the Greek *oky* = quick and *tokos* = birth; it refers in no way to oxygen.

Insulin:

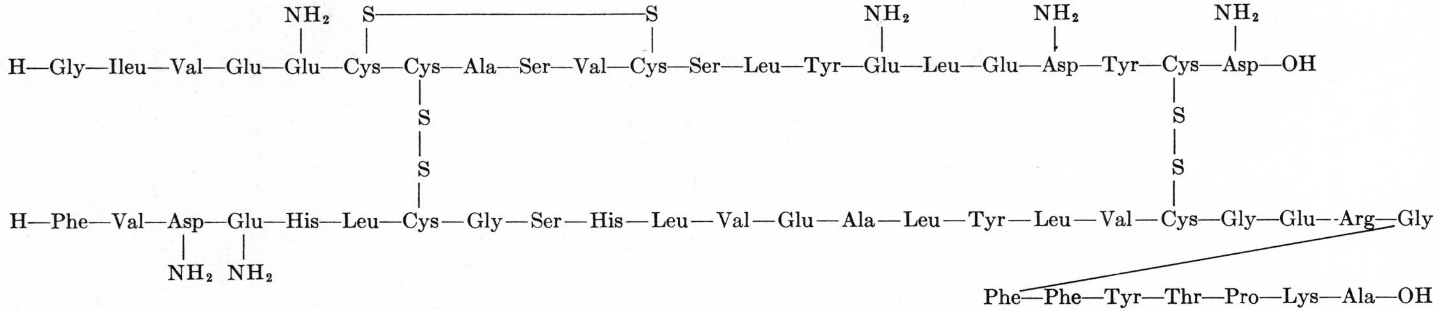

H—Gly—Ileu—Val—Glu—Glu—Cys—Cys—Ala—Ser—Val—Cys—Ser—Leu—Tyr—Glu—Leu—Glu—Asp—Tyr—Cys—Asp—OH

$\;\;\;\;\;\;\;\;$ NH₂ $\;\;\;\;\;$ S $\quad\quad\quad\quad\quad\quad\quad\quad$ S—S $\quad\quad\quad$ NH₂ $\quad\quad\quad\quad$ S—S $\quad\quad$ NH₂

H—Phe—Val—Asp—Glu—His—Leu—Cys—Gly—Ser—His—Leu—Val—Glu—Ala—Leu—Tyr—Leu—Val—Cys—Gly—Glu—Arg—Gly

$\quad\quad\quad\quad\quad$ NH₂ NH₂

Phe—Phe—Tyr—Thr—Pro—Lys—Ala—OH

*Insulin* is secreted by the pancreas. This hormone causes a lowering of blood sugar (cf. Chap. XX). Its molecular weight is 6000 and it should, for that reason, be classified as a peptide. However in solution, particularly in the presence of metal ions, it readily aggregates to form molecules with relative weights of 12,000, 36,000 or 48,000. It is evident that there is no clear distinction between peptides and proteins. Insulin, for this reason, is considered to be the first protein whose structure has been determined completely. The establishment of the sequence of the 51 amino acid residues through Sanger's efforts was an immensely important step for science in general and provided great impetus to protein research in particular.

Sanger and his co-workers broke insulin into small peptides by partial hydrolysis and separated them by paper chromatography. The sequences in these peptide fragments were determined by the dinitrophenyl method and compared with the composition of larger fragments resulting from enzymic cleavage of the insulin molecule. The partial formulas were finally integrated to the complete formula of insulin shown above. The sequence of another pancreatic hormone *glucagon*, composed of 29 amino acid residues, is also known.

*Parathormone*, secreted by the parathyroid gland, is the largest polypeptide analyzed at present. Its molecular weight of 8500 brings it pretty close to that of proteins.

**Antibiotics and Toxins.** Fungi and microorganisms produce various substances with characteristic chemical peculiarities. Either they contain amino acids which are not found in any other proteins or peptides or they have highly unusual linkages.

One of the best known representatives is *penicillin*:

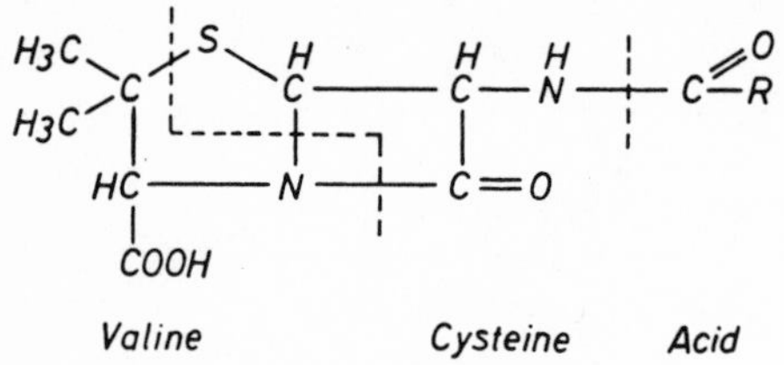

Valine                    Cysteine        Acid

e.g. : $R = -CH_2-\langle\text{phenyl}\rangle$

Penicillin                                         Benzyl penicillin
General formula

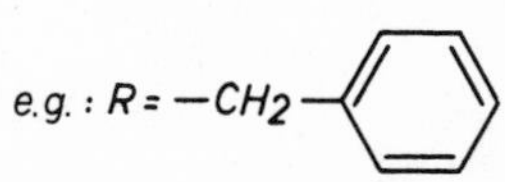

It is produced by the mold *Penicillium notatum* and excreted into the culture medium. Its biogenesis involves the amino acids valine and cysteine; the formula can easily be derived especially if one remembers that the molecule also contains a highly strained four-membered $\beta$-lactam ring and another S-containing ring. The amino group of the cysteine component is acylated; several different radicals may be attached in place of R. At present the bulk of manufactured penicillin carries a benzyl radical, $C_6H_5CH_2$. Recently it has become possible to induce the mold to produce penicillanic acid (lacking the entire group labeled "acid" in the general formula above) and to manufacture from it all the different penicillin derivatives.

Penicillin is the prototype of an *antibiotic*, which is generally defined as a substance that inhibits the growth and multiplication of bacteria and other microorganisms and is of biologic origin. These were the properties responsible for the discovery of penicillin by Fleming in 1928. Antibiotics affect only specific groups of bacteria; they exhibit a definite spectrum of action. Antibiotics are an invaluable aid for the control of infections, because they prevent the rapid growth of the causative agents. Excessive doses occasionally cause undesirable side effects such as destroying the natural intestinal flora and permitting a colony of resistant strains of bacteria or fungi to lodge there. Many antibiotics in high doses are toxic, and only a few have proved generally useful in therapy.

Antibiotics belong to very diverse chemical classes of compounds. *Azaserine* and *chloramphenicol* have already been mentioned (Chapt. II–2). Another peptidic antibiotic is *gramicidin S* which contains an amino acid of the rare D-series, D-phenyl-alanine. It is a cyclic peptide with ten amino acids:

$$\text{Pro} \to \text{Val} \to \text{Orn} \to \text{Leu} \to \text{D-Phe}$$
$$\uparrow \qquad\qquad\qquad\qquad\qquad \downarrow$$
$$\text{D-Phe} \leftarrow \text{Leu} \leftarrow \text{Orn} \leftarrow \text{Val} \leftarrow \text{Pro}$$

*Phalloidin* is one of the poisons of the mushroom *Amanita phalloides* with great toxicity. Only 50 $\mu$g are lethal for a mouse. Seven different amino acids are involved in its structure including such unusual hydroxy amino acids as hydroxyleucine and allothreonine (T. Wieland). There is a bridge between tryptophan and the SH group of cysteine which yields hydroxytryptophan upon hydrolysis. The formula is not reproduced here.

### BIBLIOGRAPHY

E. Bricas and C. Fromageot, Naturally occurring peptides, *Advances in Protein Chem.* **8**, 4 (1953).

C. H. Li, Hormones of the anterior pituitary gland. Part I. Growth and adrenocorticotropic hormones. *Advances in Protein Chem.* **11**, 102 (1956); Part II. Melanocyte-stimulating and lactogenic hormones. **12**, 269 (1957).

R. C. Sheppard, Amino acids and peptides, *Ann. Rept. Chem. Soc., London,* **60**, 448–466; D. G. Smyth, Proteins and peptides, *ibid.,* 468–485 (1963).

# CHAPTER IV

# Proteins

## 1. Structure of Proteins

When a peptide chain is extended by more and more amino acids until a chain length of from one hundred to several thousand amino acid residues[1] is reached, it is classified as a protein.

The term *protein* (Greek: *proteuo*, I occupy first place) was first suggested by Berzelius and used by Mulder (about 1840) in his textbook. The name *protein* is well chosen; all the basic functions of life depend on specific proteins. Indeed, we know no form of life without proteins; they are present in every cell; they make up the contractile elements and the enzymes that catalyze the release of energy for maintenance of life, and they are present in blood where they have a transport function.

The properties of proteins may differ extremely. Consider two generally familiar proteins: Egg-white protein denatures on heating, dissolves easily in water and is quite reactive, while keratin of nails and hoofs is wholly insoluble, tough, and chemically quite inert and resistant.

It is not easy to classify proteins. We distinguish here simply between *scleroproteins*, which are insoluble and fibrous, and function as structural material, and *globular proteins*, which may be characterized for the present time by the properties of such representatives as egg white or serum proteins. Proteins of this second group are soluble in water or salt solution and consist of spherical rather than thread-like molecules. (Globular proteins are further subdivided in Chapt. IV–8.

**The Chemical Structure of Proteins** is comparatively simple in principle: Numerous amino acids are joined to form peptide linkages. A segment of a peptide chain may

---

[1] This corresponds to molecular weights of from over 10,000 to several million. The distinction between protein and polypeptide (mol. wt. below 10,000) is quite arbitrary.

be represented by the following structural formula:

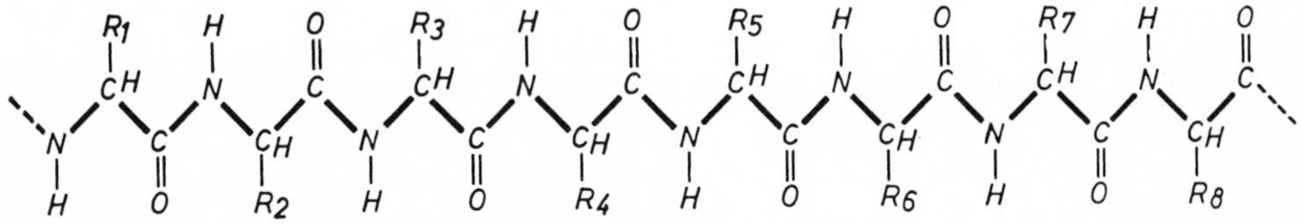

The problem of protein structure is primarily a question of the sequence of amino acids, i.e. what amino acid residues take the place of $R_1$ and $R_x$ in the above formula.

The sequence of amino acids determines the primary structure, but this is not the only problem in protein chemistry. When several hundred amino acids join to form an extended chain molecule, it is easy to imagine that such a molecule may be arranged in space in various ways. For example, it may retain a straight linear form, or bunch up randomly in a ball, or arrange itself in a highly ordered helix (screw shape). These arrangements are called the secondary structure. We shall see that only a few types of secondary structures are actually found in nature.

The problem is complicated further when several chains line up and form aggregates as globular soluble proteins do. Chains with their own secondary structure orient themselves into larger molecules of definite shape, the tertiary structure of proteins. Neither the secondary nor the tertiary structure are revealed by chemical methods. They must be determined by physical or physico-chemical methods.

## 2. Primary Structure

For Determining the Sequence of amino acids various methods have been developed during the past twenty years, as discussed under peptides (Chapt. III–1). Usually the N-terminal amino acid is determined first, by labeling the amino end with the dinitrophenyl radical. Chemical degradative methods are also available that can remove one amino acid at a time, as exemplified by the Edman degradation.

For the degradation from the carboxyl end, the enzymic cleavage with carboxypeptidase (Chapt. VIII–3) has frequently proved valuable. This enzyme clips off amino acids one at a time, and from the order in which they are liberated the sequence in the peptide chain can be deduced.

It is more practical, however, to resolve bigger proteins into a mixture of long peptides by a very carefully conducted digestion with the enzyme trypsin. These peptides are separated and their individual amino acid sequences are determined, often a rather tedious task.

The order in which the tryptic peptides occur must then be determined by another technique, e.g. according to a scheme of overlapping cleavages with other proteases (pepsin, chymotrypsin, papain, and others). The first extensive sequence of amino acids was determined on insulin (Sanger 1954), which is a polypeptide consisting of 51 amino acids. The sequential analysis of true proteins was still beset with serious obstacles. Finally in 1959, ribonuclease with 124 amino acid residues was analyzed completely (Hirs, Stein, and Moore; Anfinsen). In 1960–61 followed the publication of the complete primary structures of the protein of the tobacco mosaic virus with 158 amino acid residues (Schramm and co-workers), of hemoglobin with 574 amino acid residues (Braunitzer and co-workers), and of cytochrome (Tuppy; Margoliash and Smith).

As an example of the primary structure of a protein we can use that of hemoglobin. Normal human hemoglobin is composed of four polypeptide chains (and four heme groups; cf. Chapt. IX–2), or two identical pairs, where each pair consists of an $\alpha$- and a $\beta$-chain. The $\alpha$-chain is made up of 141 amino acid residues and contains relatively more acidic groups than the $\beta$-chain (with 146 residues); the two chains are held together by ionic and hydrogen bonds. The exact sequence of the two chains is reproduced in the Appendix (the reverse side of the folding chart). The arrangement chosen emphasizes certain homologous sequences between each other and in comparison with myoglobin. Homology is achieved by leaving certain spaces blank. In this way a large number of positions contain the same amino acid residues in the different chains. This observation suggests that the two chains have both evolved from one common ancestral hemoglobin by the exchange of some individual amino acid residues (cf. also Chapt. VII–6).

**Regularities in Sequences.** Earlier it had been supposed that the arrangement of amino acids in the chains would be subject to certain periodicities. None of these hypotheses, however, have been substantiated and it is doubtful that there is any regularity in the sequence of the various amino acids. If any conclusion can be drawn from the available data, it is that acidic amino acids tend to group themselves together, and the basic and aromatic amino acids do the same. Often the same amino acid appears several times in a row. It is certain that every molecule of any one protein displays exactly the same sequence, and evidence supports the assumption that this sequence is determined genetically (Chapt. VII–6).

The same peptides and proteins of different animal origin actually show differences in composition. Such a species difference has already been pointed out with the peptide hormones. Analogous differences have been uncovered in hemoglobins. In man there appear a fetal hemoglobin, a normal hemoglobin of adults, and a number of variants usually connected with pathological conditions. Sickle-cell anemia (a blood disease predominantly of the Negro race, characterized by morphologic changes of erythrocytes in oxygen-poor, venous blood) results from an altered hemoglobin and is hereditary. Several other hereditary hemoglobins are known. A careful analysis of the cleavage peptides of about ten different pathologic hemoglobins has revealed that the differences are limited to only a few positions; usually only one amino acid is exchanged. In the following examples, glutamic acid in position 6 of the $\beta$-chain is replaced first by valine and then by lysine:

| | |
|---|---|
| Normal Hemoglobin | Val—His—Leu—Thr—Pro—*Glu*—Glu—Lys— |
| Sickle-cell Hb S | Val—His—Leu—Thr—Pro—*Val*—Glu—Lys— |
| Hemoglobin C | Val—His—Leu—Thr—Pro—*Lys*—Glu—Lys— |

These genetically controlled exchanges of amino acids have corroborated the hypothesis which states that sequence is predetermined by heredity. Such a conclusion agrees closely with other theoretical considerations. And the species differences of peptide hormones are explained readily by the same hypothesis.

## 3. Secondary Structure

Methods for determining secondary structure are entirely different. The most valuable insight was provided by X-ray diffraction, particularly on the fibrous scleroproteins.

The technique of X-ray diffraction, which presupposes an ordered molecule, is quite suited for scleroproteins with their highly stretched structures and orderly bundles of fibers. If the molecule is in an orderly arrangement, then regularities in molecular structure, i.e. regularly recurring groups, will show up as so-called *identity periods*. From X-ray interference patterns, the identity periods are calculated and expressed in Ångström units ($1 \text{ Å} = 10^{-7} \text{ mm} = 0.1 \text{ m}\mu$). Scleroproteins may be classified according to their identity periods (and other properties) into three divisions:

    1. Silk fibroin-$\beta$-keratin group:             Identity period 6.5–7.0 Å

    2. $\alpha$-Keratin-myosin-fibrinogen group:      Identity period 5.1–5.4 Å

    3. Collagen group:                        Identity period 2.8–2.9 Å

X-ray data alone do not permit rigorous calculation of spatial arrangement, except where a series of analogous crystals can be measured thoroughly. (Crystals are far more ordered than fibers.) As a result, it is necessary to conceive of models and to test these models empirically. It is possible to calculate precisely what types of X-ray diffraction will be shown by any given model.

Thanks to Pauling and Corey we possess both very stringent conditions and the necessary information to construct models. They are:

1. Amino acids must be of the L-configuration. All amino acids are equivalent; the various side chains do not influence structure.[2]

2. Bond angles and bond distances must be reproduced exactly as they are found in glycylglycine (cf. Fig. 6).

3. All atoms of the peptide bond

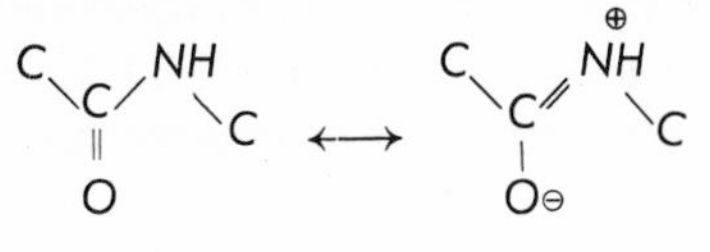

must lie in a plane. This planar requirement arose from actual measurements on glycylglycine and other simple peptides. In addition, theoretical considerations

[2] An exception is proline. Furthermore, the model must provide enough room for the side chains.

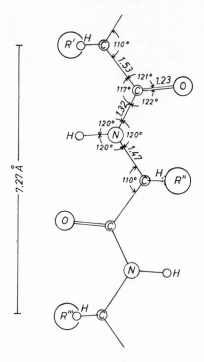

FIG. 6. Dimensions within the peptide chain

dictate the same; for example, resonance, as shown above, favors planarity energetically.

4. The model must allow a maximal number of hydrogen bonds[3] between the groups CO and HN, for only then can the molecular configuration be expected to be energetically stable.

By extending the chain drawn in Fig. 6 for some distance, the simplest model of a protein thread can be obtained. It would be a straight peptide chain with an identity period of 7.27 Å. The greatest number of hydrogen bonds would be attained between two chains running side by side in opposite directions; the chains would thus attach to each other and form a planar grid (Fig. 7). This simple model does not, however, conform to reality. Scleroproteins of the β-keratin type have a structure which Pauling calls pleated sheet. The *pleated-sheet structure* comes about when the planes of the individual peptide groups (Rule 3) are at an angle to

---

[3] In biochemistry, a hydrogen bond may be described as the interaction of a hydrogen atom (either from an NH or OH group) between a nitrogen and an oxygen atom. This bond is much weaker than a primary valence (about 1/10 the bond energy). A hydrogen bond is symbolized by a dotted line: $C=O\cdots H-N$; the distance between O and N may not exceed 2.8–3.0 Å.

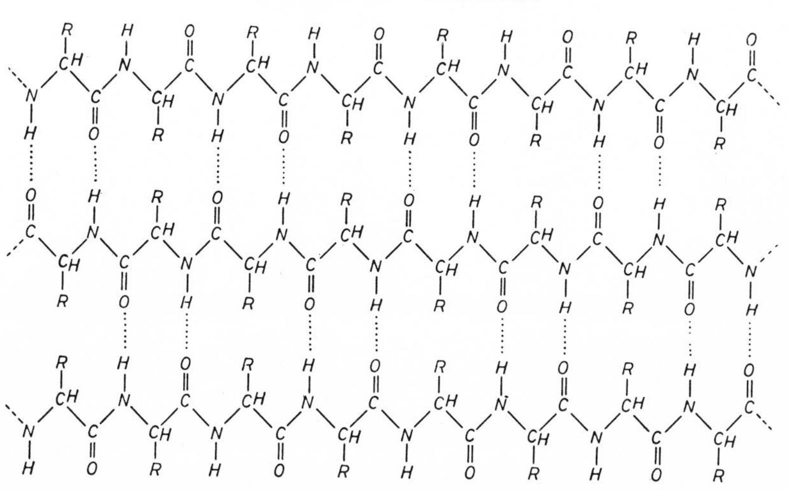

FIG. 7. Peptide chains with hydrogen bonds ("peptide grid"). In juxtaposed chains, the peptide bonds (CO→NH) run in opposite direction.

each other; the $\alpha$-C atom,

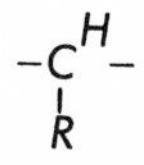

$$-\overset{\displaystyle H}{\underset{\displaystyle R}{C}}-$$

simultaneously belongs to two different planes (Fig. 8).[4]

The side chains enjoy more room in this way; they stick out nearly perpendicularly. Hydrogen bonds may be inserted just as in the "peptide grid." The pleated sheet model adjusts for the observed discrepancy that the identity period is actually shorter by 5–10% than calculated for the straight chain. In addition, it provides sufficient space for the side chains, whereas in the straight model the side chains come in contact. Pleating also permits hydrogen bonding between peptide chains running in the same direction. Consequently we must accept the existence of two pleated sheet structures (one with parallel, unidirectional chains and another with antiparallel chains in opposing directions).

The pleated sheet structure applies to proteins of the silk fibroin-$\beta$-keratin group. For silk fibroin itself it may be assumed that the structure has been proved correct by Pauling's calculations (antiparallel chains). A pleated sheet structure with parallel chains is proposed for stretched hair ($\beta$-keratin). Investigations on some other natural representatives have not yet been concluded. Possibly, amorphous or differently arranged sections occur in combination with pleated-sheet areas.

---

[4] It is easy to fabricate such a model for oneself by drawing the peptide chains on a sheet of paper and folding it at the appropriate places.

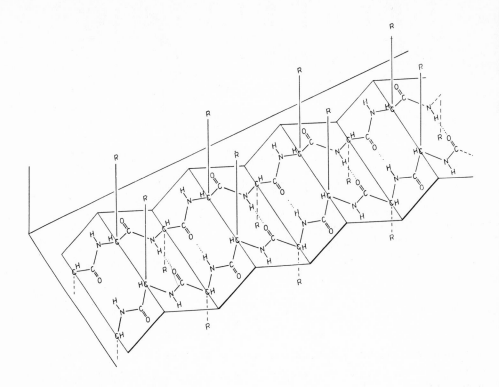

FIG. 8. Pleated sheet structure

**The α-Helix (α-Screw).** In pleated-sheet structures or "peptide grids" hydrogen bonds link the individual chains. But a structure in which the hydrogen bonds are all satisfied within a single chain should be favored. Such a preferred structure is achieved by winding the peptide chain around an imaginary cylinder in a way that from one turn to the next, CO and HN face one another with the proper distance. Several models of this concept are possible. The one that is found widely distributed in nature is the α-helix with 3.7 amino acid residues per turn and with an identity period of about 5.44 Å.

The α-helix is probably the most significant result of the work of Pauling and Corey, although authors before them had already discussed spiral structures. Innovations introduced by Pauling's model are, first, the abandonment of whole numbers of amino acids per turn; second, the use of exact distances and bond angles; and, third, the strict adherence to the planarity of peptide bonds. Subsequently, it became evident that the α-helix is also involved in the structure of soluble proteins.

During construction of an α-helix care must be taken to keep the peptide groups planar. Free rotation is possible only at the α-C atom. These peptide planes form

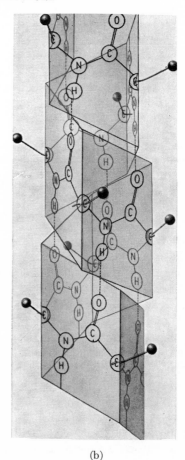

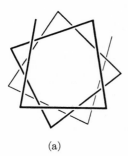

(a)                                    (b)

Fig. 9a. Top view of the α-helix. The planes of the peptide groups are at an angle of about 80° to each other.

Fig. 9b. Side view of a model of the α-helix (original). Each surface represents the plane of a peptide group; the protruding balls indicate side chains.

angles to each other of 80°, so that when viewed from the top the planes are arranged as indicated in Fig. 9a (shown are 10 amino acid residues). At the points of intersection the CO and HN groups approach each other to a distance of one hydrogen-bond length, i.e. 2.8 Å, as seen from the side (Fig. 9b). Each amino acid residue advances the chain in the direction of the cylinder axis by 1.47 Å; with 3.7 amino acid residues per turn, the identity period becomes 5.4 Å. As shown, hydrogen bonds connect consecutive turns; this feature grants unusual stability to the α-helix. In this model, which may be built up either as a right-handed or left-handed screw, side chains stick out radially from the body of the screw proper. They can interact among themselves or with the solvent. The secondary amino acid proline does not fit into the helix, and wherever it occurs in the amino acid sequence there is a break in the regular structure.

The structure of the $\alpha$-helix, initially devised merely as a model, is followed most faithfully by some synthetic peptides of high molecular weight, which is an indication that it can form spontaneously. The occurrence of the $\alpha$-helix in many natural proteins seems even more probable since the scatter line corresponding to the 1.47 Å period, predictable from the model, actually was found (Perutz). Several other properties, such as the extent of optical rotation, also correspond to the theoretical demands of the model.

Although the model suggests an identity period of 5.4 Å, keratins of hair and feathers did not measure more than 5.1 Å. Pauling refined his model for these scleroproteins by twisting a few helices around one another like the strands in a rope or cable. The identity period in the direction of the fiber is shortened that way, since the helices no longer lie perfectly parallel to the fiber, but are skew to it. Wet hair may be stretched to twice its original length, forcing the $\alpha$-keratin structure ($\alpha$-helix) to pass over to the $\beta$-keratin structure (pleated sheet).

**Configuration of Collagens.** This important group of scleroproteins is the chief component of supportive and connective tissue, primarily skin and the organic part of bone. The cells of the connective tissue at first form a *tropocollagen*, with a molecular weight of 360,000, which consists of three chains, helical themselves (three amino acids per turn and an identity period of 8.6 Å), intertwined like the strands of a cable, and held together by hydrogen bonds. The whole molecule is 3000 Å long. Of three consecutive amino acid residues two may be proline or hydroxyproline—these amino acids predominate in collagen—the third invariably is glycine (Fig. 10a). The fibers arise when many tropocollagen molecules line up alongside each other, shifted by one-fourth of the length along its neighbor molecule, and become cross-linked by primary valence bonds. This cross-linking increases with age. Basic and acidic amino acids occur in much greater proportions at certain places of the fiber and are responsible for the transverse stripes observed with the electronmicroscope after staining with metal salts (Fig. 10b).

## 4. Tertiary Structure and Denaturation

The types of organization discussed under the section on secondary structure are the "raw material" for tertiary structure, which can be described as the particular distribution of peptide chains and segments of $\alpha$-helices in the space available to the molecule. The interpretation for the structure of hair presented above actually refers to its tertiary structure, in which large numbers of molecules are grouped together to broad, organized regions, called micelles. But of greater interest is the tertiary structure of globular proteins. Here, the individual molecules exist free in solution, and the peptide chain must be held together in a very definite way to allow the formation of a relatively compact structure. Approximate molecular dimensions of some globular proteins are illustrated in Fig. 17 (Chapt. IV–9).

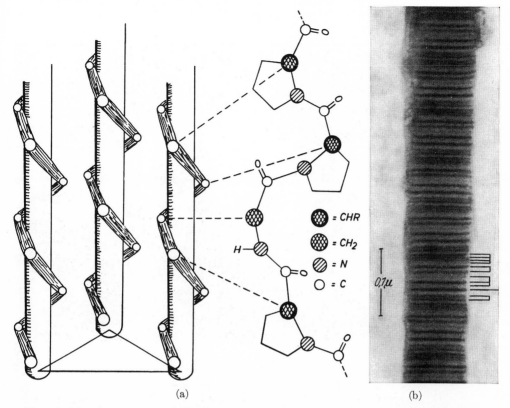

(a)          (b)

Fig. 10a. Structure of Collagen. Columns were inserted to bring out the intertwining of the individual chains. The bundle of three chains must be imagined to continue to be twisted over some distance.

Fig. 10b. Electronmicrograph of a single collagen fibril. Staining with chromate clearly brings out the transverse stripes. A pattern of 12 stripes in five groups is repeated periodically. Note that Fig. 10a is enlarged about 200 times compared with Fig. 10b. (Original photograph by Dr. Klaus Kühn.)

The most successful method for studying tertiary structure is again X-ray analysis. Only crystallized proteins can be used, since in globular proteins no order is obtained along the direction of a fiber. But the orientation is even more precise in crystals, and much clearer pictures are taken. This method depends, for physical reasons, on the availability of a series of isomorphous crystalline derivatives containing some heavy atoms (e.g. heavy metal atoms). Under such conditions the method produces three-dimensional representations of the structure without the need for further assumptions.

The measurement of optical rotation has also become useful. The helix, as an ordered system, contributes a definite amount to the over-all rotation of the molecule, permitting an estimate of the helical portion of the whole protein molecule; it usually falls between 30 and 70%.

Almost nothing is known about the tertiary structure of most proteins, because crystal-structure analyses are unusually laborious. *Hemoglobin* and *myoglobin* are the only proteins whose arrangement of peptide chains in space is known (Perutz; Kendrew). Fundamentally, the structure consists of $\alpha$-helix portions that are draped in an irregular double loop around the prosthetic group. Myoglobin is

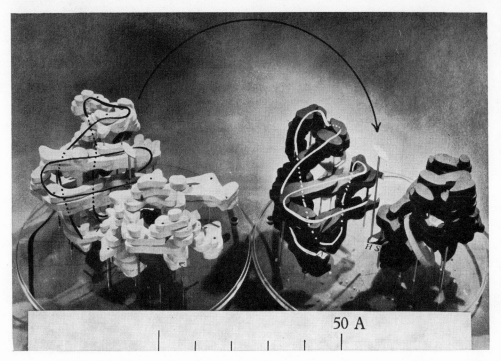

FIG. 11. Models of hemoglobin subunits (according to Perutz). Two "black" and two "white" chains are so mounted that a hemoglobin molecule results when they are fitted together.

composed of one unit (with one heme); in hemoglobin four units are joined, two identical pairs. The units are tied together by salt-like bonds. In Fig. 11 and 12 they are shown as black and white chains. It is remarkable that the long peptide chains of the two hemoglobin subunits, while of different amino acid composition, possess such similar tertiary structure. It is supposed that this typical spatial arrangement is predetermined by the amino acid sequences in the two chains which do possess rather striking similarities. This is probably true in general: It is easy to see that the position of cysteine residues determines the place for sulfur bridges and hence the linkage between sections of the helix; that proline residues necessitate kinks in the helix; that histidine, serine, and glutamine residues determine the place for hydrogen bonds, which stabilize the tertiary structure; and that acidic and basic side chains also play a big role in the tertiary structure.

If the hypothesis that primary structure largely predetermines tertiary structure were correct, then "folding isomerism" would become irrelevant. The theory states that a given peptide chain may be folded in two or more different ways, with each mode of folding having its own biologic property.[5] Refolding has been

---

[5] An example of folding isomerism might be the transition of $\alpha$-keratin to $\beta$-keratin. But the transition is forced by mechanical stretching and it is not accompanied by a change in biologic properties. The example, therefore, has no argumentative value.

FIG. 12. Model of the hemoglobin molecule (according to Perutz). One "white" chain is removed for the sake of clarity. The lines are drawn in to show the course of the peptide chain (usually in the form of the α-helix). The light disk in the "black" chain at right represents the porphyrin ring.

Figures 11 and 12 were taken from M. F. Perutz, M. G. Rossmann, A. F. Cullis, H. Muirhead, and G. Will, Structure of hemoglobin, *Nature* **185**, 416 (1960).

used to explain antibody formation (Pauling, 1940), but this ingenious hypothesis remains unsupported by experimental evidence. Our present knowledge leaves the existence of folding isomerism an open question.

**Denaturation.** Almost all soluble proteins coagulate upon heating, particularly in slightly acidic solution. This is a common, but not a necessary, sign of denaturation. The term *denaturation* is applied to structural changes of protein with the concomitant loss of biologic properties such as enzymic or hormonal action, with a big drop in solubility, and with general changes of chemical and physical properties. Under special conditions denaturation may be reversible; usually it is irreversible.

There is an abundance of substances with denaturing action; namely, acids, bases, organic solvents, concentrated solutions of urea or guanidine, aromatic acids, like salicylic acid, and detergents, such as dodecylsulfate. Proteins are not all equally susceptible to these substances nor even to physical treatment like heat or radiation. Susceptibility itself depends to different degrees on pH, salt content, etc.

Denaturation is really the transition from a highly ordered to a less ordered state, as evidenced by the large gains in entropy[6]: Denaturation is a strongly endothermic reaction; yet, it becomes exergonic above a certain critical temperature. There is more than a superficial analogy to the process of melting.

While dissolved protein molecules possess a definite secondary and tertiary structure, denatured proteins are unfolded extensively. Their X-ray diagram resembles the one of $\beta$-keratin, i.e. one of almost straight peptide chains. This structure is firmly held in place by intermolecular forces (hydrogen bonds and salt bonds), which develop randomly. During the reorientation process, at least some of the disulfide bonds (if present) must be ruptured; and, in fact, the number of reactive HS groups does grow. Other functional groups of the side chains, e.g. of tyrosine, often become more reactive in denatured proteins.

## 5. Molecular Weights of Proteins

During the classification of peptides we have already designated proteins as high molecular weight substances. The actual size of protein molecules, however, was measured first with the ultracentrifuge developed by T. Svedberg (1925–1930).

The usual methods of physical chemistry for determining molecular weights in solution cannot be applied to proteins, since the effects of proteins in solution are too small (e.g. melting point depression). The measurement of osmotic pressure may also provide useful results; however, it is quite difficult. Only when the technique of measuring sedimentation in the gravitational field of an ultracentrifuge was developed, did determinations of molecular weight and checks of homogeneity of particle size become routine methods.

The measurement of sedimentation requires that a protein solution be exposed to gravitational forces over one-hundred-thousand times gravity. Such fields of gravity are obtained in very rapidly spinning centrifuges (up to 60,000 rpm). Protein molecules, which are denser than water, slowly sink to the bottom of the tube, i.e., they sink to the outside. The rate of sedimentation is recorded by optical methods which do not interfere with the operation of the centrifuge. From this rate the sedimentation constant (a specific constant for each protein) is evaluated.

The molecular weight in turn is calculated from the measured sedimentation constant $S$, according to the formula:

$$M = \frac{R \times T \times S}{D(1 - \rho_s/\rho_{\text{prot}})}$$

$R$ = gas constant;

$T$ = absolute temperature

---

[6] Entropy is a measure of the probability of a certain state; unordered states are always more probable (see also Chapt. V-2).

It is evident that the diffusion constant $D$ must be known (usually it is obtained from the same solution); further, the density of the dissolved protein $\rho_{prot}$ and the density of the solvent $\rho_s$. A large sedimentation constant indicates a high molecular weight. Because of the hydrate layer enveloping the protein molecules, the measured values exceed those calculated from the amino acid composition by about 5%.

Instead of sedimentation measurements, the molecular weight can be calculated from light scattering: Protein solutions opalesce and show the Tyndall effect. A measure of the intensity of light scattered sidewise permits calculation of molecular weight. X-ray measurements on crystalline proteins yield very exact data for molecular weights.

TABLE V

MOLECULAR WEIGHTS OF PROTEINS

| | | | |
|---|---|---|---|
| Ribonuclease | 12,700 | Pepsin | 35,500 |
| Cytochrome C | 15,600 | Egg albumin | 44,000 |
| Myoglobin | 16,900 | Serum albumin (human) | 69,000 |
| Lactalbumin (cow) | 17,400 | Diphtheria toxin | 74,000 |
| Trypsin | 24,000 | Urease | 480,000 |
| Gliadin | 27,500 | Hemocyanin (lobster) | 760,000 |
| $\beta$-Lactoglobulin (cow) | 35,400 | | |

(cf. also Fig. 17, Chapt. IV-9)

The molecular weights of several proteins are listed in Table V. It should be noted that values close to 17,500, 35,000, and 70,000 occur rather often. Some time ago, this was interpreted as a regularity (Svedberg's rule) and it was assumed that all proteins are composed of units of molecular weight 17,500 (corresponding to about 144 amino acids). The discovery in recent times of too many exceptions to this rule finally forced its abandonment.

Beyond this, it became evident that proteins in solution may form molecular aggregates, which dissociate upon dilution or other changes in the medium (e.g., pH shift, addition of urea to break hydrogen bonds).[7] A classical example is insulin, whose molecular weight was first found to be 36,000. Upon dilution it dissociates to units of 12,000 which in turn are composed of two molecules, each with a molecular weight of 6000 and probably held together by ions (e.g. zinc). The structural determination (Chapt. III-2) demonstrated that the molecule itself, i.e. the smallest unit held together by primary valence bonds, consists of 51 amino acid residues (two chains linked by sulfur bridges) and possesses a molecular weight of around 6000. These units associate, as shown in Fig. 13. Hemoglobin with a molecular weight of 67,000 may dissociate into four peptide chains, or two identical pairs. The smallest true molecule, therefore, is composed of two chains and has a molecular weight of 33,500. As yet, it is impossible to state how general such dissociation is. Certainly many proteins consist of a single chain; their molecular weight must then agree with their particle weight.

---

[7] Generally, secondary valence bonds are firm enough that the statement in the next section about the monodisperse state of solution remains correct.

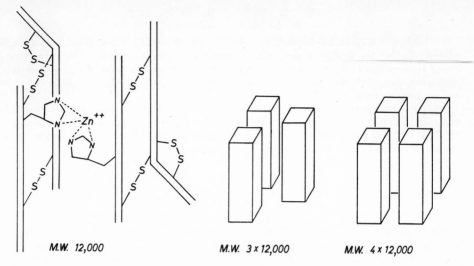

M.W. 12,000          M.W. 3 x 12,000          M.W. 4 x 12,000

FIG. 13. Association of insulin molecules. At left two monomers are represented with their disulfide linkages. The histidyl residues can form a complex with zinc, thereby stabilizing the dimer. In the further associations the dimers are drawn schematically as columns.

## 6. Colloidal Nature of Proteins

Applying the knowledge of colloid chemistry to biologic phenomena and to proteins caused considerable confusion during the first half of the 20th century. It has been overlooked for a long time that by use of the statement, "the cytoplasm is a colloidal system," no knowledge was gained at all; on the contrary, deeper insight was actually foregone. Hence, it is important for us to develop clear concepts and definitions.

Colloid chemistry distinguishes molecular (or micromolecular) solutions, colloidal (or macromolecular) solutions, and coarse suspensions (e.g. mud). Molecular solutions are solutions of salts or any simple organic or inorganic molecules which exist individually in the solution. Such a solution often is converted into a *colloidal solution* when large numbers of molecules aggregate so that the individual particles no longer are single molecules, but rather consist of whole collections of molecules. Colloidal particles may be large or small, i.e. they may consist of many or of a few individual molecules. Such colloidal solutions are contrasted with "true solutions," i.e. molecular solutions.

With this distinction in mind, we find that most protein solutions are molecular solutions, for the individual molecules are free in solution; there are no molecular aggregates. The protein is truly dissolved. A finer subdivision is impossible without destroying the molecules; whereas, in most examples of colloidal solutions, particularly inorganic colloids, further subdivision is achieved readily.

Protein molecules, however, are composed of several hundred amino acids; they possess high molecular weights, between 10,000 and several millions. For comparison, the molecular weight of glycine is 75, of glucose 180. The diameter of a single glucose molecule amounts to 0.5 m$\mu$; the size of protein molecules ranges between 5 m$\mu$ and 100 m$\mu$. The same sizes prevail among colloidal particles. For this reason, in the beginning of colloid chemistry, inorganic colloids and protein molecules were thought to be essentially identical. Table VI presents an outline of particle size and

TABLE VI

| Type of Material | Particle Size | Kind of Solution | Dispersion |
|---|---|---|---|
| Low molecular substances "Crystalloid" | below 1 m$\mu$ | molecular | monodisperse |
| High molecular substances | 1–100 m$\mu$ | molecular | monodisperse |
| Colloids | 1–100 m$\mu$ | colloidal | polydisperse |
| Coarse particles | above 100 m$\mu$ | suspension | polydisperse |

kind of solution. The classification of colloidal solutions according to type of phase into suspensions, emulsions, and aerosols is meaningless in protein chemistry, since we deal with free molecules. A phase arises only from an aggregation of molecules.

Modern colloid chemistry makes an important distinction between monodisperse and polydisperse systems. In monodisperse solutions all particles of the dissolved substance are of the same size and same shape, and have the same properties; in polydisperse solutions we find the most diverse particle sizes and varying charges, in short, different properties. Polydisperse systems do not behave like monodisperse solutions whose particles have the size of colloidal particles.

Protein solutions are monodisperse solutions whose particles, namely the protein molecules, are of the same size as the composite particles of colloidal solutions. It is to be expected, therefore, that protein solutions will manifest certain properties in common with colloidal polydisperse solutions of organic or inorganic materials, as well as certain different properties.

We are forced to make one more minor restriction. Some proteins tend to aggregate: Two, three, four, or more molecules may associate (cf. Chapt. IV-5). The resulting particles have a range of definite sizes, which differ by whole-number factors of two, three, four, or more. Such systems are called paucidisperse.

Molecular size prevents the diffusion of protein molecules through membranes whose pores measure less than a few millimicrons, as for example collodium, parchment, and cellophane, while small molecules and ions can pass through. This fact is put to use in dialysis in order to separate salts from proteins.

When equilibrium is reached between the inside and outside of a membrane, the solution inside is under greater pressure—in principle the same situation as in an ordinary osmotic cell where no solute at all can pass through the membrane. This pressure difference is called the colloid osmotic pressure. Its magnitude depends on the molarity of the protein solution, and is generally rather low due to the high molecular weight. A serum albumin solution of 35 gm per liter (3.5%) is only 1/2000 $M$; its osmotic pressure is 22.4/2000 atm or 122 mm of water. Nevertheless, colloid osmotic effects do play a role in physiology.

# 7. Purification and Check of Purity

To purify proteins is often very difficult. In the first place, body fluids and tissue extracts are comprised of very complex mixtures; second, proteins are very unstable, thus precluding the use of many of the methods of organic chemistry, and third, the check for purity—necessary for the control of each purification step—presents a formidable problem.

Ultracentrifugation, discussed before, may be used for the separation of proteins with different particle weights and is very valuable as a criterion for homogeneity. It is one of the standard methods used in protein research.

**Electrophoresis.** As discussed in Chapt. II–1, the acidic and basic amino acids are largely ionized in aqueous solution. The charges of the $\alpha$-carboxyl group and the $\alpha$-amino group disappear, of course, during formation of peptide bonds. Nevertheless, proteins are multivalent ions: Acidic groups in the side chains of glutamic acid and aspartic acid residues are dissociated and bear negative charges; while the basic groups of lysine and arginine (and to a lesser degree histidine) bear positive charges. Insulin, for example, carries six acidic and six basic groups (including the end groups); with all of them ionized, the insulin molecule carries six positive and six negative charges.

The degree of ionization depends on the pH of the solution. An excess of $H^+$ ions (low pH) retards dissociation of the acidic groups; at high pH, the basic groups remain uncharged. At a certain pH, the number of positive and negative charges will be exactly equal. This particular pH is called the *isoelectric point* (pI). At the isoelectric point, proteins are found to be least soluble and can be precipitated most easily.

If an electric field is applied to a solution of proteins, the multivalent protein ions will migrate at rates depending on the voltage applied. The velocity of migration depends also on the number of charges (which determines the effective electric force) and on the size and shape of the molecule (which determines the extent of fluid friction; cf. Fig. 14). At the isoelectric point no net electric force exists, since the effects of positive and negative charges cancel each other. On the acid side of this point, the protein migrates toward the cathode. If the pH exceeds the pI, then the molecules are negatively charged and migrate toward the anode.

Electrophoresis is a very effective method for separating proteins and for determining impurities in a protein preparation. It is used primarily as an analytical tool, but has also been applied to the preparative separation of various proteins.

Electrophoresis of serum proteins has become an outstanding diagnostic tool in medicine. It is usually carried out on some inert support (paper or starch gel), and the proteins are made visible by staining. The resulting "electropherogram" can be evaluated quantitatively. Normally a curve is obtained, as in Fig. 15. For identification of the fractions see Table VII.

**Precipitation of Proteins.** Proteins can be precipitated from solution in various ways. Irreversible denaturation is of interest only for the total analysis of precipitable protein (trichloroacetic acid or uranyl acetate being used) or for removal

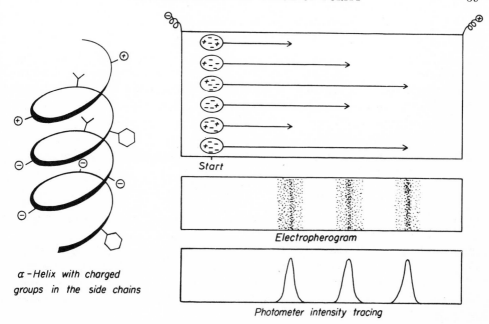

*α-Helix with charged groups in the side chains*

*Start*

*Electropherogram*

*Photometer intensity tracing*

FIG. 14. Schematic representation of electrophoresis. At left, a segment of an α-helix which shows the location of certain charged groups. At right, three proteins with different charges are applied to the supporting medium; these proteins migrate during a given time (e.g. 15 hours) as far as the arrows indicate. The "electropherogram" is made visible by staining and evaluated quantitatively by photometry.

of proteins which might interfere in some other analytical procedure, as in blood-sugar determinations. A reversible process is attempted whenever a certain component has to be isolated in pure form from a mixture of proteins. The most common examples are the isolation of a peptide hormone or an enzyme from tissue extracts.

One of the most important methods is salting out with a neutral salt such as ammonium sulfate, sodium sulfate, or magnesium sulfate, since highly concentrated solutions of these salts can be prepared. The salt content of a protein solution is increased stepwise, and after each addition the precipitated protein is centrifuged off. The pH may be varied to allow multiple fractionation (around their isoelectric points proteins become least soluble). Another method is precipitation with organic solvents (alcohol, acetone) according to E. Cohn. This must be carried out under refrigeration (cf. Chapt. IV–9).

**Chromatography.** Separation of proteins has recently been accomplished by chromatographic methods. The adsorbing material is usually a chemically modified cellulose; the proteins are eluted with buffer solutions. In principle, this is ion-exchange chromatography, since the groups which have been attached to the cellulose are all charged. Chromatographic homogeneity is another criterion of purity.

**Immunologic Differentiation of Proteins.** Immunology provides the basis for one of the most sensitive methods for differentiation and identification of proteins. It entails the reaction of a protein solution with certain serum proteins of an experimental animal.

When proteins which are foreign to the body, or also more complex structures like bacteria or viruses, have penetrated into an organism (or have been injected), the organism responds by forming "antibodies" to the foreign proteins, which are known as "antigens." The antibodies are proteins (part of the γ-globulin group of serum, Chapt. IV–9) which form an insoluble complex with the antigens. This precipitation[8] constitutes a positive antigen-antibody reaction. It is also used for identification of proteins (with immuno-electrophoresis, cf. Chapt. IV–9).

The nature of antibody formation is still unclear. The only thing known is that the biosynthesis of proteins is so influenced that in place of the regular γ-globulins, these specific antibodies are produced. Chemically, antibodies resemble normal globulins very closely; they have the same molecular weight and the same amino acid composition. Very recently, however, some differences in primary structure among antibodies of varying specificities have been detected. Every antibody molecule has two specific sites of attachment; the area between these sites does not appear to possess any specificity.

So-called antiserum usually contains different antibodies which react with different groups or areas on the causative protein, the antigen. This reaction is highly specific, particularly when carried out quantitatively; it permits the most sensitive distinction between closely related proteins. Nevertheless, cross reactions do occur sometimes: An antiserum to protein A reacts with the closely related protein B, but not as strongly. This is taken as a sign of close relationship and may possibly be due to the presence of some identical areas on the protein surfaces. Antibodies can also be generated against specific chemical groups (e.g. benzene sulfonic acid, iodotyrosyl residue) by attaching such groups to proteins and then using the modified proteins as antigens.

At present it is difficult either to describe the secondary valence forces that bind antibody to antigen, or to give a chemical interpretation of the high specificity of the reaction. Perhaps some day exact structural analysis of antigens and antibodies will solve the problem.

## 8. Classification of Globular Proteins

In the past, globular proteins were classified according to their solubilities and some of their chemical characteristics. This classification is no longer satisfactory, especially because the "classes" cannot be defined precisely enough. We want to distinguish[9] only among (1) histones, (2) albumins, and (3) globulins.

---

[8] Precipitation occurs only when the relative concentrations are chosen correctly.

[9] Often additional classes are listed for glutelins, gliadins, and protamines which are small groups of vegetable proteins occurring in grain kernels. There is no reason to grant them special significance by the establishment of exclusive classes.

We have relegated the strongly basic protamines, which in the past were considered members of a special class of proteins, to the polypeptides because of their relatively low molecular weight (around 5,000).

*Histones* are basic proteins found in the cell nucleus, where they are bound to nucleic acids by ionic bonds. Histones have not yet been studied sufficiently. At present it is impossible to decide whether their function goes beyond mere neutralization of the negative charges of nucleic acids.

*Albumins* are proteins which dissolve in pure water and precipitate from solution only at high ammonium sulfate concentrations (70–100% of saturation).

*Globulins*, on the other hand, are at best slightly soluble in pure water, dissolve easily in dilute solutions of neutral salts, and precipitate again when the ammonium sulfate concentration reaches half-saturation.

In many individual cases, globulins and albumins can be distinguished only with difficulty. Furthermore, such a distinction contributes little to further understanding; its value is historical only.

Lastly, the *complex proteins* have been gathered into a separate classification. They are composed of a protein part and an additional, nonprotein, "prosthetic" group. It is rather difficult to maintain the distinction between proteins which adsorb metals and carbohydrates or incorporate them in small quantities, and proteins with a definite metal or carbohydrate component. The usual division of complex proteins comprises the following: (1) metalloproteins, (2) phosphoproteins, (3) lipoproteins, (4) nucleoproteins, (5) glycoproteins, and (6) chromoproteins.

(Instead of *lipoproteins*, *glycoproteins*, etc., the terms *lipoproteid*, *glycoproteid*, etc. are sometimes used.)

Such a heteregeneous combination of components is not always of biologic significance. For example, it is uncertain whether the protein in nucleoproteins possesses any specific functions. On the other hand, we are well aware of the role of both the protein component and the prosthetic group in many enzymes. (cf. Chapt. V and VI.)

In some modern textbooks and handbooks proteins are classified according to where they are found as blood proteins, milk proteins, plant-seed proteins, etc.; or alternately, they are classified by biologic properties as enzymic proteins, hormonal proteins, etc. Following these principles we shall discuss in some detail blood proteins and let them serve as illustrations. Then enzyme proteins will be treated mainly with regard to their catalytic properties, but without overlooking their protein nature.

## 9. Plasma Proteins

Blood plasma is the clear liquid which remains as the supernatant after centrifugation of the erythrocytes. It contains 7–8% protein, which is actually a mixture of different proteins including the clotting factors. If plasma (or whole blood) is allowed to clot before centrifuging, serum is obtained. It differs from plasma essentially in the absence of fibrinogen (cf. this section, below). Approximate molecular dimensions of blood proteins are illustrated in Fig. 17. The red blood pigment, hemoglobin, is localized inside erythrocytes; its function is discussed in Chapt. IX–4.

**Separation of Plasma Proteins** has been carried out in the past by fractional salting-out with either ammonium or sodium sulfate. The analytical characterization of individual plasmas or sera is now accomplished by electrophoresis, usually paper electrophoresis (Turba; Grassmann and Hannig). In a normal electropherogram, run at pH 8.6, all proteins migrate toward the anode (cf. Fig. 14). Albumin travels fastest, followed by the $\alpha_1$, $\alpha_2$, $\beta$-, and $\gamma$-globulins. Though these fractions are not homogenous, their relative abundance permits the drawing of important clinical conclusions. The electropherogram of a normal serum with its evaluation diagram is presented in Fig. 15. Pathological sera deviate considerably from the normal pattern; "paraproteins," absent in normal sera, appear occasionally.

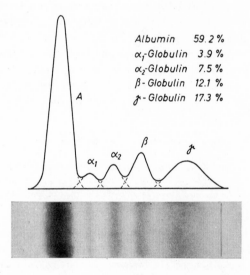

Albumin         59.2 %
$\alpha_1$-Globulin      3.9 %
$\alpha_2$-Globulin      7.5 %
$\beta$-Globulin       12.1 %
$\gamma$-Globulin      17.3 %

FIG. 15. Electropherogram of a human serum: below, the stained paper strip; above, the photometric curve. (By Dr. Knedel.)

A further separation of serum proteins is possible with immunoelectrophoresis. Electrophoretically separated proteins are allowed to diffuse toward an antiserum; wherever the protein meets an antibody a precipitation ring develops (cf. Fig. 16). Apart from electrophoretic mobility, the rate of diffusion and serological specificity govern the position of these precipitation lines. More than 20 serum components have been distinguished this way.

The individual proteins can be isolated from larger quantities of plasma by a method of E. Cohn and co-workers.

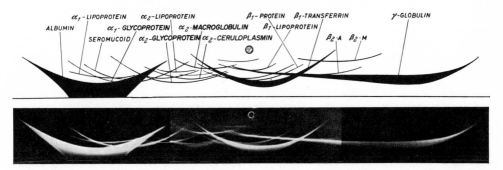

FIG. 16. Immuno-electrophoretic separation of a normal human serum and sketch of the positions of resulting precipitation lines. The cross-hatched circle indicates the point of application for electrophoresis. Antibodies were applied in a trough-shaped indentation at the lower border.

The method may be described briefly with the aid of a diagram. Plasma is adjusted to a pH of 7.2; addition of alcohol to a concentration of 8% precipitates fraction I, (mainly fibrinogen), which is centrifuged off. The supernatant is then brought to a pH of 6.9 and to an alcohol concentration of 25%. Precipitated fractions II and III consist of $\beta$- and $\gamma$-globulins and contain all immunoproteins and blood-type specific isoagglutinins, in addition to part of the lipoproteins.

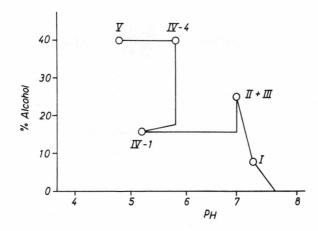

The solution is then diluted to 18% alcohol content and adjusted to pH 5.2; fraction IV-1 containing lipoproteins is precipitated and collected. The remaining solution is adjusted to pH 5.8, and 40% alcohol concentration; this removes the remaining globulins from solution. At pH 4.8 and the same alcohol content, the albumins precipitate as the largest uniform fraction of plasma proteins. The entire procedure must be performed between −2° and −5°, otherwise denaturation sets in and the proteins become insoluble.

**Properties and Biologic Functions of Plasma Proteins.** The important properties of plasma proteins are listed in Table VII.

TABLE VII

PROPERTIES OF BLOOD FRACTIONS

| Protein | Molecular Weight | Isoelectric Point (pI) | Normal Content | Composition and Function |
|---|---|---|---|---|
| Albumin | 69,000 | 4.8 | 52–62% | Plasma volume; transport vehicle |
| $\alpha_1$-Globulins | 130,000 | 5.0 | 3–5% | Contain glyco- and lipoproteins; transport function |
| $\alpha_2$-Globulins | 200,000 | 5.0 | 6–9% | |
| $\beta$-Globulins | up to 1,300,000 | 5.12 | 9–14% | Lipoproteins, prothrombin, agglutinins |
| $\gamma$-Globulins | 150,000 | 6.8–7.3 | 11–17% | Antibodies |
| Fibrinogen | 400,000 | — | 5% | Blood clotting |

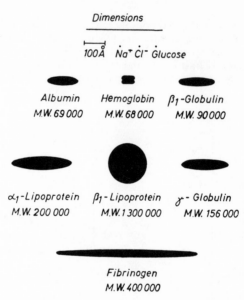

Dimensions

100Å   Na⁺ Cl⁻ Glucose

Albumin    Hemoglobin    $\beta_1$-Globulin
M.W. 69 000   M.W. 68 000   M.W. 90 000

$\alpha_1$-Lipoprotein   $\beta_1$-Lipoprotein   $\gamma$-Globulin
M.W. 200 000   M.W. 1 300 000   M.W. 156 000

Fibrinogen
M.W. 400 000

Diameter of erythrocytes with same enlargement: 4.5 meter.

FIG. 17. Molecular dimensions of blood proteins

*Albumin* is an ellipsoidal molecule 150 Å long; the ratio of the axes is 4:1 (cf. Fig. 17). The chief functions of albumin are the regulation of osmotic relationships in blood and the provision of a reserve of protein for the organism. In addition, albumin easily binds reversibly to various substances, especially negatively charged ones, so that it also plays the role of a carrier; in other words, it has a transport function.

A great many different proteins are found among the *globulins*. Some of them are metalloproteins, containing iron, zinc, or copper. Copper-containing *ceruloplasmin* (mol. wt. 150,000) possesses the enzymic activity of a laccase (cf. Chapt.

X–7), although it is still uncertain whether this fact has any biologic significance. The $\alpha$- and $\beta$-globulins include glyco- and lipoproteins, which contain cholesterol and phospholipids. $\beta_1$-Lipoprotein has been studied extensively; it is spherically shaped and of very high molecular weight: 1.3 million. Only one fourth of this is due to the protein component itself; about 30% consists of cholesterol (partly free, but mostly esterified) and phospholipids. The significance of these lipoproteins, whose composition varies, probably lies in their ability to transport water-insoluble substances in an aqueous medium, the blood. The organism uses this same principle in various other ways. In spite of their low protein content—not even enough to cover their spherical surface—lipoproteins do behave as proteins. But since their density is low, they rise to the surface during centrifugation in 1 $M$ sodium chloride or sodium bromide solution.

**Immunoproteins and Isoagglutinins.** These are a part of the $\gamma$-globulins, which comprise a very heterogenous fraction of serum proteins that cannot easily be further fractionated. Individual antibodies, for which one can test with the appropriate antigens, comprise only an infinitesimal part of the $\gamma$-globulin fraction. After an infection, however, $\gamma$-globulins are often observed to increase (in the electropherogram) (cf. this section, above).

Isoagglutinins are proteins which have an antibody-like specificity against foreign blood corpuscles, but which are present normally without the need to introduce an antigen artificially. Along with the blood-type substances of blood corpuscles, these isoagglutinins are responsible for the incompatibility in some blood transfusions (see Chapt. XVII–7).

**Enzymes.** Normal plasma contains only a few esterases in addition to ceruloplasmin and the blood clotting enzymes. However, in certain pathologic conditions enzymes from tissue can enter the blood plasma; examples are glutamate-oxaloacetate transaminase (with cardiac infarction) or lactate dehydrogenase (with several liver diseases). Hence, enzyme assays in plasma have acquired diagnostic value.

**Fibrinogen, Fibrin, and Clotting.** The key feature of blood clotting is the conversion of soluble fibrinogen into insoluble fibrin, a skeleton of protein fibers. Certainly not all details of blood clotting have been explained, but at present ten different factors, designated by Roman numerals, are implicated. We shall restrict ourselves to the principal components of the system.

*Fibrinogen* is a soluble, elongated fibrillar protein of the $\alpha$-keratin type; its molecular weight is 400,000. The conversion of fibrinogen to fibrin, involving the removal of peptides, is catalyzed by *thrombin*, which acts as a proteolytic enzyme.

Circulating blood contains practically no thrombin, only its precursor *prothrombin*. The conversion of prothrombin to thrombin is usually considered to be the first phase of blood clotting. Numerous factors are involved in this preliminary phase: First, *thrombokinase* from *tissue* with the *accelerators* and $Ca^{++}$; second, *thrombokinase* from *blood*, which is formed by the thrombocyte factor in presence of at least four plasma factors and $Ca^{++}$. The conversion prothrombin $\rightarrow$ thrombin proceeds autocatalytically; the process is accelerated by the action of newly formed thrombin on factor V (*proaccelerin*) by converting this factor into the active factor

VI (accelerin). The accelerins in turn activate prothrombin. In this way, all prothrombin is very quickly transformed to thrombin, which can then catalyze the conversion fibrinogen → fibrin, as mentioned. Initially, monomeric fibrin (or activated fibrinogen) is produced, which then polymerizes spontaneously. The last reaction is the clotting phase.

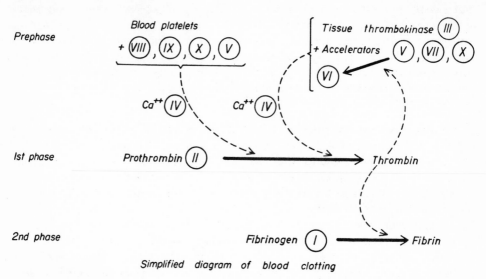

Simplified diagram of blood clotting

Clotting may be inhibited or disturbed in several ways. The well-known bleeding condition hemophilia is caused by the absence (or inactivity) of any one component of the thrombokinase system from blood, i.e. of some plasma factor. In classical hemophilia A it is factor VIII (*antihemophilic globulin*); in hemophilia B, factor IX (*Christmas factor*). Due to a deficiency in these factors insufficient amounts of plasma thrombokinase are formed, and consequently the transition prothrombin → thrombin is delayed greatly or even prevented.

One physiological inhibitor of clotting is *heparin*, which is formed in mast cells. Heparin acts at different steps in the complicated process: First, it inhibits the formation of plasma thrombokinase; second, the activation of prothrombin; third, the enzymic activity of thrombin. Many animal poisons (e.g. the blood poison, hirudin, extracted from leeches) also inhibit blood clotting. *In vitro*, clotting is prevented commonly by binding $Ca^{++}$ ions (precipitation with fluoride or oxalate; complex formation with citrate, etc.).

Prothrombin is produced in the liver by a process which requires vitamin K. The drug dicumarol blocks the action of vitamin K; consequently little prothrombin is made available and the clotting time is prolonged.

Great physiological significance is attached to the dissolution of clots that may have formed in the blood stream. This lysis is effected by the enzyme fibrinolysin (plasmin), whose precursor, profibrinolysin (plasminogen), occurs normally in plasma. Several different activators can change profibrinolysin to fibrinolysin.

BIBLIOGRAPHY

C. B. Anfinsen, "Molecular Basis of Evolution," Wiley, New York, 1959.

K. M. Brinkhous, Blood cootting: the plasma procoagulants, *Ann. Rev. Physiol.*, **21**, 271–298 (1959).

F. Haurowitz, "The Chemistry and Function of Proteins," p. 193, Academic Press, New York, 1963.

H. Neurath (editor), "The Proteins," 4 vols., Academic Press, New York, 1963–1965.

R. G. Macfarlane, The blood coagulation system, *in* "The Plasma Proteins," F. W. Putnam, ed. Vol. 2, p. 137, Academic Press, New York, 1960.

G. E. Perlmann and R. Diringer, Structure of proteins, *Ann. Rev. Biochem.*, **29**, 151–182 (1960).

F. J. Reithel, The dissociation and association of protein structures, *Advances in Protein Chem.* **18**, 123–226 (1963); annual volumes published by Academic Press, New York.

H. E. Schultze, On glycoproteins, *Deut. med. Wochschr.*, **83**, 1742 (1958).

D. G. Smyth, Proteins and peptides, *Ann. Rept. Chem. Soc., London*, **60**, 468–485 (1963).

C. Tanford, "Physical Chemistry of Macromolecules," Wiley, New York, 1961.

# CHAPTER V

# Enzymes and
# Biocatalysis

## 1. Chemical Nature of Enzymes

The enzymes are a very important group of proteins. All the chemical reactions in the organism (i.e. metabolism) are made possible only through the actions of the catalysts which we call *"enzymes."* The substance transformed by an enzyme is termed *"substrate."*

Although the German literature still uses both the terms "ferment" and "enzyme," only the latter is used in the English language, and "fermentation" is restricted to describing bacterial actions. The use of the word "enzyme," proposed by Kühne in 1878, for soluble "ferments" avoids the historical controversy concerning "formed ferments" (yeast and other microorganisms, i.e. intact organisms) and "unformed ferments" (pepsin, trypsin, saccharase). After Buchner's epoch-making discovery that alcoholic fermentation is indeed possible outside the living cell, the concept of formed ferment was dropped, and the designations "ferment" and "enzyme" became synonymous.

Chemically every enzyme known so far is a protein. About one hundred enzymes have been prepared in pure and crystalline state by the methods of protein chemistry; the first of these was *urease* (Sumner, 1926). Ribonuclease is the only enzyme whose structure, i.e. its amino acid sequence, has been analyzed; the sequences of other enzymes are only partially known. The assumption is that a certain sequence of amino acids at and around the active site of the enzyme is responsible for the catalytic effect. This theory is supported by the observation that part of the molecule may be split off some enzymes without loss of activity. Denaturation abolishes catalytic activity, of course, without changing the sequence of amino acids.

Many enzymes are complex proteins; they consist of a protein component and a "prosthetic group." In many cases it is possible to remove the prosthetic group reversibly. In such a case the protein part is called *"apoenzyme"*; the prosthetic group, *"coenzyme"*;

$$\text{Coenzyme} + \text{apoenzyme} = (\text{holo-}) \text{ enzyme}$$

The apoenzyme, the protein itself, has also been called a "colloidal carrier." This terminology is based largely on Willstätter's idea that "the molecule of an enzyme consists of a colloidal carrier and an active group with purely chemical activity." Today the concept of a colloidal carrier must be rejected, because it implies that the protein component is inactive, and we now know that it is not.[1] For one thing, the protein component decides the *substrate specificity*; it determines which substances react and which do not. In many cases this same protein component also determines the direction of the reaction (*reaction specificity*), in other words, which reaction out of the numerous possible ones is undergone by the substrate. This point becomes especially clear in cases where the same coenzyme, i.e. the same prosthetic group, catalyzes different reactions, as does, for instance, pyridoxal phosphate (see Chapt. VIII–4) or heme (see Chapt. IX–3).

The frequently heard statement, "substrate specificity resides in the apoenzyme; reaction specificity resides in the coenzyme," needs therefore to be corrected in its second part, but in any case, coenzymes are essentially involved in enzyme activity, as will be discussed in a separate chapter (VI).

Enzymes have been called catalysts, or loosely speaking, accelerators of reactions. In order to understand their action we must first ask why chemical reactions really take place.

## 2. Chemical Equilibria and Chemical Energetics

**Equilibria of Chemical Reactions.** A large number of chemical and biochemical reactions attain a measurable equilibrium between their reactants. Two well-known examples are given here:

$$CH_3COOH \rightleftharpoons CH_3COO^- + H^+ \qquad (1)$$

$$CH_3COOH + C_2H_5OH \rightleftharpoons CH_3COOC_2H_5 + HOH \qquad (2)$$

General chemistry teaches that the law of mass action applies to equilibria. For reaction (1) it may be formulated as follows:

$$\frac{C_{CH_3COO^-} \times C_{H^+}}{C_{CH_3COOH}} = K$$

Here, $C_{CH_3COOH}$, $C_{CH_3COO^-}$, and $C_{H^+}$ stand for the concentrations (in moles per liter) of the reactants as they are found when equilibrium is established. In the case of the dissociation of acetic acid the equilibrium is established nearly instantaneously; the ester formation of reaction (2), for which we can write an analogous concentration equation, takes more time to reach equilibrium. Finally, the state of equilibrium can be attained from either side of the reaction, i.e. from a mixture of acetic acid and alcohol as well as from ethyl acetate and water.

---

[1] In Willstätter's time (around 1920) this statement nevertheless represented scientific progress, because it identified the action of enzymes with chemical properties. Now we recognize the "chemically active group" as the active site of the protein.

Every chemical reaction is, in theory, reversible; the equilibrium of some reactions, however, lies too far on one side for the reverse reaction to be detected.

**Chemical Energetics.** Let us look at a general equation:

$$A + B \rightleftharpoons C + D; \qquad \frac{[C] \times [D]}{[A] \times [B]} = K \qquad (3)$$

It is easy to appreciate that the more vigorously the reaction between substance A and B proceeds, the farther the equilibrium lies to the right, i.e. to the side of C and D, or in other words, the greater is the equilibrium constant $K$.[2] We can say then that the reaction mixture possesses a high potential energy and during the course of the reaction it drops to a lower potential. This energy change is related quantitatively to the equilibrium constant by the following expression:

$$\Delta F^\circ = -RT \ln K \qquad (4)$$

In this expression, $R$ stands for the gas constant 1.987 cal/mol·degree, $T$ for absolute temperature, ln for the natural logarithm, and $K$ for the equilibrium constant at temperature $T$.

The superscript° indicates that the quantity $\Delta F^\circ$ refers to the "standard state," where the reactants are dissolved in a pure solvent at a concentration of 1 mole/liter. It is further supposed that exactly 1 mole of material is reacted. $\Delta F^\circ$ corresponds to that amount of energy which can be released under these prescribed conditions and is called "free energy," or more precisely, "the change of free energy of the system" during the reaction.

Starting with any arbitrary concentration other than the "standard state," the value for the free energy change is calculated from the standard value by the relation:

$$\Delta F = \Delta F^\circ + RT \ln\left(\frac{C_C \times C_D}{C_A \times C_B}\right) \qquad (5)$$

Here, $C_A$, $C_B$, etc. are again the concentrations of the reactants. The expression within the parentheses is the same as is found in the law of mass action, equation (3). At equilibrium, i.e. at the concentrations of equilibrium, $\Delta F = 0$.

A reaction which releases energy to its surroundings is called *"exergonic."* In this case the free energy $\Delta F$ bears a negative sign, because, by convention, all quantities of energy which are lost by a system (in the form of heat or work) are negative. A comparison may be drawn from a business accounting system: Expenditures (released energy) are entered with a negative sign; income (added heat or work) is given a positive sign.

Every spontaneous reaction is exergonic. In other words, every reaction proceeds as long as free energy is still decreasing. If no further decrease is possible,

---

[2] This presupposes an uninhibited reaction. To *initiate* a reaction, the energy of activation is of decisive importance (cf. Chapt. V-3).

then the state of equilibrium is reached, and $\Delta F = 0$. For better visualization this concept is diagrammed here:

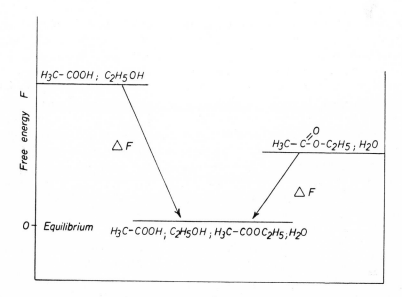

Again we use ester formation, reaction (2), as an example. The potential energy depends on the concentrations. At the left is the mixture of acid and alcohol with its own potential; at right, ester and water. The equilibrium mixture has the lowest potential. Hence, either of the two reaction mixtures will approach the equilibrium mixture with a release of corresponding amounts of energy in an exergonic reaction.

The direction of the reaction, therefore, depends on the concentrations, and in many cases it is important for us to be able to calculate from the *standard change* of free energy $\Delta F°$ by equation (5) the actual free energy change $\Delta F$, which depends on the concentrations actually at hand. If this $\Delta F$ is negative, then the reaction runs from left to right, as usually written; if $\Delta F$ is positive, then it runs in the reverse direction.

Physical chemistry teaches that the change of free energy during a chemical reaction is defined by two other thermodynamic quantities of state:

$$\Delta F = \Delta H - T \Delta S \qquad (6)$$

$\Delta H$ means change of heat content[3] (enthalpy; basically the change of "internal energy"); $\Delta S$ means change of entropy content. (Entropy is a measure of molecular order.)

A more detailed explanation of the thermodynamic concepts must be omitted here, except to mention that in several processes, such as protein denaturation, the increase in entropy, the rise of molecular disorder, is the driving force of the reaction.

---

[3] The change in enthalpy differs from change of heat content (developed or absorbed quantity of heat) only by its sign: $\Delta H = -Q_p$

### 3. Catalysts and Enzymes

If equilibrium were always reached quickly, then there could be neither any organic chemistry nor any life on our planet. The equilibrium of most organic compounds in the presence of atmospheric oxygen greatly favors the oxidation products $CO_2$ and $H_2O$. If the reactivity of such substances is raised by heating them, they burn. At room temperature they are metastable; though they are not at equilibrium, they do not change. Only when a certain amount of energy, the energy of activation, has been applied will they react with atmospheric oxygen. The same holds true for other reactions. As a result, we must correct our diagram of energy levels as shown in Fig. 18. At first some energy of activation must be absorbed (usually from thermal motion), before the reactants—hydrogen and oxygen in this case—can react to attain equilibrium and form water. The energy of activation can frequently be calculated from empirical data. The greater this energy, the less reactive the substances.

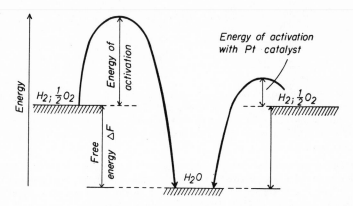

FIG. 18. The function of catalysts

There is one way to lower the energy of activation: the addition of a catalyst. An example may help to explain this. A mixture of oxygen and hydrogen at room temperature will remain unchanged for a long time, because the energy of activation is quite high. Local heating, as through an electric spark, can initiate the reaction, which is violent because of the large release of free energy. If instead we introduce a catalyst, say a platinum sponge, then the reaction starts at room temperature and will finish quickly, with the release of heat. The catalyst's job here is to lower the energy of activation, or in other words, to make the molecules more reactive.

Everything explained here by the example of water formation applies also to biochemical reactions. The vast majority of them become possible solely through the aid of catalysts, which we call enzymes. Thermodynamically, catalysts lower the necessary energy of activation of the reaction and thus facilitate reaching equilibrium. Catalysis "beyond the state of equilibrium," i.e. a shift of equilibrium, is not possible, however. Every reaction, though catalyzed by an enzyme, proceeds only until equilibrium is reached. This same equilibrium would have been reached just as well in the presence of some inorganic catalyst, or even without the aid of a catalyst; the equilibrium is defined only by the equilibrium constant $K$.[4] This fundamental law of biochemistry must never be forgotten.

There is only one possible way to maintain a continuous reaction: two enzymic reactions in tandem, with the second reaction continually using up a substance—often present in low concentration—which is being produced by the first reaction. Such a situation is not unknown in nonenzymic reactions, e.g. in inorganic chemistry. Loosely speaking, the equilibrium is "shifted" by the removal of the reaction product. More correctly we say that equilibrium concentrations are never established, simply because one of the reaction products reacts further and continuously disappears; and has to be supplied by the first reaction.

In this way even an endergonic (energy requiring) reaction can be made to occur. The subsequent reaction, however, must be exergonic so that the overall $\Delta F$ for both reactions has a negative value, i.e. the combination of reactions must be exergonic.

## 4. Dynamic Equilibrium and the Steady State

The above-mentioned common example of water formation also points out the limits of the equilibrium theory. In biochemistry this theory is very useful in explaining energetics and the nature of biocatalysis, but it would be a gross mistake to assume that the organism is anywhere near chemical equilibrium ($\Delta F = 0$). L. v. Bertalanffy put it succinctly: "A closed system[5] at equilibrium neither needs energy for its maintenance, nor can energy be obtained from it. The chemical equilibrium, for this reason, is unable to produce work. In order for a system to perform work, it must *not* be at equilibrium, but rather it must *tend* toward equilibrium. And in order for the system to be able to persist in its tendency, it must be kept in a steady state. Such is the situation with the organism, whose constant capacity for work is insured by the fact that it is an open system."

In a dynamic equilibrium or steady state substances flow in continuously and reaction products escape. It is part of the nature of dynamic equilibria to have

---

[4] Were it different, i.e. were an enzyme able to influence the position of equilibrium, one could construct a *perpetuum mobile*; according to the laws of thermodynamics, however, this is not possible.

[5] In physical chemistry, the expression "system" is used for that segment of the universe which is being studied at the time. A *closed system* exchanges with its environment neither matter nor energy; material transport and exchange of energy is the mark of an *open system*.

transport phenomena at the boundaries of the system. Along with other parameters, the transport phenomena determine the steady state concentrations of individual substances within a system. Evidently the organism fulfills these conditions: Food and oxygen are taken up; $CO_2$ and waste products are eliminated. The organism is truly an open system and can develop and maintain itself only as an open system, i.e. a system in exchange with its environment. Different laws apply for an open system at dynamic equilibrium than for a closed system at true equilibrium. The theory behind this is very complicated and has not yet been developed completely; we will not discuss it further save for one point:

In a closed system a catalyst, or an enzyme, does not disturb the position of equilibrium. In an open system, in contrast, an enzyme is very well able to regulate the steady state concentration of a reacting substance. For example, the substrate concentration may drop because more substrate is turned over than is supplied from the environment whenever there is more enzyme present. Furthermore, the system is capable of developing forces to counteract disturbances of the steady state.

A very good example from biochemistry is the respiratory chain, which in a limited way represents a system in dynamic equilibrium. It depends on steady state concentrations of the various redox systems. It will be discussed further in Chapt. X–4.

In summary, it is impossible to comprehend the action of enzymes and to experiment with biochemical systems and their energetics without a firm foundation in chemical equilibria. In many experimental situations the enzyme governs the arrival at equilibrium, but not its position. In contrast, the organism, like its own individual cells, must be considered as an open system which normally maintains a dynamic equilibrium. In a dynamic equilibrium, steady state concentrations will always be established different from those of the chemical equilibrium, which is governed by thermodynamics. Hence, reactions tending toward equilibrium take place continuously, and it is these reactions which provide the energy necessary for the organism's vital processes.

## 5. Energetic Coupling and Energy-Rich Compounds

The laws of thermodynamics do not permit endergonic reactions to run either spontaneously or through enzymic catalysis. An endergonic reaction has to be coupled with another reaction which is sufficiently exergonic to let the sum of $\Delta F$ for both be equal to zero or be negative (cf. this section). The most important mechanism of coupling is the formation of an energy-rich (hence, very reactive) intermediate compound. The same principle is employed in organic chemistry when acid chlorides are prepared for the synthesis of amides and esters (cf. Chapt.

I–2, II–1). In biochemistry this energy-rich, "activated" component is very often *adenosine triphosphate* abbreviated as ATP:

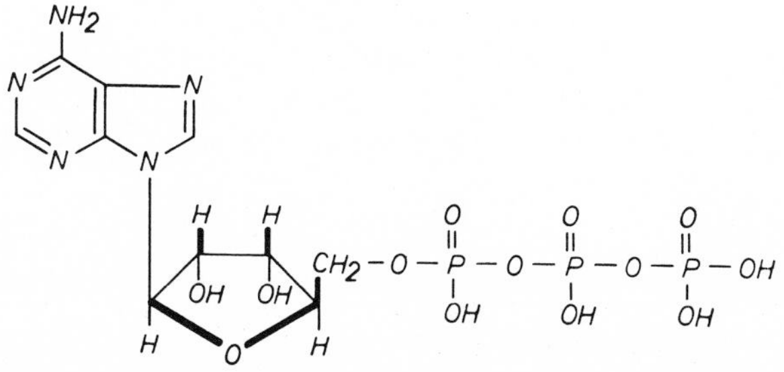

Let us consider for example the formation of glucose 6–phosphate, i.e. an ester of phosphoric acid.[6] In the reaction between $H_3PO_4$ and the alcohol group of glucose $\Delta F° = +3$ kcal/mole, and at equilibrium one would find only minute amounts of glucose 6-phosphate. If phosphoric acid is, however, first raised to a high energy level by being attached to adenosine diphosphate (ADP) to give the triphosphate (ATP), then the reaction with glucose becomes exergonic ($\Delta F° = -4$ kcal/mole) and runs nearly to completion. Here phosphoric acid is bound in an energy-rich way, which we can formalize:

$$ADP + P = ATP + H_2O \qquad \Delta F = +7 \text{ kcal}$$

The reaction requires an energy expenditure of 7 kcal/mole, which has to be provided by some other exergonic reaction. This may come, e.g. from the cleavage of phosphoenolpyruvate[7]:

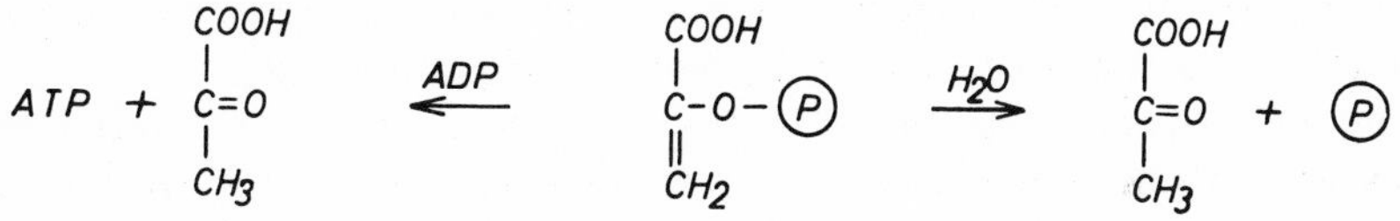

$$\Delta F° = -5 \text{ kcal} \qquad\qquad \Delta F° = -12 \text{ kcal}$$

In the following diagram the necessary energy is provided by the oxidation of glyceraldehyde to glyceric acid:

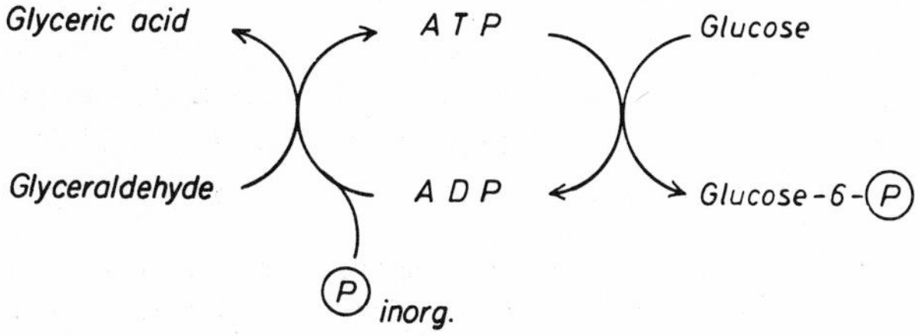

---

[6] This reaction is discussed in more detail in Chapt. XV-7.

[7] The phosphate radical, symbolized in the text by P, will appear as (P) in the drawings, which are taken from the German edition.

Here the adenylic acid system is subjected to a cyclic process: ATP is consumed, but regenerated through a coupled reaction, and the cleavage of ATP in turn is linked to an endergonic reaction, the sugar phosphate formation. We frequently encounter this type of interrelationship in the study of metabolism; the living cell is comparable to a chemical machine which converts chemical energy in a variety of ways and tries to keep it in the form of chemical energy as long as possible. For this purpose several versatile "energy carriers," such as ATP, acyl-coenzyme A, and others, are of particular importance, since they can exchange energy among various reactions (cf. also Chap. VI).

At this point we must warn of a possible misunderstanding. Although chemical energy (free energy of chemical reactions) is measured and expressed in kcal units, it is nevertheless not identical with heat energy. The organism is incapable of utilizing heat energy applied to it; to maintain the operations of life the organism depends on chemical energy in the form of food.[8] Chemical energy is easily converted to heat, but not the reverse. One ought to be aware of the confusion arising from the use of the same units (kcal) for different forms of energy.

**The Energy-Rich Bond.** In modern biochemistry the energy-rich bond[9] is an important concept. The expression applies to all those bonds which release a large amount of energy upon their hydrolysis (more than about 6 kcal/mole), and which have therefore a large potential energy. The energy-rich bond is usually symbolized by the sign $\sim$, as a reminder that a group bound in such a way will react exergonically with many other substances; in other words, that it is highly reactive.

Chemical energy which is released from "combustion" processes of the cell is largely trapped in the form of these energy-rich bonds and then used in a great variety of tasks. The number of ATP molecules produced is sometimes taken as a measure of the useful energy from biochemical exergonic processes.

For the sake of comparing the stored free energies in such compounds as ATP, acyl-CoA, and others, it has become conventional to refer to one common reaction partner, namely water. In effect, the free energies of hydrolysis are compared. The values for several important compounds have been compiled in Table VIII. The accuracy of the values is not very good, since they are based on rather complicated measurements.

These "standard energies" are merely theoretical values; the energy actually available to the cell depends fundamentally on the ratio of concentrations of the reactants (according to equation (5), Chapt. V-2). This dependency is represented graphically in Fig. 19 for the very important system ATP/ADP. A shift of the ratio by the factor 10 changes the free energy by 1.4 kcal.

---

[8] Plants are able to utilize the radiation energy of sunlight for biochemical reactions. This process, of course, makes life on this planet possible. No other forms of energy described in physics are used profitably.

[9] This concept diverges from the "bond energy" of physical chemistry, which refers to the free energy released when a molecule is split to atoms and radicals. Splitting molecules is a highly *endergonic* process (of the order of magnitude of 50–100 kcal/mole for primary valences and about 8 kcal for secondary valences such as hydrogen bonds; cf. Chapt. IV-3).

TABLE VIII

STANDARD FREE ENERGY OF HYDROLYSIS OF SOME ENERGY-RICH COMPOUNDS

| | |
|---|---|
| Adenosine triphosphate, ATP ($\rightarrow$ADP + orthophosphate) | 7 kcal/mole[a] |
| Adenosine triphosphate, ATP ($\rightarrow$AMP + pyrophosphate) | 8 kcal/mole |
| Pyrophosphate ($\rightarrow$2 orthophosphate) | 6 kcal/mole |
| Creatine phosphate | 8 kcal/mole |
| Phosphoenolpyruvate | 12 kcal/mole |
| Phosphoglyceryl phosphate | 11 kcal/mole |
| Acetyl-Coenzyme A (Chapt. VI-5) | 8 kcal/mole |
| Aminoacyl-AMP (Chapt. VII-8) | 7 kcal/mole |

[a] It can be estimated that in the cell the cleavage of ATP releases not 7 but 9–10 kcal per mole of available chemical energy.

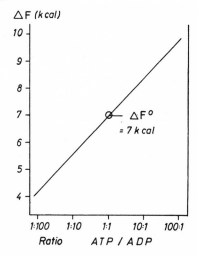

FIG. 19. Dependency of the free energy of ATP hydrolysis on the ratio of concentrations of ATP/ADP. The ordinate is negative free energy.

## 6. Specificity of Enzyme Catalysis

Reaction Specificity. The foregoing discussion of the role of enzymes has emphasized that enzymes cannot shift the equilibrium; rather they accelerate the establishment of equilibrium or, in cases of very sluggish reactions, they make the reactions possible. But the enzyme is capable of selecting a single reaction from a number of possible reactions and catalyzing that one alone. The energy of activation is depressed enough to restrict the attainment of equilibrium exclusively to this particular reaction. This phenomenon is called *"reaction specificity"* of the enzyme. The enzyme catalyzes only one out of numerous thermodynamically possible conversions of a substance. (The same applies, incidentally, for many inorganic catalysts employed by the chemical industry.) Another enzyme with another reaction specificity initiates another reaction. Here is an example:

$$R-C-COOH + NH_3$$
$$\overset{\|}{O}$$

Oxidase
$-2[H] + H_2O$

$$R-\overset{H}{\underset{NH_2}{C}}-COOH$$

Decarboxylase $\longrightarrow$ $R-CH_2-NH_2 + CO_2$

$+HOOC-CH_2-CO-COOH$ Transaminase

$$R-C-COOH + HOOC-CH_2-\overset{H}{\underset{NH_2}{C}}-COOH$$
$$\overset{\|}{O}$$

Amino acid oxidase oxidatively deaminates the amino acid at the left (one of many); the enzyme specifically catalyzes this particular reaction as described extensively in Chapt. VIII–7. Another possible reaction, decarboxylation, does not occur. The catalysis of $CO_2$ loss requires a different enzyme, and a third reaction, transamination, requires a third enzyme assisting in the exchange of functional groups (the keto group of oxaloacetic acid with the amino group). Obviously each of the three enzymes possesses a characteristic reaction specificity; this is true for all enzymes.

The last two enzymes happen to use the same coenzyme (pyridoxal phosphate, (Chapt. VIII–4). The reaction specificity therefore depends on the protein component, and not on the coenzyme (cf. Chapt. VI–1). This selectivity of reactions by the enzymes is of prime importance for life processes in general.

The following mechanism furnishes a likely (but still incomplete) explanation of reaction specificity: Enzyme and substrate form a weak bond from which the reaction on the substrate may then proceed. The kind of bond between enzyme and substrate prepares for the specific reaction. In bimolecular reactions, two substrates must be bound simultaneously to the enzyme surface to let the substrates react with each other. Frequently, one of the reaction partners is a coenzyme (see Chapt. VI).

**Substrate Specificity.** The principle of selection operates furthermore in the binding of the substrate to the enzyme. Certainly not every substance which might be able to undergo a particular reaction is bound. In the example of the amino acid decarboxylase, a few amino acids are bound tightly, some loosely, and others not at all. The latter do not react, i.e. their decarboxylation is not catalyzed. This kind of selectivity is called *"substrate specificity."* It is especially characteristic for optical antipodes (mirror image isomers). Usually only one of the two isomers reacts, or at least one antipode reacts much faster.

The extent of substrate specificity varies from enzyme to enzyme. A few hydrolases are relatively nonspecific, others require substrates containing certain groups (group specificity; e.g., $\beta$-galactosidase and $\alpha$-glucosidase, which cleave all β-galactosides and α-glucosides respectively; cf. Chapt. XVII–3). Other enzymes interact very specifically with one substrate only; closely related substances may be bound by the enzyme but are not brought to reaction and thus behave as inhibitors (examples: succinate and malonate[10] with succinate dehydrogenase) (cf. also Chapt V–9).

The metabolism of fluoroacetate, $CH_2F—COO^-$, illustrates this point very nicely. Fluoroacetate is very similar to acetate, $CH_3—COO^-$, and is converted just like the latter to the CoA derivative, in which form it condenses with oxaloacetate to fluorocitrate (cf. Chapt. XI-1). Both the activating enzyme and the condensing enzyme, the citrogenase, treat fluoroacetate like acetate itself. Aconitase, on the other hand, the next enzyme in the citric acid cycle, is very strongly inhibited by fluorocitrate. Fluorocitrate is bound by the enzyme surface (thus replacing citrate) but cannot undergo the reaction (hence competitive inhibition, Chapt. V-9). Aconitase appears to be an enzyme of high specificity. The great toxicity of fluoroacetate is explained, therefore, by its blocking of the citric acid cycle.

## 7. Michaelis' Theory

The hypothesis that the enzyme binds the substrate led to a very fruitful theoretical treatment of the mode of enzyme activity (Michaelis and Menten). We can apply the law of mass action to the reversible formation of the enzyme-substrate complex from its components,

$$\text{Enzyme} + \text{Substrate} \rightleftharpoons \text{Enzyme-Substrate} \qquad (7)$$
$$\text{E} \quad + \quad \text{S} \quad \rightleftharpoons \qquad \text{ES}$$

obtaining the following expression:

$$\frac{[E] \cdot [S]}{[ES]} = K_{eq} \qquad (8)$$

According to the fundamental precepts of the "catalysis of intermediates" the enzymic reaction itself can proceed only *via* the complex. The products A and B are formed this way:

$$\text{ES} \rightarrow \text{A} + \text{B} + \text{E} \qquad (9)$$

This reaction is assumed to run practically to completion (presupposing the likely situation that the reaction is exergonic and the equilibrium lies far to the right). At the same time, the catalyst is being regenerated. Michaelis and Menten then supposed that this last reaction (9) is rate limiting, i.e. that it runs much slower than the formation of the enzyme-substrate complex. The speed of the overall reaction, which is directly measurable, is therefore proportional to the concentration of enzyme-substrate complex [ES], and conversely, the speed of the reaction can be taken as a measure of the ES concentration.

Equation (8) can be interpreted as follows: Starting with a given amount of enzyme, if the substrate concentration is raised gradually, more and more enzyme will be converted into the complex ES and the rate of reaction will increase until

---

[10] Malonic acid $HOOC—CH_2—COOH$ cannot be dehydrogenated by insertion of a double bond, as is possible with succinic acid $HOOC—CH_2—CH_2—COOH$, for simple chemical reasons.

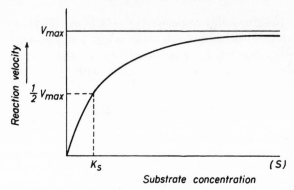

FIG. 20. Dependency of reaction rate on substrate concentration (at constant enzyme concentration).

finally virtually all the enzyme is in the form of ES. The enzyme is then saturated; at this point the reaction rate is maximal. This relationship is represented graphically in Fig. 20.

**Michaelis Constant.** The saturation concentration differs from enzyme to enzyme, and for any one enzyme it differs from substrate to substrate. In contrast to maximum velocity, it cannot be read easily from the graph. But the situation is better defined by choosing as a point of reference the half-maximal velocity. According to our hypothesis, at this point half of the entire enzyme is in form of the ES complex and the other half as free E, since the reaction rate should be proportional to the ES concentration. In equation (8) the terms E and ES cancel, leaving

$$[S]_{\text{at half-maximal velocity}} = K_m$$

To express this in words: That substrate concentration at which half-maximal reaction velocity is reached equals the dissociation constant of the enzyme-substrate complex. This constant is named the "Michaelis constant," $K_m$, after the originator of the theory. Its dimensions are those of the substrate concentration (moles/liter); when $[S] = K_m$ the enzyme is only half saturated.

It is relatively easy to determine experimentally the Michaelis constant, $K_m$ (i.e. the substrate concentration at which half-maximal reaction speed is attained), while it is not always possible to test the assumption that the turnover of [ES] is rate-determining. Hence, the distinction is now made between the substrate constant,

$$K_s = \frac{[E] \cdot [S]}{[ES]},$$

which is equivalent to the dissociation constant of the enzyme-substrate complex, and the Michaelis constant, $K_m$, which is determined solely from the reaction rate. The two constants ordinarily are numerically equal, which means that the limiting condition is fulfilled.

An "inhibitor constant" may be defined similarly whenever a certain substance becomes reversibly attached to the enzyme and inhibits or prevents the reaction:

$$K_i = \frac{[E] \cdot [I]}{[EI]}$$

A large Michaelis constant means that a high substrate concentration is necessary to attain half saturation; the enzyme possesses a low affinity for the substrate in question. It will preferentially bind another substrate whose Michaelis constant is smaller and probably bring that substrate to reaction, too. Michaelis constants usually range between $10^{-2}$ and $10^{-5}$ moles/liter.

The reaction rate of an enzyme-catalyzed reaction is also used to define *"enzyme units."* One unit (U) is that amount of an enzyme which will catalyze the transformation of 1 $\mu$mole of substrate per minute under optimal conditions (saturation with substrate, optimal pH, etc.). Enzyme units may be determined even in crude preparations.

**Molecular Activity.** Many enzymes have thus far been isolated in pure and crystallized form. In these cases, the *molecular activity* can be determined; it is defined as the number of molecules of substrate transformed per minute per molecule of enzyme (or the number of $\mu$moles of substrate per $\mu$mole of enzyme, i.e. the number of enzyme units per $\mu$mole of enzyme). The term *"turnover number"* has also been applied to this definition (and similar ones). For the calculation of molecular activity, the activity of the enzyme and its molecular weight must be known. A large molecular activity indicates a rapid reaction. Very large molecular activities have been found in the cases of acetylcholinesterase ($18 \times 10^6$). The usual values range from several thousand to ten thousand molecules of substrate per enzyme molecule per minute, still a rather rapid turnover.

## 8. The Mechanism of Enzyme Catalysis

In spite of all our knowledge of the structure of enzymes and the thermodynamics and kinetics of enzyme-catalyzed reactions, we are still far from an adequate understanding of the enzymic mechanism of action. In modern organic chemistry reactions are explained on the basis of the electron theory and the chemical bond. In principle, this explanation should also apply to enzymic transformations, but so far it has been possible only in a few instances to arrive at the detailed reaction mechanism.

Very often, enzymic reactions are assisted by coenzymes or prosthetic groups. The chemical structure of these cofactors is discussed in the following chapter. They are low molecular weight substances of much simpler structure than the high molecular weight proteins (apoenzymes). Some of the coenzymes, e.g. pyridoxal phosphate, by themselves, without the apoenzyme, exhibit catalytic properties which can be explained by modern electron theory (cf. Chapt. VIII-4). Such explanations, however, do not answer the question why enzymic reactions occur so much faster and why they are guided in a very specific direction. The apoenzyme, the protein component of the enzyme, evidently is responsible for the latter phenomena, but to interpret its role in the reaction is much more difficult, although a few concepts have been developed very recently.

Michaelis' and Menten's assumption that initially an enzyme-substrate complex is formed has been corroborated fully. The kinetic data fit this hypothesis very well (even though the formation of the complex is sometimes slower than the setting-up of a true equilibrium according to the equation E + S ⇌ ES). In some cases the existence of such enzyme-substrate complexes has been proved directly by spectroscopic methods. The bonds in the complex most probably are ionic or secondary valence bonds. Certain areas on the protein surface contain a pattern of charges or of reactive groups such that the substrate molecule can become attached there.

This area on the protein molecule is called the *active site*, where the catalysis itself takes place. In some cases, it has become possible to label the active site of an enzyme and to investigate its structure. The active site usually includes amino acid residues with reactive side chains (histidine, serine, cysteine, and others), which can interact with the substrate.

The reaction on the enzyme protein may also proceed in two steps. A reactant (or a part of it) at first is bound to the protein by primary valence bonds, and only in a second step does the formation of the product proceed from the intermediate complex. The proteolytic action of chymotrypsin is an example of this; the enzymic cleavage of the bound peptide is presumed to follow the scheme shown on page 83.

The diagram shows that the catalytic action depends on a serine and a histidine residue. The histidine residue functions as a proton donor and acceptor. The reaction proceeds first by eliminating the group NH—X and by binding the acyl radical (the carboxyl group of the peptide bond under attack) to the enzyme, more specifically, to the serine residue. (Very careful hydrolysis has permitted the isolation of such serine-O-acyl compounds.) The ester bond is then hydrolyzed; the enzyme thus is returned to its original reactive form, and the second product of the hydrolysis, the acid, is liberated. The reactions are reversible to an extent depending on the equilibrium positions.

The key feature of this two-step hydrolysis is the primary valence bond of a part of the molecule to the enzyme protein, whereby the first product of the enzymic reaction is already released. The active enzyme is then regenerated by the hydrolysis. A very analogous mechanism has been proposed for some other hydrolases, e.g. acetylcholinesterase and glucose 6-phosphatase. Several transferases, too, appear to follow the same scheme.

The *kinases* (phosphate-transferring enzymes, e.g. hexokinase, creatine kinase) do not form an intermediate product in which phosphate is bound to the enzyme. Instead, the phosphate group is transferred directly between the reaction partners, more in the nature of a many-center reaction. Such a mechanism has been proposed for creatine kinase, which catalyzes the transfer of a phosphate group on a high energy level, according to the equation:

$$\text{creatine} + \text{ATP} \rightleftharpoons \text{creatine} - \text{P} + \text{ADP}$$

Though the mechanism is still hypothetical, it illustrates the mechanism of the many-center reaction rather well. The diagram on p. 84 shows two groups of the enzyme participating in this reaction, namely an —SH group and a histidine residue. The binding of the two substrates involves a $Mg^{++}$ ion. The reaction itself consists of a *simultaneous* shift of seven electron pairs, partly in the two substrate molecules and partly in the reactive groups of the enzyme protein.

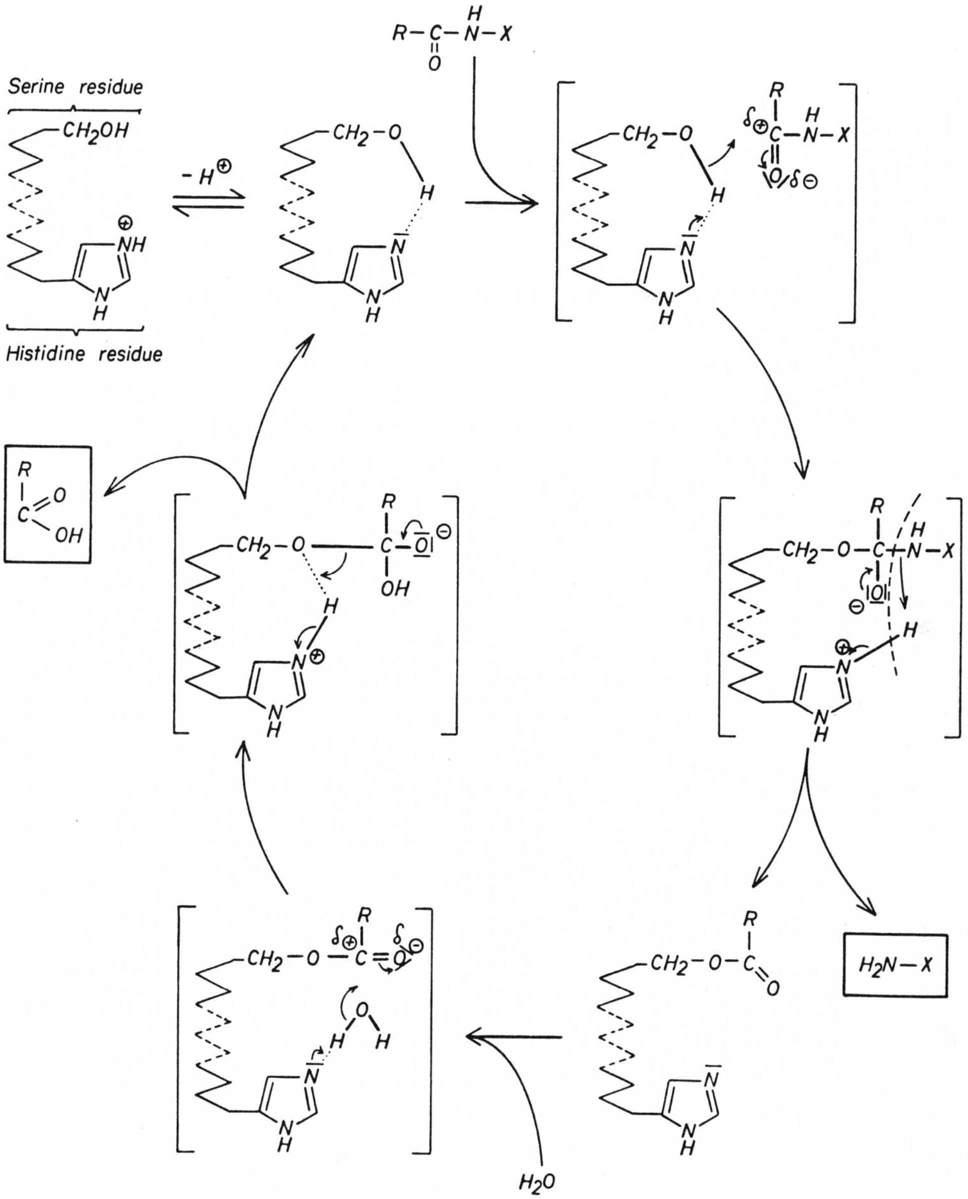

The two examples are hypothetical to a considerable degree. They should provide some idea, however, of probable mechanisms of enzyme action and of possible ways in which active sites on the protein can participate in the reaction. Many questions, of course, remain unanswered: We do not know yet what forces bring the reactive groups into favorable spatial relation to each other; nor do we know what determines the very high specificity of the enzyme-substrate bond. Some of these problems will perhaps be solved once the tertiary structure of the corre-

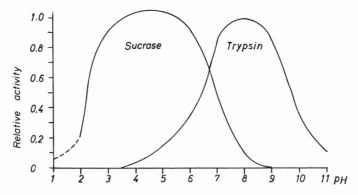

sponding proteins becomes known, because this would enable us to construct models of these proteins.

## 9. Conditions for Enzyme Activity

Since enzymes are proteins, their properties are affected by the ionic strength of the solution, particularly by the pH. The majority of enzymes exhibit their specific catalytic activity only at one particular range of pH values. The most favorable $H^+$ concentration is called the *optimum* pH. The pH dependence may be more or less striking and is usually expressed in the form of a curve, by plotting enzyme activity (e.g. $\mu$moles turned over per unit time) versus pH (Fig. 21). For most enzymes the optimum pH is in the neutral or slightly acid region. Extreme pH optima occur with several digestive enzymes, e.g. pepsin (1.5–2.5), trypsin (8–11), pancreatic lipase (8.0).

FIG. 21. Dependency of the action of an enzyme on pH

Temperature is just as important for the speed of enzymic reaction as it is for uncatalyzed reactions; a temperature rise of 10° accelerates the rate of reaction two- to four-fold, but the phenomenon quickly reaches a limit because of the sensitivity of the proteins; some enzymes are damaged irreversibly even at 40 to 50°, and only a few continue to be active above 60°.

Many enzymes require certain ions for their activity. Amylases need $Cl^-$ ions; enzymes turning over ATP nearly always require $Mg^{++}$. Numerous peptidases are activated by $Mn^{++}$, $Zn^{++}$ or $Co^{++}$. Occasionally, divalent ions can replace one another. The mechanism by which ions exert their influence, however, is known only in a few cases. The assumption is that complexes with ions somehow "loosen up" the substrates.

Beside these activators, many inhibitors are also known. Some of them are quite specific: Heavy metal-containing enzymes are inhibited by HCN; many SH-group-containing enzymes, by $Cu^{++}$ or $Hg^{++}$ ions. Arsenate generally inhibits wherever phosphoric acid is metabolized, etc.

*Competitive inhibition* occurs whenever the place on the enzyme which should be occupied by the substrate molecule is taken by another molecule which cannot itself react. The inhibiting molecule blocks the enzyme. One classical example is the pair succinate (substrate) and malonate (inhibitor) with succinate dehydrogenase. Raising the substrate concentration replaces the inhibitor (malonate) on the surface of the enzyme according to the law of mass action. Mathematical analysis of the extent of inhibition as a function of inhibitor and substrate concentrations can easily distinguish between competitive and noncompetitive inhibition.

**Isoenzymes.** Isoenzymes are enzymes with very similar chemical and physical properties. They catalyze the same reaction but can be separated by the methods of protein chemistry. This phenomenon has been studied thoroughly in the case of the five forms of lactate dehydrogenase which can be distinguished by electrophoresis. The relative amounts of the five isoenzymes differ from organ to organ and species to species.

## 10. Classification and Nomenclature of Enzymes

Enzymes known for a long time have trivial names that are still in use (e.g. *trypsin, pepsin, emulsin*). More recently, names have been devised more systematically with the suffix -*ase*. To designate a group of enzymes with a specific property, the suffix is attached to the name of the reaction catalyzed. Thus, dehydrogenating enzymes are called dehydrogenases; enzymes that transfer groups are called transferases; etc. The suffix -*ase* attached to the name of a substrate indicates hydrolytic enzymes: Proteases are enzymes that cleave proteins; phosphatases those that hydrolyze phosphate esters. The complete designation of individual enzymes includes the full chemical name of the substrate and of the reaction. Examples are lactate dehydrogenase, cytochrome oxidase, and glucose 6-phosphatase.

Until very recently the naming of the individual enzymes has been entrusted largely to the discoverers. This resulted often in such descriptive names as "zwischenferment" or "pH 5 enzyme." An international commission meanwhile has drafted specific rules for the classification and nomenclature of enzymes.[11] The commission has established six main classes, which are further subdivided into sub-classes and sub-sub-classes, according to the nature of the reaction catalyzed and to the type of bond formed or severed. In Table IX several examples of each main class are listed to illustrate the system.

---

[11] Report of the Commission on Enzymes, International Union of Biochemistry Symposium, Vol. 20, Pergamon Press, New York, 1961. A discussion and an outline of this Report is given by R. H. S. Thompson, *Nature*, **193**, 1227 (1962).

TABLE IX

CLASSIFICATION OF ENZYMES

| Main Class and Sub-Classes | Example | Chapter |
|---|---|---|
| **1. Oxidoreductases** | | |
| 1.1 Acting on the >CH—OH group of donors | | X |
|   1.1.1 With NAD or NADP as acceptor | Alcohol dehydrogenase, lactate dehydrogenase | XV-7 |
|   1.1.3 With $O_2$ as acceptor | Glucose oxidase | |
| 1.2 Acting on the aldehyde or keto-group of donors | | |
|   1.2.1 With NAD or NADP as acceptor | Glyceraldehyde-3-phosphate dehydrogenase | XV-7 |
|   1.2.3 With $O_2$ as acceptor | Xanthine oxidase | VII-2 |
| 1.3 Acting on the >CH—CH< group of donors | | |
|   1.3.1 With NAD or NADP as acceptor | Dihydrouracil dehydrogenase | |
|   1.3.2 With a cytochrome as an acceptor | Acyl-CoA dehydrogenases | XII-3 |
| 1.4 Acting on the >CH—$NH_2$ group of donors | | |
|   1.4.3 With $O_2$ as acceptor | Aminoacid oxidases | VIII-7 |
| etc. | | |
| **2. Transferases** | | |
| 2.1 Transferring $C_1$-groups | | |
|   2.1.1 Methyltransferases | Guanidinoacetate methyltransferase | VI-5 |
|   2.1.2 Hydroxymethyl- and formyltransferases | Serine hydroxymethyltransferase | VIII-12 |
|   2.1.3 Carboxyl- and carbamoyltransferase | Ornithine carbamoyltransferase | VIII-8 |
| 2.3 Acyltransferases | Choline acetyltransferase | XXIII-7 |
| 2.4 Glycosyltransferases | | |

| Classification | Example | Code |
|---|---|---|
| 2.6 Transferring N-containing groups | | |
|   2.6.1 Aminotransferases | Transaminases | VIII-6 |
|     etc. | | |
| **3. Hydrolases** | | |
| 3.1 Cleaving ester linkages | | |
|   3.1.1 Carboxylic ester hydrolases | Esterases, Lipases | XII-2 |
|   3.1.3 Phosphoric monoester hydrolases | Phosphatases | VII-9 |
|   3.1.4 Phosphoric diester hydrolases | | VII-9 |
|     etc. | | |
| 3.2 Cleaving Glycosides | | |
|   3.2.1 Glycosidases | Amylase | XVII-3 |
| | $\beta$-glycosidase, etc. | XVII-6 |
| | Nucleosidases | XVII-3 |
|   3.2.2 N-Glucosidases | | VII-9 |
| 3.4 Cleaving peptide linkages | | |
|   3.4.1 $\alpha$-Aminopeptide aminoacidhydrolases | Leucine aminopeptidase | VIII-1 |
|   3.4.2 $\alpha$-Carboxypeptide aminoacidhydrolases | Carboxypeptidases | VIII-3 |
|   3.4.4 Peptidopeptide hydrolases | Pepsin, trypsin, chymotrypsin | VIII-3 |
|     (= endopeptidases) | | VIII-2 |
|     etc. | | |
| **4. Lyases** | | |
| 4.1 C—C Lyases | | |
|   4.1.1 Carboxy Lyases | Pyruvate decarboxylase | XV-7 |
|   4.1.2 Aldehyde Lyases | Aldolase | XV-7 |
| 4.2 C—O Lyases | | |
|   4.2.1 Hydrolyases | Fumarate hydratase | XI-2 |
| 4.3 C—N Lyases | Histidine-ammonia lyase (= histidase) | VIII-13 |
| **5. Isomerases** | | |
| 5.1 Racemases and epimerases | | |
|   5.1.3 Acting on carbohydrates | Ribulose-5-phosphate epimerase | XV-5 |
| 5.2 *Cis-Trans* isomerases | Maleylacetoacetate isomerase | VIII-11 |
| 5.3 Intramolecular Oxidoreductases | | |
|   5.3.1 Interconverting aldoses and ketoses | Glucosephosphate isomerase | XV-7 |
| 5.4 Intramolecular transferases | Methylmalonyl-CoA mutase | XII-5 |

TABLE IX—Continued

| Main Class and Sub-Classes | Example | Chapter |
| --- | --- | --- |
| **6. Ligases** | | |
| 6.1 Forming C—O bonds | | |
| 6.1.1 Aminoacid-RNA ligases | Amino-acid activating enzyme | VII-8 |
| 6.3 Forming C—N bonds | | |
| 6.3.1 Acid-ammonia ligases | Glutamine synthetase | |
| 6.3.2 Acid-amino acid ligases | Peptide synthetase, glutathione synthetase | VII-8 |
| 6.4 Forming C—C bonds | | |
| 6.4.1 Carboxylases | Acetyl-CoA carboxylase | XII-6 |

Obviously only a small selection of the more than 700 known enzymes has been incorporated into the table; the mere enumeration of all sub-groups would have occupied too much space. The hydrolases, which before were commonly placed at the head of the table, now make up the third main class, following the transferases. The term *desmolase*, which used to designate the entirety of the nonhydrolytic enzymes, has been dropped. Enzymes with a degrading action are classified as *"lyases,"* while enzymes that catalyze synthetic processes may be called "synthases." Synthetases, on the other hand, are enzymes that catalyze the joining of two molecules with the aid of ATP or a similar nucleoside triphosphate, i.e. by the cleavage of an energy-rich phosphate bond. This main class has received the systematic name "ligases," to avoid confusion with the above-mentioned synthases.

Since this whole book deals with biochemical reactions and hence with enzymic activity, it appears superfluous to discuss the individual enzymic reactions again here. Accordingly, after each name a reference is made to the section where the reaction is discussed more thoroughly.

BIBLIOGRAPHY

R. Ammon and W. Dirscherl, *in* "Fermente—Hormone—Vitamine," Vol. I: "Fermente," 3rd ed., Georg Thieme, Stuttgart, 1959.

L. v. Bertalanffy, "Problems of Life," Wiley, New York, 1952.

P. D. Boyer, H. Lardy, and K. Myrbäck (editors), "The Enzymes," Vol. I: "Kinetics, Thermodynamics, Mechanism, Basic Properties," Academic Press, New York, 1959; for specific enzymes see Vols. 2–8, 1960–1963.

M. Dixon and E. C. Webb, "Enzymes," 2nd ed., Academic Press, New York, 1964.

F. Haurowitz, "Progress in Biochemistry Since 1949," pp. 1–25, Karger Verlag, Basel, 1959.

Lloyd L. Ingraham, "Biochemical Mechanisms," Wiley, New York, 1962.

I. M. Klotz, "Some Principles of Energetics in Biochemical Reactions," Academic Press, New York, 1957.

D. E. Koshland, Correlation of structure and function in enzyme action, *Science* **142**, 1533–1541 (1963).

H. Netter, "Theoretische Biochemie,ʼ Springer Verlag, Berlin, 1959.

J. B. Neilands and P. K. Stumpf, "Outlines of Enzyme Chemistry," Wiley, New York, 1958.

B. L. Vallee, Active center of carboxypeptidase A, *Federation Proc.* **23** (No. 1, Pt. I), 8–17 (1964); a symposium paper.

# CHAPTER VI

# Coenzymes

## 1. Coenzymes and Prosthetic Groups

We have already indicated (Chapt. V–1) that all enzymes are proteins, and that many have in addition a "prosthetic group," the coenzyme. These groups often dissociate:

$$\text{Coenzyme} + \text{Apoenzyme} \rightleftharpoons \text{Holoenzyme}$$

The terms *"coenzyme"* and *"prosthetic group"* are frequently used synonymously.[1] Lately, the tendency has been to call the tightly bound groups that cannot be removed (for example by dialysis) prosthetic groups, and those which dissociate easily, coenzymes. Naturally it is often difficult to decide what is easily dissociable and what is not, for there is a complete range of possibilities.

The following considerations may lead to a sensible distinction between coenzyme and prosthetic group. Both types of groups participate chemically in the catalyzed process; they are thereby altered and their original condition is restored only in a second reaction, usually through the mediation of a second enzyme. In this sense they do not conform to the strict definition of a catalyst, because they do not emerge from the reaction unaltered. This process of restoration differs between the coenzymes and the prosthetic groups.

Typically dissociable coenzymes might better be called *"cosubstrates."* They assume the role of a hydrogen or group donor; e.g., ATP contributes a phosphate radical in the hexokinase reaction (Chapt. V–5, diagram), and nicotinamide-adenine dinucleotide (formerly coenzyme I or DPN) accepts hydrogen from the substrate. Each substance functions therefore as a second substrate, which reacts with the real substrate itself strictly stoichiometrically; i.e., mole per mole and

---

[1] "Prosthetic group" is a generic term which comprises all groups bound to proteins including even those without any catalytic effect (cf. Chapt. IV-8). In this chapter we always refer to prosthetic groups of *enzymes*.

*not* catalytically. In a second reaction, catalyzed by another enzyme protein, the hydrogenated $NAD \cdot H_2$ can then relinquish its hydrogen (or ADP can again pick up phosphate); even at this point the coenzymes are "cosubstrates," which react stoichiometrically. The catalytic nature of a coenzyme begins to appear only when it is coupled to two enzymes in an enzyme system. The process, illustrated schematically below, is realized in anaerobic glycolysis.

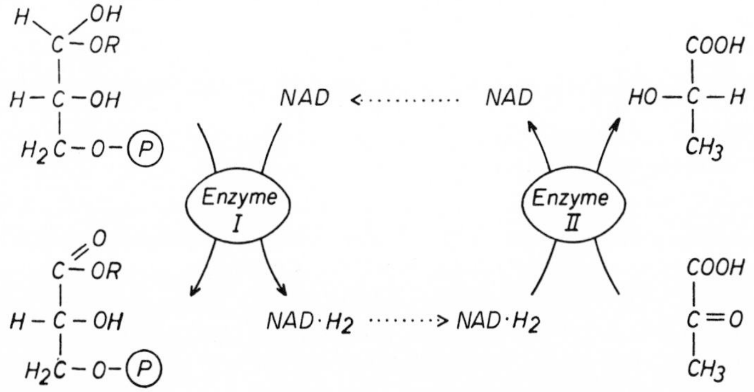

It is precisely because coenzymes couple different enzymes that they are important in metabolism: They are the links by means of which the exchange of material—be it hydrogen, phosphoric acid, or some organic group—becomes possible.

In other enzyme systems, in contrast, the "active group" is tightly bound to the enzyme protein. In this case catalysis occurs when the holoenzyme reacts with two different substrates simultaneously (or in rapid succession). This is illustrated in the following diagram. The amino acid is dehydrogenated by the enzyme; the hydrogen is accepted by the prosthetic group and transferred to a molecule of oxygen in a second reaction (with formation of $H_2O_2$). The active group reacts stoichiometrically even here, but is returned to the original state on the same enzyme by reaction with the second substrate. Further examples of this are found in transamination (Chapt. VIII–6) and in the respiratory chain (Chapt. X–4); in these cases we would speak of the *prosthetic group* of the enzyme.

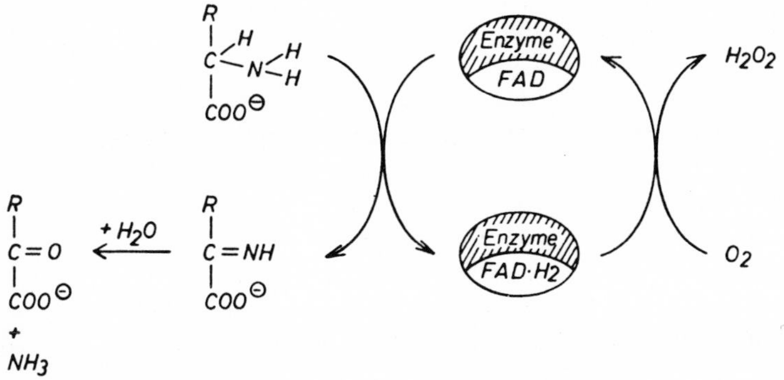

The distinction drawn here between coenzyme and prosthetic group has not been adopted generally, nor has the concept of coenzymes as cosubstrates been accepted universally. It has been difficult to free ourselves of the ideas of "active group" and "colloidal carrier."

It is true even with our terminology that coenzymes take a decisive role in the activity of the enzyme. The individual specificity of the enzyme—including the reaction specificity—does reside, however, with the protein component. Many cases are known in which the same coenzyme is involved in completely different reactions, depending on the protein to which it is bound. Not a single case is known, however, where one protein in conjunction with various coenzymes shows various activities, although this is theoretically possible.

The chemical nature of coenzymes has been established for a much longer time than that of the enzymes themselves. The explanation is that all enzymes are proteins and, as indicated before, the methods for their structural determination (sequential analysis) have been developed only very recently. Coenzymes, on the other hand, are low molecular weight compounds which can be studied by the methods of organic chemistry.

## 2. Coenzymes and Vitamins

Many coenzymes are closely related to vitamins. Vitamins are active compounds which must be ingested in food. They are necessary for the proper functioning of life processes and cannot be replaced by other substances. The organism is itself incapable of synthesizing them, except possibly from direct precursors, the *provitamins*. The amounts of vitamins which must be supplied daily are relatively minute (cf. Table XIX, Chapt. XXII). This means that vitamins are not "foodstuffs" in the ordinary sense, but rather function catalytically. The biocatalytic function is known for many vitamins; generally, a vitamin is the main (or sole) component of a coenzyme (see Table X). An insufficient supply of one of the vitamins results in arrested growth and deficiency diseases; avitaminoses were the starting point of vitamin research. The connection between the biochemical role of the coenzyme and the clinically observable manifestations of vitamin deficiency is still unknown. It is remarkable that many deficiency diseases have skin and mucosal symptoms. In animal experiments it is possible, however, to observe deviations from normal metabolism, based on vitamin deficiency, before the characteristic symptoms of the avitaminosis become discernible.

In this chapter the chemical structures of those vitamins which are components of presently known coenzymes will be discussed; their nutritional significance will be treated in Chapt. XXII.

## 3. Structure and Classification of Coenzymes

Almost all coenzymes contain phosphoric acid as an essential component, often in a type of bond called "nucleoside phosphate," or better "*nucleotide*." Nucleotides consist of a base, a monosaccharide (nearly always ribose), and phosphoric acid. The base and sugar are linked through an N-glycoside bond (cf. Chapt. VII–1); the phosphoric acid is esterified with one hydroxyl group of the ribose. Nucleotides

TABLE X
COENZYMES

| Coenzymes | Usual Abbreviation | Group Transferred | Corresponding Vitamin | cf. Chapt. |
|---|---|---|---|---|
| **1. Hydrogen-transferring coenzymes:** | | | | |
| Nicotinamide-adenine dinucleotide | NAD (formerly DPN) | Hydrogen | Nicotinamide | X-4 |
| Nicotinamide-adenine dinucleotide phosphate | NADP (formerly TPN) | Hydrogen | Nicotinamide | X-4 |
| Nicotinamide mononucleotide | — | Hydrogen | Nicotinamide | X-4 |
| Flavin mononucleotide (Riboflavin phosphate) | FMN | Hydrogen | Riboflavin | X-4 |
| Flavin-adenine dinucleotide | FAD | Hydrogen | Riboflavin | X-4 |
| Cell hemins | — | Electrons | — | X-4 |
| Lipoic acid | Lip(S$_2$) | Hydrogen and acyl groups | — | VIII-10 |
| **2. Group-transferring coenzymes:** | | | | |
| Adenosine triphosphate | ATP | Phosphate group (and AMP group) | — | VI-5 |
| Phosphoadenyl sulfate | PAPS | Sulfate group | — | VI-5 |
| Adenosylmethionine | — | Methyl group (methionine) | — | VI-5 |
| Uridine diphosphate | UDP | Sugar, uronic acid | — | XVII-4 |
| Cytidine diphosphate | CDP | Phosphoryl choline and related groups | — | XIII-3 |
| Coenzyme A | CoA | Acyl group | Pantothenic acid | XII-6 |
| Tetrahydrofolic acid | THF | Formyl group | Folic acid | VI-5 |
| Biotin | — | Carboxyl group (CO$_2$) | Biotin | XII-6 |
| Thiamine pyrophosphate | TPP | C$_2$-aldehyde groups | Thiamine | XV-5 |
| Pyridoxal phosphate | PALP | Amino group | Pyridoxine | VIII-6 |
| **3. Coenzymes of isomerases and lyases:** | | | | |
| Uridine diphosphate | UDP | Sugar isomerization | — | XVII-4 |
| Pyridoxal phosphate | PALP | Decarboxylation | Pyridoxine | VIII-6 |
| Thiamine pyrophosphate | TPP | Decarboxylation | Thiamine | VIII-10 |
| B$_{12}$ Coenzyme | — | Carboxyl displacement | Cobalamin | XII-5 |

were originally discovered as components of nucleic acids and received their name in that way (cf. Chapt. VII–1).

It seems convenient to classify coenzymes according to the reactions in whose catalysis they are instrumental. Such a classification parallels that of the enzymes (see Table X). Accordingly, the hydrogen transferring coenzymes are listed first. A second and particularly comprehensive class is made up by the group-transferring coenzymes. The hydrolases frequently require metal ions for activity but have no true coenzymes. Group-transferring coenzymes also participate often in reactions catalyzed by the isomerases, lyases, and ligases; a few special cases will be discussed in Section 6, at the end of this chapter.

Understanding of coenzymes necessarily involves knowledge of the reactions in which they participate. These are treated thoroughly later in this book, and this chapter will be referred to in many places. It is hoped that any initial difficulties in understanding this topic will be gradually overcome as the reader proceeds.

## 4. Coenzymes of the Oxidoreductases

**The Nicotinamide Nucleotides.** The hydrogen-transferring enzymes of fermentation, of glycolysis, and of many other reactions utilize as their coenzymes, dinucleotides, one of whose bases is the pyridine derivative nicotinamide. These dinucleotides are therefore pyridine nucleotides.

Pyridine nucleotides are the coenzymes longest known. In 1906, Harden and Young noticed that Buchner's "zymase" could be separated by ultrafiltration into a high molecular weight component and a low molecular weight component, or coenzyme. These results were later extended and served as a basis for theories of enzyme structure. This "coenzyme" (then called *"codehydrogenase I," "coenzyme I," "DPN,"* now *NAD*) was isolated by H. v. Euler and co-workers in 1931; shortly afterwards, Warburg and Christian discovered the closely related *coenzyme II* (*"TPN,"* now *NADP*).

Pyridine nucleotides are intimately associated with *niacin*, another B vitamin (the pellagra-preventive factor). Niacin is a simple pyridine derivative, pyridine-3-carboxylic acid or nicotinic acid. The amide (niacinamide, *nicotinamide*) also prevents pellagra. The vitamin appears in the coenzyme in this form:

| Nicotinic acid | Nicotinamide | Nicotinamide |
| (Niacin) | (Niacinamide) | pyridinium salt |

The pyridine ring in the coenzyme is attached in N-glycosidic linkage (cf. Chapt. VII–1) to ribose. Such a linkage evidently is possible only with the pyridinium cation, which bears one hydrogen atom on the nitrogen. Pyrophosphoric acid provides the link between nicotinamide riboside and adenosine. The complete formula for the nicotinamide-adenine dinucleotide is given here:

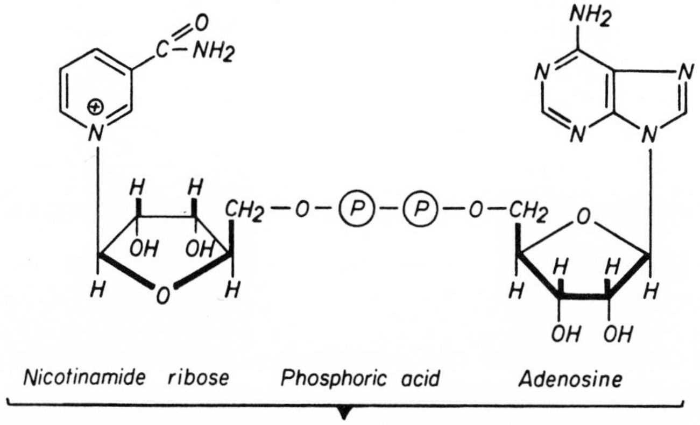

Nicotinamide  ribose      Phosphoric acid      Adenosine

Nicotinamide adenine dinucleotide = Diphosphopyridine nucleotide
NAD  or  NAD$^{\oplus}$                              DPN$^{\oplus}$

The common designation *"diphosphopyridine nucleotide"* is incorrect and confusing. We are not at all dealing with a nucleotide of diphosphopyridine. We are concerned, however, with a *dinucleotide*, one of whose base components is a pyridine derivative. The Commission on Enzymes of the International Union of Biochemistry, therefore, has proposed the name *"nicotinamide-adenine dinucleotide,"* abbreviated NAD, for the so-called diphosphopyridine nucleotide. *"Nicotinamide-adenine dinucleotide phosphate,"* abbreviated NADP, is suggested for the coenzyme triphosphopyridine nucleotide.[2] Since this improved nomenclature has now been introduced officially, we will adopt it throughout this book (see also footnote 2, Chapt. XVIII-1).

In nicotinamide-adenine dinucleotide phosphate the adenosine moiety carries the additional phosphate group in the 2'-position:

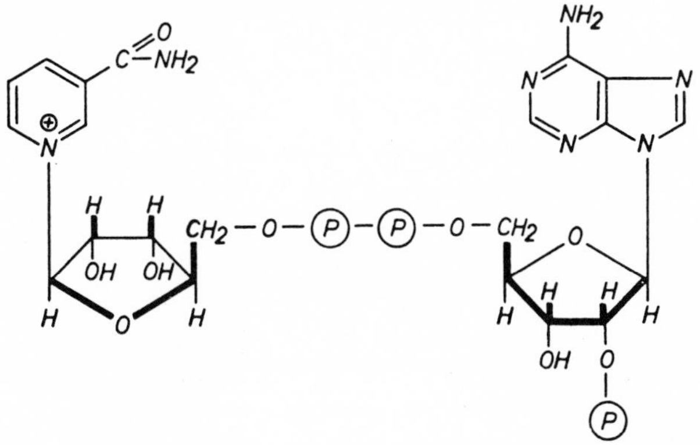

Nicotinamide adenine dinucleotide phosphate = Triphosphopyridine nucleotide
NADP or NADP$^{\oplus}$                    =                    TPN$^{\oplus}$

---

[2] See M. Dixon, *Science,* **132,** 1548 (1960) and R. H. S. Thompson, *Nature,* **193,** 1227 (1962).

Because of the positive charge in the pyridine ring these coenzymes are also abbreviated NAD+ and NADP+. Their function is the reversible uptake of hydrogen. The pyridine ring becomes reduced, retaining only two double bonds, while the nitrogen loses its positive charge:

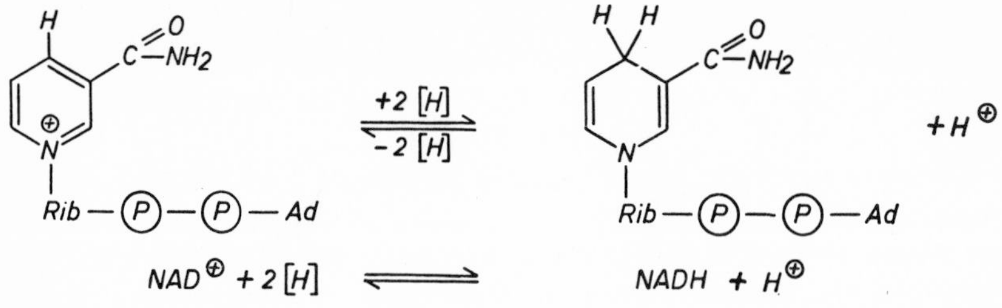

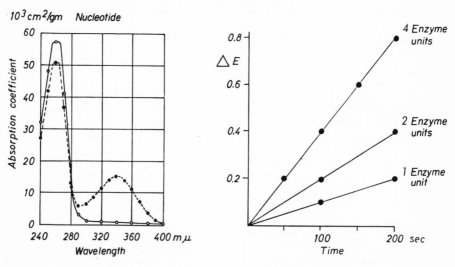

Obviously, the aromatic nature of the pyridine ring is lost, too. This changes the light absorption very characteristically. The dihydropyridine system has a broad absorption maximum at 340 m$\mu$, whereas the pyridine system does not absorb at that wavelength (cf. Fig. 22). If NADH is produced during a reaction, the absorption at 340 m$\mu$ rises gradually. This rise in light absorption can be measured quite easily and thus the transition NAD+ $\rightleftharpoons$ NADH can be followed optically. The increase of absorption per unit time is proportional to the enzyme concentration (cf. Fig. 23). This optical test for enzyme activity, or enzyme assay, is of extreme practical importance in the laboratory.

FIG. 22. Ultraviolet absorption of pyridine nucleotides. There is a maximum at 340 m$\mu$ for the reduced form.

FIG. 23. Optical assay of a dehydrogenase. The change in absorption is plotted against time. With more enzyme used, the reaction runs faster.

Since the reduction of pyridine nucleotides occurs very frequently in biochemical equations, the structural formulas are usually not written out and the reaction is symbolized in the following manner:

$$NAD^+ + CH_3{-}CH_2OH \rightleftharpoons CH_3{-}CHO + NADH + H^+$$

The pyridine nucleotides NAD and NADP are coenzymes (more correctly, co-substrates) of a large number of dehydrogenases, especially for dehydrogenation of primary and secondary alcohol groups. The reactions are generally reversible. The particular significance of these coenzymes rests on their role of reversibly transferring hydrogen according to the scheme in Chapt. VI–1. Bücher has named them properly "transport metabolites" because they take care of the hydrogen transport within the cell. The two coenzymes have different functions: NADPH$_2$ usually supplies the required hydrogen or generally the reduction equivalent for biosynthesis (cf. Chapt. X–3, XII–6, XIV–6), while NADH$_2$ usually releases its hydrogen to the enzymes of the respiratory chain, in which the reaction with O$_2$ to form H$_2$O is used for the synthesis of ATP (cf. Chap. X).

During careful analysis of the reaction mechanism for the addition of hydrogen to the ring, two noteworthy observations were made. First, the hydrogen that is added to the ring is transferred *with its electron pair*, i.e. as *hydride ion*. NAD$^+$ reacts through one of its resonance structures with the charge in position 4. An example (with alcohol dehydrogenase) will help to explain this (cf. also Chapt. X–2):

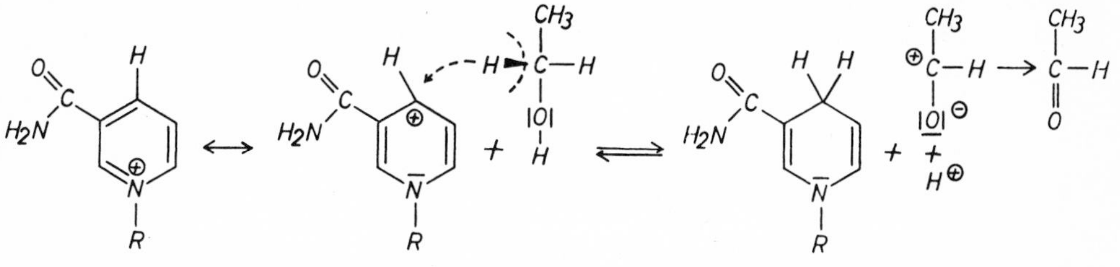

Second, the reaction is stereospecific, as was shown by deuterium labeling. It is easy to imagine that the deuterium ion can approach the ring only from the top when the ring is assumed to rest on the protein surface (Fig. 24).

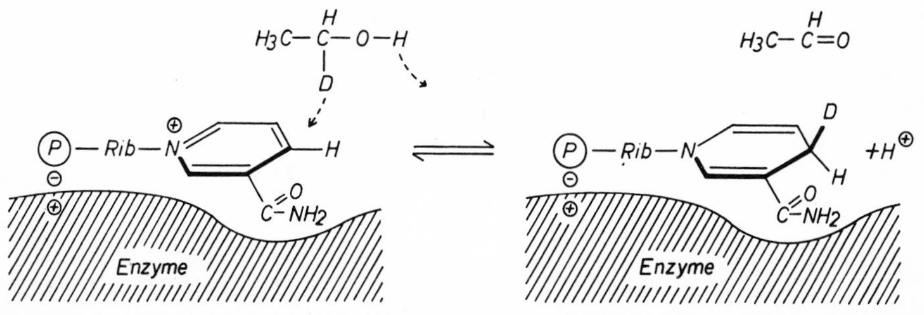

FIG. 24. Stereospecificity of the catalysis of pyridine nucleotides

The points of attachment for rib-P and for —CONH$_2$ on the enzyme surface[3] will then determine exactly which side of the pyridine ring is available for reduction.

By convention, that side which accepts a hydrogen during the dehydrogenation of ethyl alcohol by alcohol dehydrogenase and of lactate by lactate dehydrogenase is designated as the $\alpha$-side; the other side, the $\beta$-side, is attacked by glucose dehydrogenase and triose phosphate dehydrogenase. This type of specificity is but a special case of common stereospecificity: During the reduction of pyruvate, for instance, hydrogen is also attached on one particular side, yielding only L(+)-lactate, or D(−)-lactate, depending upon the particular enzyme used.

Two enzymes which approach the nicotinamide-adenine dinucleotide from opposite sides are able to cooperate especially closely; At first, hydrogen is transferred to the $\alpha$-side, then the $\beta$-oriented H is removed and a new H added on the $\alpha$-side. (In the dehydrogenated, aromatic form of NAD$^+$, hydrogen is in the plane of the ring, and therefore between the $\alpha$- and $\beta$-position.) There is evidence that in addition to freely dissolved enzymes there are also ordered enzyme complexes which work in just this manner.

Many apoenzymes react with NAD analogs, too. These are compounds in which the amide group of the pyridine part has been replaced by some other group. Thus nicotinic acid, 3-acetylpyridine (with a —COCH$_3$ group), and thionicotinamide (with —CS—NH$_2$) can be coupled to give pyridine nucleotides, all of which are reduced enzymically. These compounds have achieved importance in several studies of reaction mechanism and in distinguishing different apoenzymes.

**Flavin Nucleotide.** Vitamin B$_2$ or *riboflavin* is a component of the prosthetic group of flavoproteins. The isolation of the vitamin from biologic material was accomplished by György and R. Kuhn in 1933. Almost simultaneously, the first "yellow enzyme" was obtained in pure form and the close relationship between these active substances was recognized.

Riboflavin is an isoalloxazine derivative, i.e. a pteridine ring with a benzene ring fused on to it. The side chain is a C$_5$-polyhydroxy group. Note that this is not an N-glycoside of ribose, but rather a derivative of ribitol, a pentahydroxy compound. The systematic name is 6,7-dimethyl-9-ribityl-isoalloxazine:

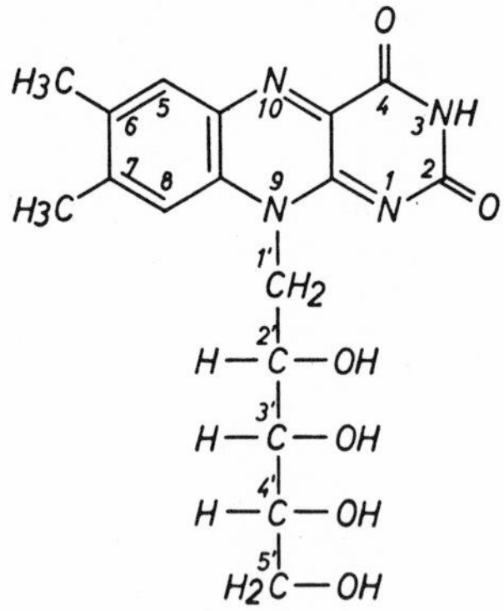

*Riboflavin*

---

[3] In the figure the acid amide group is shown to point to the front. With $\beta$-dehydrogenases it would point to the back; the pyridine ring would appear to be turned around. This assignment, however, was chosen entirely arbitrarily. In addition, the adsorption to the surface has been oversimplified greatly.

The active component of the "old yellow enzyme" is riboflavin 5′-phosphate, usually called *flavin mononucleotide* and abbreviated FMN. This nomenclature is somewhat incorrect again, since we do not have a nucleotide, i.e. an N-glycoside of a ribose phosphate. In spite of this, the name and abbreviation have been adopted, and actually the close similarity to real nucleotides must be conceded.

Most flavoproteins, however, do not contain the mononucleotide, but rather *flavin-adenine dinucleotide*, abbreviated FAD. As in the pyridine nucleotides, adenosine monophosphate and riboflavin phosphate are joined by a pyrophosphate bond. The formula is shown below.

The isoalloxazine ring acts as a reversible redox system with the codehydrogenases; hydrogen is added at $N^1$ and $N^{10}$, as shown:

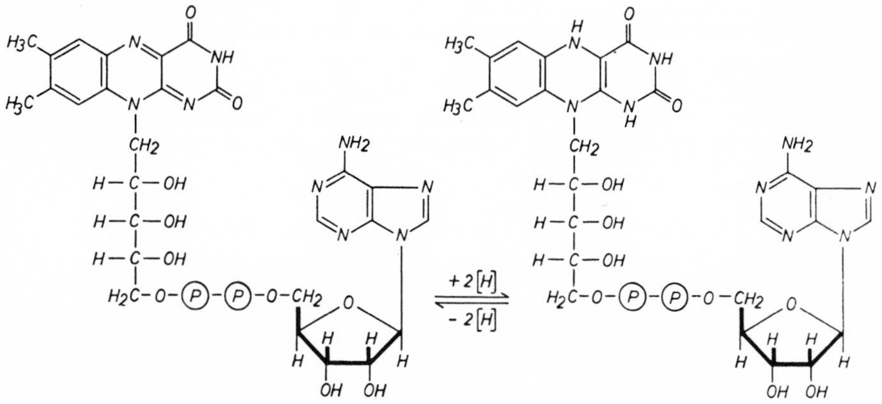

*Flavine adenine dinucleotide (oxidized and reduced form)*

Hydrogen is transferred to the prosthetic group through the action of the enzyme. For the enzyme to retain its catalytic property the flavin system must be reoxidized. This is usually accomplished by another enzyme system (Chapt. X-4). A few yellow enzymes are able to transfer their hydrogen onto oxygen directly, yielding $H_2O_2$. Such enzymes function as aerobic dehydrogenases (cf. Chapt. X-7).

Flavin, as the name reveals, is yellow; the dihydro compound, however, is colorless (the situation is similar with other dyes, e.g. methylene blue, indigo, etc.). This property is used to follow the reduction of flavin by optical methods, as previously discussed in connection with the pyridine coenzyme.

There is some recent evidence that in the reduction of several flavoproteins only *one* hydrogen atom is taken up. The result is a semiquinone with radical properties (unpaired electron). The semiquinone is very reactive and can easily donate the accepted hydrogen atom, for example, to $Fe^{3+}$ ions or to oxidized cytochrome.

Some flavin enzymes may be separated into the apoenzyme and coenzyme components by a shift of pH and dialysis, or protein precipitation procedures. The old yellow enzyme was the first example of this, in that the active enzyme protein could be regenerated from coenzyme and apoenzyme (Theorell, 1934). But the bonds often are much tighter, and the flavin groups generally do not dissociate from the protein. According to our definition, they are prosthetic groups. Some flavoproteins also contain tightly bound metal ions which probably participate in catalysis (cf. Chapt. X-4).

**Hemin as a Prosthetic Group.** The cytochromes often are associated with the flavoproteins. They are oxidoreductases because they transfer electrons. Iron is involved in the electron transport by a reversible change of its valency between $Fe^{++}$ and $Fe^{+++}$. The cytochromes contain a complex porphyrin system, which is either identical with or closely related to the heme of hemoglobin. Because of their importance, a separate chapter (Chapt. IX) has been devoted to hemoproteins. The cooperation between pyridine nucleotides and the flavoproteins in the respiratory chain is discussed in Chapt. X-4.

**Lipoic Acid** or *thioctic acid* was discovered in 1950 as a growth factor for certain microorganisms, then was isolated, and finally its constitution determined. It is a cyclic disulfide and in its side chain contains a carboxyl group, which is usually bound to the enzyme protein in amide or amide-like linkage. Lipoic acid is another hydrogen-transferring cofactor. Its prime role is in oxidative decarboxylation, a very complicated reaction.

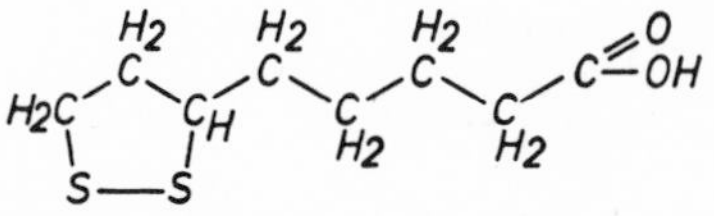

*Lipoic acid or thioctic acid*

The reaction sequence of oxidative decarboxylation and the role of thioctic acid therein are discussed in detail in Chapt. VIII-10. Here it suffices to mention that it cooperates in the conversion of the primary decarboxylation product, an active aldehyde, to the activated acid. Its job, therefore, is both dehydrogenation and group transfer. When acetate arises from active acetaldehyde, chosen here as the example (see diagram on page 101), dihydrothioctic acid with an opened ring and two sulfhydryl groups remains. The cofactor must now be returned to the oxidized form by a dehydrogenase in order to be able to repeat its part in the reaction; this explains its classification as a hydrogen-transferring enzyme.

The dehydrogenase has recently been found and studied. It transfers hydrogen from dihydrothioctic acid to nicotinamide-adenine dinucleotide. Peculiarly, it is a flavoprotein but its redox potential (cf. Chapt. X-3) is much farther on the negative side than that of the familiar flavoproteins, so that hydrogen is able to switch over to NAD.

# 5. Group-Transferring Coenzymes

Ranking first in this list is *adenosine triphosphate*, commonly abbreviated as ATP. A nucleotide which is composed of the base adenine, the sugar ribose, and phosphoric acid esterifying the OH group in position 5 of ribose is called *adenosine monophosphate*, abbreviated AMP (cf. also Chapt. VII-1). With one further phosphoric acid attached in anhydride linkage we have *adenosine diphosphate*,[4] ADP; with three phosphoric acid residues we come to the triphosphate ATP.

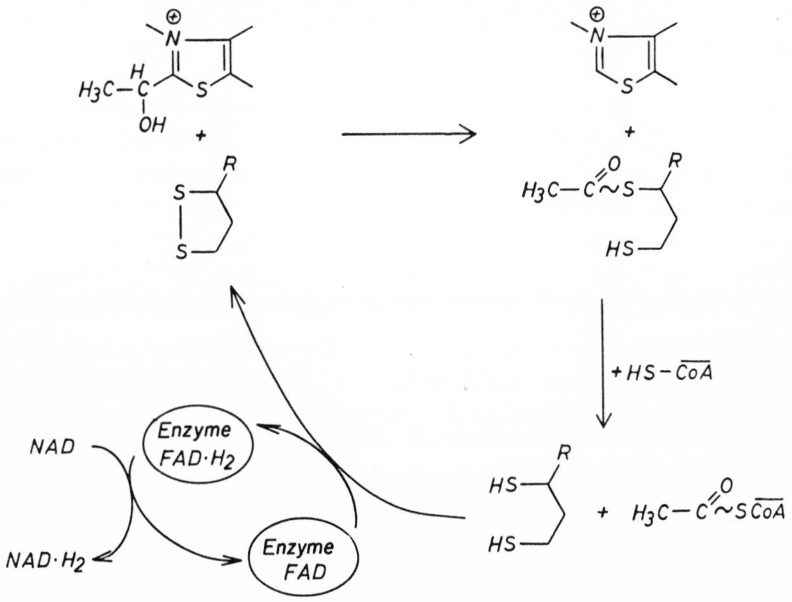

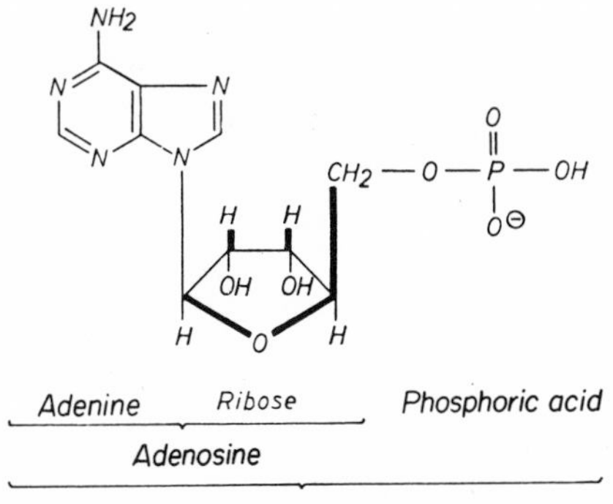

Adenine    Ribose        Phosphoric acid

Adenosine

Adenosine monophosphate
AMP

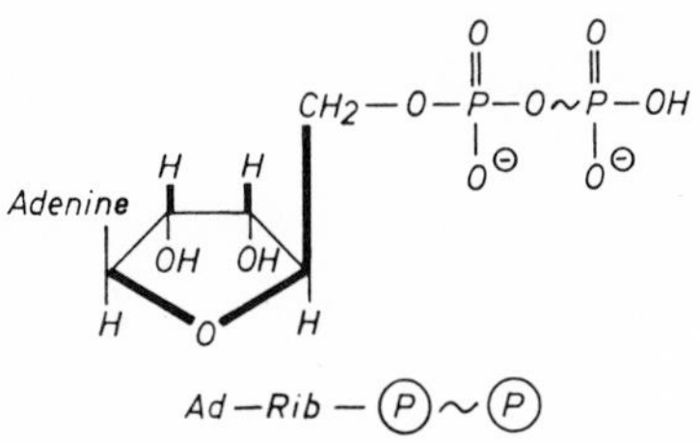

Ad—Rib — (P) ~ (P)

Adenosine diphosphate
ADP

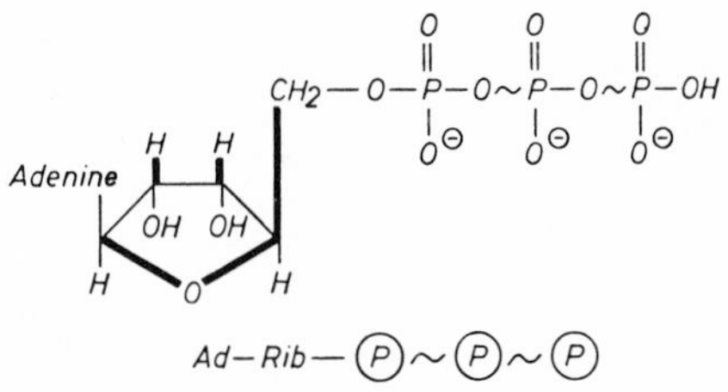

Ad—Rib — (P) ~ (P) ~ (P)

Adenosine triphosphate
ATP

[4] The compound ad—rib—P $\sim$ P should be named more correctly adenosine pyrophosphate instead of diphosphate, but the name diphosphate is too well established.

Our symbol for the phosphoric acid residue is P, or as used in the above diagram Ⓟ

ATP contains two energy-rich bonds; it has a high potential for group transfers. Different types of groups can be transferred. Depending on what bond reacts the result is:

a. Transfer of the orthophosphate group; release of ADP.
b. Transfer of the pyrophosphate group; release of AMP.
c. Transfer of adenosyl monophosphate group; release of pyrophosphate.
d. Transfer of the adenosyl group; release of both orthophosphate and pyrophosphate.

These reactions are illustrated in Fig. 25.

Reaction a is the most common. If the orthophosphate residue is transferred onto water, HOH, we have hydrolysis; the free energy of this reaction is strongly negative, $\Delta F = -7.0$ kcal/mole.

**Kinases.** The highly exergonic nature of the phosphate transfer onto water explains the generally great transfer potential of the phosphate groups of ATP. ATP can transfer phosphate onto alcoholic hydroxyl groups, onto acyl groups, or amide groups. All these transfer reactions are catalyzed by specific enzymes which are usually called *"kinases."* The hexokinase and pyruvate kinase reactions have already been mentioned under the section on coupled reactions (cf. also Chapt. V–5, XV–7).

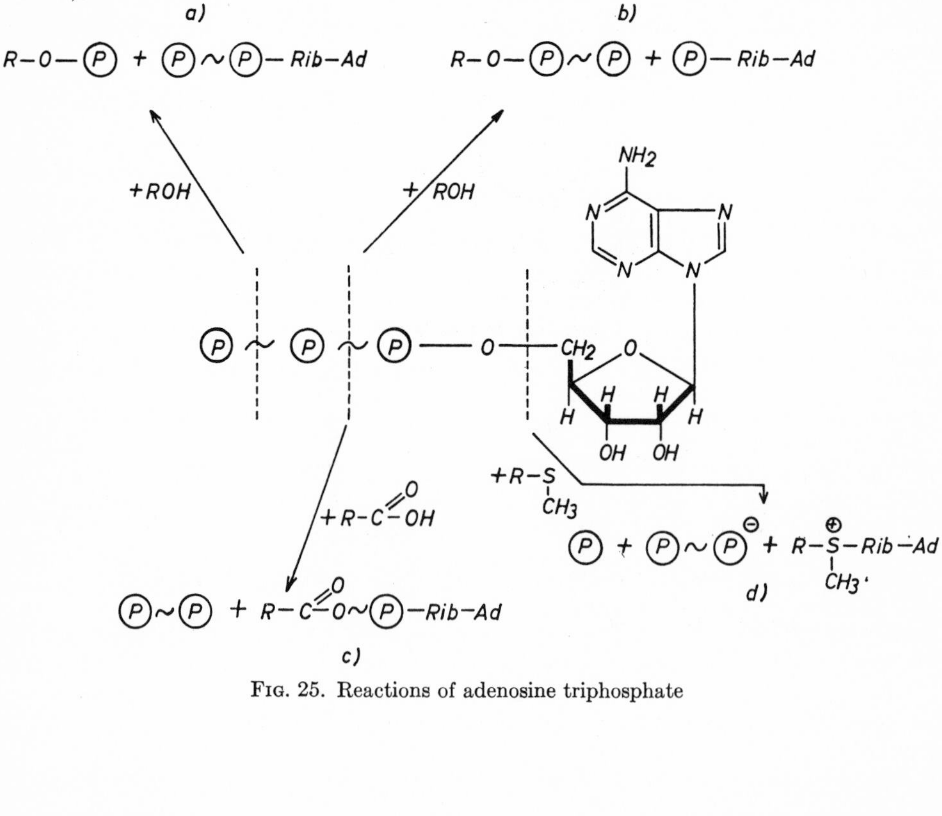

FIG. 25. Reactions of adenosine triphosphate

The reaction is reversible whenever the compound formed is energy rich. Otherwise the equilibrium would be too unfavorable to let the reverse reaction proceed to more than a minute extent (concerning energy-rich bonds, cf. Chapt. V–5).

For most kinases, the phosphate donor is ATP. Since the reaction frequently is irreversible, the resynthesis of ATP must take place through another enzymic reaction. Many authors, therefore, do not include ATP among coenzymes; the situation is nevertheless entirely analogous to that of the typical "coenzyme" (NAD).

Another important function of the kinases is the synthesis of ATP from ADP and energy-rich bound phosphate in "substrate-linked phosphorylation" (cf. Chapt. XV–7) and in "respiratory-chain phosphorylation" (Chapt. X–6). ATP hence represents a "pool" for energy-rich phosphates—and, in a sense, for chemical energy in general.

Reaction b, a transfer of pyrophosphate, occurs comparatively rarely. One example is the conversion of ribose 5-phosphate to 5-phosphoribose-1-pyrophosphate (cf. Chapt. VII–2).

The transfer of adenosine monophosphate to an acceptor with removal of pyrophosphate, reaction c, is again quite common. A compound with a high potential for group transfer, i.e. an "activated compound," is usually generated. Such compounds include, among others, the intermediates of fatty acid activation (Chapt. XII–6) and of amino acid activation in protein synthesis (Chapt. VII–8).

As another example, cyclic *adenosine-3′,5′-monophosphate* (formula is in Chapt. XVII–6), which activates phosphorylase, arises from ATP by intramolecular transfer onto the 3′-hydroxyl group, with pyrophosphate elimination.

The reaction mentioned under d, the transfer of the adenosyl residue, plays a part in the formation of the "active methyl groups" (Chapt. VI–5).

The equilibrium of reaction c is occasionally unfavorable to the formation of the new activated compound $R{\sim}P$—Rib—Ad. In that case, the free energy of hydrolysis of the $P{\sim}P$ bond ($-5$ kcal) can be drawn upon through the action of pyrophosphatase, which splits pyrophosphate and forces the reaction to proceed to completion by removing one of the reaction products from the equilibrium mixture. A fine example of a coupled energetic reaction of this type is provided by the formation of active sulfate, according to Lipmann's scheme:

1. $Ad$—Rib—$P{\sim}P{\sim}P + H_2SO_4 \rightleftharpoons Ad$—Rib—$P{\sim}SO_3H + P{\sim}P$ $\qquad \Delta F° = +11$ kcal
2. $P{\sim}P \rightleftharpoons P + P$ $\qquad \Delta F° = -6$ kcal
3. $Ad$—Rib—$P{\sim}SO_3H + ATP \rightleftharpoons Ad$—Rib—$P{\sim}SO_3H + ADP$ $\qquad \Delta F° = -5$ kcal

$\qquad\qquad\qquad\qquad\qquad |$ $\qquad\qquad\qquad\qquad\qquad\qquad\qquad\qquad\quad \overline{\Delta F° = \quad 0\ \text{kcal}}$
$\qquad\qquad\qquad\qquad\qquad P$

Adenosine phosphorylsulfate from reaction 1 can scarcely be detected in the equilibrium mixture. Only in the presence of pyrophosphatase are appreciable amounts produced, because then the reverse of reaction 1 (thermodynamically enormously favored) is no longer feasible. Even so, the energy is balanced only when the activated sulfate reacts with a further ATP and takes up a phosphate at the 3′-hydroxyl group of ribose. (The values for free energies are approximate.)

104                               VI. COENZYMES

**Active Sulfate** therefore has the formula:

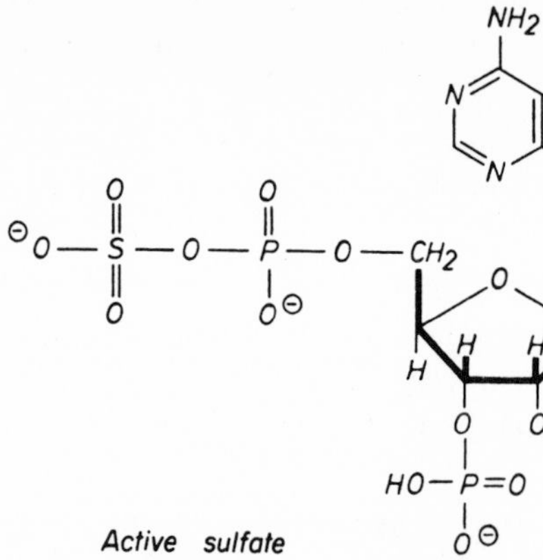

*Active sulfate*

The sulfate group can be transferred easily, i.e. in exergonic reactions, to phenols and alcohols. These sulfuric esters have long been known as "detoxication" and excretion forms of various foreign substances and metabolic products. They include phenol sulfuric acid, indoxyl sulfuric acid (indican), and estrone sulfuric acid. The sulfuric esters of carbohydrates arise presumably in a similar manner (Chapt. XVII–7).

**Active Methyl; Adenosylmethionine.** Methionine, one of the sulfur-containing amino acids, is the chief donor of methyl groups, which are transferred to various substances, but especially to amino groups (cf. Chapt. VIII–12). The methyl group bound in thioether linkage does not possess a high potential for group transfer; it is activated by the reaction with ATP, yielding, according to Fig. 25d, a very reactive sulfonium compound:

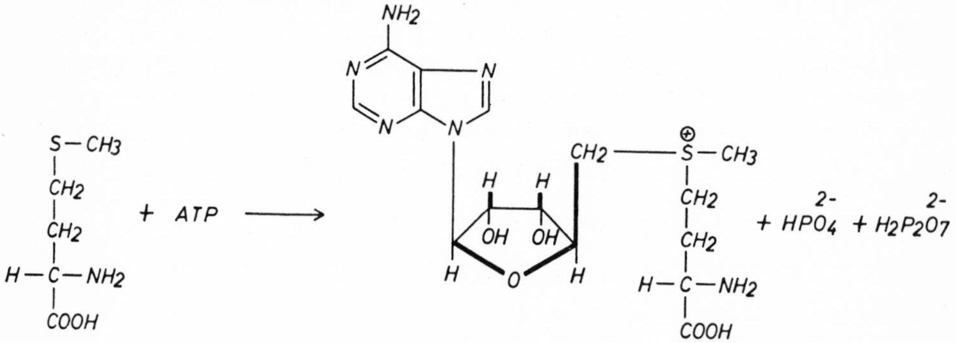

*Adenosylmethionine,"active methyl"*

The group bound to sulfur is transferred as $+CH_3$ to an atom with a free electron pair (e.g. N); thus the sulfonium structure is lost and an adenosine thioether remains. The following example shows the conversion of guanidinoacetate to creatine, which then can pick up phosphate in an energy-rich bond (cf. Chapt. V-5, V-8, XXIII-6).

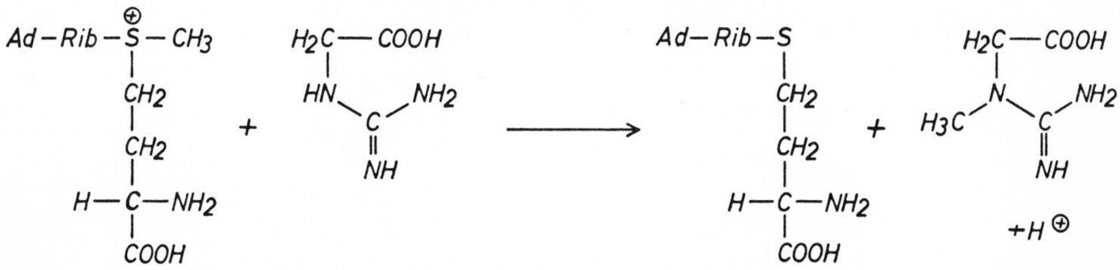

Adenosylmethionine + Guanidinoacetic acid → Adenosylhomocysteine + Creatine

ATP is not the only reactive triphosphate. Other purine or pyrimidine bases (guanine, cytosine, hypoxanthine, uracil; cf. Chapt. VII–1) may take the place of adenine in the molecule; the corresponding triphosphates replace ATP in several metabolic reactions. We will mention two examples: The uridylic acid system in the interconversion of carbohydrates and the cytidylic acid system in the synthesis of phosphatides.

**Uridine diphosphate** is the carrier of "active glucose." Uridine triphosphate, entirely analogous to ATP, can exchange the third phosphate group for a sugar molecule and hold it in an energy-rich bond:

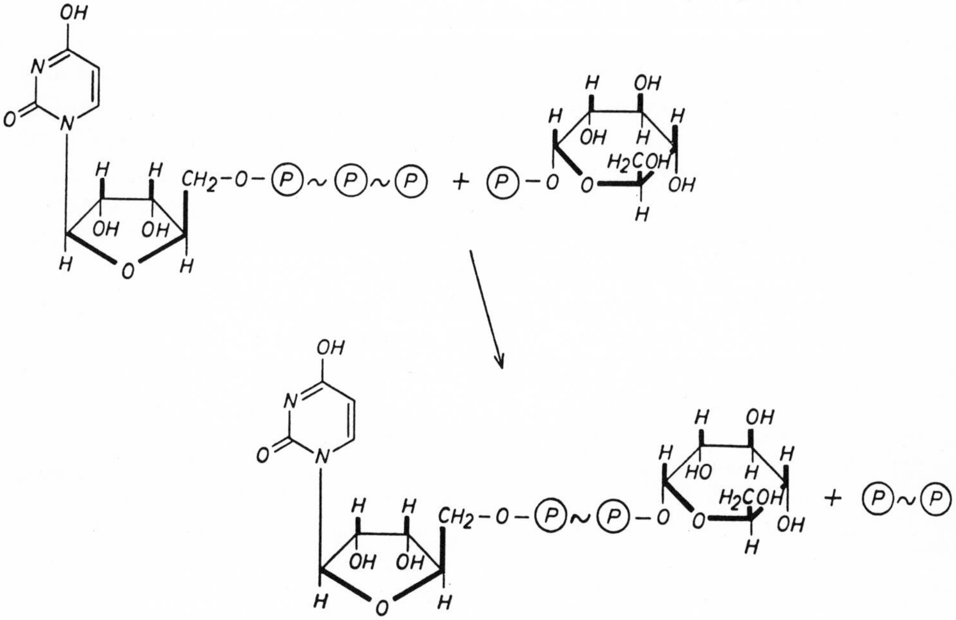

Uridine diphosphate glucose

The sugar molecule—glucose in the above example—can be transferred to other molecules with OH groups. Glycosides and disaccharides are synthesized in this manner. These reactions will be discussed more extensively in Chapt. XVII–4.

**Cytidine diphosphate** is the coenzyme of phosphatide biosynthesis; it ties together a diglyceride and phosphorylcholine. Cytidine triphosphate first binds choline phosphate through a high energy bond:

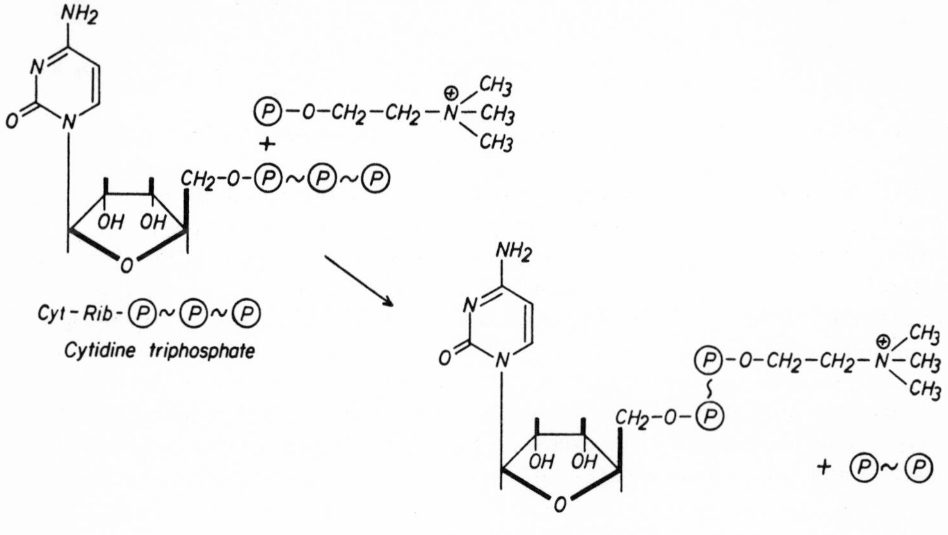

Cytidine diphosphate choline

The choline moiety can then be transferred to some acceptor molecule—e.g. a diglyceride—forming a phosphodiester bond while cytidine monophosphate is split off (cf. diagram of formulas in Chapt. XIII–3). In contrast to the reaction with uridine diphosphate glucose, one phosphate group enters the product. Ethanolamine, instead of choline, can also be activated in this manner. Furthermore, both N-acetyl-sphingosine and glycerophosphate can function as acceptors in place of diglycerides. Thus a great number of phosphatides are synthesized.

**Coenzyme A.** This coenzyme transfers carboxylic acids. Acids bound to CoA (the usual abbreviation for coenzyme A, the "A" standing for acylation) have a high potential for group transfer. Hydrolysis of acyl-CoA compounds is exergonic to the extent of about 8 kcal/mole.

The chemical structure of coenzyme A is considerably more complex than that of the preceding coenzymes. It is helpful to divide it mentally into adenosine-3′,5′-diphosphate and pantetheine phosphate. *Pantetheine* is a growth factor for several microorganisms, e.g. *Lactobacillus bulgaricus*. It, in turn, consists of pantoic acid, β-alanine, and mercaptoethylamine, the decarboxylation product of cysteine. The pantetheine component of CoA therefore contains three constituents in amide linkage.

The combination of pantoic acid ($\alpha,\gamma$-dihydroxy-$\beta,\beta$-dimethylbutyric acid) and β-alanine is also called *pantothenic acid*; this name is derived from its nearly universal occurrence. Pantothenic acid is listed as one of the B vitamins. Pantothenic acid deficiency in experimental animals produces various symptoms (chicken pellagra, graying of hair in the rat); but in man deficiency diseases are not known.

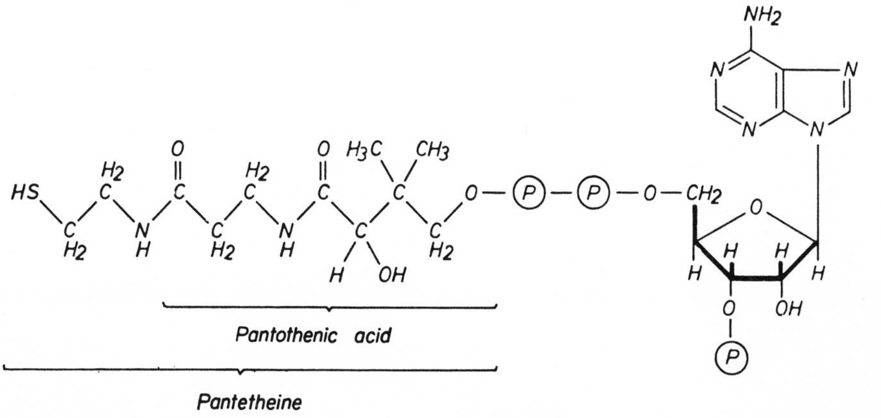

Pantothenic acid

Pantetheine

Coenzyme A

The biochemical significance of the vitamin resides in its being a necessary precursor in the biosynthesis of CoA. Depending on the capabilities of the organism, pantoic acid (or $\beta$-alanine), or pantothenic acid, or pantetheine must be supplied.

The most important CoA compound undoubtedly is acetyl-CoA, *activated acetate*. Here the acetyl residue $CH_3CO-$ is bound to the free SH group[5] (belonging to the mercaptoethylamine component). Chemically this constitutes a thioester, and thioesters are known to be very reactive.

To bring acetic acid (or any other carboxylic acid) into this compound, with its high potential for group transfer, it is necessary, of course, to expend energy. This energy can be derived either from cleavage of ATP—whereby an intermediate arises, an anhydride with adenylic acid according to reaction c in Fig. 25—or from a strongly exergonic reaction (oxidative decarboxylation; cf. Chapt. VIII-10).

The reactions of activated ˙acetate (acetyl-CoA) can be indicated here only sketchily. There are two groups: (1) reactions of the carboxyl group, and (2) reactions of the methyl group (or, in the case of higher homologs, of the $\alpha$-methylene group).

1. *Reactions of the Carboxyl Group.* Ester and amide formation may be mentioned first; one H atom of an alcohol or an amine is replaced by the acyl group. But C-acylation ("ester condensation" in organic chemistry) is also known, along with the reverse reaction, thioclastic cleavage:

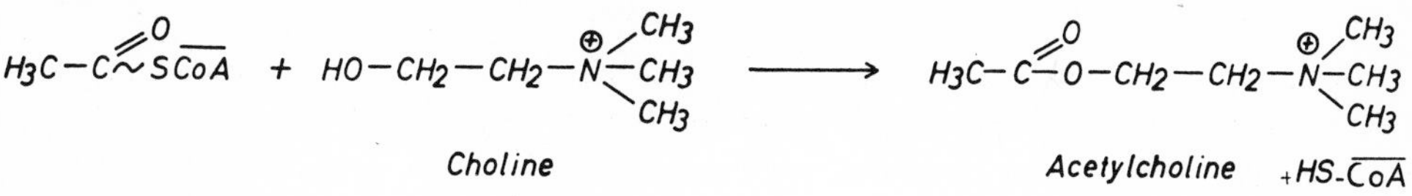

Choline                    Acetylcholine  +HS-CoA

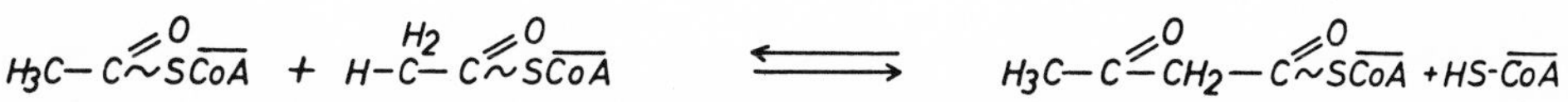

---

[5] If it is desired to emphasize the reactive group itself, then HS—$\overline{CoA}$ (or $H_3C$—CO—S—$\overline{CoA}$) is written, where $\overline{CoA}$ stands for "coenzyme A less —SH."

2. *Reactions of the Methyl Group* usually occur on carbonyl groups. These reactions can be understood more easily from the polarized form of the acetyl-CoA in which the $\alpha$-C atom receives a partial negative charge from the coenzyme (i.e. through the thioester bond). The polarized $\alpha$-C atom then joins with the partially positive C atom of the carbonyl group:

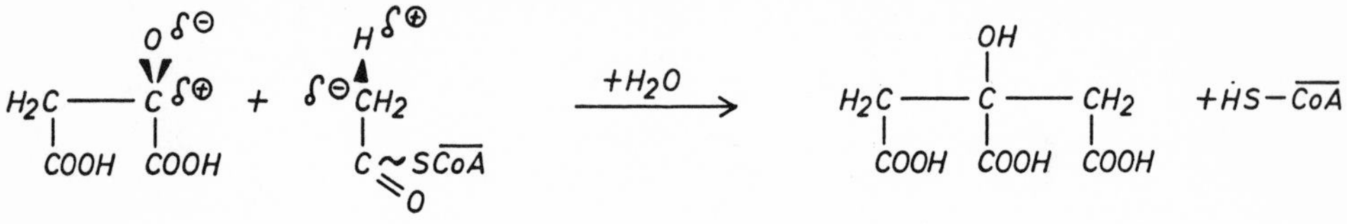

The formation of citric acid, as in the above scheme,[6] is quantitatively most important. These reactions are treated more thoroughly in Chapt. XI.

**Tetrahydrofolic Acid; "Active C₁ Fragment."** Just as acetyl-CoA represents the active $C_2$ fragment of metabolism, so is formyltetrahydrofolic acid the active $C_1$ fragment.

Folic acid was originally discovered and isolated as a vitamin by several different laboratories independently. The compound contains a pteridine ring, a heterocyclic ring system with one pyrimidine ring fused onto one pyrazine ring. Pterins are colored substances occurring in butterfly wings, e.g. *xanthopterin* in the brimstone butterfly, and in wasps. The work of H. Wieland, C. Schöpf, and co-workers on these insect pigments gained particular interest with the discovery of folic acid.

The structure and function of every biologically important pterin is not yet known. *Biopterin* was isolated recently; its formula is presented below. It is a growth substance for the unicellular *Crithidia fasciculata*. Biopterin is widely distributed in very minute amounts; it is found in urine, in *Drosophila* extracts, and in the food juice of queen bee larvae (royal jelly). The biologic significance of biopterin for bees is still obscure.

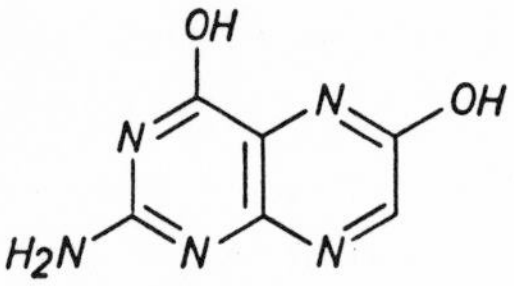

Xanthopterin 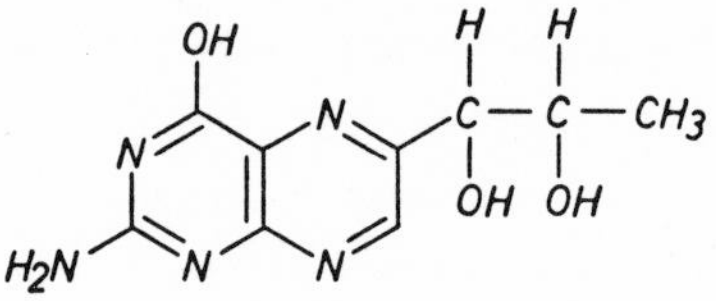                                    Biopterin

Folic acid contains, in addition to the substituted pteridine ring, *p*-aminobenzoic acid, which is a growth factor for a number of microorganisms. The growth effect can be repressed by sulfonamides, and the mode of attack of the sulfonamides, which are used frequently as medications (chemotherapeutics), appears to be interference with folic acid formation in bacteria.

---

[6] The wedge-shaped bond symbols stand for electron pairs which tend to stay more on the side of the broad end of the wedge thus imparting an excess charge on that side.

Finally, folic acid also contains glutamic acid. The complete formula, therefore, looks like this:

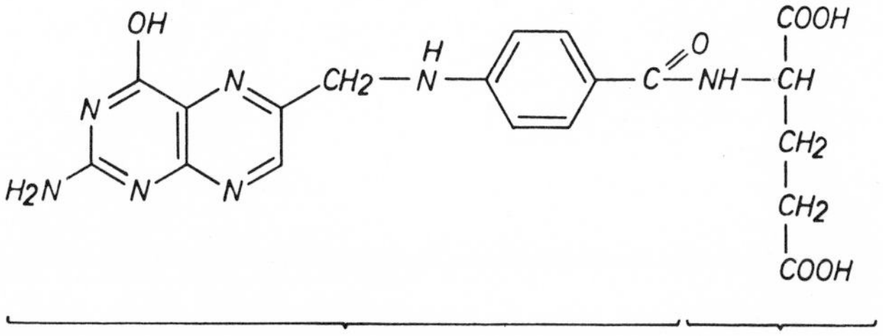

Pteroic acid · Glutamic acid

*Pteroylglutamic acid or folic acid*

In addition to the folic acid, which has but one glutamic acid residue, various polyglutamic acid conjugates are known, which stimulate growth of certain bacterial strains and which cannot be replaced by folic acid. Pteroylheptaglutamic acid in particular has drawn attention; it has seven glutamic acid residues in peptidic linkage (through the γ-carboxyl groups). It is really a polypeptide with one folic acid group.

*Leucovorin* is a folic acid derivative closely related to the true coenzyme. It is a growth factor for the bacterium *Leuconostoc citrovorum*. Leucovorin contains a reduced ring and bears a formyl group on the 5 nitrogen atom ($N^5$), but has only a low potential for group transfer.

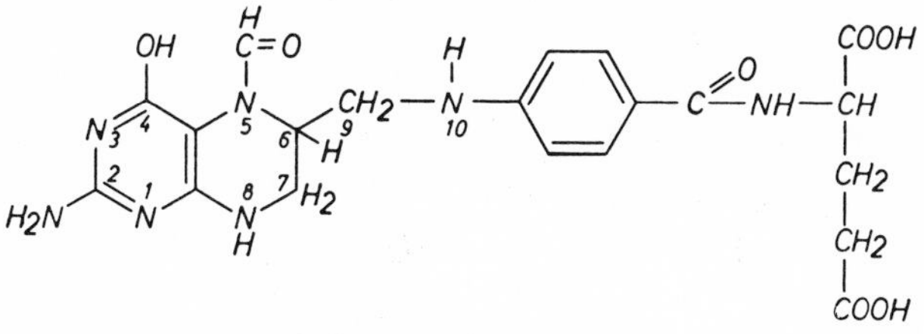

*Leucovorin = $N^5$-Formyltetrahydrofolic acid*

*Active formate* is $N^{10}$-formyltetrahydrofolic acid. Another immediately reactive intermediate with an even greater energy content is the anhydro derivative $N^5,N^{10}$-methenyltetrahydrofolic acid. It can revert to the $N^{10}$-formyltetrahydrofolic acid in slightly alkaline media by the addition of $OH^-$ (Jaenicke). The cooperation of ATP is required to convert the $N^5$-formyl derivative to the $N^{10}$-formyl derivative. Ordinarily, however, it is not free formate which is activated; the $C_1$ fragment arises rather from metabolism and is bound immediately to *coenzyme F* (tetrahydrofolic acid) (cf. Chapt. VIII–12). Donors of active formate are, for example, histidine and glyoxylic acid. Active formate is used, among other things, in purine synthesis (Chapt. VII–2). Beside formate, *active formaldehyde* also plays a role as a $C_1$ fragment. Formaldehyde is bound just like formate, i.e. at $N^{10}$; one donor is serine (cf. Chapt. VIII–12). The metabolism of $C_1$ fragments is discussed in more detail in connection with purine biosynthesis and amino acid metabolism (Chapt. VII–2, VIII–12).

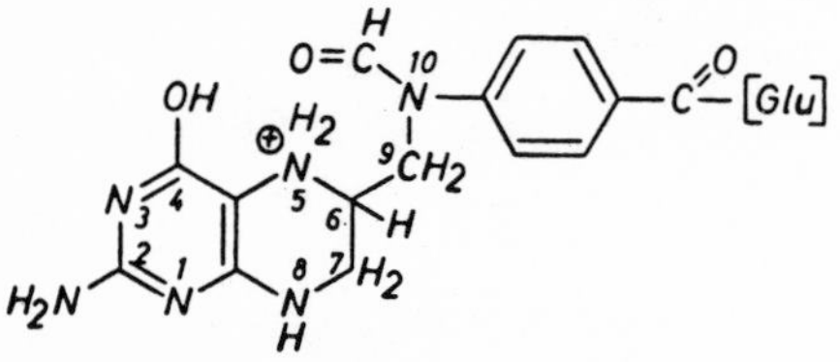

$N^{10}$-Formyltetrahydrofolic acid

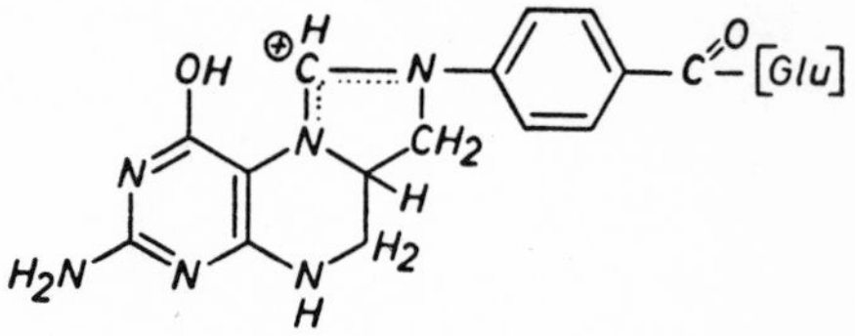

$N^5 \cdot N^{10}$-Methenyltetrahydrofolic acid

Biotin has been isolated as "vitamin H" from liver extracts (DuVigneaud and co-workers) and as one of the "bios factors" (yeast growth factor) from egg yolk (Kögl and co-workers). It is a cyclic derivative of urea with an attached thiophane ring. The structural formula has been substantiated by synthesis.

Biotin adheres very tightly to a specific protein of egg white, avidin, and consequently is inactivated by it. Large doses of raw egg white fed to animals are able to evoke biotin deficiency. A similar phenomenon is seen occasionally in man. Avidin is denatured and inactivated by heat.

Biotin is linked to the enzyme protein by a peptide bond to the ε-amino group of a lysyl residue; hence, it represents a prosthetic group. Charging biotin with carbon dioxide is an endergonic process requiring the assistance of ATP.

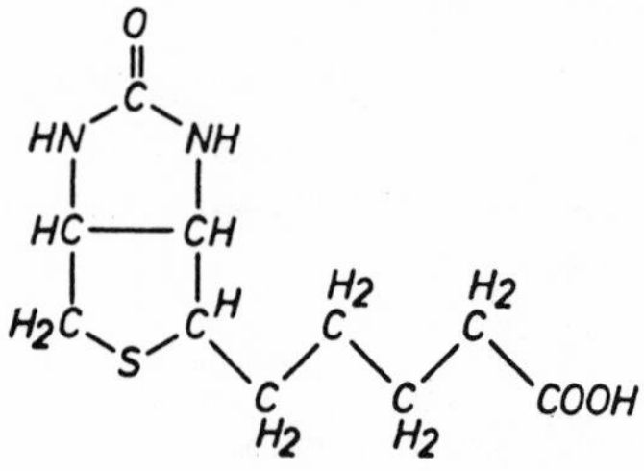

Biotin

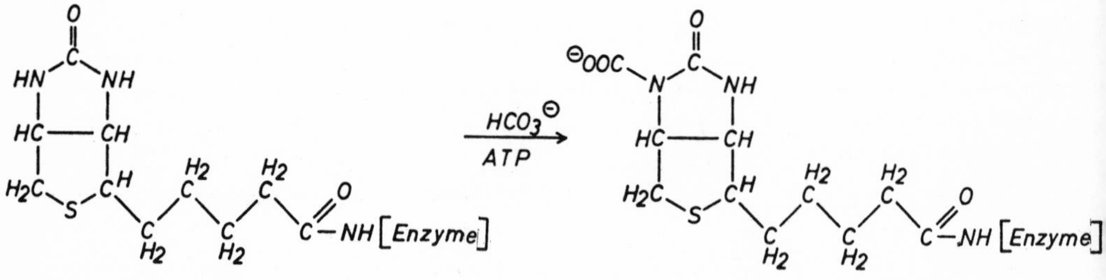

Biotin - enzyme

Carboxy-biotin - enzyme

The $CO_2$ attached to the nitrogen of biotin is the *active form of carbon dioxide* which participates in numerous carboxylation reactions (e.g. acetyl-CoA to malonyl-CoA, Chapt. XII–6, and related reactions). The very labile carboxy-biotin has now been isolated as a methyl ester (Lynen and co-workers).

**Thiamine Pyrophosphate** is the coenzyme responsible for transferring "active acetaldehyde" and "active glycolaldehyde." Simultaneously, it acts as "co-decarboxylase,"[7] i.e. as the coenzyme for a lyase. The characteristic component is *thiamine* (vitamin $B_1$), one of the vitamins whose biologic role has been known longest; the symptoms of thiamine deficiency (beriberi in man; polyneuritis in animals) comprised one of the starting points in the study of vitamins. The name thiamine refers to its sulfur content.

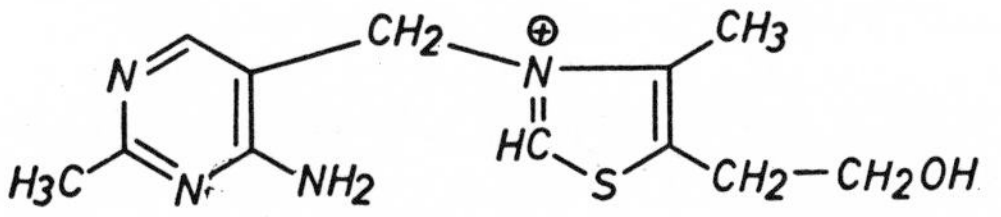

*Thiamine*

The structural formula of thiamine has two heterocyclic rings, which are not condensed: one pyrimidine and one thiazol ring. They are connected at the quaternary nitrogen of the thiazol ring; thiamine, therefore, always carries a charge. The coenzyme is the pyrophosphate of thiamine. Aside from the pyridine nucleotides, thiamine pyrophosphate was one of the first recognized coenzymes. In conformity with our definition, however, it must be considered a prosthetic group, since it remains tied to the enzyme protein.

The mode of action of thiamine pyrophosphate was debated for some time. Today it is clear that the active aldehyde group, which is formed or transferred by thiamine pyrophosphate enzymes, is attached to the thiazol ring at position C–2 (cf. formula scheme in Chapt. VIII–10).

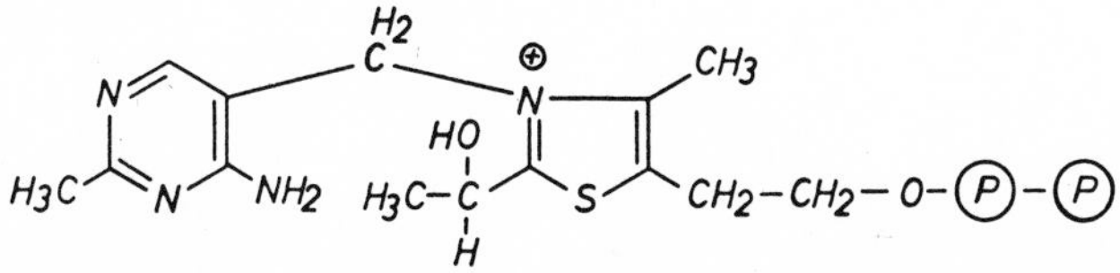

*Active acetaldehyde*

The most important reaction in which thiamine pyrophosphate collaborates is the oxidative decarboxylation of $\alpha$-keto acids (cf. formulas in Chapt. VI–4, VIII–10, and XI–2). $CO_2$ is split off and the aldehyde residue is transferred by thiamine

---

[7] The older term *cocarboxylase* is used frequently, because the latter stems from *carboxylase*, the older name of the decarboxylating yeast enzyme. It would seem more useful to reserve the name *carboxylase* exclusively for those enzymes whose main job is carboxylation; it follows then that *cocarboxylase* should be the name for biotin.

pyrophosphate to lipoic acid, which functions as an oxidizing agent (cf. end of Section 4, above). However, in the transketolase reaction thiamine pyrophosphate serves only as a group-transferring coenzyme (cf. Chapt. XV–5).

**Pyridoxal Phosphate** is the coenzyme of amino acid metabolism. It is closely related to pyridoxine, a vitamin of the B group, which is also called vitamin $B_6$.[8] The German name *"Adermin"* refers to skin disorders that appear in connection with vitamin $B_6$ deficiency.

Due to its vitamin nature, five separate groups of investigators almost simultaneously isolated, established the constitution of, and synthesized pyridoxine. For some bacteria, however, extracts from natural material were more effective than expected from the content of pyridoxine; this led to the discovery of pyridoxal and pyridoxamine. Later, pyridoxal phosphate was recognized as the active group of various enzymes of amino acid metabolism.

*Pyridoxine, pyridoxal,* and *pyridoxamine,* as the names suggest, are all pyridine derivatives; the various substitutions are seen in the following formulas:

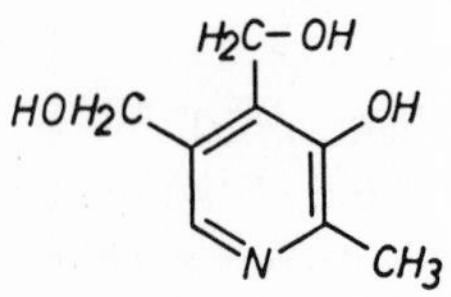

Pyridoxine 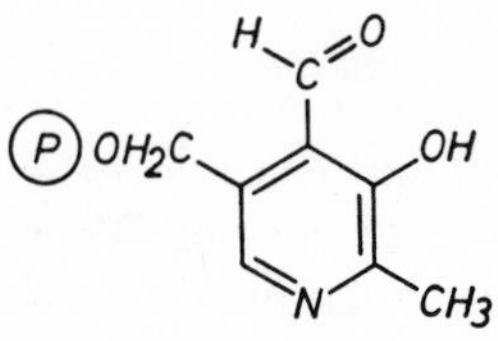                      Pyridoxal                    Pyridoxamine
                                phosphate                    phosphate

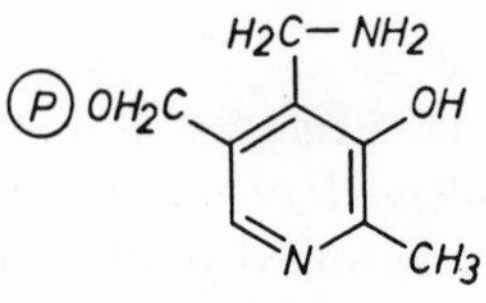

Pyridoxal phosphate is an excellent example of the fact that a single coenzyme is able to catalyze completely different reactions. It is the active group not only for the aminotransferases, but also for the decarboxylases and various lyases and synthetases as well. A hypothesis by Snell endeavors to derive all types of reactions from one intermediate product, a type of Schiff's base:

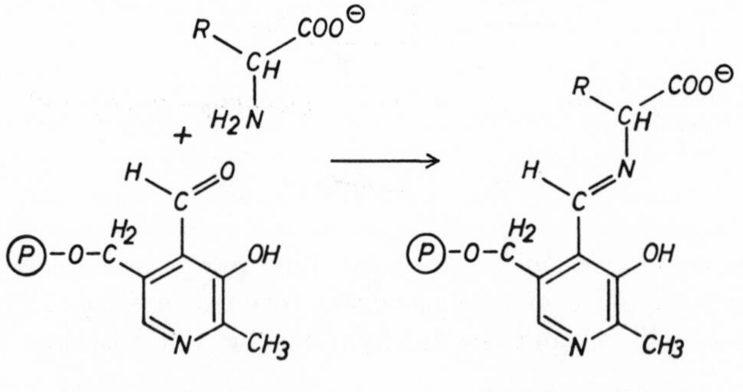

Pyridoxal   phosphate                    Schiff's     Base

---

[8] *Vitamin $B_6$* is still in use as a generic term for pyridoxine, pyridoxal, and pyridoxamine.

The intermediate can react further in various ways, as discussed extensively in Chapt. VIII–4. The choice of the reaction catalyzed is made by the apoenzyme, i.e. the protein.

Pyridoxal phosphate and pyridoxamine phosphate should not be classified as coenzymes, but rather as prosthetic groups, because they are not split off during the reaction, are not handed along to another enzyme protein, and are regenerated on the same enzyme protein.

## 6. Coenzymes of Lyases, Isomerases, and Ligases

**Lyases and Synthases** are enzymes which catalyze the cleavage of a compound into two fragments or, in reverse, which catalyze the joining of two substances to form a third (synthases). The latter reaction is frequently equivalent to a group transfer. While it is still possible to draw up boundaries for the classification of the enzymes in this respect, for the coenzymes it ceases to be possible. Numerous groups activated by coenzymes participate in the reactions of synthases, as e.g. acetyl-CoA, carboxy-biotin, and thiamine-bound active aldehyde.

One important subgroup of the lyases are the *decarboxylases*. The decarboxylation of amino acids is assisted by pyridoxal phosphate as a prosthetic group, whereas in the decarboxylation of pyruvate to acetaldehyde, thiamine pyrophosphate (TPP) plays that role. Oxidative decarboxylation, lastly, depends on the cooperation of no fewer than five cofactors: thiamine pyrophosphate, lipoic acid, coenzyme A, flavin-adenine dinucleotide, and nicotinamide-adenine dinucleotide.

**Isomerases** usually do not require cofactors. Sugars sometimes need uridine diphosphate and a firmly bound pyridine nucleotide. In some reactions of carboxyl compounds, yet another coenzyme, vitamin $B_{12}$, is involved.

An interesting phenomenon is presented by the *mutases* which shift phosphate residues in the metabolism of carbohydrates. They catalyze, for example, the transition *glucose 1-phosphate* $\rightleftarrows$ *glucose 6-phosphate*. In this case, the intermediate glucose 1,6-diphosphate is at the same time "coenzyme" (i.e. phosphate donor), and the stoichiometrically reacting "coenzyme" is regenerated from the substrate (cf. Chapt. XV–7, XVII–6).

**Vitamin $B_{12}$,** also called *cobalamin* (because of its content of tightly bound cobalt), protects against pernicious anemia. Its structure is rather involved; there is a certain kinship to the hemin system. There is a whole series of compounds of this type with vitamin properties; they are distinguished by the various base components in nucleotide-like linkage and by the anions present to balance the charge of cobalt ($CN^-$, $OH^-$, $Cl^-$, etc.).

How this vitamin enters the process of blood formation is still entirely unknown. More can be said, however, about its biochemical action: It is a component of the coenzyme to carboxylation reactions. The $B_{12}$-coenzyme in which the cyanide group is replaced by adenine is instrumental in carboxyl shifts within molecules. One of these reactions is the rearrangement of methylmalonate to succinate (formulas in Chapt. XII–5), important in the degradation of several branched-chain fatty acids.

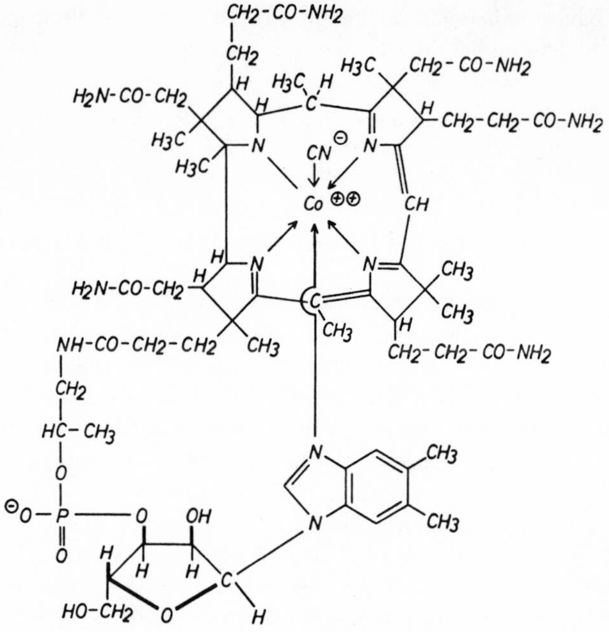

Vitamin $B_{12}$
$(C_{63} H_{90} O_{14} N_{14} PCo)$

**Ligases** are defined by the new system of nomenclature as enzymes which aid the formation of new bonds coupled with the breakdown of a pyrophosphate bond. Consequently either ATP or a similar triphosphate must participate; occasionally biotin is involved (in carboxylation reactions).

The amino-acid activating enzymes are also ligases. The so-called "soluble ribonucleic acids" may well be called coenzymes, although they are not low molecular substances (molecular weight is around 25,000). The structure and function of nucleic acids will be discussed in the following chapter.

BIBLIOGRAPHY

P. Boyer, H. Lardy, and K. Myrbäck (editors), "The Enzymes," Vols. II and III, Academic Press, New York, 1960.
"Significance of Free Nucleotides," 11th Mosbach Colloquium der Gesellschaft für physiologische Chemie, Springer Verlag, Berlin, 1961.
C. P. Fawcett, The nicotinamide coenzymes and their apoenzymes, Ann. Rept. Chem. Soc. London, **59**, 413–426 (1962).
A. M. White, Vitamin $B_{12}$, Ann. Rept. Chem. Soc. London, **95**, 400–413 (1962).

# CHAPTER VII

# Nucleic Acids and

# Protein Biosynthesis

Nucleic acids were discovered by Miescher in 1869; he found them in pus cor-puscles, in fish sperm, and other biologic material. They are high molecular weight polymeric substances which are hydrolyzable into heterocyclic organic bases, carbo-hydrate (pentose), and phosphoric acid.

The preparation of pure nucleic acids is as yet an unsolved problem. It is quite easy to prepare nucleic acid fractions that are free of proteins, polysaccharides, etc., but invariably they are mix-tures of many very similar nucleic acids whose further separation becomes extraordinarily difficult. Most investigations on the chemical structure of nucleic acids have been carried out on such nucleic acid fractions, just as in the beginning of protein research all structural principles were derived from heterogeneous protein mixtures. The validity of the results need not be doubted on this account, however.

The chemistry of the carbohydrates will be treated extensively in Chapt. XV and XVII. Here we mention that they are polyhydroxyaldehydes or ketones, which exist in the form of cyclic hemiacetals. The OH group arising from the hemiacetal structure is particularly reactive and can react with amines with loss of water (cf. formulas in Chapt. VII–1). Compounds resulting from this reaction are called N-glycosides (cf. Chapt. VI–3, XVII–1).

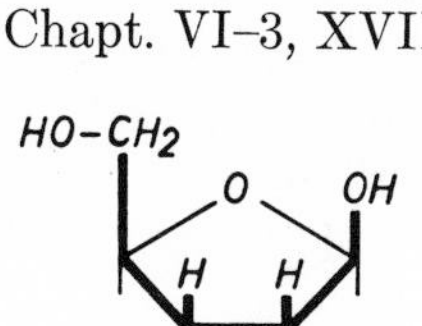

$\beta$-D-Ribose          $\beta$-D-Deoxyribose

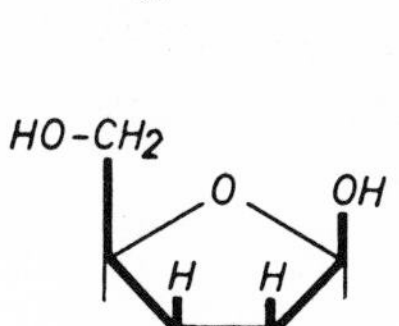

According to the type of carbohydrate which they contain, we distinguish (1) *ribonucleic acids* (abbreviated RNA), containing ribose, and (2) *deoxyribonucleic acids* (abbreviated DNA), with 2-deoxyribose as the carbohydrate. With this purely chemical distinction there go different biologic functions: Deoxyribonucleic acids represent the genetic material, and the ribonucleic acids participate intimately in all phases of protein synthesis. First, however, the cleavage products of nucleic acids will be discussed: the bases, the nucleosides, and the nucleotides.

## 1. Bases, Nucleosides, and Nucleotides

**Pyrimidines.** The pyrimidine ring is a six-membered ring with two nitrogen atoms; the pyrimidine bases of nucleotides bear an amino or hydroxy group in position 6 (for numbering see formula below), and always have an oxygen function in position 2. This situation allows for tautomerism: The H atom can belong either to the oxygen or to the ring nitrogen, as shown below for uracil. Among these tautomeric forms, the most interesting is the one that has a hydrogen on $N^3$ (in nucleosides, ribose has replaced this hydrogen; the ribose is bound in N-glycosidic linkage).

The main pyrimidine bases are *cytosine, uracil,* and *thymine.* Uracil is found virtually only in RNA; thymine almost exclusively in DNA. The formulas of all the bases and corresponding nucleosides are presented in the list below.

**Purines.** Emil Fischer named the ring system which is the skeleton of uric acid "purine" (from Latin *purum uricum*). The positions on the rings are numbered as shown:

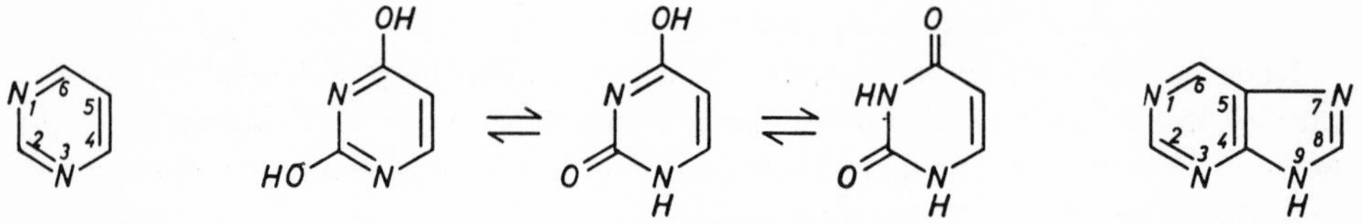

Pyrimidine        Uracil (tautomeric forms)        Purine

*Adenine* (6-aminopurine). We have already seen this as a component of ATP and other low molecular weight nucleotides (nucleotide coenzymes). The replacement of the amino group with a hydroxyl gives *hypoxanthine.*

Another common component of nucleic acids is *guanine* (2-amino-6-hydroxy-purine). Its name stems from its original discovery in guano. Guanine has the grouping of guanidine ($NH=C(NH_2)_2$) in its molecules, and indeed, guanidine (amino urea) was first obtained by degradation of guanine.

**Nucleosides.** The structural features of nucleosides have already been explained briefly in connection with the coenzymes. Base and sugar are linked through a C—N bond (N-glycoside bond; cf. also Chapt. XVII–1), which formally derives from loss of a water molecule. The arrow indicates that the equilibrium favors the side of the components:

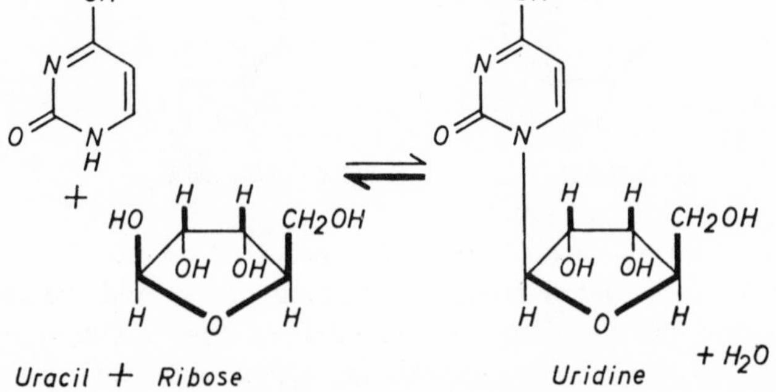

Uracil + Ribose        Uridine        $+ H_2O$

Nucleosides have trivial names, derived from the bases; pyrimidine derivatives end in -idine and those of purine end in -osine (see structures on page 118):

| Base | Nucleoside | Base | Nucleoside |
|------|-----------|------|-----------|
| Cytosine | Cytidine | Adenine | Adenosine |
| Uracil | Uridine | Guanine | Guanosine |
| Thymine | Thymidine | Hypoxanthine | Inosine |

In distinction to the ring numbering, the C atoms of the sugar component are numbered 1' to 5' (see formula of adenosine on the following page).

Beyond the well-known base components, several other bases and nucleosides occurring only in special nucleic acids have recently been discovered. Some bacterial viruses (bacteriophages) contain in their nucleic acids the bases *5-hydroxymethylcytosine* and *5-hydroxymethyluracil*. "Soluble ribonucleic acid" (i.e., transfer ribonucleic acid, see Section 6) contains *pseudouridine*, a 5-ribosyluracil in which the sugar and the pyrimidine moieties are linked through a C—C bond. Transfer ribonucleic acid also contains a small proportion of methyl derivatives of the main nucleosides (especially N-methyl derivatives).

**Nucleotides,** in addition, carry phosphoric acid in ester linkage with the ribose (or deoxyribose) component. The 5'-esters are biologically important; here the phosphoric acid (or pyrophosphoric or triphosphoric acid) is bound to the —$CH_2OH$ group of the sugar moiety (cf. ATP, uridine and cytidine diphosphate; Chapt. VI–5).

Alkaline hydrolysis of RNA, however, does not release the 5'-phosphates, but rather a mixture of 2'- and 3'-phosphates. This mixture arises because an intermediary cyclic 2',3'-phosphodiester[1] forms during hydrolysis. (Deoxyribonucleotides, of course, cannot form such cyclic 2',3'-phosphates.) The cyclic phosphate finally opens up either to the 3'-monoester or the 2'-monoester. These isomers can be separated successfully by ion-exchange chromatography or paper chromatography. For the discussion of enzymic hydrolysis of nucleic acids, see Section 9 of this chapter.

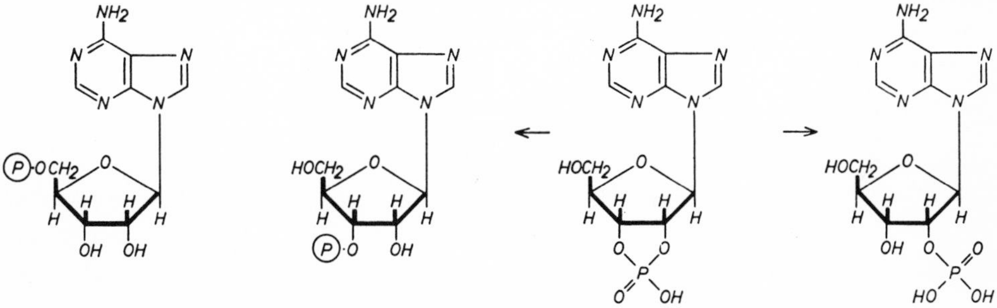

---

[1] Whenever two hydroxyl groups of phosphoric acid have been engaged in ester bonds, one speaks of phosphoric diesters or simply phosphodiesters.

Purine derivatives:

Bases:

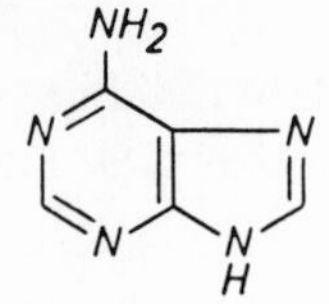

Adenine 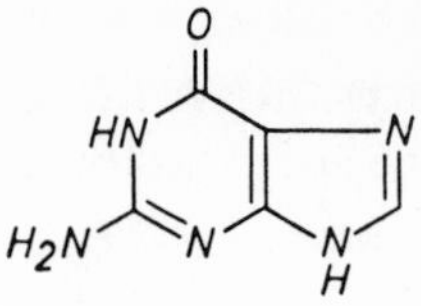   Guanine 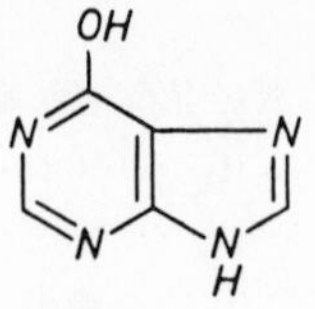   Hypoxanthine

Nucleosides:

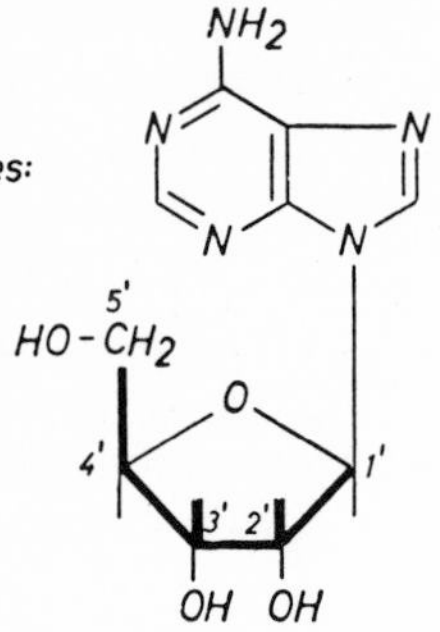

Adenosine 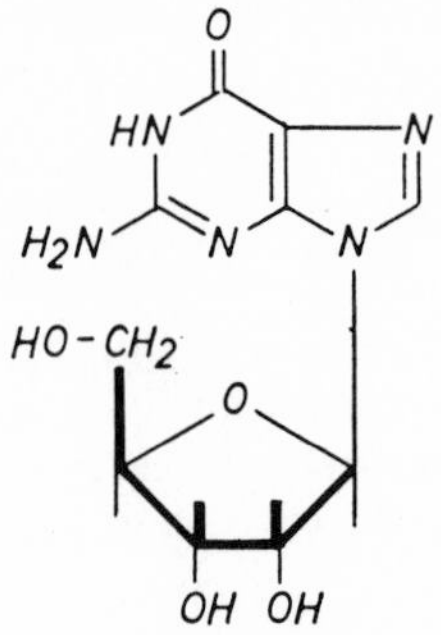   Guanosine 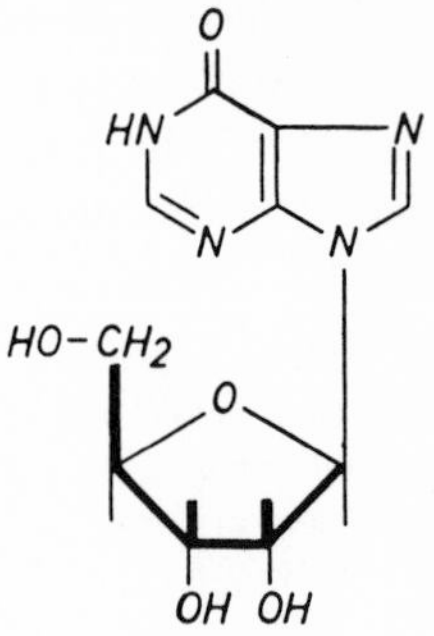   Inosine

Pyrimidine derivatives:

Bases:

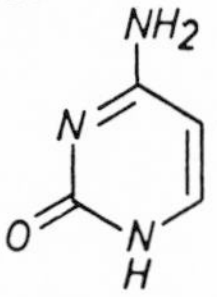

Cytosine 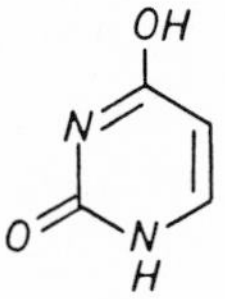   Uracil 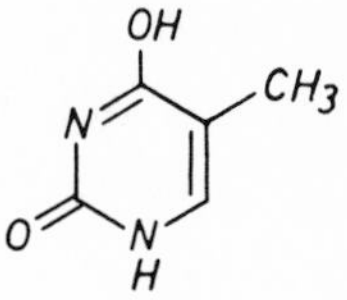   Thymine

Nucleosides:

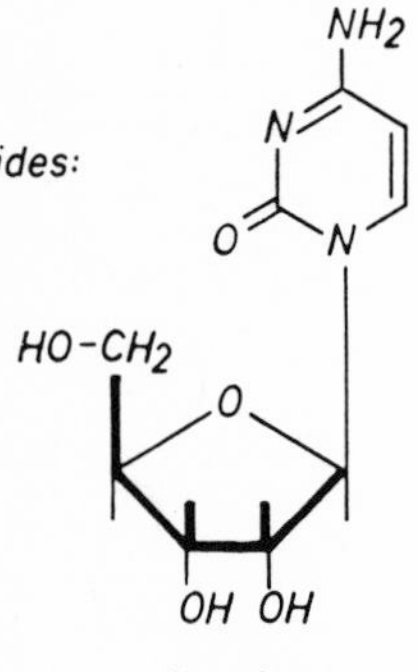

Cytidine 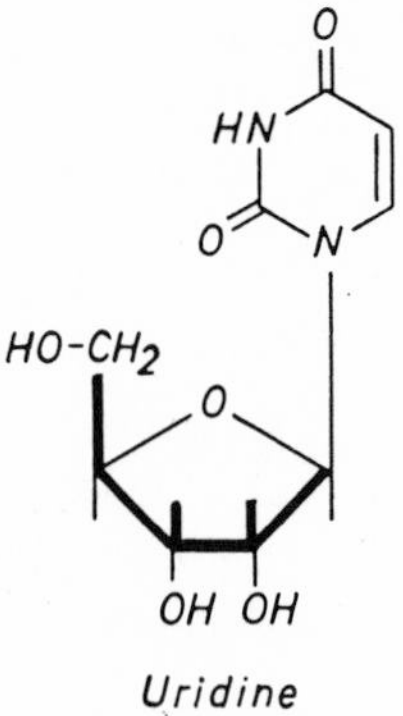   Uridine 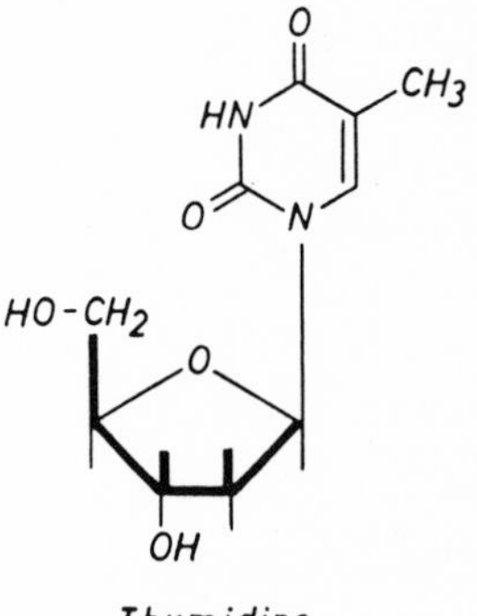   Thymidine

Rare bases:

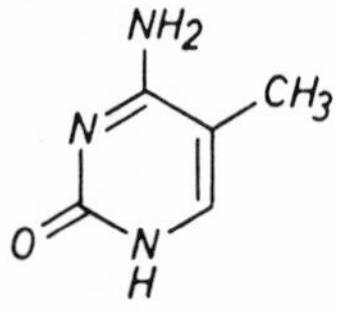

5-Methylcytosine 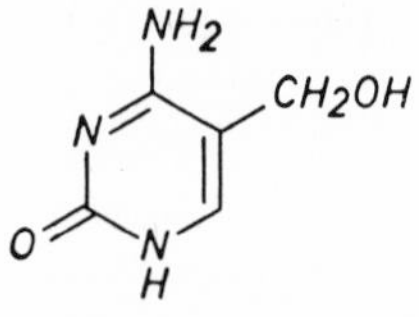   5-Hydroxymethylcytosine 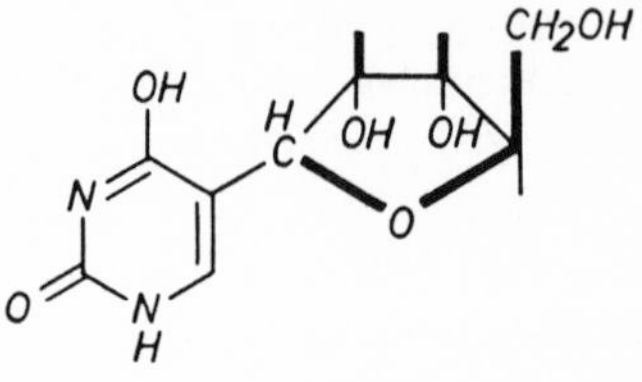   5-Ribosyluracil

## 2. Biosynthesis and Degradation of Nucleotides

**The Biosynthesis of the Pyrimidine Ring** begins with aspartic acid and carbamyl phosphate. The latter is an energy-rich compound which reacts with the former to give carbamylaspartic acid. Ring closure consumes ATP and is in principle an acid amide formation (peptide synthesis). The intermediate *dihydro-orotic acid* is dehydrogenated to orotic acid, probably by action of a flavoprotein. *Orotic acid* is the key precursor of pyrimidine nucleotides. It reacts with phosphoribosyl pyrophosphate. The removal of pyrophosphate yields the nucleotide of orotic acid, whose enzymic decarboxylation produces uridine 5'-phosphate. Phosphorylation with ATP yields uridine pyrophosphate and, finally, uridine triphosphate. Beside the above pathway, there is the further possibility of converting free uracil and ribose 1-phosphate to the nucleoside and from there with ATP to the nucleotide.

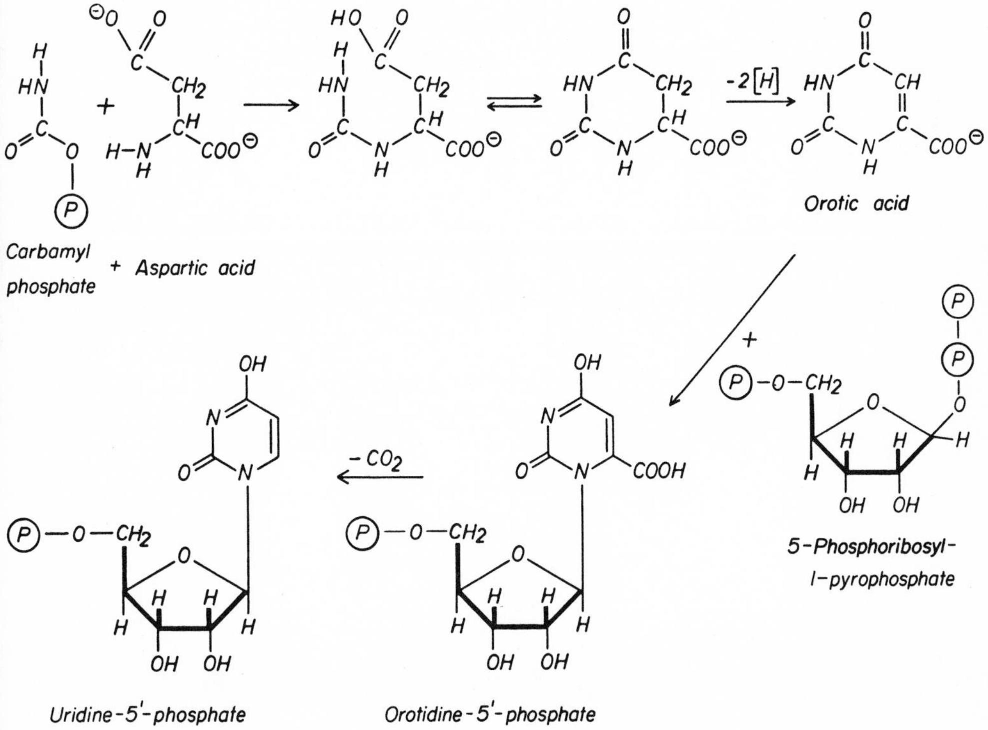

Carbamyl phosphate + Aspartic acid

Orotic acid

Uridine-5'-phosphate    Orotidine-5'-phosphate

5-Phosphoribosyl-1-pyrophosphate

**The Degradation of Uracil** is the reverse of its biosynthesis; in other words, the ring is hydrogenated partially and cleaved hydrolytically between N–1 and C–6. But since $CO_2$ was split off in the conversion of orotic acid → uridine, the degradation product is $\beta$-alanine instead of aspartic acid.

The other pyrimidines arise from the uridine derivatives. One enzyme converts the C–6 hydroxyl group of uridine triphosphate with the aid of ammonia or glutamine to an amino group. Uridine triphosphate thus becomes cytidine triphosphate. The transition to deoxyribose derivatives occurs at the level of the diphosphates by reduction of the sugar moiety. Finally, "active formaldehyde" (cf. Chapt. VI–5) can introduce a methyl group into deoxyuridine 5'-phosphate producing thymidine 5'-phosphate, a characteristic component of DNA.

**The Biosynthesis of Purine Nucleotides** is considerably more involved. Two principles should be noted: In the first place, the sugar-phosphate component of the nucleotide is prepared first, and subsequent reactions take place on it (every chemist would first synthesize the ring system and then attack the carbohydrate synthesis); second, this synthesis uses very small units and molecular groups. Everything is arranged around one glycine molecule. Figure 26 illustrates the origin of the individual groups of atoms and provides the basis of the biosynthesis:

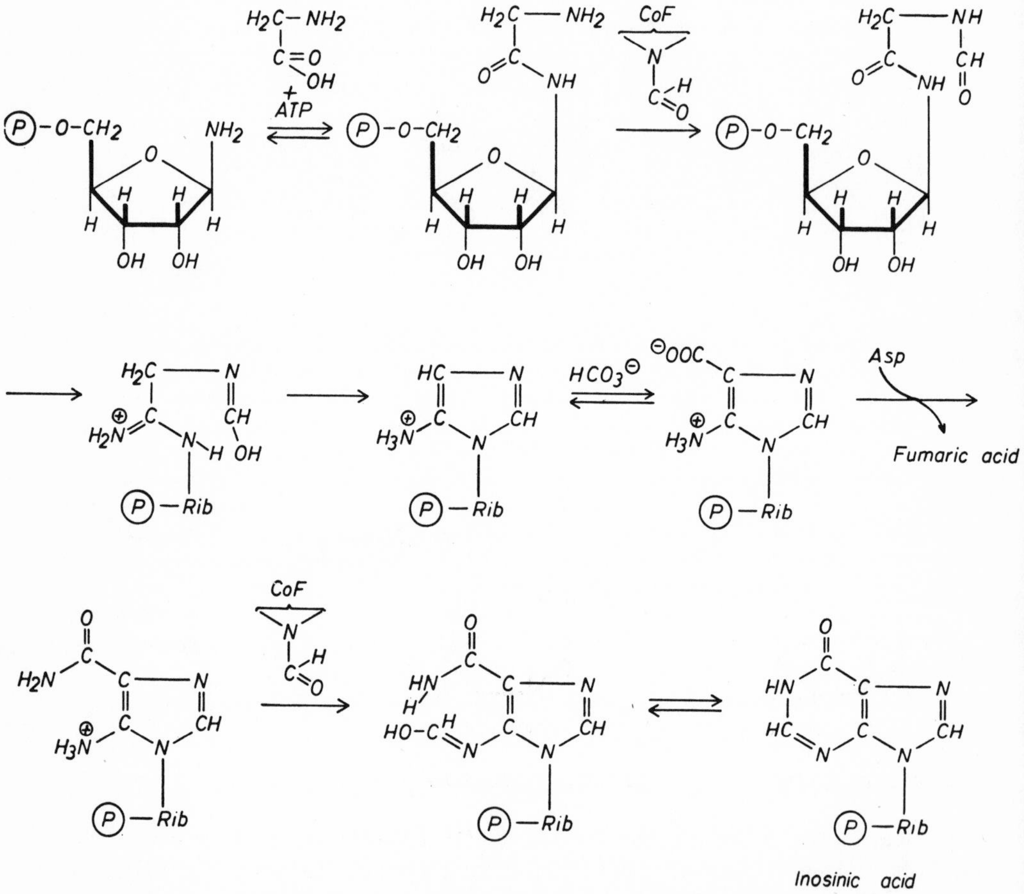

Inosinic acid

In detail, the synthesis as studied by Buchanan and Greenberg takes the following route: 5-phosphoribosylamine (stemming from phosphoribosyl pyrophosphate and glutamine, as mentioned under pyrimidines) condenses with glycine to form the amide with the aid of ATP; the

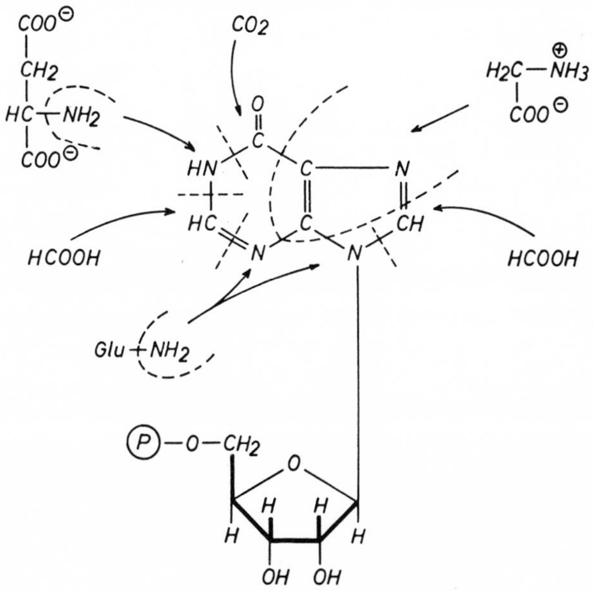

FIG. 26. Biosynthesis of purine nucleotides

central piece of the purine ring is established. The five-membered ring is then prepared by attaching a C atom which is transferred by formyl-coenzyme F. After the addition of another N group—later to become $N^3$—the imidazole ring is closed, whereby 1 mole ATP is consumed. Carbon dioxide (as bicarbonate) next enters the molecule. Remarkably, no activation by ATP is necessary here; the reaction is freely reversible. The acid is then converted to the amide; the nitrogen (later $N^1$ of the purine ring) is supplied by aspartic acid, which becomes fumaric acid (in analogy to urea formation, Chapt. VIII-8). Throughout all these enzymic reactions phosphoribose remains attached to the molecule. Lastly, the six-membered ring is closed, just as the five-membered ring, by the insertion of an active formyl group. The first purine derivative emerges then in the form of inosinic acid, which occurs free in muscle.

*Inosinic acid* is the parent substance of the two purine nucleotides adenosine 5'-phosphate (*adenylic acid*) and guanosine 5'-phosphate (*guanylic acid*), both components of nucleic acids. It is also the parent compound of uric acid, which is the final excretion form of nitrogen in birds and in reptiles.

**Degradation of Purine Bases.** Most purine derivatives are converted to uric acid. Ribose is first removed from guanosine; then the remaining guanine is deaminated to *xanthine*. Adenosine is deaminated as a nucleoside. Phosphorolytic cleavage of the ribose produces *hypoxanthine*, which is oxidized *via* xanthine and through the action of xanthine oxidase to *uric acid*. Xanthine oxidase is a flavoprotein with very low substrate specificity (identical with Schardinger's aldehyde-dehydrogenating enzyme from milk).

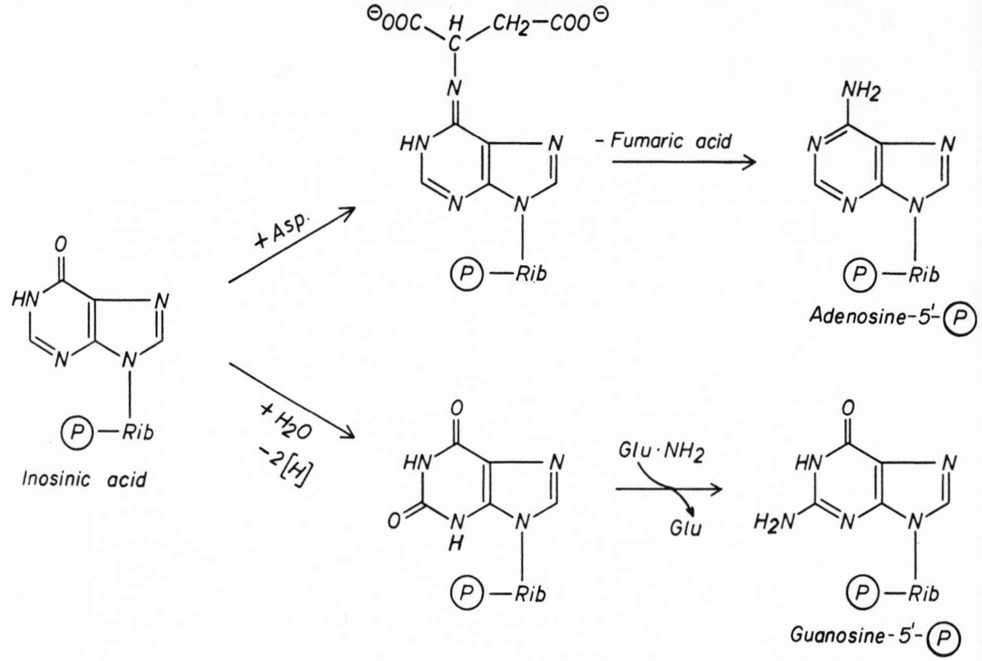

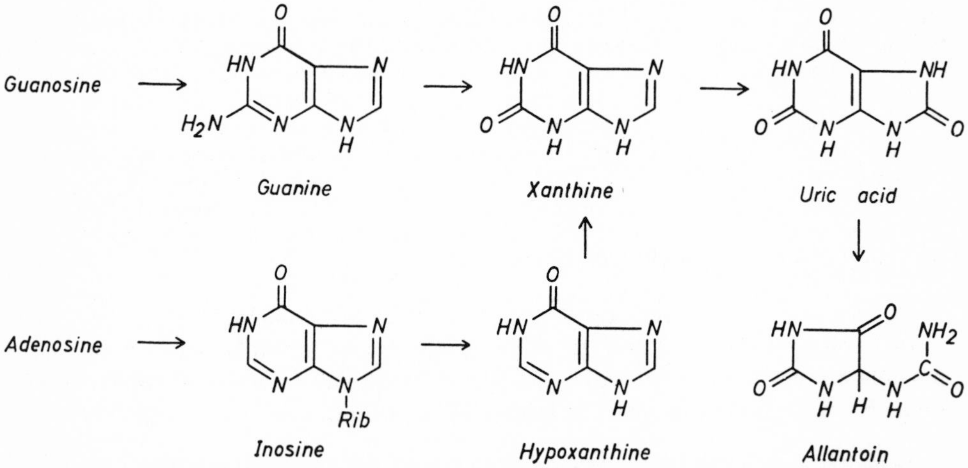

In most mammals uric acid is further degraded to *allantoin*; in man and other higher primates, however, uric acid is excreted as such. In certain pathologic conditions (gout) it is deposited in the joints.

Methylated xanthines have pharmacologic applications (theophylline = 1,3-dimethylxanthine, caffeine = 1,3,7-trimethylxanthine). Certain analogs of the purines (8-azaguanine, 6-mercaptopurine) have antibiotic and cytostatic properties; they have been used as chemotherapeutic agents against tumors.

## 3. Structure of Nucleic Acids

**The Chain Structure of Deoxyribonucleic Acids.** The nucleic acids are high molecular weight polynucleotides: Innumerable nucleosides are linked together with phosphoric acid (in diester bonds). Because in deoxyribonucleosides, which we shall consider first, position 1' of deoxyribose is occupied by the base and position 4' is in the furanose ring, phosphoric acid must tie together the hydroxyls of 3' and 5'. A section of a hypothetical chain is represented here:

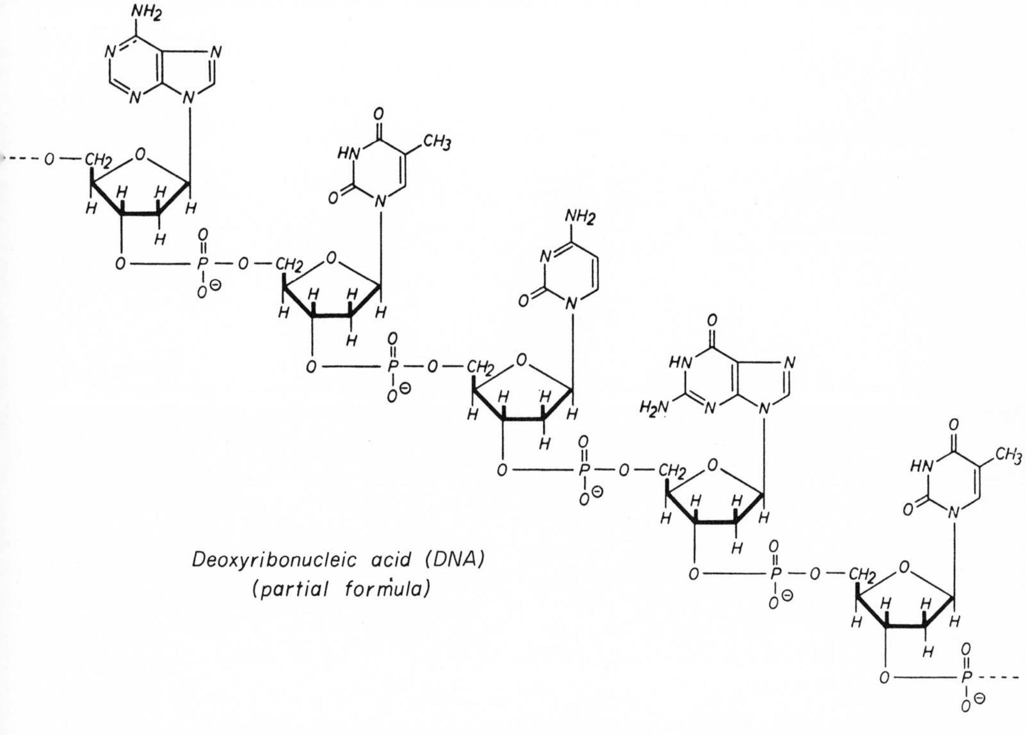

*Deoxyribonucleic acid (DNA)*
*(partial formula)*

The molecular weight of native DNA is very high. Carefully isolated preparations have measured more than 100 million; with the lower values frequently found in the literature one suspects that fragments may have arisen during preparation.

As the base constituents of DNA, the above formula shows the purines adenine and guanine and the pyrimidines cytosine and thymine. The occurrence of thymine is typical for DNA (RNA contains uracil instead).

Quantitative analysis revealed a molar ratio of 1:1 for adenine and thymine, and the same ratio for guanine and cytosine (hence there always are equal proportions of purine and pyrimidine bases). In most animals there is more adenine plus thymine than guanine plus cytosine (molar ratios of the pairs range from 1.3 to 1.5); in bacteria the opposite may be found.

The order of occurrence of bases in the molecule is almost entirely unknown, since methods for sequential analysis are still missing. The sequence will be of great significance, and the individual kinds of DNA (which today cannot even be separated neatly) will differ precisely in their base sequence.

**Ribonucleic Acid** is constructed very similarly to deoxyribonucleic acid. It consists of numerous nucleosides linked together by phosphoric acid. A segment of such a chain is represented by the following formula:

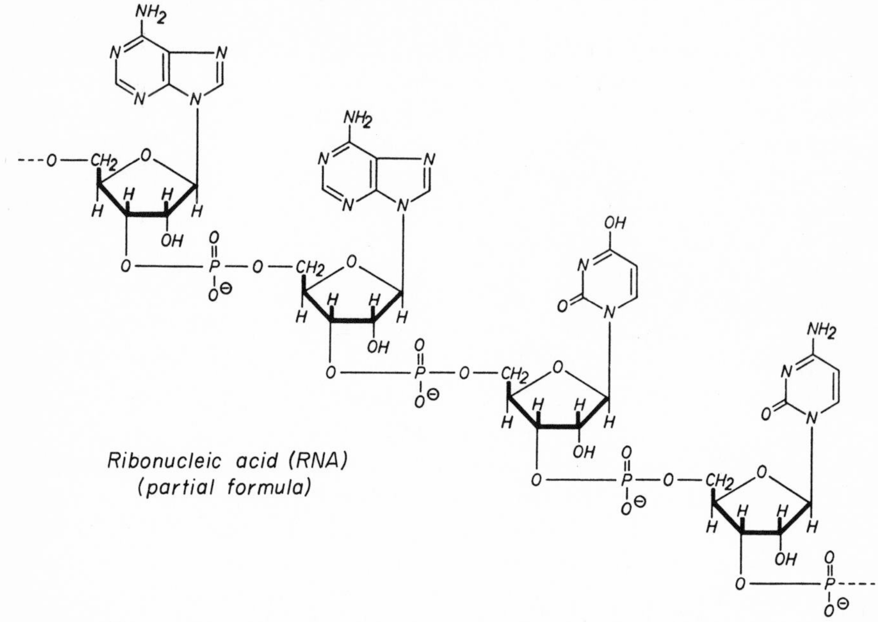

*Ribonucleic acid (RNA)*
*(partial formula)*

The diester of phosphoric acid constitutes the link between the individual ribose units. The 3'-5'-type linkage is found in RNA. The bases are arranged like "side chains" of the sugar-phosphate chain. Some RNAs, in addition to the usual bases adenine, guanine, uracil, and cytosine, contain trace amounts of other bases. Among the latter *pseudouridine* is the most interesting; it is a uracil which carries its ribosyl residue on C atom 5 in a C—C bond (not glycosidic).

The formula above illustrates the principle of the structure of RNA. Again, the actual structural formula of RNA depends on the sequence of the bases. The elucidation of the base sequence of pure and homogeneous nucleic acids is being conducted presently with intense interest.

According to their molecular weights, ribonucleic acids may be grouped into two classes. There are the "soluble ribonucleic acids" found in the cytoplasm with molecular weights between 20,000 and 30,000,[2] and the ribonucleic acids with high molecular weights ranging from several hundred thousand to over a million. The bulk of the latter RNA is a structural component of certain submicroscopic cellular particles, the ribosomes. The remainder, the so-called messenger RNA (or template RNA), attaches itself loosely to these cytoplasmic particles. For the biologic function of the different nucleic acids see Section 6.

---

[2] It is called "soluble" RNA because it remains unsedimented after centrifugation at about 100,000 $g$ for 1–2 hours, in contrast to the RNA bound to structures (ribosomes).

High molecular weight ribonucleic acids of exceptional purity have been prepared from certain viruses. The RNA of the tobacco mosaic virus, for example, has a molecular weight of 2 million.

**Secondary Structure of Deoxyribonucleic Acid.** Watson and Crick have developed a model on the basis of X-ray data obtained by Wilkins, which has been substantiated by other analyses.

The basis for the structural model is the assumption that two bases are always connected by hydrogen bonds (cf. Chapt. IV–3); this is quite possible for the pair adenine-thymine and for the pair guanine-cytosine. The analytic data referred to firmly support the assumption of base pairing.

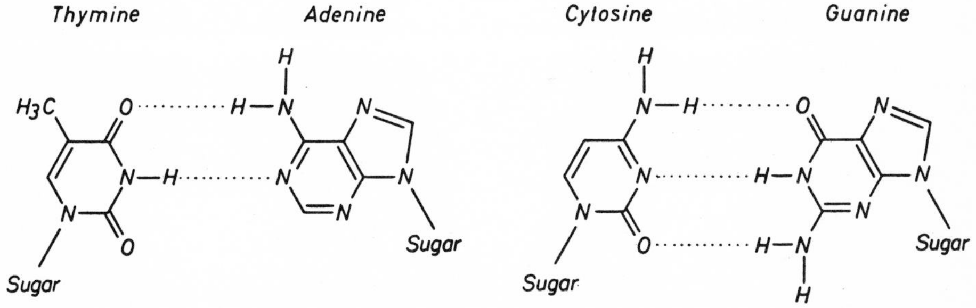

The pairing of the bases holds together two strands of polynucleotides (or two halves of one strand). At the same time, each base predetermines its other pair member, so that *one* strand alone determines the complete sequence of bases in the other strand. This situation is illustrated in Fig. 27a; each unit can correspond with only one other partner and thus determines it.

If the two-stranded tape is imagined twisted, then one gets a fair picture of Watson and Crick's model for DNA: Two molecules (or two halves of one molecule) form a double strand and turn around one another like threads of a screw. Figure 27b is a schematic drawing of this helix model.

**The Helical Nature of Nucleic Acids.** The double helix of nucleic acids has a diameter of 20 Å. Dimensions such as these can be made visible in modern electron microscopes. In the photograph of a deoxyribonucleic acid preparation of bacteriophages (Fig. 28), even the twisted structure of the DNA can be distinguished. The entire, multiply looped thread is 500,000 Å (= 50 μ) long, which corresponds to a molecular weight of 130 million.

The double helix does not withstand the disruptive forces of heating (denaturation) any more than the tertiary structure of proteins does (cf. Chapt. IV–4). When DNA in salt solution is warmed up to 70–80°, the structure separates into single strands and certain physical properties change (viscosity, light absorption, and optical rotation). By cooling the solution very slowly, the molecules are given the opportunity to order themselves partially back to the double strand; with rapid cooling the single strands remain largely separated. This breaking-up of the secondary structure is similar to the melting process, in which the crystal lattice disintegrates, and hence one talks about the "melting point" of DNA.

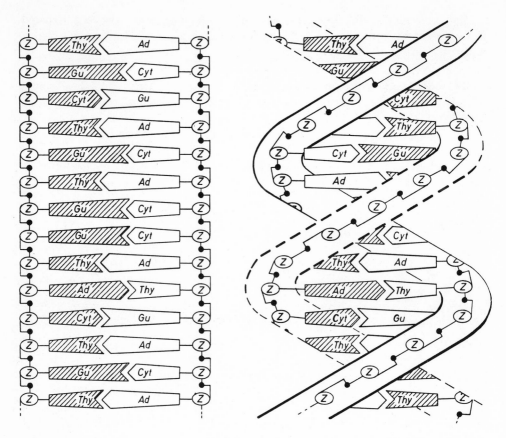

FIG. 27a and b. Structures of Deoxyribonucleic acids. Z stands for the sugar deoxyribose; ● for phosphoric acid.

**Secondary Structure of Ribonucleic Acid.** Compared to the DNA, very little is known about the spatial arrangement of the RNA chain, i.e., about its secondary structure. For soluble RNA it is assumed that a single strand is folded back on itself giving rise in parts of the molecule to a "DNA-like" double helix (cf. Fig. 30 and "Adaptor Hypothesis," Section 6). Base pairing and possibly double strandedness play a role also with high molecular weight ribonucleic acids, but a well-substantiated model does not exist yet.

**Hybridization.** Very closely related nucleic acids, i.e. possessing complementary base sequences over greater portions of the molecules, can form double helices consisting of one strand of each of the two nucleic acids. *Hybridization*, as this phenomenon is called, between a molecule of DNA and a complementary RNA molecule can occur also when the dissolved components are heated above their melting points and allowed to cool slowly.

Hybridization is achieved only, of course, if the two nucleic acid strands possess complementary structure. Only then can hydrogen bonds form between the individual bases along the whole length

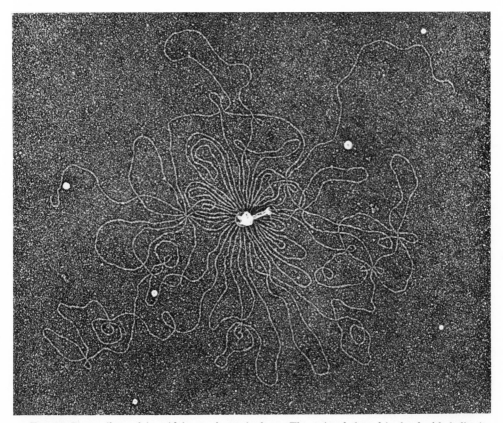

FIG. 28. Deoxyribonucleic acid from a bacteriophage. The twisted thread is the double helix; it is 50 $\mu$ long and is a single DNA molecule with a molecular weight of 130 million. [A. K. Kleinschmidt, et al., Biochim. Biophys. Acta **61,** 857–864 (1962).]

of the molecule and hold the strands together. Moreover, the observation of hybridization affords proof that different nucleic acids possess complementary structure (cf. "messenger RNA," Section 5).

The principle of base pairing, developed by Watson and Crick, has been important in elucidating the structural problems of DNA. Now it has become very fruitful in explaining the chief functions of DNA as carrier of information or hereditary factors and the transmission and utilization of this information.

## 4. Deoxyribonucleic Acid as Carrier of Genetic Information

**Definition of the Gene.** Hereditary factors or genes were at first defined as biologic entities by their *ability to induce characteristics*, by *identical reproduction*, and by *mutation*. In experiments on heredity, certain inherited characteristics (e.g., skin color, morphologic peculiarities, presence or absence of certain substances or metabolic functions) are studied. The hereditary factors or genes are localized on the chromosomes and are inherited according to the well-known Mendelian laws.

From the appearance of a certain characteristic (taking dominance and recessivity into consideration) the presence of a hereditary factor is inferred. The fact that genes can be handed over unchanged from generation to generation, often to many thousand offspring and to millions of generations of cells, compels us to ascribe to genes the capacity for identical replication. Only in this way can daughter nuclei contain the same stock of genes after division.

In all these experiments we can recognize a characteristic to be truly hereditary only when we also find individuals that do not possess this characteristic. Today we have evidence for the assumption that every important property and developmental potential is determined by a gene, i.e., the information for it is carried by a gene.

Very rarely one can observe the phenomenon of sudden changes in hereditary characteristics. The altered gene is then handed on in the same way as the original one. Such mutation explains the multiplicity of species.

**Deoxyribonucleic Acids as Genetic Material.** The substance that makes up the hereditary factors or genes is deoxyribonucleic acid. In general, the current concept is that for each individual gene there is as the chemical equivalent an appropriate DNA characterized by a definite base sequence. The *information* carried by the gene and finally expressed as a particular character consists in the sequence of the bases. The *base sequence* in turn determines the primary structure, i.e., the *sequence of amino acids*, of proteins. There is a direct correlation: A certain group of bases of the DNA stands for a certain amino acid in the final protein.

The ability of DNA for identical replication becomes plausible with the aid of Watson and Crick's structural model. Through the pairing of bases each individual strand determines a second and complementary strand. The mechanism of the biosynthesis of DNA follows the same concept. More will be said about this in the following section.

DNA is localized in the cell nucleus, more specifically in the chromosomes. This has been demonstrated by Feulgen's reaction (Feulgen's nuclear staining) which is specific for DNA and stains only the chromosomes. Optical methods (measurements of ultraviolet absorption) have corroborated these observations.

The amount of DNA per cell is constant; it is the same regardless in what kind of cell of the organism it is. This is not surprising since the chromosomal set and gene content is the same for every cell (except in cases of polyploidy). Only gametes (germ cells and egg cells) have half as much DNA as somacells. The gametes are haploid; they have only half the chromosome content.

**Mutagenesis.** Mutation means a change of information. Chemically it is a change of the DNA, particularly of its base sequence. It has been known for some time that high energy radiation (such as X-rays or γ-rays of radioactive substances) can cause mutation. In recent years mutagenic substances have been discovered. The latter can modify the bases of DNA by introducing alkyl groups and thus interfere with base pairing. As a result certain sections of the base sequence may not be replicated. *Proflavin* interferes with replication in another manner: It penetrates the helix and usurps the place of a base pair. *5-Bromouracil*, a base analogous to thymine (the bromine is in place of the methyl group), is incorporated into DNA as thymine; but during replication it is mistaken occasionally for cytosine. This finally leads to an exchange of adenine for guanine and to an altered base sequence. *Nitrous acid* ($HNO_2$) also can change the base sequence; cytosine is converted to uracil:

$$NH_2 \quad + O=N-OH \rightarrow \left[ N=N-OH \right] \longrightarrow OH \quad + N_2$$

In the same manner, $HNO_2$ converts adenine to hypoxanthine. Uracil or thymine pair with adenine, while hypoxanthine pairs with cytosine and therefore takes the place of guanine. Systematic studies of controlled mutations of this kind have yielded valuable insights into the process of information transfer.

**Transformation and Transduction.** Transformation factors of bacteria have produced important proof for the genetic role of DNA. Of some bacteria, e.g., the *Pneumococci*, different strains are known which produce different capsular material. The material (a polysaccharide; cf. Chapt. XVII–7) must be regarded as one of the hereditary properties, just like hair coloration of mammals. It is possible to convert (to transform) bacteria of one type (e.g. type II) to another (e.g. type III) by treating them under certain conditions with an extract of type III: The active factor in the extract was prepared in pure form by Avery (1944); it is high molecular weight DNA. The assumption is that transformation is a transplantation of a gene. In the host bacterium, the transplanted nucleic acid, used in the process of transformation, acquires the capacity to induce characteristics—here the synthesis of type-specific capsular material. It also acquires in the host the capacity for identical replication, since the very same transformation factor can be isolated in quantity from a new harvest of transformed bacteria.

In other bacteria genetic material is transferred by *transduction*. In this process part of a bacterial chromosome is transported (transduced) by a bacteriophage (virus; cf. Section 8) into the receptor bacterium. Bacterial genetics has become a very valuable tool for many fundamental questions in genetics.

## 5. The Transfer of Information: Biosynthesis of DNA and RNA

The passing-on of genetic information requires, as we have seen, "identical replication" of DNA, which means *de novo* synthesis of deoxyribonucleic acid in strict conformity with an existing template.

**Enzymic Synthesis of DNA.** Enzymes catalyzing the biosynthesis of DNA were first discovered by Kornberg in *Escherichia coli*. The required substrates of the *polymerase* are the triphosphates of all four nucleosides, i.e., deoxyadenosine triphosphate, deoxyguanosine triphosphate, deoxycytosine triphosphate, and deoxythymidine

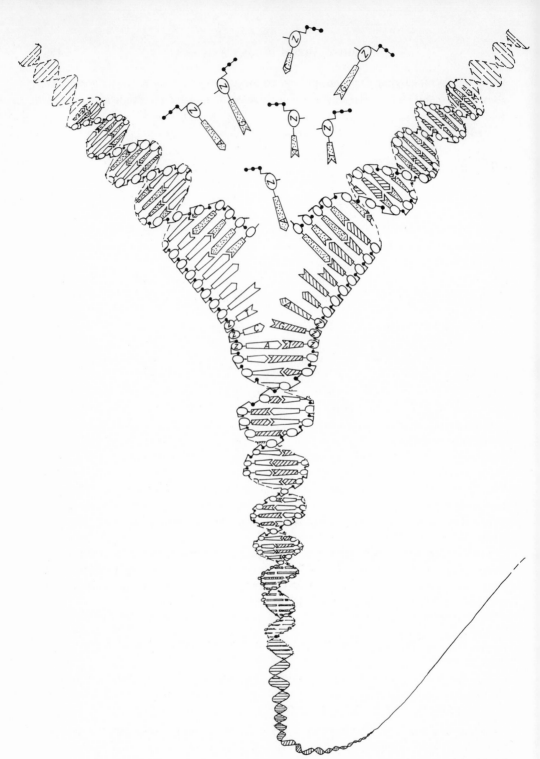

Fig. 29. Biosynthesis of nucleic acid represented schematically according to the principle of base pairing. The threads of the double helix separate; each strand serves as template to which the complementary base components attach. The newly produced parts are shaded on the figure. After replication each double strand consists of half old and half new material ("semiconservative replication").

triphosphate. The chemical mechanism of the synthesis of the macromolecule consists in a nucleophilic attack of the free 3'-hydroxyl group of deoxyribose on the triphosphate group. The chain is extended in this way link by link.

In addition to the four deoxyribonucleoside triphosphates, all of which must be present, there must also be a small amount of high molecular weight DNA which functions as the primer (or starter) of the reaction. Watson and Crick's model makes the need for a primer molecule intelligible: Each single strand of the helix becomes a template for the "stringing-up" of the bases. The assumption is that the primer DNA unwinds to single strands and that the corresponding bases line up along the single strand. The job of the enzyme is to establish the phosphodiester linkages (with elimination of pyrophosphate). This mechanism of identical replication is represented schematically in Fig. 29.

It is no surprise then that nucleic acid synthesized *in vitro* according to this mechanism has the same base composition, the same physical properties (molecular weight), and even the same biologic activity (as a transformation factor) as the primer nucleic acid. The polymerase is not species specific; primer nucleic acids of different species origin are multiplied indiscriminately by the enzyme from *E. coli*.

Biologic observations of the formation of viral nucleic acid in bacteria and of the replication of bacterial chromosomes have essentially substantiated this mechanism, although a host of individual problems remains to be solved.

**The Biosynthesis of Ribonucleic Acids** in the cell takes place to a large extent directly on the chromosomes. At the chromosomes of the salivary gland a very intense incorporation of radioactively tagged RNA precursors has been found (cf. also Chapt. XIX–1). The newly synthesized RNA, according to modern theory, is the working copy of a gene and carries the information from nucleus to cytoplasm. This role has lent it the name *messenger RNA* (mRNA); it has also been called *template RNA*, because this RNA serves as the template for protein synthesis (see following section).

The formation of messenger RNA should also conform to the rule of base pairing. In any case, it can be demonstrated that template RNA is complementary to DNA since one can make hybrid nucleic acids, which are double-stranded molecules consisting of one DNA and one RNA chain (cf. Section 3).

The enzymes involved in RNA biosynthesis have been found and purified recently. One enzyme investigated by Weiss and Hurwitz requires not only the four nucleoside triphosphates (ATP, GTP, CTP, and UTP) as substrates but also a "primer" DNA, to which must be assigned the function of template for the orderly arrangement of the nculeosides. This permits the formation of a "negative" copy of the primer, resulting in the template RNA.

Another RNA-synthesizing enzyme has been isolated from bacteria by Ochoa and his collaborators. The enzyme polymerizes nucleoside *diphosphates* with the elimination of orthophosphate:

$$n(\text{nucleoside—P—P}) \rightleftharpoons \text{polynucleotide} + n\text{P}$$

The reaction is reversible. Cleavage with the uptake of orthophosphate is analogous to the phosphorolysis of glycogen (Chapt. XVII–6), and perhaps the biologic significance of the enzyme rests more on its lytic rather than synthetic activity.

Products are formed which resemble natural RNAs to a greater or lesser degree: They are of high molecular weight, form viscous solutions, and are attacked by nucleic acid-cleaving enzymes. Their molecular skeleton, therefore, must be the same (unbranched chains; the components linked through 3'-5'-diester bridges of phosphoric acid). These preparations, however, do differ from natural nucleic acids in their base composition. The ratio of the bases is largely determined by the relative concentrations of nucleoside diphosphates in the substrate mixture and, indeed, it is possible to prepare with these enzymes polymers of only one nucleotide, i.e. a polyadenylic acid or a polyuridylic acid, etc. Such synthetic polynucleotides can substitute for messenger RNAs under certain conditions and catalyze the incorporation of amino acids into polypeptides (cf. this chapter, Section 6).

## 6. Protein Biosynthesis

The problem of the biosynthesis of proteins has two parts: How is the peptide linkage made possible energetically, and how is the sequence of amino acids determined?

**Activation of Amino Acids.** Proteins cannot be formed from free amino acids by a reversal of proteolysis. We have emphasized that the equilibrium of this process lies very far to the side of hydrolysis; peptides decompose very readily to amino acids, but amino acids never recombine to give peptides. Consequently, the amino acid must first be activated, i.e. raised to a high potential for group transfer.

The reactions which result in the activation of amino acids have basically been elucidated during the past few years. Chemical energy is supplied by adenosine triphosphate (ATP), which with elimination of pyrophosphate produces a mixed carboxylic-phosphoric anhydride with the acid group of the amino acid (see Fig. 25 in Chapt. VI–5, reaction c). As shown in the first line of the diagram on page 133, the reaction is reversible.

In a second reaction, the amino acyl group is transferred onto a molecule of soluble ribonucleic acid, to the 2'- (or 3'-) hydroxyl of ribose. An ester is evidently formed with the hydroxyl group of ribose. This ester has a high enough potential for group transfer so that peptide bonds can be formed. The "activating" ribose is part of an adenosine residue which makes up the end group of a transfer RNA molecule. For every amino acid there is a specific activating enzyme and at least one specific transfer RNA. Hence, "soluble RNA" of the cell consists of a mixture of different transfer ribonucleic acids. Several individual components of this mixture have been isolated in pure form.

**Ribosomes.** The job of transfer RNAs is to bring activated amino acids to the ribosomes, which are small, submicroscopic particles with a diameter of about 15 mμ and which can be photographed electronoptically (see Fig. 49, Chapt. XIX–2). About 65% of a ribosome is ribonucleic acid; the remainder is made up of protein and some low molecular weight material. In the cell the ribosomes are situated in the *ergastoplasm*; in thin sections they are seen lined up on the lamellae.

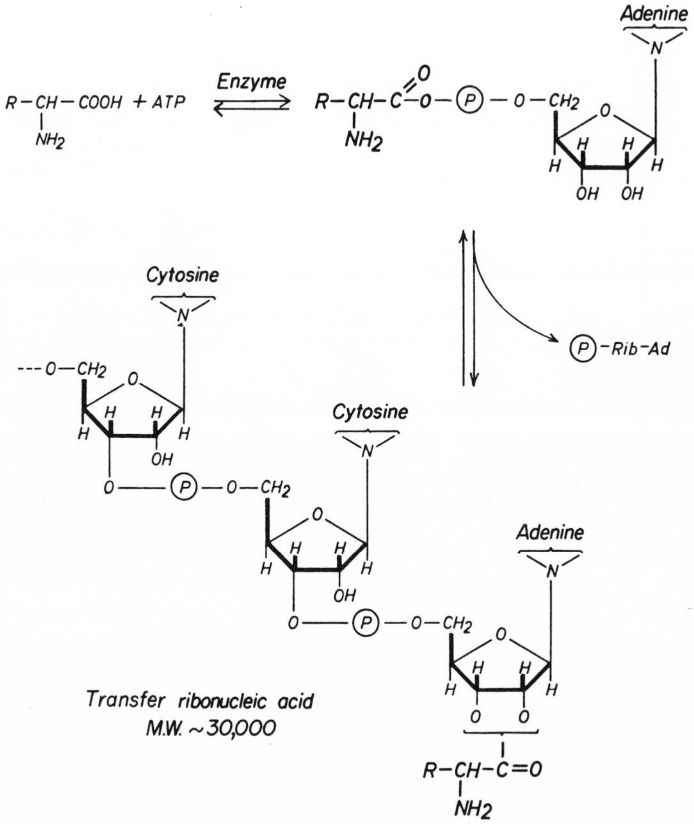

Transfer ribonucleic acid
M.W. ~30,000

Normal ribosomes, with a particle weight of about 3 million (sedimentation constant of 70–80 S), are aggregates of two dissimilar subunits which sediment with 30 S and 50 S and contain RNA of 0.55 and 1.1 million molecular weight, respectively. This aggregation is reversible and is strongly dependent on the $Mg^{++}$ content of the solution. The complexes dissociate in low $Mg^{++}$ concentrations. Ribosomal RNA also appears to be complementary to certain portions of the DNA.

Ribosomes can synthesize protein only when they are loaded with template RNA. Electron micrographs have indicated that four to six ribosomes combine with one mRNA molecule (template RNA). Such combinations are called *polysomes* or *ergosomes*.

**Fixing the Amino Acid Sequence.** We have learned that the sequence of amino acids in proteins is determined genetically and that the information for it resides in the base sequence of the DNA. For protein synthesis a "working copy" of the gene is produced, the template or *messenger RNA* (mRNA). Its formation was discussed in the preceding section. The following diagram (Fig. 30) shows how messenger RNA attaches to ribosomes and how it acts as the template. This mechanism enables all ribosomes to synthesize the great number of different proteins depending on the template with which they are loaded.

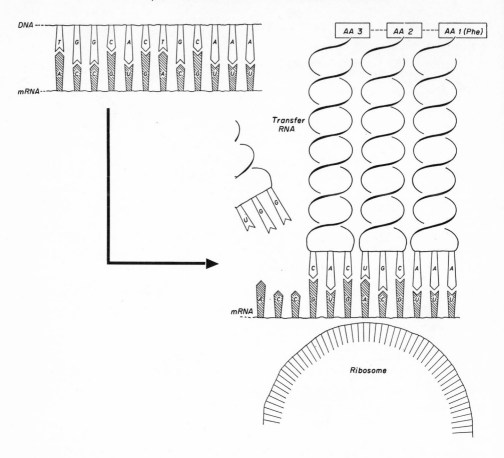

Fig. 30. Diagram of protein biosynthesis. First, complementary messenger RNA (mRNA) is formed at the DNA and then attaches itself to ribosomes. Second, each base group of the mRNA is paired with the corresponding, amino acid-charged transfer RNA. Last, the activated amino acids are linked up to become the peptide chain.

**The Coding Problem.** Now we may ask how the amino acid sequence is coded into the sequence of bases in the messenger RNA. RNA has only the four bases (adenine, guanine, cytosine, and uracil) with which to determine the twenty amino acids. In other words, there are only four letters, $A$, $G$, $C$, $U$, in the alphabet to make up the code words or *codons*.

If a code word consisted of only two letters then $4^2 = 16$ combinations would result; evidently not enough. But three symbols per combination brings it up to $4^3 = 64$ possibilities—more than enough to provide each of the twenty amino acids with one codon. Probably there are two or even three codons for each of several amino acids. This situation is called a *degenerate code*, which means that several combinations stand for the same thing. Other combinations probably are nonsense, i.e., they do not stand for any amino acid.

The assumption is that each codon consists of three adjacent bases, although this "triplet code" has not yet been proved rigorously. Another requirement is that the start for reading off a series of triplets must be signaled in an as yet unknown manner. As a result of mutation, either by deletion of a base or by insertion of a new one, the sequence is misarranged and so many nonsense triplets are created that no protein is formed for a given gene. Such a mutation is called a deletion mutation.

A direct experimental approach to the code problem was afforded by the surprise discovery that in place of the regular messenger RNA relatively simple polynucleotides also can direct the incorporation of amino acids if they are incubated with ribosomes, activated amino acids, and enzymes (Matthaei and Nirenberg; Ochoa). With polyuridine phosphate in place of the natural messenger RNA, a polypeptide is formed which consists only of phenylalanine. The base sequence U—U—U therefore must be the code word for phenylalanine. If the polynucleotide also contains some cytidine, then leucine is included in the polypeptide as well. The codon for leucine apparently has the symbols C, U, and U. The probable code triplets for most amino acids have been deciphered by this procedure.

**The Adaptor Hypothesis.** The translation of the base code into amino acid sequence, according to a hypothesis of Crick, again depends on the principle of base pairing. The individual transfer nucleic acids are postulated to bear in a highly prominent position (pictured as a loop in Fig. 30) a base group which pairs with the complementary codon on the messenger RNA. It is likely that an enzyme protein catalyzes this binding. The transfer nucleic acids charged with amino acids would arrange themselves in this way and the amino acids would link up. The peptide chain would grow till the end of the template had been reached and finally peel off.

We can summarize as follows: The specificity of the protein, its amino acid sequence, is determined by a specific RNA, which is synthesized in immediate contact with DNA and whose base pattern is the complement of that of the DNA. This messenger RNA attaches to the ribosomes and serves as a template for the protein synthesis. Each group of three bases represents one of the 20 possible amino acids. The amino acids which are bound to soluble (or transfer) RNA in an energy-rich bond are lined up along the ribosome template according to the code groups and linked together by a special enzyme (see Fig. 30). After the peptide chain is completed, the protein is separated from the ribosome by an unknown mechanism and released to the cytoplasm.

## 7. Mode of Action of Genes

In preceding sections we have developed the significance of DNA, the genetic material, in protein synthesis. Again, let us remember that genes are defined primarily by the *expression of a characteristic*. The process by which the gene determines the hereditary characteristics in general is extraordinarily complex, especially with morphologic characteristics, and is as yet far beyond biochemical analysis. With some hereditary biochemical anomalies, or biochemically differentiated races, however, it has been possible to study the way hereditary factors operate.

**Biochemical Mutants.** Mutants with such anomalies were first found and studied (A. Kühn, A. Butenandt) among insects (e.g. the flour moth *Ephestia* and the fruit fly *Drosophila*). Later, biochemical mutants were generated (Beadle) from the easily grown bread mold *Neurospora crassa*.

Often the result of a metabolic defect in a mutant is that some substance which was synthesized by the wild strain now must be provided as an essential growth factor.[3] The mutant is said to be auxotrophic for that factor (e.g. for tryptophan or nicotinic acid); it is also called a deficiency mutant. The question then remains what biochemical reaction has been interrupted.

In the above-mentioned insect mutants, a chain of syntheses which forms the brown pigment of the eyes was interrupted; the insects became conspicuous because of their light eyes. It was found that the pigment xanthommatin arises from tryptophan, and that in one group of mutants the step from tryptophan to kynurenine, and in another mutant the step from kynurenine to 3-hydroxykynurenine was blocked (Butenandt and co-workers):

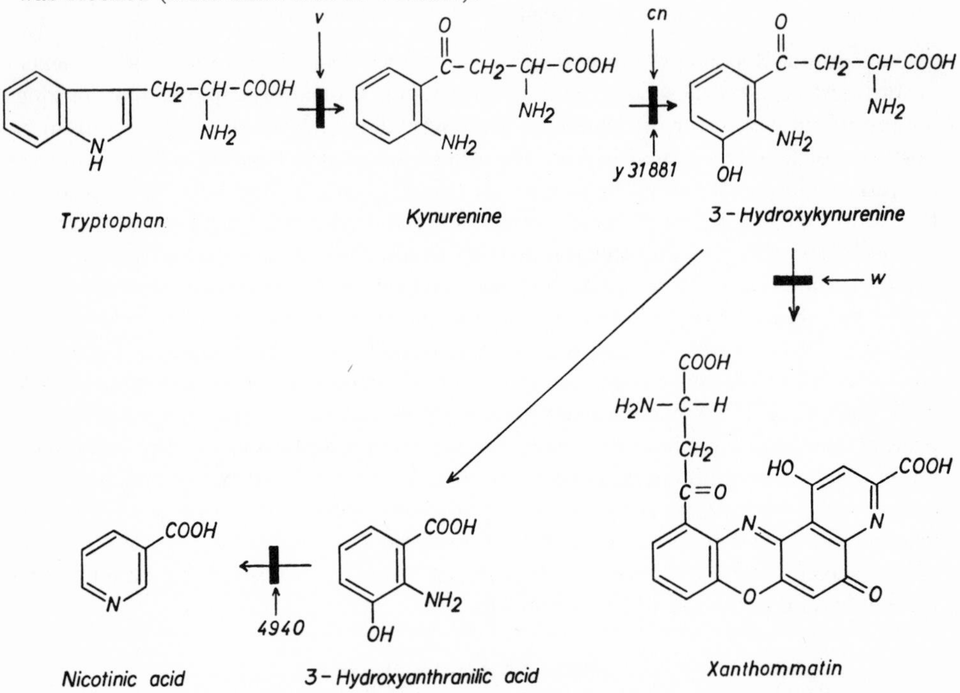

Tryptophan　　　　　　Kynurenine　　　　　3 - Hydroxykynurenine

Nicotinic acid　　3 - Hydroxyanthranilic acid　　　　Xanthommatin

The same reaction sequence was then discovered in *Neurospora*, but there 3-hydroxykynurenine yields nicotinic acid rather than the pigment (cf. also Chapt. VIII-11). The designations of the mutants are written near the arrows (above)[4] wherever the particular reaction seems to be blocked. It is more correct to say that in the wild form the corresponding gene permits the reaction while in the deficient mutant the altered gene no longer has that ability.

[3] The requirement for vitamins in higher organisms is to be explained in the same way.

[4] Letters refer to mutants of *Drosophila*; numbers to those of *Neurospora*. The corresponding wild strains are identified by the added + sign (e.g. cn+).

The simplest explanation is that the gene collaborates in the production of the enzyme which catalyzes the particular metabolic reaction. In the above diagram, the gene v+ of *Drosophila* controls the production of the enzyme which effects the conversion of tryptophan to kynurenine; the gene cn+ (*Drosophila*) or Y 31881+ (*Neurospora*) controls the biosynthesis of the enzyme kynurenine hydroxylase. In some cases it could be demonstrated that the mutant indeed lacked the enzyme. Occasionally it is replaced by a very similar, but enzymically inactive, protein.

Corresponding situations are found in man. Phenylalanine-tyrosine metabolism is especially subject to congenital defects (cf. diagram of formulas in Chapt. VIII– 11): In Fölling's imbecility (phenylketonuria) the step phenylalanine → tyrosine is blocked; in alcaptonuria, the breakdown of homogentisic acid. In albinism the side pathway leading to melanin is interrupted. These "inborn errors in metabolism" had already been recognized as effects of the genes by Garrod in 1923.

Generalizing, it can be stated that genes act by controlling the production of enzymes (or other proteins). As an example, sickle cell hemoglobin, a congenital anomaly prevalent among Negroes (cf. Chapt. IV–2),

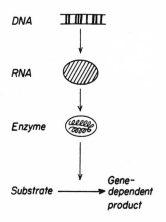

DNA

RNA

Enzyme

Substrate ————→ Gene-dependent product

differs from "normal" hemoglobin by having valine in place of the usual glutamic acid. It has, therefore, one less negative charge and can be separated from normal hemoglobin electrophoretically. The difference in hereditary stock is manifested here in a changed protein molecule, through an exchange of amino acids. Numerous other examples of this kind have also been noted. This is direct proof for the assertion with which we began in Section 4, namely, that genes determine the amino acid sequence. This closes our discourse. Research on the biochemical action of genes, on the genetic code, and on protein biosynthesis has led to a uniform picture which is presented here in outline form in the accompanying diagram.

**The Regulation of Gene Activity** is an old but still unsolved problem of genetics and developmental physiology: All genes are, of course, present equally in every cell of the organism for its entire life-span. Yet genes exert their influence only in very specific organs or tissues and only during highly specific phases of development. Is this activity being directed? A conceptual model to solve this problem has evolved from the study of enzyme induction of microorganisms.

**Enzyme Induction.** The formation of certain enzymes is enhanced dramatically by the substrate entering the cell. The yeast cell, for example, produces β-galactosidase, a milk-sugar cleaving enzyme, when the medium contains lactose. Formerly, this was looked upon as a mysterious enzymic adaptation to the environment. Today the phenomenon is called *enzyme induction*; it has been studied in detail mainly in microorganisms. Related substances, even enzyme inhibitors, not only the substrates, can also induce enzyme formation. Many investigations have borne out that the induced enzyme is identical with the enzyme protein normally present and that it can be induced only if the corresponding gene has already existed in the organism. Further, the induced enzyme is known to be newly synthesized from amino acids. The *inducer*, therefore, must act, somehow, directly on the mechanism of protein synthesis and stimulate it.

One hypothesis of Jacob and Monod's, supported essentially by genetic experiments, postulates that in addition to structural genes (which determine the structure of the proteins) there are also *regulator genes* whose job is to *control* protein synthesis. They are responsible for the formation of *repressor* molecules which block the structural genes and thus prevent the synthesis of messenger RNA. The repressor, however, can react with the inducer, i.e., the substrate or substrate analog. The repressor is removed from equilibrium, and the blocking of the structural gene, in turn, is ended. Now the synthesis of messenger RNA can begin.

It remains to be seen whether Jacob and Monod's hypothesis will stand or whether it will have to be modified. In any case, it is a regulatory mechanism, which has the formation of enzyme proteins adapting itself to the requirements, and which could, accordingly, be of physiological significance. The same mechanism has now been detected in mammals, and considerable evidence indicates that several hormones operate through this mechanism (cf. Fig. 52 in Chapt. XX–1).

## 8. Biochemistry of Viruses

**Viruses and Genes.** Viruses exhibit the three fundamental properties of genes: In host cells they replicate identically, i.e., the virus multiplies; they express some characteristic—in this case the symptom of a disease; and they may undergo mutation. Mutants differ, among other things, in the symptoms that they cause and in the constitution of viral protein. Mutants have also been developed artificially (e.g., with nitrous acid; cf. Section 4).

Viruses have become invaluable as models for genes because they can easily be obtained in large lots. Protein and nucleic acid are the components of simple viruses. But not long ago Schramm was able to single out the nucleic acid as the sole agent responsible for infectivity. Therefore, here too the expression of characteristics and the ability to replicate depend on the nucleic acid.

**Virus and Host.** Viruses depend very generally on the metabolism of their host cells; hence they cannot be grown in artificial culture media. They have neither energy metabolism nor enzymes for the biosynthesis of their own substance, the viral protein and the nucleic acid. They merely carry the information of their own "specificity," e.g. the amino acid sequence of the proteins, and are able so to influence the metabolism of the host cell that virus-specific substances are formed, usually at the cost of cellular material already present. The host cell then either perishes or recovers from the disease.

The question whether viruses are alive can only be answered with an exact definition of "alive." They are able to mutate and to reproduce identically, but are not able to metabolize, and show no (or only very limited) reaction to stimuli. There is justification for saying that viruses gain the attributes of life only in conjunction with the host cell.

**Composition of Virus Particles.** Many viruses have been prepared pure, some even in crystalline form. The simplest among them chemically are nucleoproteins; they consist of protein and nucleic acid (usually DNA; with some plant viruses, e.g. tobacco mosaic virus, it is RNA). Larger viruses are more variable, which means they can no longer be regarded as chemically definable nucleoproteins.

The internal structure of the elementary particle of virus has been studied in great detail in a few cases. The *tobacco mosaic virus* surely is the best known among them. It is one of the smaller pathogenic plant viruses. Its particle weight[5] amounts "only" to 40 million; it is rod-shaped, 260 m$\mu$ long, and 15 m$\mu$ thick (cf. Figs. 31 and 32).

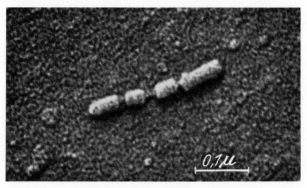

FIG. 31. Tobacco mosaic virus partially broken down (photograph by Prof. Schramm). Careful treatment with a weakly alkaline salt solution removed the virus protein completely in some places, exposing the thread of nucleic acid. 150,000-fold enlargement.

Each tobacco mosaic virus particle consists of one long thread of nucleic acid embedded in protein. The protein surrounds the nucleic acid in loops or in the fashion of screw threads making up the "super-molecule." Treatment with phenol separates nucleic acids from protein. The nucleic acid obtained in this mild way remains infectious, and in a host cell can cause virus multiplication and consequent symptoms of disease. About 95% of the material is protein; it consists of individual subunits with a molecular weight of 17,500, which exhibit a marked tendency to aggregate: At neutral or slightly acidic pH the protein molecules aggregate to little rods, very similar to the intact virus particles both in shape and size. The amino acid sequence is now known. Mutants obtained by nitrous acid treatment (see above) show up differences in the amino acid sequence; usually only one amino acid has been replaced, for example, serine by leucine, or leucine by phenylalanine.

[5]With viruses it is more meaningful to speak of particle weight than molecular weight, since the higher viruses especially are quite variable. Particle weight, of course, is also measured on the scale of atomic weights.

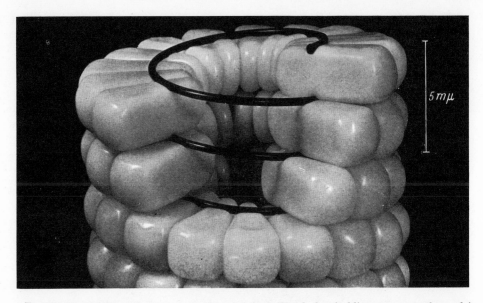

Fig. 32. Model of the tobacco mosaic virus (section). The dark spiral line represents the nucleic acid molecule; the bread-loaf-like structures, the protein subunits—of which there are altogether about 2300. The model is sectioned and partly opened to show the internal structure. (Model and photograph by the author).

*Bacterial viruses* (*phages*) have been very popular subjects in recent decades for many fundamental experiments in molecular genetics. A few relatively small phages contain RNA, the majority, however, DNA. The bacteriophage $\phi$X174 recently has been enjoying unusual popularity. It possesses a comparatively small DNA with the molecular weight of 1.7 million and a single-stranded and, probably, cyclic structure.

The very well studied $T_2$-phage of *Escherichia coli* is much larger (particle weight of 200 million) and begins to exhibit morphologically and functionally distinguishable structures. Figure 34a is a diagram and Figs. 33 and 34b are electron microscopic photographs of the phage.

The large hexagonal head is enveloped by a protein membrane. It contains the nucleic acid (of the DNA type). The tail has three different proteins. One is responsible for the attachment of the phage to the bacterial membrane. Another is an enzyme; it dissolves the membrane during infection. Finally, the DNA is injected through the tail portion into the bacterial cell and there begins the process of forming new phage material, i.e. of nucleic acid and protein. The synthesis of phages uses the host's metabolic setup, which is commandeered by the intruding DNA in a way still incompletely understood. When all components are formed and the finished phages are put together, the bacterial membrane bursts open (lysis of bacteria) and the phages stream out.

Viruses of vertebrates and man have not been studied nearly as well as those of the plants and bacteria mentioned. Many of them are considerably bigger: The *influenza virus* (shown in Fig. 35 has a particle weight of 350 million; the smallpox virus, several billion. These viruses contain components which are host specific and not virus specific. The introduction of tissue culture for growing virus and the use of the electron microscope for their characterization has permitted substantial progress in virus research.

FIG. 33. T₂-Phages of *E. coli*. Careful removal of tail protein exposes the tail rod which bores through the cell wall and is injected into the cell. (Photograph by Dr. Hofschneider, 100,000-fold enlarged).

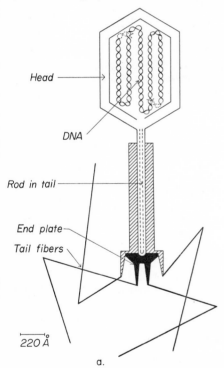

Head

DNA

Rod in tail

End plate

Tail fibers

220 Å

a.

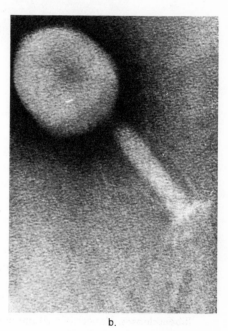

b.

FIG. 34. a. Schematic representation of the T₂ bacteriophage of *Escherichia coli*. The various structural features of the tail facilitate the penetration of deoxyribonucleic acid into the host cell. Compare with the accompanying photograph (Fig. 34b). b. Electron micrograph of the *E. coli* phage T₂. Enlargement: 250,000 times. The technique of "negative staining" was used to bring out the details of the end plate and the tail fibers. (Original photograph by Dr. Hofschneider.)

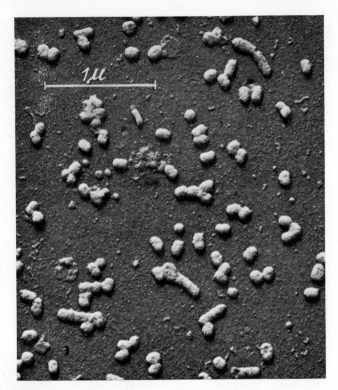

FIG. 35. Influenza virus of the Asiatic type (original photograph by Prof. Schäfer). A larger spherical virus with a tendency to aggregate.

## 9. Nucleic Acid-Cleaving Enzymes and Phosphatases

A number of different enzymes attack nucleic acids. Systematically they are all classified as hydrolases, subgroup phosphodiesterases. Furthermore, a few mono-esterases (cleaving only phosphomonoesters, i.e. mononucleotides) and nucleo-sidases will be mentioned.

**Deoxyribonucleases.** The enzyme from the pancreas has been studied best and has been crystallized; its molecular weight is 60,000; the pH optimum is around 6.0 to 7.0. It splits the 3'-phosphoester bond, freeing oligonucleotides. There remain also some nondialyzable, large fragments.

The spleen and other tissues contain an enzyme which splits the other bond, the 5'-phosphate bond.

**Ribonucleases.** Pancreatic ribonuclease has already been mentioned in the chapter on proteins. Its molecular weight is not very high (13,000), and its amino acid sequence has been unraveled. As an enzyme it has one remarkable property: It is relatively heat stable; solutions may briefly be warmed up to 80°.

Ribonuclease has a very pronounced specificity. It cleaves only those phosphodiester bonds that leave the pyrimidine 3'-phosphates. The first step of enzymic catalysis is transphosphorylation:

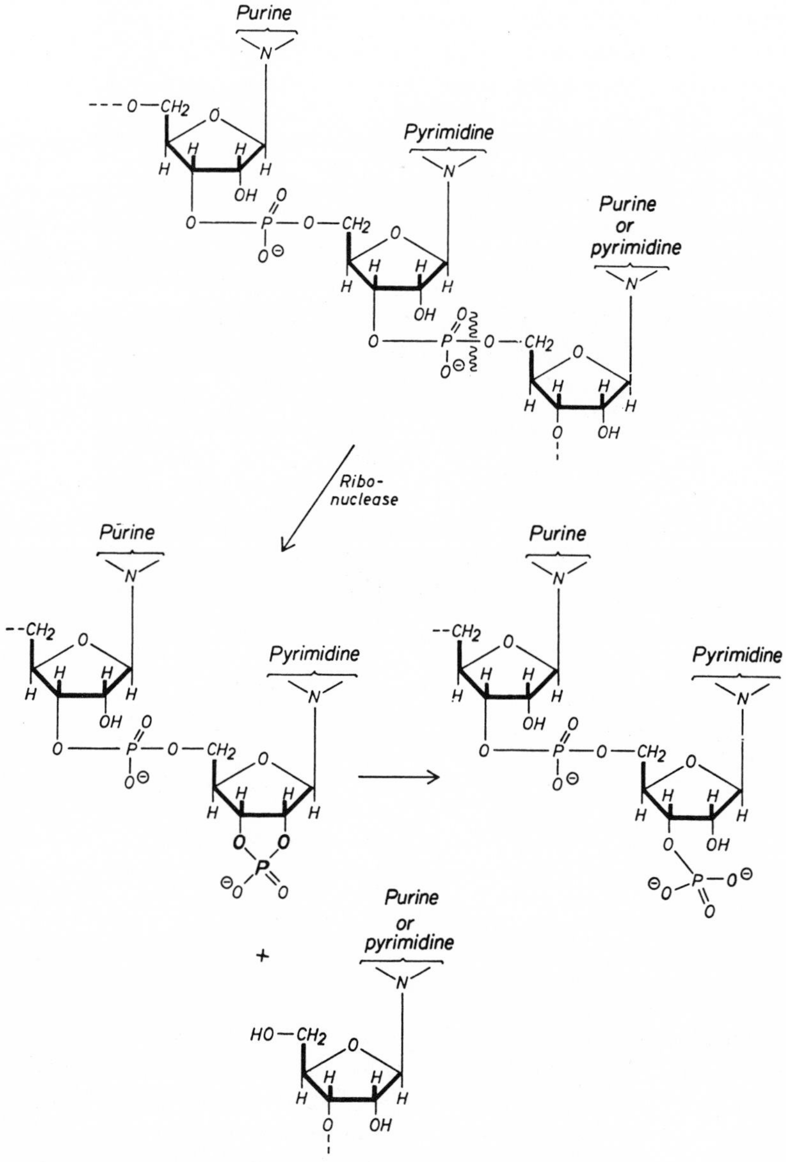

The ester bond going to the C atom 5' is transferred to the 2'-hydroxyl group establishing first a cyclic diester (see also Section 1). This cyclic ester is then hydrolyzed specifically to the 3′-monoester. Purine nucleoside-3′-phosphodiester groups, strangely, are not changed to the cyclic form; they are resistant to ribonucleases. The cleavage products therefore are, in addition to uridine 3′-phosphate and cytidine 3′-phosphate, various oligonucleotides with one pyrimidine nucleoside-3′-phosphate end group.

Besides ribonuclease from the pancreas, enzymes from a mold are known to split specifically at certain purine bases (Egami). This is important for the sequence analysis of nucleic acids.

**Nonspecific Phosphoesterases.** These enzymes cleave a variety of phosphoric acid derivatives, even synthetic substrates and lecithins (diesters of phosphoric acid with glycerol and choline). Such enzymes occur among other places in *snake venom*, and in the intestinal mucosa. Snake venom phosphatases specifically split 3′-phosphate bonds, giving rise to 5′-monophosphates, whereas chemical hydrolysis yields a mixture of the 2′- and 3′-monophosphates. Free 3′-phosphate groups (the monoesters) are inhibitory in the enzymic reaction.

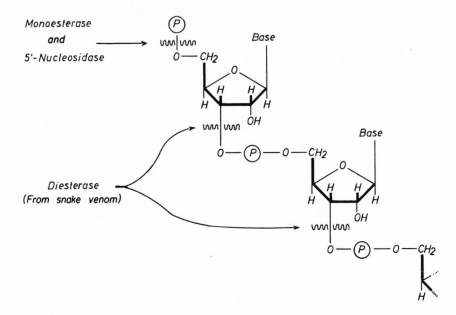

**Phosphomonoesterases.** Enzymes with this specificity are widely distributed. They are simply called "phosphatases;" we usually distinguish acid phosphatases with a pH optimum of about 5 and alkaline phosphatases with a pH optimum around 7 to 8. They split monoesters exclusively, the 3′-monophosphates as well as the 5′-monophosphates. One acid phosphatase occurs in remarkably high concentration in the human prostate gland. The enzyme active at the higher pH is found in the small intestine and in bones where it participates in the formation of bone tissue.

In addition to these enzymes, whose physiological substrates are probably not nucleotides, but more likely sugar phosphates, there exist specific 5'-nucleotidases. One of these enzymes was detected in muscle and in the seminal fluid; it splits optimally in slightly alkaline media (pH 8.5).

**Nucleosidases** are enzymes which cleave the bond between the sugar residue and the base. The cleavage of the nucleoside bond does not go *via* hydrolysis, but through phosphorolysis. Usually orthophosphate is involved, but occasionally pyrophosphate in conjunction with an appropriate enzyme accomplishes the same result, which is equivalent to the reverse of nucleoside synthesis from base and phosphoribosyl pyrophosphate (cf. Section 2).

All the numerous cleavage possibilities listed probably are more significant for research on nucleic acids than for *in vivo* processes. In the cell the decisive role is played by the nucleases that break the high molecular nucleic acids into fragments of oligonucleotide size. These enzymes are able to degrade nucleic acids swiftly and to abolish their biologic activity.

BIBLIOGRAPHY

F. M. Burnet and W. M. Stanley (editors), "The Virsuses," 3 Vols., Academic Press, New York, 1959.
A. Butenandt, On the analysis of hereditary factors and their significance in biochemical problems, *Arbeitsgemeinschaft Forsch. Landes Nordrhein-Westfalen* **62,** (1960).
E. Chargaff and J. N. Davidson (editors), "The Nucleic Acids," 3 vols., Academic Press, New York, 1955 and 1960.
J. N. Davidson, "The Biochemistry of Nucleic Acids," 4th ed., Methuen, London, 1960.
J. R. S. Fincham, Genetically controlled differences in enzyme activity, *Advances in Enzymol.* **22,** 1–44 (1960).
F. Jacob and J. Monod, Genetic regulatory mechanisms in the synthesis of proteins, *J. Mol. Biol.* **3,** 318–356 (1961).
F. Lipmann, Messenger ribonucleic acid, *in* "Progress in Nucleic Acid Research" J. N. Davidson and W. E. Cohn (eds.), Vol. I, pp. 135–161, Academic Press, New York, 1963; also several other pertinent articles in the same volume.
I. D. Raacke, The synthesis of proteins, *in* "Metabolic Pathways" (D. M. Greenberg, ed.), Vol. II, pp. 263–388, Academic Press, New York, 1961.
R. Schweet and J. Bishop, Protein synthesis in relation to gene action, *in* "Molecular Genetics" (J. H. Taylor, editor), Part. I, pp. 353–404, Academic Press, New York, 1963.
G. Stent, "The Molecular Biology of Bacterial Viruses," W. H. Freeman and Co., 1963.
"Synthesis and Structure of Macromolecules," *Cold Spring Harbor Symp. Quant. Biol.* **28,** 610 pp. (1963); held June 1963.

# CHAPTER VIII

# Metabolism of

# Proteins

In the organism, most of the proteins are constantly being built up and broken down again. In man, for example, the biologic half-time of liver proteins amounts to 20–25 days; this is the span of time required to degrade half of the liver protein and replace it with new material. This turnover raises two problems, namely the mechanisms of degradation and of biosynthesis. The latter problem was discussed in Chapt. VII in connection with the function of nucleic acids. The problem of degradation will be treated here, and at the same time the utilization of nutritional proteins will be discussed. Like many animals, man depends on a fairly regular diet of either animal or plant protein; its digestion and utilization will therefore be the focus of our discussion.

Proteolytic enzymes initiate protein degradation whereby amino acids are set free. The amino acids either are used to form new body protein or are broken down further: Nitrogen from the amino acids is transformed to urea, which is excreted as such; the carbon skeletons are oxidized through various intermediate steps to $CO_2$ and $H_2O$.

## 1. Proteolytic Enzymes

Proteases, along with amylases, probably are the most important hydrolytic enzymes. Both have been known for a long time. In systematic nomenclature the proteases would be called C–N hydrolases, since they catalyze the cleavage of peptide bonds, i.e. C—N bonds:

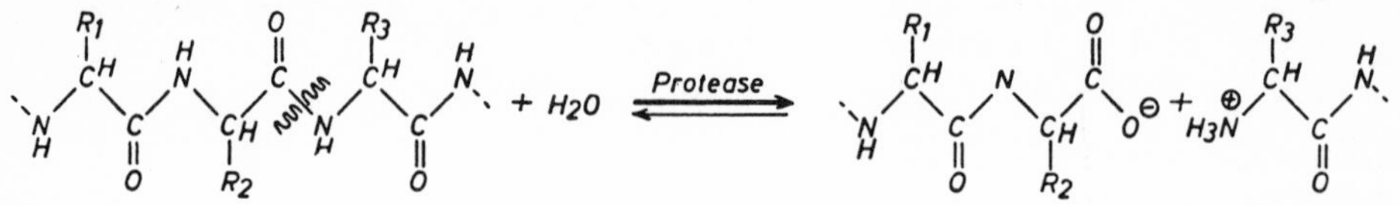

As mentioned in the chapter on peptides (Chapt. III–1), the equilibrium greatly favors cleavage. A coupling to an energy-producing reaction is therefore not necessary. The organism does not appear to make use of the free chemical energy of hydrolysis; it is lost as heat.

Some proteases function as digestive enzymes. They usually occur extracellularly, in the gastro-intestinal tract, but some animals secrete proteases to the outside of their bodies. Intracellularly occurring proteases have been studied relatively little; they are called *cathepsins*.

**Classification of Proteases.** All peptide-cleaving enzymes are divided customarily into endopeptidases and exopeptidases, according to their specific mode of action. *Exopeptidases* are so called because they attack peptide chains only at the ends, in other words, they remove terminal amino acids only. A further distinction is made between *carboxypeptidases* acting on the carboxyl end and *aminopeptidases* acting on the amino end of the chains. The preferred substrates for exopeptidases are smaller protein fragments, oligopeptides and polypeptides; hence they are also called simply "peptidases."

*Endopeptidases* split proteins at certain points along the chain and do not usually attack its end. Consequently, they tend to act on proteins and higher polypeptides and are also called proteinases. The well-known digestive enzymes pepsin, trypsin, and chymotrypsin belong to this group. Several important proteases are listed in Table XI.

TABLE XI

PROTEOLYTIC ENZYMES

| | | Occurrence | pH Optimum | Specific for |
|---|---|---|---|---|
| Endopeptidases | Pepsin | Stomach[a] | 1.5–2.5 | x$\overset{\downarrow}{-}$Phe$\overset{\downarrow}{-}$x, x$\overset{\downarrow}{-}$Tyr$\overset{\downarrow}{-}$x, —Leu$\overset{\downarrow}{-}$Glu— |
| | Trypsin | Small intestine[b] | 7.5–8.5 | Lys$\overset{\downarrow}{-}$x, Arg$\overset{\downarrow}{-}$x |
| | Chymotrypsin | Small intestine[b] | 7.5–8.5 | Phe$\overset{\downarrow}{-}$x, Tyr$\overset{\downarrow}{-}$x |
| | Cathepsin | Intracellular and stomach | 5.0–6.0 | — |
| | Papain | Plants | 5 | — |
| Exopeptidases | Carboxypeptidase | Small intestine[b] | | Terminal —COO$^-$ |
| | Aminopeptidase | Intestinal mucosa | | Terminal —NH$_3^+$ |
| | Dipeptidase | Intestinal mucosa | | Dipeptides |

[a] Formed as proenzyme in the gastric mucosa.
[b] Formed as proenzyme in the pancreas.

**Specificity of Proteases.** Some proteases are not strictly specific for peptide linkages; they can also hydrolyze amino acid esters, which are unnatural substrates. Intact proteins are less easily hydrolyzed than denatured ones.

Endopeptidases cleave the peptide chain only at specific points, determined by the kind of amino acid residue. In Table XI, this is indicated by the column headed "specific for." The specificity of trypsin is particularly striking. It cleaves only lysyl and arginyl bonds in such a way that all resulting peptides have either lys or arg as their carboxy terminal amino acid (except for the peptide that carries the original terminal carboxyl group). Pepsin is somewhat less specific; though bonds with aromatic or acidic amino acids are split preferentially, the neighboring amino acid residues seem to have an influence, too. For example, in insulin one leu-val bond is split; another is not. This bond is not hydrolyzed in synthetic substrates.

Exopeptidases, as the name indicates, attack only the ends of a peptide chain: Carboxypeptidase attacks the carboxyl end, with a preference for some amino acids (see below); amino-peptidase, the amino end. The first group of exopeptidases evidently requires, beside the peptide bonds, a negative charge; the second group requires, beside the peptide bonds, a positive charge. Lastly, there are also dipeptidases, which need both charges and cleave only dipeptides.

The specificity of the various proteolytic enzymes was established with synthetic substrates, namely peptides or substituted peptides. Only through use of these compounds was it possible to devise unambiguous experiments. Much later it became possible to check the results on proteins or polypeptides of known constitution, e.g. insulin or ribonuclease. The check actually revealed a few deviations from the rules established earlier.

## 2. Endopeptidases

The endopeptidases of the gastro-intestinal tract are synthesized in the form of inactive enzyme precursors (zymogens). The active digestive enzymes are released from the zymogens after certain (usually proteolytic) conversions have occurred.

**Pepsin** is the protein-cleaving enzyme of the stomach. The precursor, *pepsinogen*, is formed by the gastric mucosa. It is a protein with a molecular weight of 42,600 which has been obtained in crystalline form. In an acidic medium, or by the action of pepsin itself, the zymogen is converted to the active enzyme. This conversion reaction is autocatalytic, because the catalyst, pepsin, appears as the reaction product. Nevertheless, it passes through an inactive intermediate step, a pepsin-inhibitor complex:

1. Pepsinogen $\xrightarrow{\text{acid or pepsin}}$ pepsin-inhibitor complex + 5 peptides
   42,600                                           37,600                          5000

2. Pepsin-inhibitor $\underset{\text{neutral}}{\overset{\text{acid}}{\rightleftarrows}}$ pepsin + inhibitor
   complex                      34,500    3100

3. Inhibitor $\xrightarrow{\hspace{2cm}}$ 4 peptides

Active pepsin was crystallized by Northrop. It is a protein with a molecular weight of 34,500, whose isoelectric point is unusually low (below 1). A phosphoric acid residue in the molecule, although dispensable for the catalytic action, is responsible for the very low pI. Pepsin has optimal activity at the acidity of the gastric juice (for pH optimum see Table XI).

The product of hydrolysis is commonly a mixture of polypeptides, formerly called *"peptones."* The term has now been abandoned because the substances are ill-defined (the term persists, however, in describing one component of bacterial growth media). On the average, about 10% of the peptide bonds are broken. The peptides have molecular weights ranging between 600 and 3000, depending on the duration of the digestion.

**Cathepsin** is a generic term for those proteases that are active at nearly neutral pH (5–7). They are usually found inside of cells, but the occurrence in the stomach of at least one cathepsin seems to be substantiated. Intracellular proteases have not been studied as carefully as digestive enzymes because they exist in the tissue only in low concentrations. They are usually localized in the lysosomes (cf. Chapt. XIX–2).

**Papain** is a plant protease obtained from the fruit of the papaya tree. The enzyme has been prepared from the commercial product. In its specificity it resembles pepsin and chymotrypsin, but it reacts optimally at neutral pH.

**Trypsin** is formed in the intestine from the product of the pancreatic cells, *trypsinogen*. This proenzyme or zymogen is converted by a peptidase of the small intestine, *enterokinase*, into the active enzyme trypsin. Trypsin itself has the same effect:

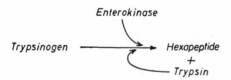

Pure trypsinogen is very unstable, because conversion in trace amounts allows the reaction rate to increase autocatalytically. During activation, the hexapeptide Val—Asp—Asp—Asp—Asp—Lys is split off. The transition can be represented schematically, showing the exposure of the active group. Whether the indicated reorientation of the molecule really takes place is not known with certainty.

In both animal and plant tissue there are proteins which inhibit trypsin. They adhere to the enzyme, but are not cleaved, and block the reaction with other substrates.

Crystalline trypsin has a molecular weight of 24,000 and acts optimally at pH values between 7 and 9, i.e. in weakly alkaline media. As mentioned, it acts on lysyl and arginyl bonds of peptide chains and hydrolyzes even esters and amides.

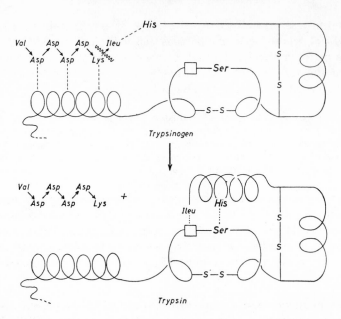

The reactive site on trypsin contains a serine residue. The sequence of amino acids known at present is:

—Asp—Ser—Cys—Glu—Gly—Gly—Asp—Ser—Gly—Pro—Val—Cys—Ser—Gly—
        S···                            ★                      S···

At ★ an inhibitor can be attached (e.g. diisopropylfluorophosphate); it marks the active site.

There is not yet any explanation why just the ★-labeled serine residue should show this special activity. Perhaps the neighboring disulfide bridge (Cys—S; Chapt. II-2) and proline bring the serine residue into proximity of a histidine residue which participates in the catalysis. The mechanism of the cleavage is discussed in detail in Chapt. V-8. The carboxyl group of lysine or arginine, forms an ester linkage with the hydroxyl of serine. By this esterification, the peptide bond is cleaved. Hydrolysis of the ester liberates the other cleavage product and regenerates the active enzyme.

Native proteins are attacked by trypsin much more slowly than denatured ones. The intact secondary structure effectively protects against proteolysis.

Chymotrypsin is formed in the pancreas, just as is trypsin, in the form of inactive *chymotrypsinogen*. Activation is performed by trypsin. The process runs through a series of intermediates which are also enzymically active. As shown in the diagram on page 149, the activation amounts to a double scission of a cyclic peptide, eliminating two dipeptides in the process.

The active site of chymotrypsin strongly resembles that of trypsin: Again there is a catalytically active serine residue which reacts with the inhibitor diisopropyl-fluorophosphate and whose immediate vicinity exhibits the same amino acid

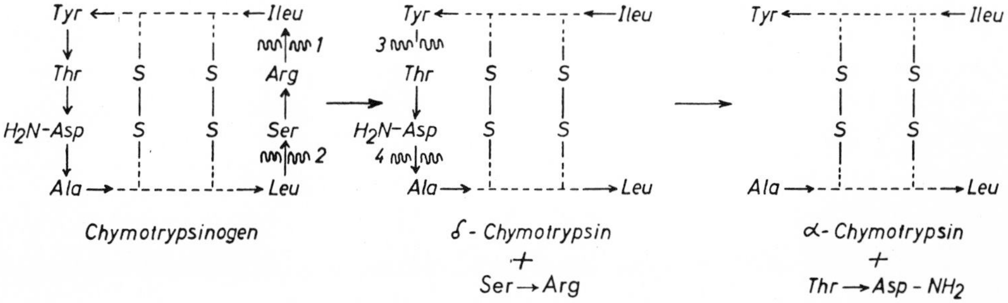

Chymotrypsinogen　　　　δ - Chymotrypsin　　　　α - Chymotrypsin
　　　　　　　　　　　　　　　　+　　　　　　　　　　　　+
　　　　　　　　　　　　Ser→Arg　　　　　　　Thr→Asp - NH₂

sequence as that in trypsin. The mechanism of the catalysis is discussed above, under trypsin. The different specificity—preferred cleavage at aromatic groups—must be due to the more distant environment of the active site. It would be extremely interesting to know precisely the complete sequence and, above all, the secondary and tertiary structure of the enzyme, so that conclusions about the catalytic function could be drawn.

**Rennin** is also found in the stomach. Its substrate is the casein of milk, which is converted by the enzyme to insoluble paracasein. This conversion is only a mild hydrolysis, which can be catalyzed just as well by pepsin, trypsin, and other proteases. For this reason, the very existence of rennin has been doubted periodically. However, rennin has now been obtained in crystalline form from the gastric juice of calves. For the calf at least, its existence has thus been established.

## 3. Exopeptidases and Dipeptidases

The other hydrolases of the gastro-intestinal tract, which prefer to act on smaller peptides, were formerly thought to be one homogeneous enzyme ("erepsin"). In fact, however, "erepsin" is a mixture of very many peptidases.

**Carboxypeptidases** may be found in the kidney and spleen, but occur in the digestive juice in particularly large amounts. One carboxypeptidase has been purified to the crystalline stage; it has a molecular weight of 34,000 and contains zinc. It is secreted from the pancreas in the form of an inactive precursor (procarboxypeptidase) with a molecular weight of 90,000.

The specificity of the enzyme reminds one of that of chymotrypsin: The end groups that are left exposed after the action of chymotrypsin are split off especially easily. Recently, a second carboxypeptidase has been discovered which splits off carboxy-terminal basic amino acids. It is therefore capable of degrading peptides which arose from tryptic action. Carboxypeptidases can remove terminal amino acids from proteins as well. Thus they have found use in protein chemistry for end group analysis.

**Aminopeptidases.** There probably is a large number of peptidases with this speci-ficity. Leucyl aminopeptidase has been studied especially well. It attacks leucyl peptides very rapidly, but its specificity is not very strict; many different peptides are split and the enzyme has been used successfully to identify amino terminal residues in proteins.

**Dipeptidases** hydrolyze, as implied by the name, only dipeptides. Here too, differ-ent enzymes must be distinguished. We should mention glycyl-glycine dipep-tidase, prolinase (prolyl peptide cleaving), and prolidase (aminoacyl proline cleav-ing).

These peptidases contain bivalent metal ions or require addition of such ions for full activity. It is assumed that metal complexes (chelates) form and change the electronic configuration; or, alternatively, the metal ion reacts with a carbonyl group and loosens up the bond in this way.

## 4. Outline of the Metabolism of Amino Acids

The cooperation of endopeptidases, which break the proteins at certain places into large fragments, and of exopeptidases, which hydrolyze these fragments further, results in a mixture of amino acids which then is absorbed and allowed to enter the bloodstream. Part of the amino acids is used to build new endogenous pro-teins. A large part, however, is degraded further. The following are the possible metabolic pathways:

a. Alteration of the side chains while maintaining the $\alpha$-amino-carboxylic acid grouping.
b. Decarboxylation.
c. Transamination to $\alpha$-keto acids.
d. Oxidative deamination to $\alpha$-keto acids.

In the reaction paths a to c, the cofactor is usually pyridoxal phosphate. Accord-ing to chemical electron theory all these reactions may be derived from one common intermediate, a Schiff's base.

The illustration shows first how a Schiff's base arises between the amino acid and pyridoxal phosphate. The electron-attracting effect of the positively charged N atom in the pyridine ring favors one of the contributing resonance structures. But this structure is realized only when one substituent is eliminated as a cation from the $\alpha$-C atom of the amino acid. That could be the group R (reaction path a, taken only in special cases, e.g. with serine; cf. Section 12) or the C atom of the carboxyl group (reaction path b; decarboxylation). In the second case, the resonating inter-mediate state is stabilized further by the addition of a proton to the $\alpha$-C atom and concomitant hydrolysis of the Schiff's base to form a primary amine. Third—and usually—the eliminated sub-stituent can be the hydrogen on the $\alpha$-C atom; the loss of the proton aids the shift of the double bond to the $\alpha$-C atom and the resulting intermediate is hydrolyzed to the $\alpha$-keto acid and pyri-doxamine phosphate. This is reaction c, a transfer of the amino group to the coenzyme with a simultaneous exchange of levels of oxidation (univalent for bivalent).

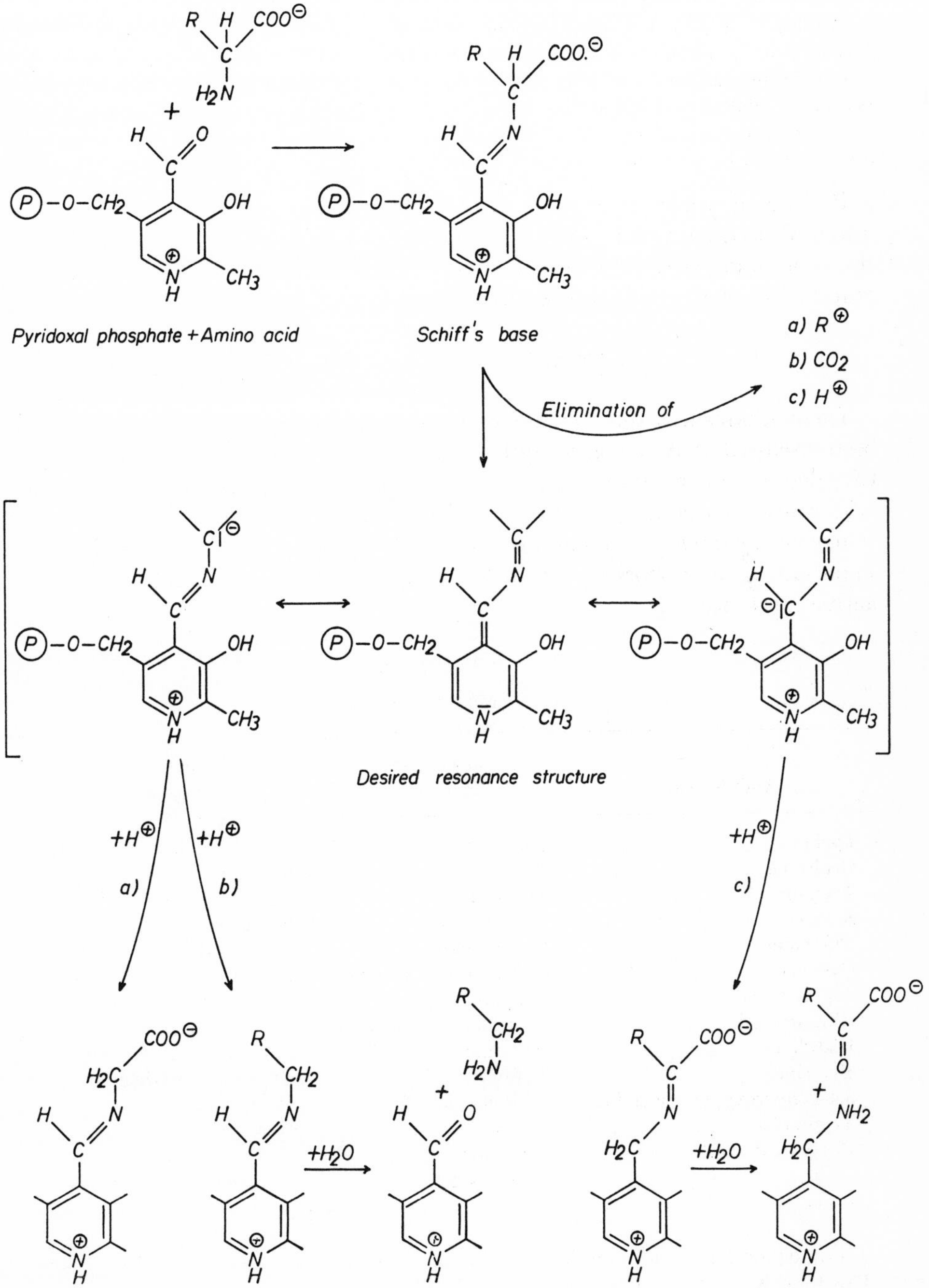
Pyridoxal phosphate + Amino acid
Schiff's base
Elimination of
a) $R^{\oplus}$
b) $CO_2$
c) $H^{\oplus}$
Desired resonance structure
$+H^{\oplus}$ a)
$+H^{\oplus}$ b)
$+H^{\oplus}$ c)
$+H_2O$
$+H_2O$

After the loss of a $H^+$ from the $\alpha$-C atom, stabilization can also be attained by eliminating $X^-$ from the $\beta$-C atom and forming a double bond. In nonenzymic model experiments *serine* and *cysteine* react according to this scheme of "$\alpha$, $\beta$-elimination" to produce aminoacrylic acid and eventually pyruvic acid and $NH_3$. And in bacterial metabolism, *tryptophan* is degraded in this fashion to indole + pyruvic acid + $NH_3$.

In higher plants we find metabolic reactions of much greater complexity; for example, amino acids enter the synthesis of alkaloids.

Reaction d, which takes place without the participation of pyridoxal phosphate, also leads to $\alpha$-keto acids. Both reactions c and d are most important for the breakdown of amino acids and the metabolism of nitrogen. But before considering this reaction, we shall briefly discuss decarboxylation.

## 5. Decarboxylation of Amino Acids

The mechanism of this enzymic reaction, catalyzed by pyridoxal phosphate, has been discussed above as pathway b (Section 4). The net result is the production of $CO_2$ and a primary amine, whose formula can easily be derived from the amino acid which was decarboxylated. Amines of this type are called biogenic amines (Guggenheim); many of them possess a strong pharmacologic effect, and others are important as precursors of hormones and as components of coenzymes and other active substances.

TABLE XII

BIOGENIC AMINES

| Amino Acid | Decarboxylation Product | Occurrence and Significance |
|---|---|---|
| Lysine | Cadaverine | Ribosomes, bacteria |
| Ornithine | Putrescine | Ribosomes, bacteria |
| Arginine | Agmatine | Bacteria (intestinal flora) |
| Serine | Ethanolamine | Phosphatides |
| Threonine | Propanolamine | Vitamin $B_{12}$ |
| Cysteine | $\beta$-Mercaptoethylamine | Coenzyme A |
| Aspartic acid | $\beta$-Alanine | Coenzyme A, pantothenic acid |
| Glutamic acid | $\gamma$-Aminobutyric acid | Brain (ganglia inhibitor) |
| Histidine | Histamine | Effective on blood pressure |
| Tyrosine | Tyramine | Uterus contracting |
| 3,4-Dihydroxyphenylalanine | ($\rightarrow$Epinephrine) | ($\rightarrow$Hormone) |
| Tryptophan | Tryptamine | Hormone (?) |
| (5-Hydroxytryptophan) | Serotonin ($\rightarrow$Melatonin) | Tissue hormone (Hormone) |

The occurrence and significance of some biogenic amines are listed in Table XII. The biogenic amines derived from aromatic amino acids are of both pharmacologic and physiological interest. They will be discussed in Chapt. XX, because of their close relationship to hormones.

Amino acid decarboxylases are especially common in bacteria; their biologic significance there is unclear. The enzymes are usually specific for one amino acid, and more particularly for the L form.

Some of the "bacterial" biogenic amines have recently enjoyed renewed interest: *Cadaverine* (from lysine) and *putrescine* (from ornithine) have been found in ribosomes (cf. Chapt. XIX-2). Decarboxylation of serine gives rise to *ethanolamine* (or aminoethanol), a regular component of phosphatides and the parent substance of choline. The analogous compound containing sulfur, called *β-mercaptoethylamine* (or cysteamine), occurs in coenzyme A, where it is the carrier of the reactive SH group. In the pantothenic-acid part of coenzyme A there is *β-alanine* (the decarboxylation product of aspartic acid). Vitamin $B_{12}$ contains *propanolamine* (or aminopropanol from threonine). It is possible that *γ-Aminobutyric* acid, derived from glutamic acid, plays a role in brain function (cf. Chapt. XX-12).

## 6. Transamination

The amino groups of many, if not all, amino acids react identically. They are transferred by transaminases to the prosthetic group, *pyridoxal phopshate*. The diagram shows the reaction with alanine as an example; for the mechanism of the reaction see Section 4.

By changing the level of oxidation one obtains pyridoxamine (which remains bound to the enzyme) and an α-keto acid containing the same carbon skeleton as

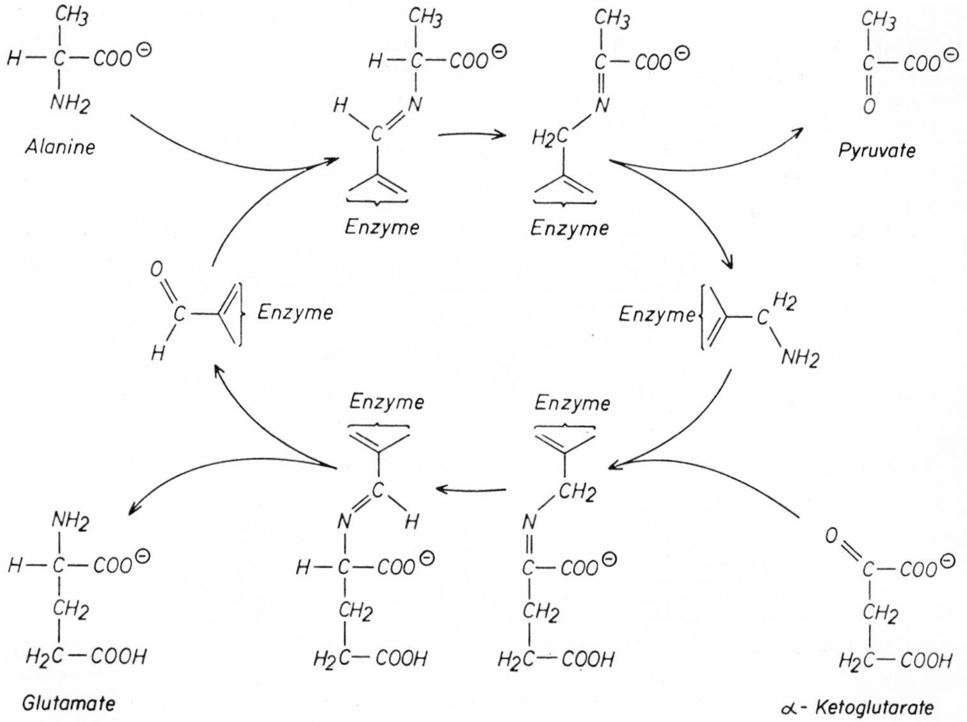

Alanine Pyruvate

Enzyme

Glutamate α-Ketoglutarate

the amino acid (upper half of diagram). Further degradation of the keto acid leads eventually to a common metabolic pool. These catabolic steps, differing for each individual amino acid, will be discussed later (Section 9).

Pyridoxal phosphate is regenerated from pyridoxamine phosphate in a reaction with a keto acid; α-keto glutarate and oxaloacetate are very effective $NH_2$ acceptors (lower half of diagram). Evidently glutamate (or aspartate) is produced in the process, and the significance of transamination reactions rests primarily on the fact that nitrogen is passed on from here, i.e. from glutamate or aspartate to the final excretion product, urea (cf. Section 8).

From glutamate the reverse path is also possible: With α-keto acids from other sources the corresponding amino acids and α-ketoglutarate can be formed[1] (the above diagram in reverse). The organism is able in this way to synthesize several amino acids: alanine out of pyruvate, serine out of hydroxypyruvate, and, of course, the two dicarboxylic acids already mentioned, glutamic and aspartic acid.

For a number of amino acids, however, neither the proper α-keto acids nor any other suitable precursors are available. These amino acids must be supplied to the organism and hence are called *essential* or *indispensable amino acids* (cf. also "Nutrition," Chapt. XXII). The list of indispensable amino acids varies somewhat for different animals. For man they are:

|            |            |               |
|------------|------------|---------------|
| valine     | lysine     | phenylalanine |
| leucine    | methionine | tryptophan    |
| isoleucine | threonine  |               |

The rat requires, in addition, histidine. Arginine, proline, serine, tyrosine, and cystine stimulate growth. Although the organism can synthesize them, it apparently cannot supply them fast enough to have optimal amounts available for the very intensive synthesis of protein which occurs during growth.

Plants and many microorganisms can make all the amino acids. Ultraviolet radiation followed by selection, permits the isolation of mutants of microorganisms (bacteria, yeasts, molds) which have lost the capacity to synthesize certain amino acids and thus have become auxotrophic[2] with respect to these particular amino acids. Biochemical mutants have acquired great significance and value for genetics and biochemistry; many biosynthetic pathways have been elucidated through the study of such mutants (cf. also Chapt. VII-6, XVI-5).

## 7. Oxidative Deamination

Besides transamination, there is another way to produce α-keto acids, namely oxidative deamination. Here two hydrogen atoms are probably removed to produce an imino acid, which is then hydrolyzed to ammonia and a keto acid:

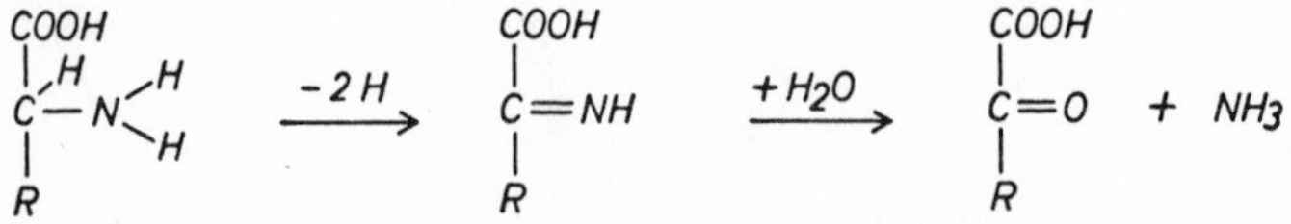

$$
\begin{array}{ccccc}
COOH & & COOH & & COOH \\
| & & | & & | \\
C-N\underset{H}{\overset{H}{<}}^H & \xrightarrow{-2H} & C=NH & \xrightarrow{+H_2O} & C=O \ + \ NH_3 \\
| & & | & & | \\
R & & R & & R
\end{array}
$$

---

[1] The transition of amino acids into keto acids and back had already been discovered by Knoop as early as 1910 from feeding experiments and later was corroborated by model reactions. Transamination was discovered by Braunstein; the role of pyridoxal phosphate by Gunsalus.

[2] A strain is called auxotrophic for a certain substance if that substance must be provided before the strain can grow.

Hydrogen is accepted at first by the prosthetic group of the enzyme, a flavin nucleotide. Amino acid oxidases therefore belong to the group of yellow enzymes. They transfer hydrogen to molecular oxygen, forming hydrogen peroxide; for this reason they are called *amino acid oxidases*. However, in addition to the reaction with oxygen, there should be other ways of reoxidizing the flavin group.

Some oxidases are specific for D-amino acids and others oxidize only the L-form. The physiological significance of the former is not known, since D-amino acids practically never appear in the organism. The one L-amino acid oxidase which was purified from rat kidneys contains *flavin mononucleotide* and has a remarkably small turnover number: One enzyme molecule acts on only six molecules per minute. It is very doubtful, therefore, whether it has a significant role in amino acid metabolism.

A specific L-glutamate dehydrogenase is, however, quite important. It catalyzes a similar type of reaction, but transfers hydrogen to nicotinamide-adenine dinucleotide. The reaction can be expressed as follows:

$$\text{Glutamate} + \text{NAD} + H_2O = NH_3 + \alpha\text{-ketoglutarate} + NADH_2$$

The reduced nicotinamide coenzyme can then transfer its hydrogen to numerous other systems. The ammonia is apparently used in urea formation.

## 8. Urea Cycle

With the formation of $NH_3$ in the dehydrogenation of glutamate nothing appears to have been gained, since ammonia is an unsuitable form for the excretion of nitrogen. Only animals living in water, crabs and some fishes, are able to excrete ammonia directly through their gills. Ammonia, a cellular poison even at relatively low concentrations, is converted by higher organisms to *urea* through a cyclic process.

The net reaction is endergonic:

$$HCO_3^{\ominus} + NH_4^{\oplus} + NH_3 \quad = \quad O = C \Big\langle {}^{NH_2}_{NH_2} + 2H_2O;$$

$$\Delta F^\circ = 3.54 \text{ kcal/mole} \qquad \Delta F_{\text{physiol}} \cong 14 \text{ kcal/mole}$$

Thus, at physiological concentrations (for the dependence of $\Delta F$ on concentration, cf. Chapt. V-2, 5), the net expenditure of energy amounts to about 14 kcal/mole. We are led to suspect, therefore, that energy-rich intermediates may participate.

The most important energy-rich intermediate is *carbamyl phosphate* (Lipmann) which arises according to the following equations:

$$NH_3 + CO_2 \rightleftharpoons H_2N - C \Big\langle {}^{O}_{OH}$$

$$H_2N - C \Big\langle {}^{O}_{OH} + ATP \rightleftharpoons H_2N - C {}^{O}\!\!- O - \text{P} + ADP$$

The first reaction occurs spontaneously; carbonic anhydrase greatly accelerates the attainment of equilibrium. The second reversible reaction is catalyzed by the enzyme *carbamyl phosphate kinase*, which is found in bacteria. In the liver of mammals, the process is more complicated; it requires another cofactor, namely N-acetyl glutamate, which forms "active carbon dioxide" with $CO_2$ and the consumption of 1 mole ATP. The —COOH group is bound presumably to the N atom, in analogy to carboxy-biotin (Chapt. VI-5). The active carbon dioxide unites with an ammonium ion, with the aid of another ATP, to form carbamyl phosphate. The enzyme system binds $NH_4^+$ even at very low concentrations ($10^{-4}\ M$); it does not bind substituted amino groups (as in amino acids, glutamine, etc.). Suggestions that the formation of free ammonia is avoided have not been born out experimentally. A considerable portion of the ammonia probably arises from the dehydrogenation of glutamate (see Section 7); glutamic acid thus assumes a key role in the metabolism of amino acids.

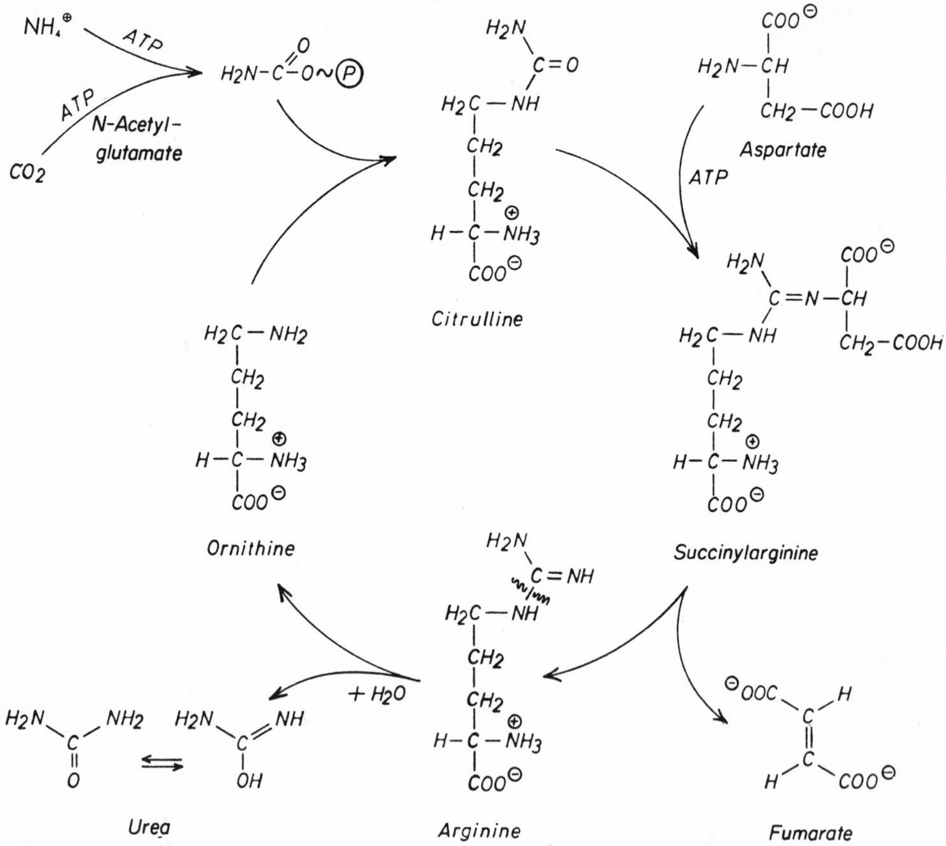

Carbamyl phosphate then reacts with the δ-amino group of *ornithine* to produce *citrulline* (ureidovaleric acid), and citrulline is transformed in two steps to *arginine*. The $NH_2$ group necessary for this is provided by aspartate which, with the consumption of 1 mole ATP and the cooperation of a "condensing enzyme," joins with citrulline to give argininosuccinate. A further enzyme helps to break the intermediate product into arginine and fumarate and, finally, arginine is cleaved by the well-known enzyme *arginase* into urea and ornithine. Urea is actually formed in its tautomeric form, iso-urea, but it rearranges spontaneously. This closes the cycle. Ornithine is then ready to accept another carbamyl phosphate.

In summary, 2 $NH_3$ (from glutamate and aspartate) join with $CO_2$ to give urea; in the process 3 moles of ATP are consumed. The formation of urea is, therefore, from an energy viewpoint, a luxury in which the cell apparently indulges in order to escape the deleterious effect of high concentrations of free ammonia.

## 9. Fate of the Carbon Skeleton of Amino Acids

The $\alpha$-keto acids arising from transamination are shunted into general metabolism and eventually are burned to $CO_2$ and $H_2O$. Since we will not study the final catabolic steps of all the other foodstuffs until later (Chapt. XI and XII), we will consider here catabolism only to the points where common intermediates are formed.

These common intermediates are, first, saturated monocarboxylic acids (often arising in their activated form, bound to coenzyme A); second, pyruvate and hydroxypyruvate; and, third, the $C_4$-dicarboxylic acids: succinate, fumarate, and oxaloacetate.

But first we will briefly discuss *acetoacetate*, a $C_4$ compound which is a pathologic constituent of urine. It is one of the "ketone bodies." Those amino acids that can give rise to acetoacetate are called "ketogenic." The *ketogenic* amino acids are *phenylalanine, tyrosine, leucine,* and *isoleucine.*

The rest of the amino acids, which can be broken down to one of the $C_4$-dicarboxylic acids enumerated above or to pyruvate, can be converted to carbohydrate. They are therefore called "glucogenic amino acids." The generation of glucose from amino acids is of considerable physiological importance. Only three carbon atoms of the amino acid are used for the synthesis of glucose. In addition to this conversion (along with the ever-present terminal oxidation to $CO_2$), it is metabolically important to produce from amino acids $C_1$ fragments at the oxidation level of formate or formaldehyde. These $C_1$ fragments arise from serine, glycine, and histidine. Finally, some amino acids are interconvertible, without deamination, merely by changes on the carbon skeleton. Excellent examples of the multiplicity of conversions are provided by the metabolism of serine (see below) and of phenylalanine.

## 10. Degradation to Activated Fatty Acids: Oxidative Decarboxylation

This pathway is followed by alanine, valine, isoleucine, and leucine. The prototype for all is the metabolism of *alanine*, which goes to activated acetate (acetyl-CoA) in two steps. Acetyl-CoA, of course, then can undergo a multitude of reactions. The first step is transamination, yielding in the usual manner the $\alpha$-keto acid, pyruvate. The latter is decarboxylated and at the same time oxidized by a complicated enzyme system (oxidative decarboxylation of the α-keto acid). The cofactors for the reaction are thiamine pyrophosphate, lipoamide, and coenzyme A. In the initial step, $CO_2$ is split out and "active acetaldehyde" is formed (see Chapt. VI-5); it is bound to C atom 2 of the thiazole ring of TPP. In a second step, the aldehyde is transferred to lipoamide, the disulfide ring is opened, and the aldehyde

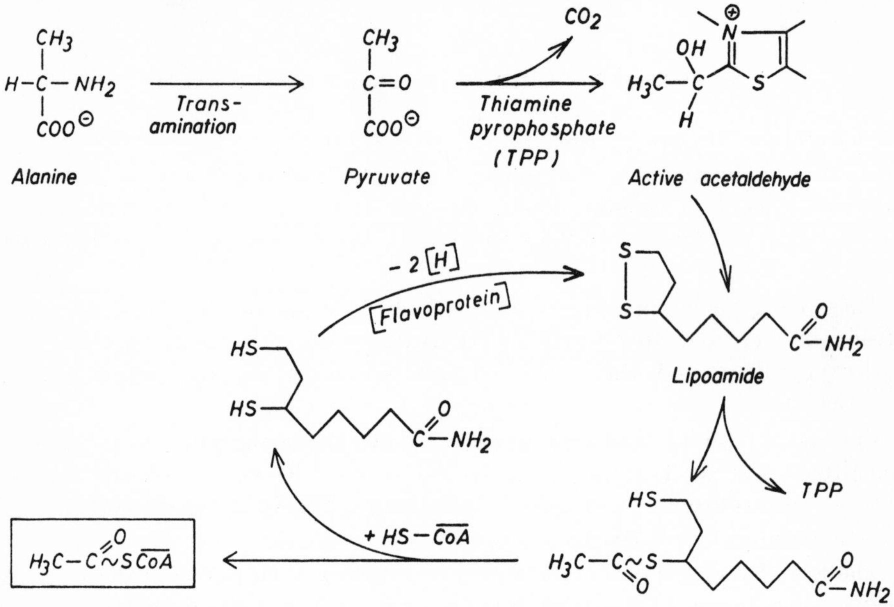

Alanine — Trans-amination → Pyruvate — Thiamine pyrophosphate (TPP) → Active acetaldehyde — Lipoamide — ( − 2 [H], Flavoprotein ) — ( + HS—CoA ) → $H_3C-C\!\!\sim\!\!S\overline{CoA}$

separated into $H_3C$—CO— and —H. This last step is really the oxidizing (more precisely, the dehydrogenating) step, because here lipoamide becomes a derivative of dihydrolipoic acid and the aldehyde actually becomes the derivative of an acid. The free energy of the aldehyde oxidation is retained by the product with the acetyl residue being held in an energy-rich bond (thioester bond); it is then easily transferred to coenzyme A. This is the "activated fatty acid"; in the case of alanine, it is activated acetate, which enters the general metabolic pool. A flavoprotein again dehydrogenates the dihydrolipoamide; the hydrogen then may end up on NAD (cf. Chapt. VI-4 and XI-2).

*Valine, isoleucine,* and *leucine* are degraded in a quite analogous manner. Activated fatty acids shortened by one C atom are treated in metabolism in essentially the same way as ordinary fatty acids. The only problem is raised by amino acids with a methyl group as a side chain of the carbon skeleton. We will discuss their degradation in connection with β-oxidation of fatty acids (Chapt. XII–5). As mentioned already, leucine is converted to acetoacetate, isoleucine partially so. Valine, however, becomes methylmalonate, and is changed further by a rearrangement of the carboxyl group to succinate; the way to the carbohydrates is thereby opened.

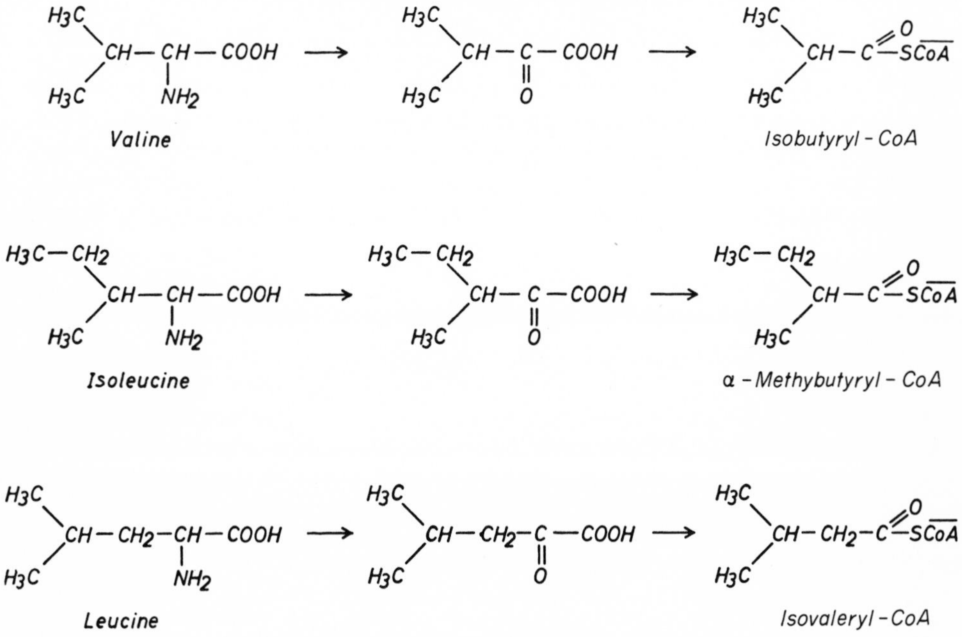

H3C
  \
   CH—CH—COOH  →
  /    |
H3C   NH2

*Valine*

H3C
  \
   CH—C—COOH  →
  /    ‖
H3C   O

H3C
  \
   CH—C≤O—SCoA
  /
H3C

*Isobutyryl - CoA*

H3C—CH2
      \
       CH—CH—COOH  →
      /    |
   H3C    NH2

*Isoleucine*

H3C—CH2
      \
       CH—C—COOH  →
      /    ‖
   H3C    O

H3C—CH2
      \
       CH—C≤O—SCoA
      /
   H3C

*α -Methybutyryl - CoA*

H3C
  \
   CH—CH2—CH—COOH  →
  /         |
H3C        NH2

*Leucine*

H3C
  \
   CH—CH2—C—COOH  →
  /        ‖
H3C        O

H3C
  \
   CH—CH2—C≤O—SCoA
  /
H3C

*Isovaleryl - CoA*

## 11. Metabolism of Aromatic Amino Acids

The aromatic ring is broken down by oxidation. One of the double bonds of a Kekulé structure is forced open enzymically and satisfied with oxygen (for the mechanism see Chapt. X–7). An analogous reaction would be the ozonolysis of benzene.

**Metabolism of Phenylalanine and Tyrosine.** These amino acids are ketogenic. The degradation of phenylalanine first of all yields tyrosine: A powerful oxygenase introduces a hydroxyl group in the para-position of the benzene ring (the oxygen is from air; for the reaction mechanism see Chapt. X–7). If through an inborn error in metabolism (cf. Chapt. VII–6) this step is blocked, then phenylalanine is converted by transamination to *phenylpyruvate* (and phenylacetate), which is excreted in urine. The resultant pathologic condition is *phenylketonuria* which is characterized by feeble-mindedness. A diet low in phenylalanine largely prevents the formation of phenylpyruvate and consequently may avoid feeble-mindedness.

Tyrosine—whether formed from phenylalanine or arising directly from ingested proteins—has various pathways available. Quantitatively, the most important is the degradation to acetoacetate + fumarate; the melanins, the dark hair and skin pigments, also come from tyrosine, as do the hormones epinephrine (Chapt. VIII–5, XX–5) and thyroxine (cf. Chapt. XX–4).

The first of the enumerated pathways proceeds *via* transamination to p-hydroxyphenylpyruvate; then there is oxidation to the quinol and rearrangement (migration of the side chain) to the p-dihydroxy derivative. This seemingly unusual step has analogies in organic chemistry. By oxidative decarboxylation one finally arrives at homogentisic acid, which has been known for a long time. It is excreted by some individuals due to another inborn error of metabolism (*alcaptonuria*).[3]

Normally, homogentisic acid is further oxidized by an oxygenase. The double bond is split open and to each end-carbon atom one oxygen is attached. The resultant compound is maleylacetoacetate which has the *cis*-configuration around

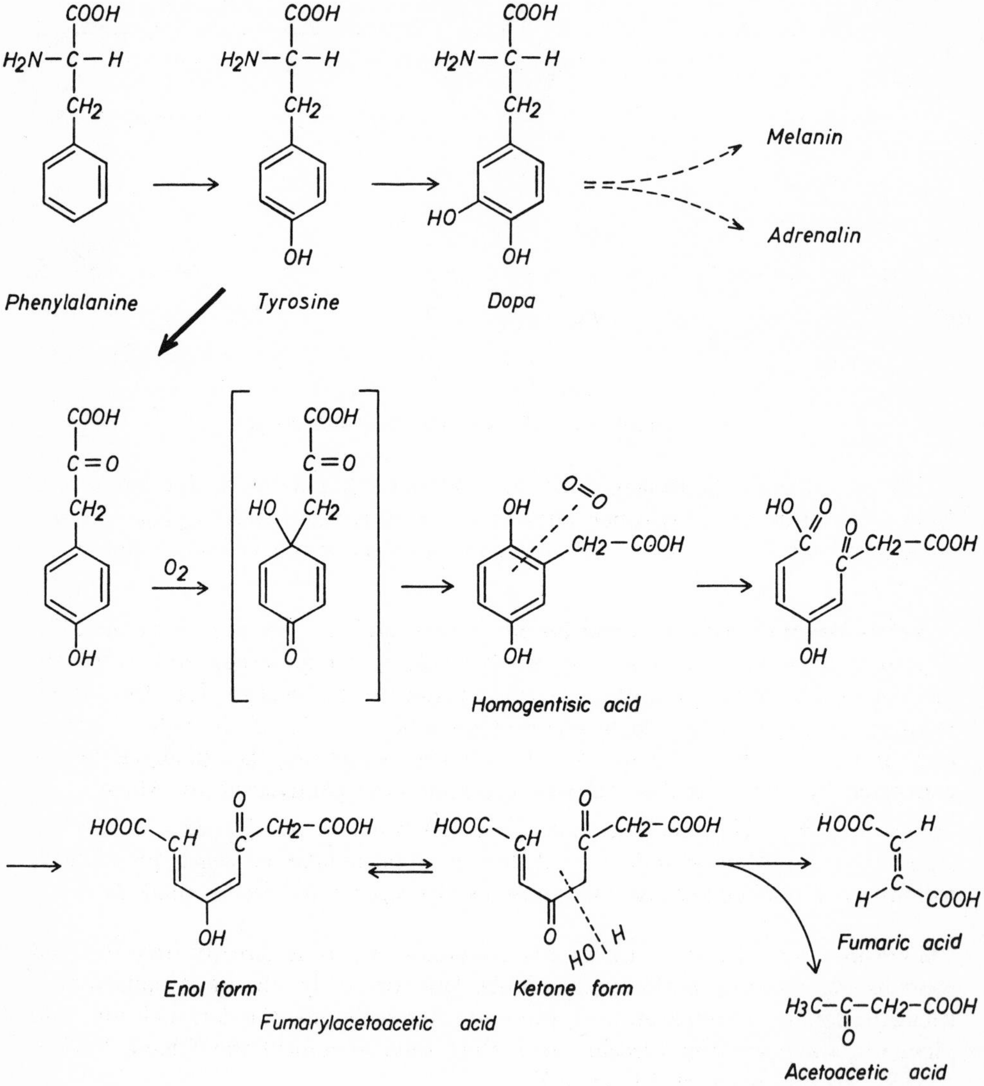

Phenylalanine → Tyrosine → Dopa ⇢ Melanin / Adrenalin

$O_2$ →  [ ] → Homogentisic acid → 

Enol form / Ketone form — Fumarylacetoacetic acid → Fumaric acid / Acetoacetic acid

$H_3C-C-CH_2-COOH$

---

[3] The presence of homogentisic acid in urine is very easily detected because the urine turns black upon standing in air (oxidation to the quinone and condensation to the pigment).

its double bonds. Interestingly enough, an enzyme catalyzes the rearrangement of the *cis*-compound to the *trans*-compound. In this reaction glutathione is a cofactor. The resulting fumarylacetoacetate is hydrolyzed into fumarate and acetoacetate. Tyrosine, therefore, provides four C atoms for acetoacetate and four C atoms for fumarate. The latter might possibly be used for glucose formation, but ultimate oxidation seems more likely.

The steps leading to melanin are of no quantitative significance for the degradation of tyrosine but are of interest because of the biogenesis of that pigment. The whole sequence of reactions is catalyzed by a single enzyme, tyrosinase, and follows essentially the scheme shown here.

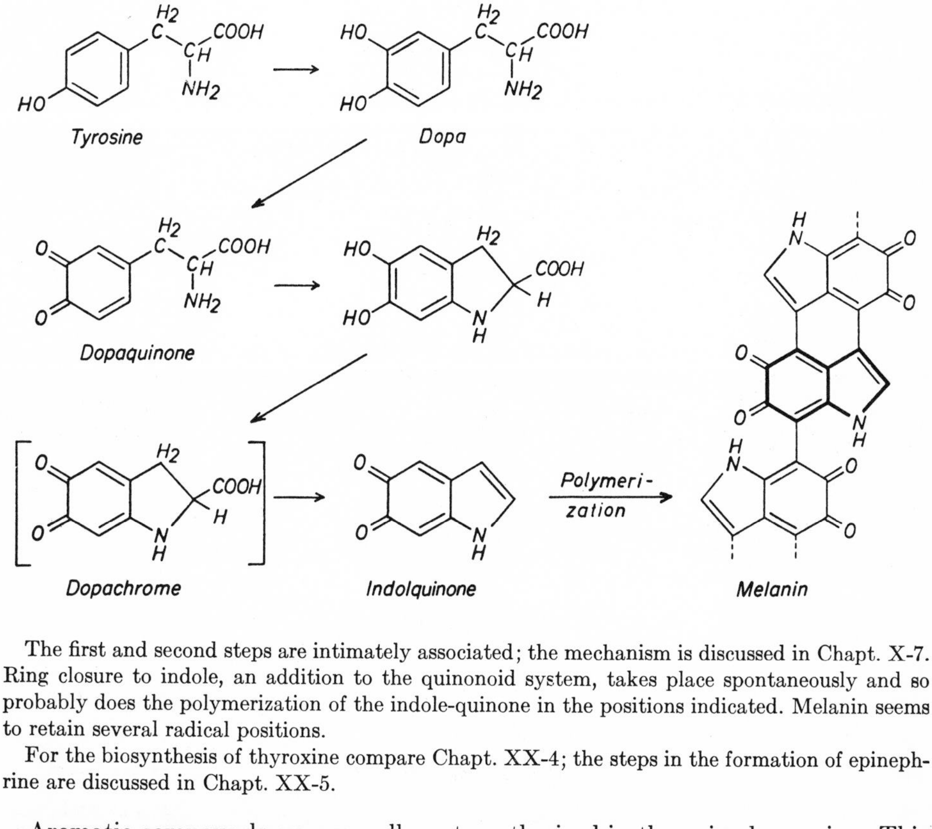

| Tyrosine | Dopa |
| Dopaquinone | |
| Dopachrome | Indolquinone | Melanin |

The first and second steps are intimately associated; the mechanism is discussed in Chapt. X-7. Ring closure to indole, an addition to the quinonoid system, takes place spontaneously and so probably does the polymerization of the indole-quinone in the positions indicated. Melanin seems to retain several radical positions.

For the biosynthesis of thyroxine compare Chapt. XX-4; the steps in the formation of epinephrine are discussed in Chapt. XX-5.

Aromatic compounds are generally not synthesized in the animal organism. This explains the indispensability of phenylalanine. Plants and microorganisms synthesize the aromatic ring out of carbohydrates (cf. Chapt. XVI-5).

**Metabolism of Tryptophan.** The catabolism of tryptophan is interesting since it leads to the biosynthesis of a vitamin, nicotinamide. It appears contradictory to state that a vitamin is formed by an organism, but nicotinamide deficiency can indeed be demonstrated only with the concurrent deficiency of vitamin B$_6$. Tryptophan largely replaces the vitamin even in man.

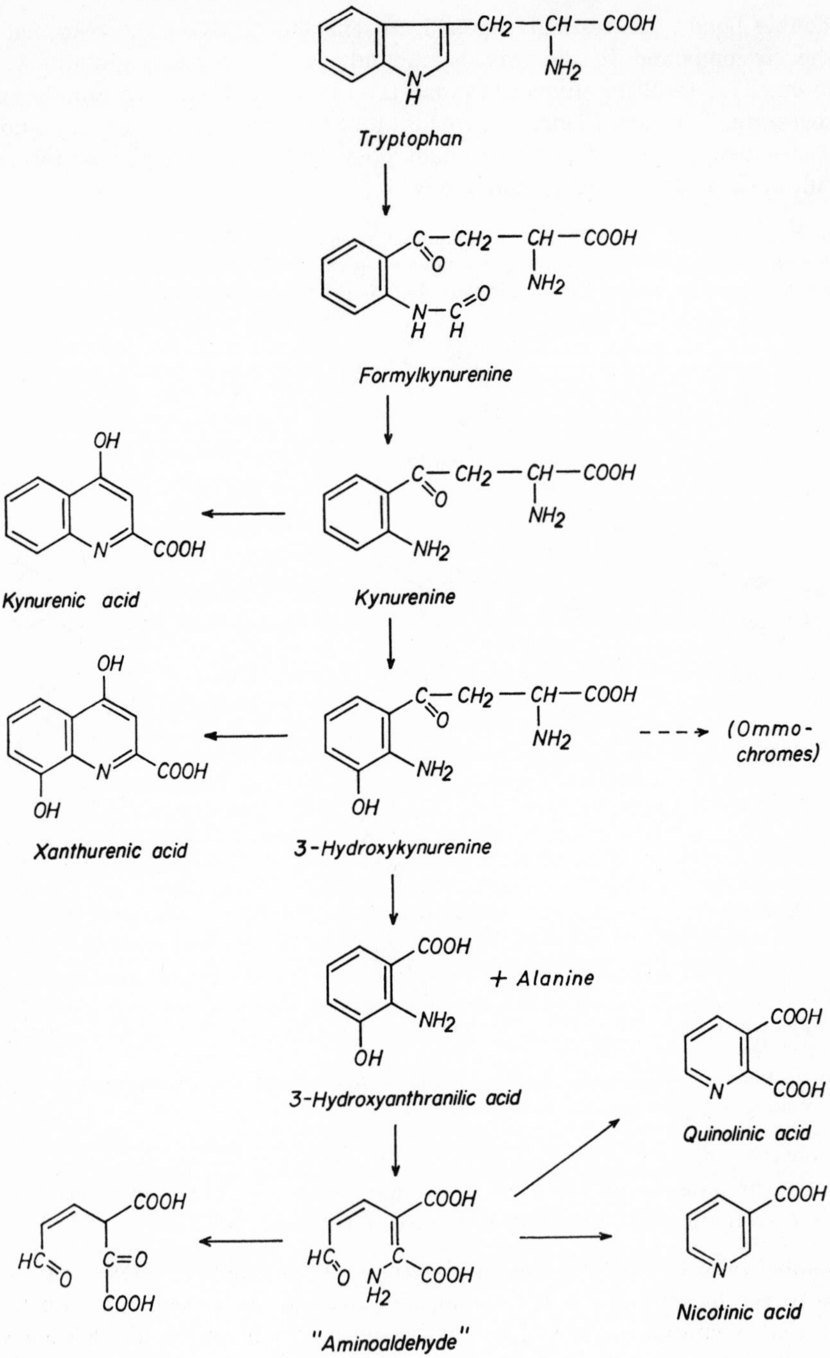

Tryptophan

Formylkynurenine

Kynurenic acid      Kynurenine

Xanthurenic acid      3-Hydroxykynurenine      (Ommo-chromes)

+ Alanine

3-Hydroxyanthranilic acid

Quinolinic acid

"Aminoaldehyde"

Nicotinic acid

The catabolism of tryptophan seems to have many steps in common with the formation of nicotinamide. The amino nitrogen is not attacked initially, but instead the indole ring is opened up by *tryptophan pyrrolase* (an iron-porphyrin enzyme). Just as in other cases of oxidative ring opening (cf. Chapt. X-7), the double bond is split and each new end receives one oxygen atom. In this way *N-formylkynurenine* is formed; it is then hydrolyzed to formate and *kynurenine*.

Kynurenine is oxidized (again by atmospheric oxygen) to yield *3-hydroxykynurenine* and subsequently is cleaved to 3-hydroxyanthranilic acid and alanine. The fate of alanine has already been presented. Sidepaths from kynurenine and 3-hydroxykynurenine lead to *kynurenic acid* and *xanthurenic acid*; this reaction is explained as a transamination followed by spontaneous ring closure.

*3-Hydroxyanthranilic acid* is subjected to another oxidative ring opening adjacent to the hydroxyl group. The unsaturated aldehyde is very unstable and easily condenses with the amino group to close the pyridine ring. Decarboxylation of the dicarboxylic acid (quinolinic acid) produces nicotinic acid; it is not clear whether this decarboxylation occurs simultaneously with ring closure or subsequently.

The formation of nicotinic acid, as important as it is for the synthesis of the two coenzymes nicotinamide-adenine dinucleotide and its phosphate (formulas in Chapt. VI-4), seems to be only a sidepath. The main degradation probably passes from the unstable, unsaturated aminoaldehyde through isomerization to the imino compound and through hydrolysis to the keto compound. The β-decarboxylation of the latter results in an α-keto aldehyde with six C atoms which is further broken down to *glutarate*.

Initially, 3-hydroxykynurenine was not discovered as the intermediate for nicotinic acid formation but rather for ommochrome formation (Butenandt and co-workers). *Ommochromes* are pigments found chiefly among insects and crabs. The simplest representative, *xanthommatine* (formula in Chapt. VII-6) is easy to prepare *in vitro* by careful oxidation of hydroxykynurenine. The synthesis of ommochromes is disrupted in several mutants of the fruitfly *Drosophila* (and other insects); either the transition from tryptophan to kynurenine or its oxidation to hydroxykynurenine is blocked. The pigmentation of insect eyes was one of the first examples of the thesis that hereditary factors control biochemical reactions (cf. Chapt. VII-6). Other examples, even in man, are provided by the metabolism of tyrosine (cf. Chapt. VII-6).

Microorganisms (including intestinal bacteria) break down the side chains of tryptophan. In the process there may be formed indolepyruvate, indoleacetate, skatole (methylindole), and indole itself. Indoleacetate is a plant hormone (*auxin*; Chapt. XX-15).

Tryptophan also can be hydroxylated to *5-hydroxytryptophan*, the parent compound of serotonin (Chapt. XX-12).

## 12. Amino Acids Supplying C₁ Fragments

We must distinguish here between methyl groups provided by methionine, on the one hand, and formaldehyde and formate arising from serine and glycine, on the other hand.

**Methionine and Cysteine Metabolism.** Methyl groups play an important role in the biosynthesis of many substances, and methionine has turned out to be the methyl donor *par excellence*. "Active methyl" arises directly out of methionine and ATP; it is a sulfonium compound (formula in Chapt. VI–5). We shall return to the active methyl group on occasion (cf. also Chapt. VI–5, XIII–2, XX–5), but now will discuss the demethylated methionine. Its name is *homocysteine*, because its carbon chain is longer than that of cysteine by one $CH_2$ group. It can provide the sulfur for cysteine by condensing with serine; the resultant thioether (cystathionine) breaks into homoserine and cysteine (formulas below).

The carbon skeleton of cysteine, therefore, comes from serine. Homoserine is further broken down *via* $\alpha$-ketobutyrate.

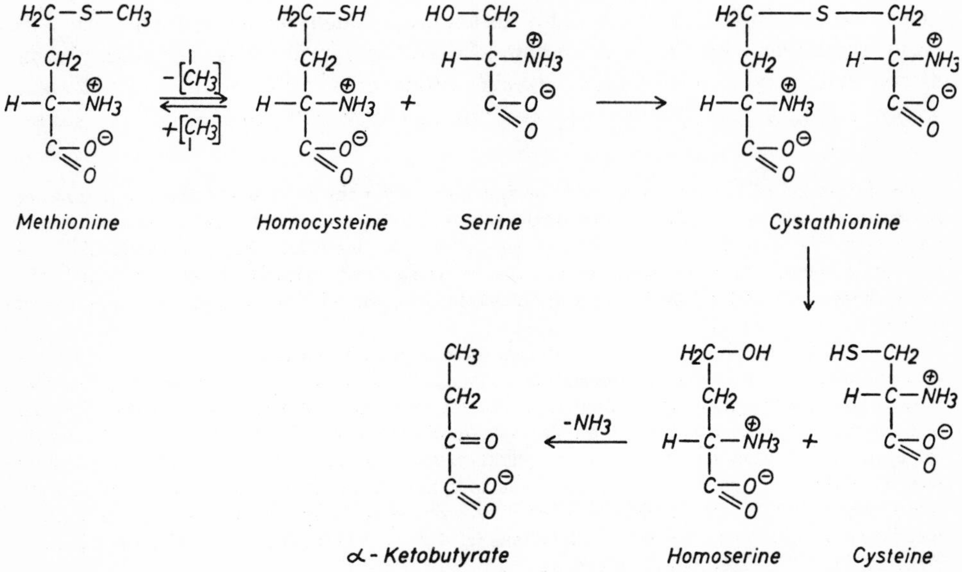

|  |  |  |  |
| --- | --- | --- | --- |
| Methionine | Homocysteine | Serine | Cystathionine |

|  |  |  |
| --- | --- | --- |
| $\alpha$ - Ketobutyrate | Homoserine | Cysteine |

*Cysteine*, whose synthesis we have just seen, is degraded chiefly through these two reaction sequences: Either to *pyruvate* + $H_2S$ + $NH_3$ (perhaps through $\beta$-mercaptopyruvate, or *via* the mechanism of $\alpha,\beta$-elimination, Section 4) or through oxidation to *cysteic acid* and subsequent decarboxylation to *taurine*:

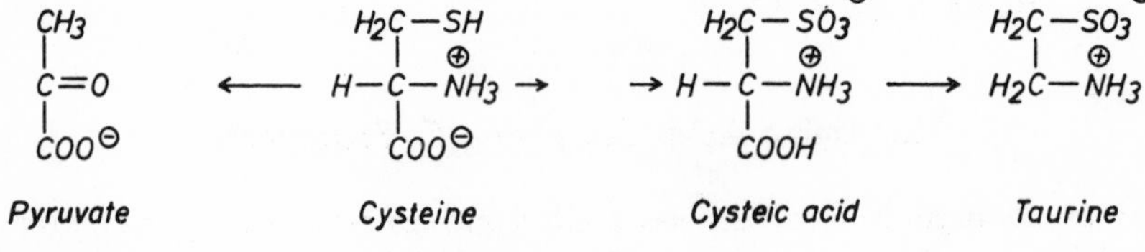

|  |  |  |  |
| --- | --- | --- | --- |
| Pyruvate | Cysteine | Cysteic acid | Taurine |

The oxidation of taurine involves several steps, which we will not discuss here; the disulfide cystine can also be oxidized in a similar manner.

**Serine and Glycine.** Serine can be converted to glycine by the loss of an active formaldehyde. This reaction is one of the most important suppliers of the $C_1$ fragment. Two coenzymes are necessary, tetrahydrofolate (Chapt. VI–5), and pyridoxal phosphate. The elimination of the $\beta$-C atom is a pyridoxal-catalyzed reaction involving the resonance structure mentioned before in Section 4. While this is taking place, the serine is also bound to tetrahydrofolate. The reaction is reversible: Serine is also formed from glycine and active formaldehyde.

Both amino acids can be metabolized through many other pathways as shown by the diagram of formulas on page 168.

Glycine can provide an active $C_1$ fragment (active formate), by oxidation or transamination (both pathways seem possible) to glyoxylate and further by "oxidative decarboxylation" to activated formate. Whether this reaction is really analogous to the normal oxidative decarboxylation (cf. Section 8; Chapt. XI-2) or passes through other intermediate steps, we do not know. With high concentrations of glyoxylate, the body can produce oxalate, but this is probably not normal. Glyoxylate can also come from sarcosine (N-methylglycine) by the action of an amino acid oxidase; the side product methylamine is oxidized to active formate during the reaction. Finally, the degradation of betaine is important. It is the oxidation product of choline and proceeds *via* dimethyl-glycine and monomethylglycine (sarcosine) to glycine. The methyl group becomes active formaldehyde, which then can join with glycine to form serine. The end effect is that sarcosine is converted to serine.

*Threonine* can be split into glycine and acetaldehyde, and this constitutes another source of glycine (threonine is essential). Finally, to mention a few more uses for glycine, the biosyntheses of the blood pigment, of purines, and of creatine require glycine and arginine (by amidino group transfer).

As shown on p. |168|, serine can be converted to pyruvate (elimination of water forms the unsaturated amino acid which goes *via* the imino acid to the $\alpha$-keto acid) as well as hydroxypyruvate or phosphoserine. The phosphorylated form, which could also come from 3-phosphoglycerate, occurs in a few proteins and phosphatides (Chapt. XIII). Other bases present in the phosphatides, i.e. ethanolamine and choline, also originate from serine.

# 13. Ketoglutaric Acid or C₄-Dicarboxylic-Acid-Supplying Amino Acids

Under this heading belong the following:

| | | |
|---|---|---|
| Phenylalanine | Histidine | Lysine |
| Tyrosine | Glutamic Acid | Proline |
| (Tryptophan) | Aspartic Acid | Arginine |

The degradation of phenylalanine and tyrosine has already been discussed. Besides fumarate, acetoacetate also occurs as a cleavage product, making these amino acids ketogenic. Tryptophan belongs to this group only to the extent that during its breakdown it passes through hydroxyanthranilic acid, the product of ring cleavage, to glutaric acid: hence, we place it in parentheses.

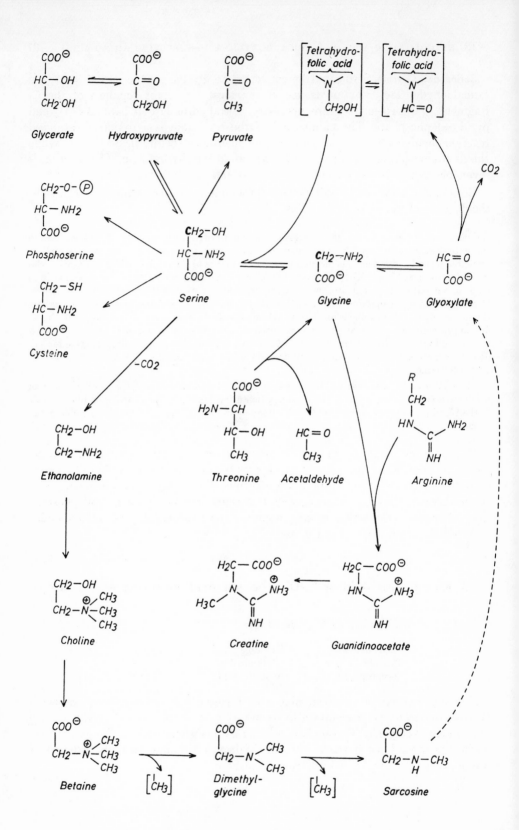

**Aspartic Acid,** as we have seen, not only can transfer its amino group to keto acids but also can supply one nitrogen directly to the urea cycle. In the second process, there arise succinoarginine and fumarate, which becomes malate by the addition of one water molecule. Malate, in turn, is dehydrogenated to oxaloacetate. The latter is also the product of the transamination of aspartate.

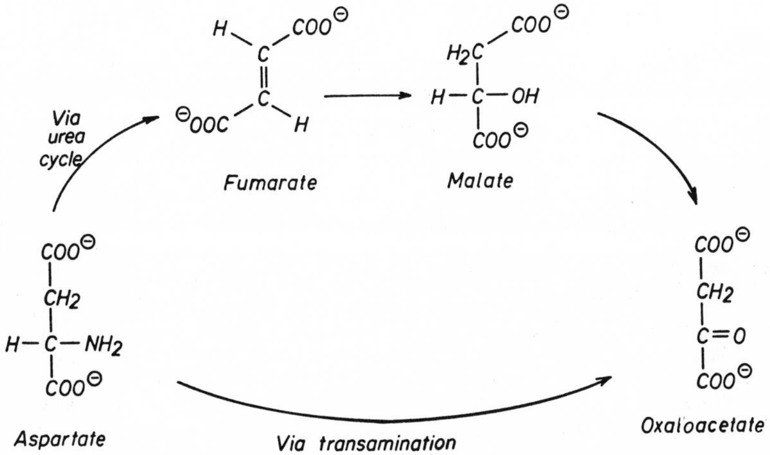

Oxalacetate is both the key substance for gluconeogenesis, i.e. glucose formation (cf. Chapt. XV), and an important intermediate in the terminal oxidation. It can be considered actually to spark the citric acid cycle. For this reason it will be discussed again in Chapt. XI.

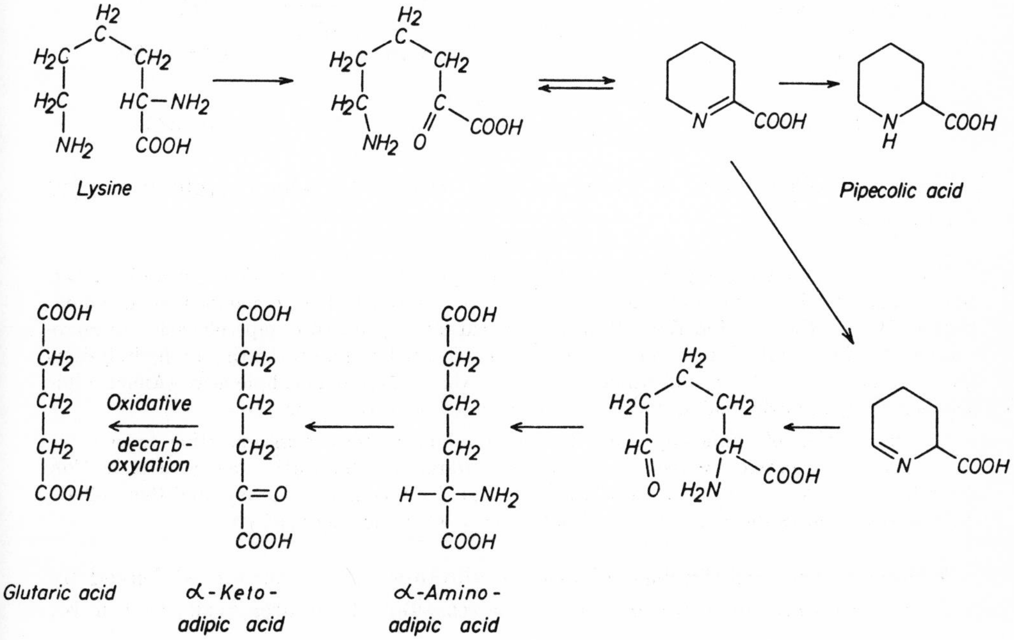

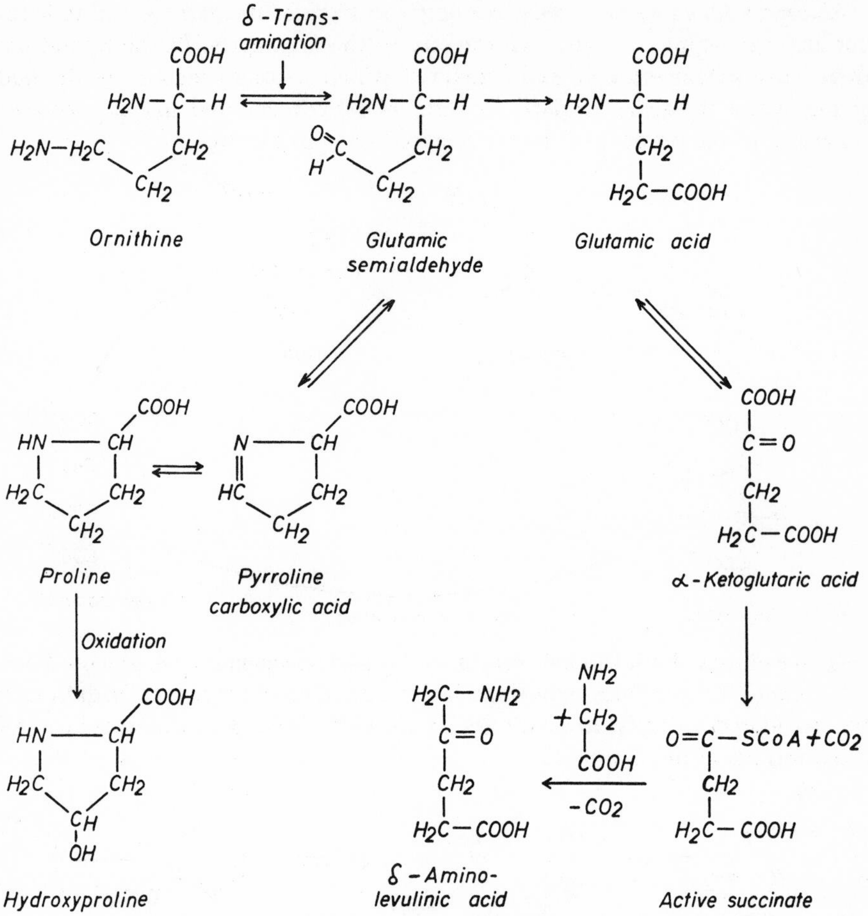

$\delta$-Trans-
amination

Ornithine      Glutamic semialdehyde      Glutamic acid

Proline      Pyrroline carboxylic acid      $\alpha$-Ketoglutaric acid

Oxidation

Hydroxyproline      $\delta$-Amino-levulinic acid      Active succinate

**Lysine** is broken down to glutarate (and thence to $\beta$-hydroxyglutarate and $\beta$-ketoglutarate).

There is considerable evidence that this reaction pathway goes through $\Delta^1$-piperidine-2-carboxylic acid, which arises from the $\alpha$-keto acid by ring closure (the two compounds are in equilibrium with each other). $\Delta^1$-Piperidine-2-carboxylic acid can be reduced to pipecolic acid (an excretion product in the rat); but it can also shift its double bond and open the ring by hydrolysis to give an $\alpha$-amino-$\delta$-aldehyde acid which is easily converted to $\alpha$-aminoadipic acid. (Aminoadipic acid is a rarely occurring amino acid found in proteins from corn, Chapt II-2).

The degradation of aminoadipic acid follows well-known steps: transamination to give the $\alpha$-keto acid and oxidative decarboxylation to form glutarate which is further degraded as the CoA derivative, just like a fatty acid. From the unsaturated compound $\beta$-hydroxy- and then $\beta$-keto-glutarate are formed; the latter in turn is split to acetyl-CoA and malonyl-CoA.

**Arginine, Proline, and Histidine,** all become glutamic acid. *Arginine* is cleaved by arginase into ornithine and urea (one of the reactions of the urea cycle, Section 8),

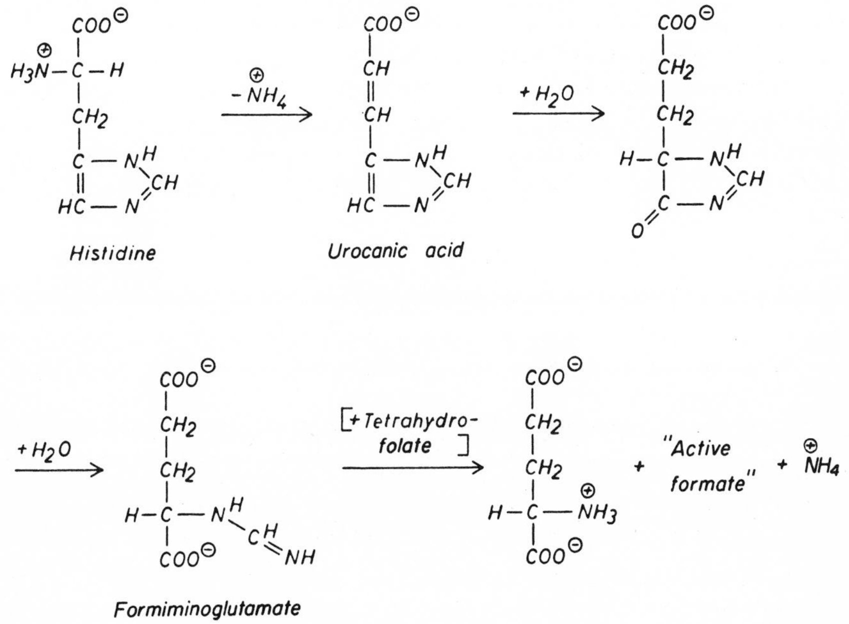

Histidine          Urocanic acid

Formiminoglutamate

and ornithine is attacked during transamination with pyridoxal phosphate primarily at the δ-amino group; it can clearly be seen that the result is *glutamate semialdehyde* which is either oxidized to glutamate or is cyclized with the elimination of water to form pyrroline carboxylic acid. Proline is produced by hydrogenation. These reactions are reversible, as shown by isotope experiments, so that the degradation of proline also goes through glutamate semialdehyde.

Proline can also be oxidized directly to hydroxyproline, probably even in peptides.

The breakdown of *histidine* is basically more complicated. It begins with an elimination of ammonia, giving an unsaturated acid, *urocanic acid*, so called because it was originally found in dog urine. But it is actually not the normal excretion product; it undergoes further changes: Addition of water and shift of the double bond yields imidazolonepropionate, which is converted by a hydrolytic ring cleavage to formiminoglutamate and further to glutamate (see diagram of formulas above).

The nitrogen of formamidine is presumably removed as ammonia and thus ends up in urea. Formate is bound to tetrahydrofolate as active formate or in general as an active C₁ fragment (cf. Chapt. VI–5).

**Glutamic acid** has appeared as a point of juncture in the network of amino acid metabolism. It is dehydrogenated with NAD to the imino acid and then converted to ketoglutarate. The ammonia liberated is used directly for urea formation (via carbamyl phosphate; Section 8 of this chapter). On the one hand, α-ketoglutarate is the universal acceptor of amino groups in transamination reactions; on the other hand, as an α-keto acid it can also be decarboxylated oxidatively. In complete analogy to the oxidative decarboxylation of pyruvate, this reaction leads to activated succinate; this is a part of the citric acid cycle, which will be discussed later (Chapt. XI). The important feature here is that a connection has been established with the terminal oxidation of all foodstuffs. Activated succinate can also condense with glycine to form a $\beta$-keto acid which decarboxylates spontaneously to give $\delta$-aminolevulinic acid (cf. diagram p. 168). This compound is the precursor for the biosynthesis of the blood pigment and cell hemins, as we shall discuss in the next chapter.

BIBLIOGRAPHY

P. Boyer, H. Lardy, and K. Myrbäck (editors), "The Enzymes," Vols. IV and V, Academic Press, New York, 1961.
P. P. Cohen and G. W. Brown, Ammonia metabolism and urea biosynthesis, *in* "Comparative Biochemistry" (M. Florkin and H. S. Mason, eds.) Vol. II, pp. 164–244, Academic Press, New York, 1960.
D. M. Greenberg, Amino acid metabolism, *Ann. Rev. Biochem.* **33**, 633–666 (1964).
J. P. Greenstein and M. Winitz, "Chemistry of the Amino Acids," 3 Vols., Wiley, New York, 1961.
M. Guggenheim, "Die biogenen Amine," S. Karger, Basel, 1951.
A. Meister, "Biochemistry of Amino Acids," 2nd ed., 2 Vols., Academic Press, New York, 1965.
H. Neurath, The activation of zymogens, *Advances in Protein Chem.*, **12**, 319–368 (1957).

# CHAPTER IX

# Porphyrins and

# Hemins

The porphyrin system is a complicated structure consisting of four pyrrole rings connected by methine groups (=CH—). It is the basis of the red blood pigment, the green leaf pigment, and of the cytochromes (redox enzymes). Efforts to determine its chemical structure occupied many decades (Küster, H. Fischer), and finally were crowned by the synthesis of the porphyrin molecule (H. Fischer). We will not follow the tortuous route of the research chemist here, but instead will construct the ring system from simple components, just as the cell does. Thus the biosynthesis will be discussed at the same time.

## 1. Biosynthesis of the Porphyrin System

**Porphobilinogen.** δ-*Aminolevulinic acid* has already been mentioned briefly (Chapt. VIII–13) as an important precursor. It is formed from *succinyl-CoA* (activated succinate), which arises either from the metabolism of amino acids (glutamate → α-ketoglutarate → succinyl-CoA) or from the citric acid cycle (cf. Chapt. XI), and which condenses with glycine (with elimination of CoA) to give *α-amino-β-keto-adipic acid*. The latter intermediate cannot be isolated; it is decarboxylated immediately to form δ-aminolevulinic acid. Condensation of two molecules of δ-aminolevulinic acid produces the pyrrole derivative porphobilinogen. The ring closure is catalyzed by an enzyme which has been purified from bovine liver.

**The Isotope Method.** The type of linkage was first studied through experiments with isotopes ($^{15}$N, $^{14}$C). The technic of labeling or tagging plays a very big role in modern biochemistry. The principle will be discussed on the basis of the example at hand.

It will be remembered that *isotopes* are atoms with different atomic weights, but with the same nuclear charge (and the same number of electrons). Chemically they are the same; physically they

173

can be distinguished frequently by their radioactive properties, such as the emission of $\beta$-rays (e.g. $^{14}C$).

An isotopic atom can be inserted into a molecule by chemical synthesis. Thus one can prepare e.g. glycine, which has in its $\alpha$-position the $\beta$-emitting carbon of atomic weight 14. The $\alpha$-position of glycine is then said to be "labeled with $^{14}C$." When one uses radioactive isotopes it suffices if only one out of ten thousand or a hundred thousand molecules contains the isotope.

If one introduces glycine labeled in this way into biochemical experiments, the pathway of the glycine can be followed readily. All substances subsequently produced from this glycine in enzymic reactions or in the intact organism must still contain the isotope and can be recognized by their radioactivity.

If such a glycine is used in our experiment, we find radioactivity in porphobilinogen; by stepwise chemical degradation it can be seen that the radioactivity is localized in the atoms marked with a solid dot in the formulas below. If we use glycine which is labeled in the carboxyl group the porphobilinogen will not be radioactive. This is proof that the carboxyl group is lost during biosynthesis. If, on the other hand, the carboxyl groups of succinic acid are labeled (indicated by °), then radioactive $^{14}C$ is found partly in the side chain and partly in the marked position of the pyrrole ring. Suitable chemical degradation procedures permit this conclusion. The path of a given carbon atom can be traced in this way to the blood pigment. For example, it has been established that the methine groups stem from glycine, whereas all the carboxyl groups derive from succinic acid.

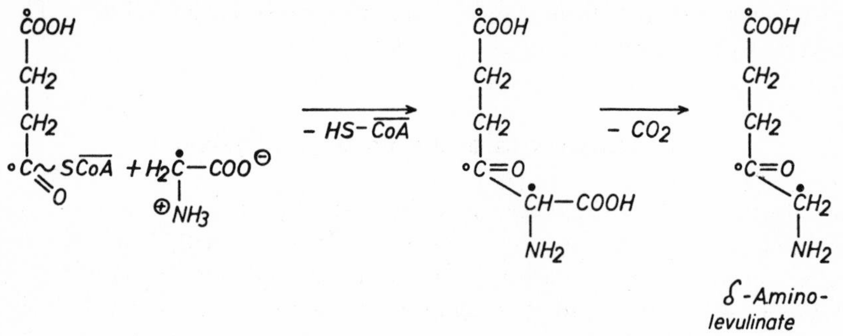

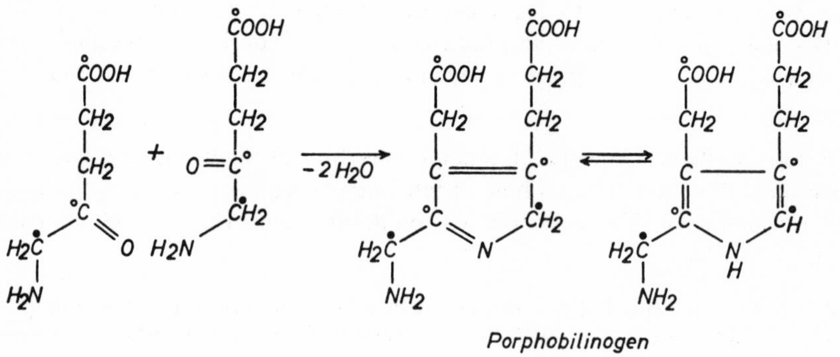

δ-Amino-levulinate

Porphobilinogen

**Formation of the Porphyrin System.** By arranging four porphobilinogen molecules in a suitable way (see formulas on page 176) and linking them, with elimination of ammonia, one obtains one of the possible porphyrin systems, namely *uroporphyrin I*. Uroporphyrin I, however, tends to be a pathological product and is the result of a "derailed" porphyrin synthesis. The actual precursor of the physiological substances, hemoglobin and cytochrome, is *uroporphyrin III*. In type III, the substituents in positions 7 and 8 are interchanged as compared to type I. Why nature prefers the isomers of type III, we do not know. In general, many a structure or reaction must be looked upon simply as a fact rather than as being causally determined. One must imagine that this structure or that path of synthesis was developed many millions of years ago and has survived through the generations.

For further clarity, a word about the possibilities of isomerism in the porphyrin system: The positions on the pyrrole rings which can bear substituents are numbered consecutively from 1 to 8. If each pyrrole ring is to have one short and one long side chain (one acetic acid $-CH_2COOH$, symbolized by $-\bullet-O$, and one propionic acid $-CH_2-CH_2-COOH$, symbolized by $-\bullet-\bullet-O$), then there are four possibilities, designated as types I–IV (cf. diagram of formulas).

In type I there is a regular sequence of short and long side chains all around the porphyrin. In the isomer important to us, type III, the fourth ring appears to be turned around or to be condensed in an inverted manner. Types II and IV have been synthesized but lack biologic significance.

Complete decarboxylation of all side chains converts each uroporphyrin to the corresponding etioporphyrin, which is characterized by short ($-CH_3$) and long ($-CH_2-CH_3$) side chains. Most textbooks derive the types I to IV from etioporphyrins. We have discussed the isomeric forms using uroporphyrins as examples because these are the naturally occurring substances.

Two enzyme systems are involved in the biosynthesis of uroporphyrin III from porphobilinogen: a deaminase and an isomerase. The initially produced colorless *porphyrinogen* is dehydrogenated to give the porphyrin system. The deaminase alone catalyzes the formation of uroporphyrin I; the isomerase suppresses the formation of type I in favor of type III.

Much discussion has centered around the problem of how the arrangement of side chains realized in type III can possibly arise during synthesis. The problem is really how a ring can be turned around without letting many side products be formed and without requiring an extra C atom for the methine bridge. Several hypotheses have been developed. One recent suggestion is at least plausible enough to be discussed briefly. Though it has not been proved experimentally, it is well supported.

The deaminase, according to this suggestion, catalyzes the condensation of four porphobilinogen molecules to form a tetrapyrrole derivative, which can fold with its particular arrangement of double bonds (shown in Fig. 36) such that the group $-CH_2NH_3^+$ of the last ring comes to rest on top of the first ring (later to be ring IV). This spatial arrangement favors ring closure with the $\alpha'$-position of the first ring. In the resulting ring system one pyrrole participates only with one corner.[1]

---

[1] A similar mechanism can be proposed to explain the formation of cobalamin (vitamin $B_{12}$; formula in Chapt. VI-6): Even more extensive folding of the linear tetrapyrrole permits ring closure between the pyrrole rings themselves and not through the methine bridges. An analogous isomerization yields a stable precursor of cobalamin.

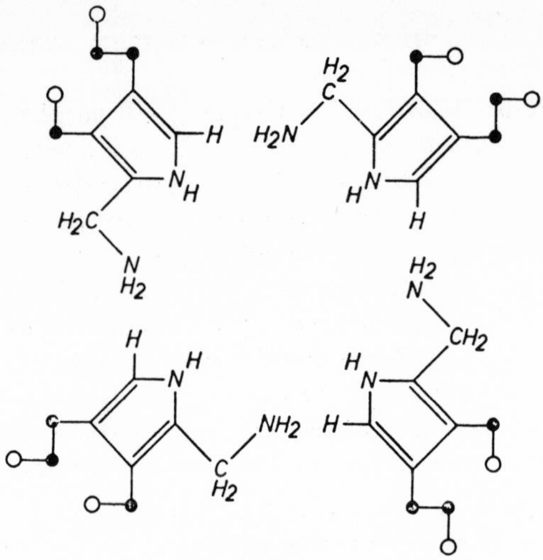

4 Porphobilinogens

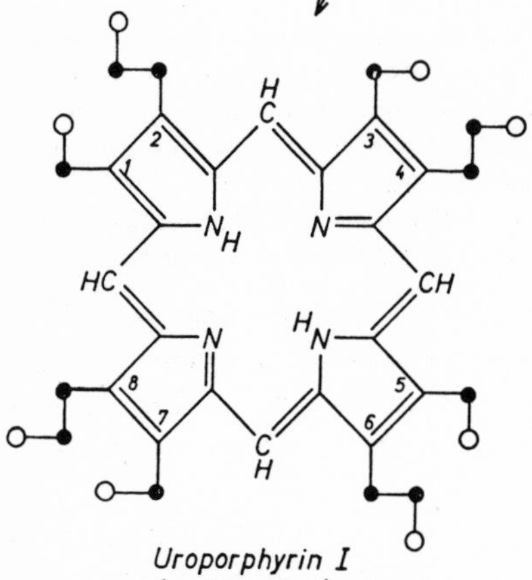

Uroporphyrin I
(pathological)

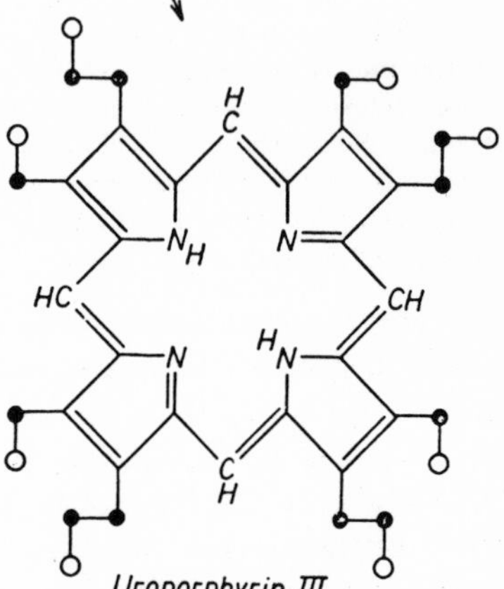

Uroporphyrin III
(precursor to heme)

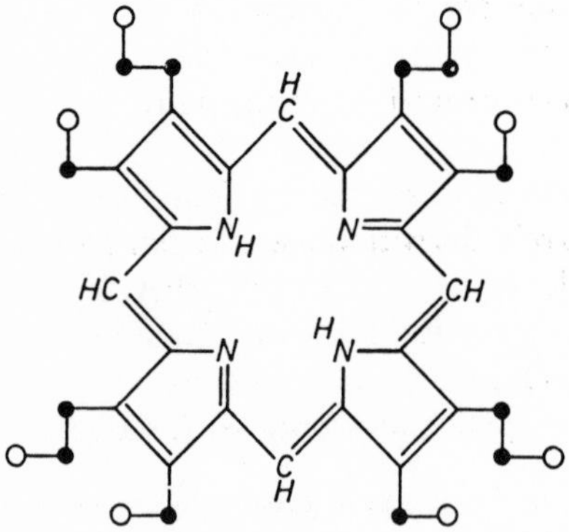

Uroporphyrin IV
(available only synthetically)

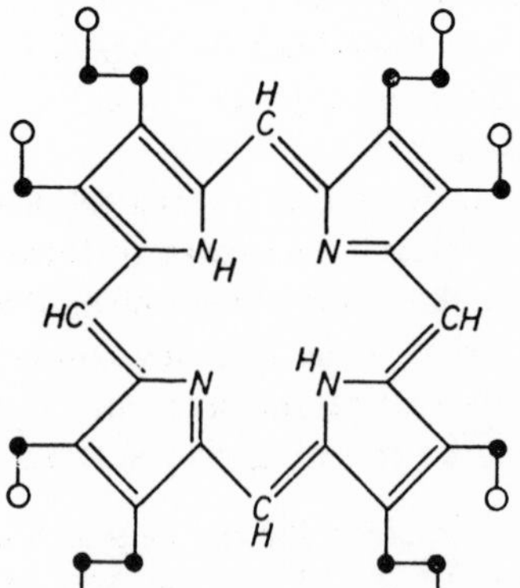

Uroporphyrin II
(available only synthetically)

176

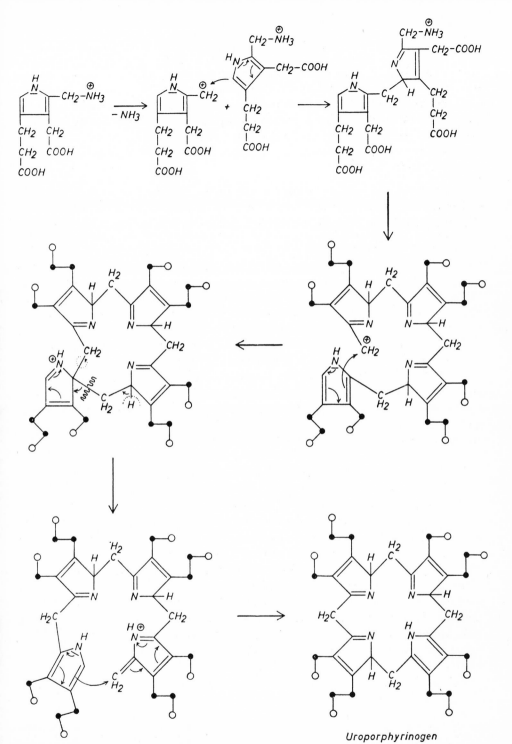

FIG. 36. Biosynthesis of porphyrin of type III. The small arrows denote the shift of electron pairs. See text for further explanation.

177

This intermediate undergoes ring cleavage at the position marked; the ring rotates around the $CH_2$—C(pyrrole) axis and condenses with the free $\alpha$-position to form *uroporphyrinogen III*. This second reaction is ascribed to the isomerase. The rotation of ring IV results in the "correct" substitution, naturally occurring in hemoglobin, and the first porphyrin produced by dehydrogenation (removal of 6 H) would be *uroporphyrin III*. In the biosynthesis of heme, dehydrogenation however appears to be the very last step.

In porphyria, a hereditary disease, synthesis takes place on a much larger scale and excess uroporphyrin of both types I and III appears in the urine. The appearance of uroporphyrin I should be explained by a relative deficiency of the isomerase.

**The Pathway from Uroporphyrin III to Heme,** the pigment of blood, is no longer difficult to describe, at least on paper. First, the acetic acid side chains are shortened to methyl groups by the stepwise loss of 4 moles of $CO_2$. The resulting compound is called *coproporphyrin III* and is usually present in small amounts in feces. In some diseases and in congenital anomalies it may appear in greatly increased amounts. (In that case, there are also found appreciable amounts of coproporphyrin of type I.) Next, the propionic acid side chains on rings I and II must be converted to vinyl groups —CH=$CH_2$ by dehydrogenation and decarboxylation, yielding protoporphyrinogen. Evidently the dehydrogenation to the porphyrin system takes place only after the ferrous ion has been inserted by enzymic catalysis. The nonplanar construction of the porphyrinogen facilitates the insertion of the central atom. From avian erythrocytes extracts have been obtained which catalyze the entire sequence of reactions from $\delta$-aminolevulinic acid to the heme.

## 2. Chemical Constitution of Heme

Heme, the colored component of hemoglobin, is ferroprotoporphyrin with the formula shown below. The ring system as such (called porphine) contains nine double bonds in uninterrupted conjugation (plus two off to the side) and in the language of organic chemistry has aromatic character. The formula can be written equally well with the primary valence bonds of iron going to rings II and IV instead of rings I and III. As a resonating structure, porphine is planar. In heme, only four of the coordination valence bonds of iron are occupied by the porphine skeleton; the two remaining ones, lying above and below the plane of the porphine ring, are both attached to the biochemically important protein (globin) by components of the protein, usually the imidazole ring of histidine (see diagram in Section 4).

The type and sequence of substituents on the porphine ring is determined during its biosynthesis (see Section 1).

The propionic acid side chains of rings III and IV have been retained, but those of rings I and II have been converted to vinyl groups. In a few cytochromes the side chains are converted further by a few more steps; in some instances, the structure of the prosthetic group is still unknown (cf. also Table XIII, Section 3).

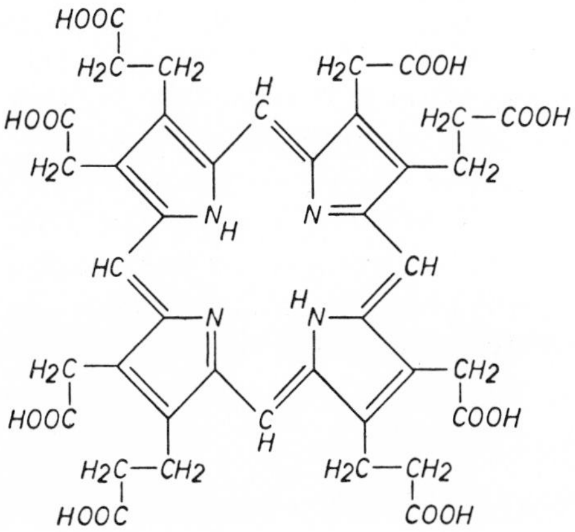

Uroporphyrin III

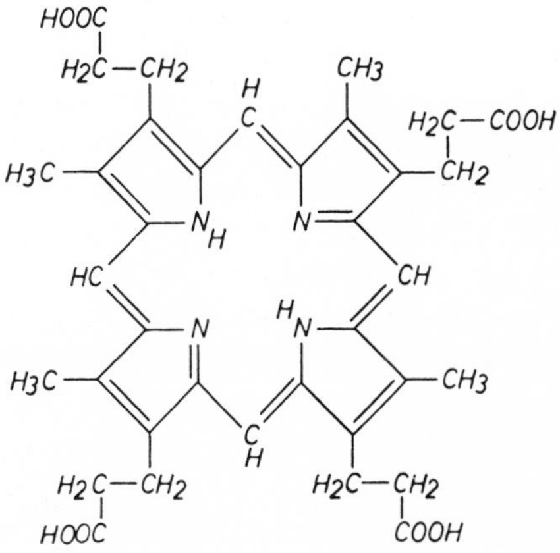

Coproporphyrin III

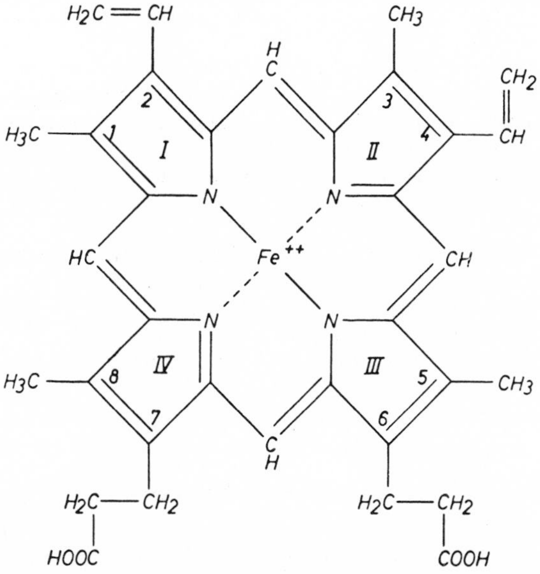

Heme

## 3. Multiplicity of Porphyrin Catalysis

The iron porphyrin molecule, called heme, and its close relatives are capable of catalyzing very many different reactions. As is generally known, hemoglobin transports oxygen in blood (this role is described in detail below). Iron does *not* change its valence in the process. A number of heme enzymes—catalases and peroxidases—interact with hydrogen peroxide $H_2O_2$, whose oxygen is transferred either to a substrate to be oxidized (peroxidase) or to $H_2O_2$ which becomes dehydrogenated to $O_2$ (catalase action, decomposition of $H_2O_2$). Another group of heme enzymes, the cytochromes, participates in biologic oxidation; they transport electrons (reduction equivalents) from suitable substrates all the way to oxygen. The type of reaction depends on the type of protein, which has a profound influence on the reactivity of the heme molecule. Again we recognize that reaction specificity of an enzyme is not determined by the prosthetic group, but rather by the apoenzyme. The various possibilities are listed in Table XIII.

TABLE XIII

FUNCTION OF SEVERAL PORPHYRIN PROTEINS

| Protein | Function | Prosthetic Group | Valence Change |
|---|---|---|---|
| Hemoglobin | $O_2$ Transport | Heme ($Fe^{++}$-protoporphyrin) | − |
| Plant peroxidase | Oxidation by means of $H_2O_2$ | Hemin ($Fe^{+++}$-protoporphyrin | + |
| Animal peroxidase | Oxidation by means of $H_2O_2$ | Green Hematin (structure unknown) | ? |
| Catalase | Decomposition of $2H_2O_2 \rightarrow 2H_2O + O_2$ | Hemin ($Fe^{+++}$-protoporphyrin) | +? |
| Cytochrome oxidase (cytochrome a) | Terminal oxidation (respiratory chain) | Cytohemin | + |
| Cytochrome c | Electron transport | Hemin; primary valence bond to the protein | + |
| Cytochrome b | Electron transport | Hemin | + |
| Oxygenase | Inserting $O_2$ into substrate | $Fe^{++}$-porphyrin | − |
| Chlorophyll | Conversion of light energy to chemical energy | Mg-containing porphyrin | − |

## 4. The Significance and Reactions of Blood Pigment

The blood pigment hemoglobin (often abbreviated as Hb) is a combination of the protein globin with heme, the prosthetic group.

By treatment with glacial acetic acid, the protein component can be removed easily and the prosthetic group isolated, e.g. in the form of the easily crystallized *chlorohemin* (in hemin iron is trivalent, in heme it is bivalent). These (Teichmann's) crystals are excellent for identifying blood.

Hemoglobin has a molecular weight of 67,000. Recently, however, it was demonstrated that it actually is an aggregate of four peptide chains. Each chain contains a heme group, and there are two identical pairs (cf. Fig. 11 and 12, Chapt. IV–4). The chains are held in place by ionic and hydrogen bonds.

It has been recognized only recently that different hemoglobins can occur in the human organism differing slightly in their protein composition. Normally there is hemoglobin A; in children one finds in addition fetal hemoglobin, HbF. All the other known hemoglobins must be considered to be genetic variants of the normal molecule (cf. Chapt. IV–2, VII–6). The differences in the protein part are slight and restricted to the exchange of a few amino acids.

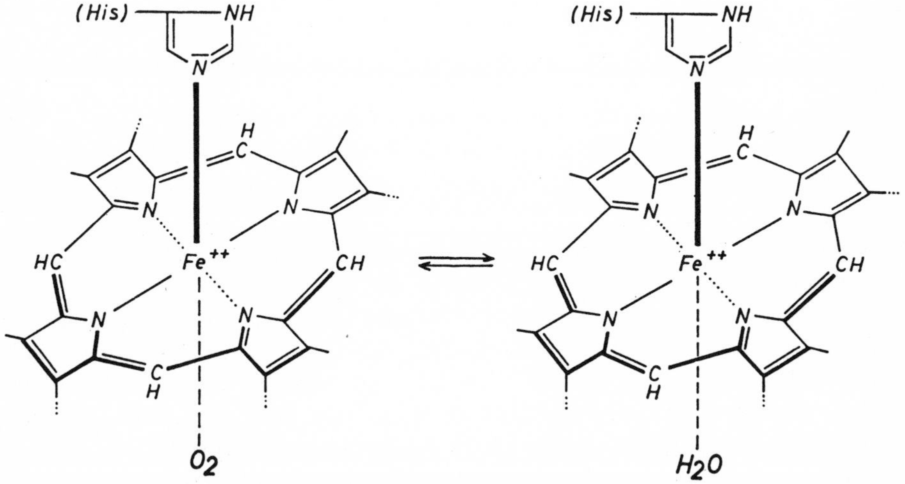

In hemoglobin (as in many other hemoproteins) one histidine residue is near the iron atom. Histidine occupies the fifth coordination position of the iron (cf. also tertiary structure of hemoglobin, Chapt. IV–4). Oxygen is held at the sixth place; it is released easily (probably in exchange for $H_2O$). The iron always remains bivalent: The amount of bound $O_2$, i.e. the ratio of $Hb \cdot O_2$ to Hb, depends on the concentration of $O_2$ or, in different units, on the partial pressure of oxygen. In the tissues, which are oxygen-deficient, oxygen is released. The reversible binding of oxygen explains the transport phenomenon. Oxygenation is accompanied by a drop in pH (Bohr effect, cf. Chapt. XXI–4), since $Hb—O_2$ is a stronger acid than Hb. This facilitates the excretion of $CO_2$ in the lungs and the release of $O_2$ in the periphery with the higher acidity (anaerobic production of lactic acid).

Substances other than the $O_2$ molecule can also be bound to the coordination places, e.g. carbon monoxide, CO. The latter is bound much more firmly than oxygen; even minute amounts in the atmosphere saturate hemoglobin with CO and thus prevent oxygen transport. But since we are dealing with an equilibrium reaction, we can slowly displace the CO with copious supplies of oxygen.

*Hemochromogens* are heme compounds with two nitrogen bases, such as pyridine and ammonia, occupying coordination places 5 and 6. The protein moiety is denatured under these conditions.

Should iron become oxidized to the trivalent (ferri) level, then the new positive charge is balanced by an anion in ionic linkage. $Hb(Fe^{+++})OH^-$ is called *methemo-*

*globin*; it cannot transport oxygen. An enzyme has been found in blood cells that reduces methemoglobin back to hemoglobin.

## 5. Degradation of the Blood Pigment

The life span of erythrocytes is limited to around four months. The hemoglobin from dying erythrocytes is broken down in the reticulo-endothelial system. At first a green pigment is produced, called *choleglobin* or *verdoglobin*, which still retains globin and $Fe^{+++}$, but whose porphine ring is opened between pyrrole rings I and II. One methine carbon is lost; it is replaced with hydroxyl groups in rings I and II. Both iron and the protein component are removed easily from the verdoglobin, and understandably so, because the porphine ring no longer exists. The result is a straight, quadrinuclear pyrrole pigment, *biliverdin*. It is reduced easily to a red substance, *bilirubin*. The latter is always found in small quantities in blood, bound to albumin.

The liver traps all of the bilirubin. The greater portion is "conjugated" with glucuronic acid to form the glucuronide and ends up in the gall bladder. Bilirubin and bilirubin glucuronide are the main bile pigments. With diazotized sulfanilic acid the glucuronide gives a red color immediately (so-called direct diazo reaction); the free bilirubin, only after addition of alcohol (indirect reaction).

In the gut, the bile pigments are further transformed. Vinyl groups are reduced to ethyl groups. The result is *mesobilirubin* which through further reduction becomes *mesobilirubinogen* (=*urobilinogen*) and *stercobilinogen*. In those pigments whose name ends in -*ogen* all the pyrrole rings are connected by methylene groups ($-CH_2-$). Dehydrogenation regenerates the pigments *urobilin* and *stercobilin* in both of which the middle rings III and IV are restored to conjugation by the new double bond. For the sake of clarity the added hydrogen atoms are marked by an asterisk in the diagram of formulas.

Part of the bile pigments are reabsorbed in the intestine and returned to the liver in the portal vein blood (entero-hepatic circulation). The greater part, however, is excreted by the intestine.

Stercobilin, urobilin, and further degradation products with but two pyrrole nuclei (mesobilifuscin) are the pigments of feces. They are produced largely by the intestinal flora. Whenever the food pulp passes through the gut rapidly, the feces have the yellow color of unchanged bilirubin.

In various liver diseases (jaundice, icterus) excess bilirubin is produced and at the same time the permeability of liver cells to the pigment is increased, so that bilirubin glucuronide ("direct bilirubin") and bilirubin itself ("indirect bilirubin") pass into blood and thence diffuse into skin tissue. Obstruction of the bile duct can cause the same symptoms. The determination of bilirubin, therefore, is important clinically.

Bile pigments have been found in various places in the animal kingdom: in egg shells of birds; among the pigments of wings and skin of insects; and finally in sea algae, where they are bound to the C-terminal group of a peptide chain.

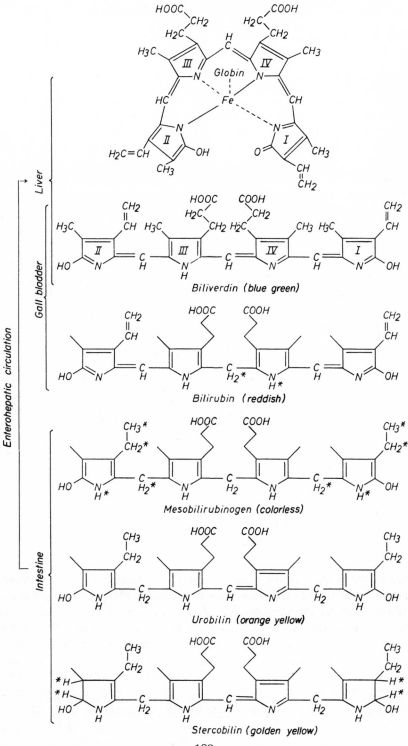

Biliverdin (blue green)

Bilirubin (reddish)

Mesobilirubinogen (colorless)

Urobilin (orange yellow)

Stercobilin (golden yellow)

183

## 6. Cytochromes, Catalases, and Peroxidases. Chlorophyll

Here we shall merely discuss structure, and in the following chapters take up the functions of these widely distributed substances.

**Cytochromes** were discovered because of their light absorption. They occur in nearly all cells, usually bound to mitochondria or similar structures. They are the catalysts of cellular respiration (function: change in valence of iron, cf. Chapt. X–4). On the basis of the absorption spectra, *cytochromes* a, b, and c were distinguished at first; later, these groups had to be further subdivided by adding subscripts, because spectroscopic studies revealed differences between members of the same group. These differences are probably determined by the protein components.

The most thoroughly studied is *cytochrome c*. It is a hemoprotein with a molecular weight of 12,000 and has one heme group per molecule. It is of particular interest that primary valence bonds are established between the protein and the porphine ring: The SH groups from two cysteine side chains have added across the vinyl groups. The resulting thiolether bonds (see formula) are very stable and are not disrupted even during hydrolysis. This fact was utilized to study the amino acid

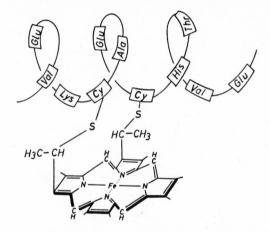

sequence in the vicinity of the heme (Theorell); meanwhile the entire amino acid sequence of horse cytochrome c has been worked out (Margoliash and Tuppy). As seen in the formula, the arrangement of the two heme-bound cysteine residues just fits into an α-helix and the adjacent histidine residue could fill another coordination place of the iron. The heme group is buried deep in the protein chains and consequently does not react with $O_2$, nor with $CN^-$, nor CO; it cannot be "poisoned" with the common inhibitors. A comparative study of the cytochromes from different animals and yeasts showed variations in some amino acid residues.

*Cytochrome b* probably has protohemin as the prosthetic group. It has recently been isolated in pure form from yeast. Cytochrome b is part of the respiratory chain, primarily in the succinate oxidation chain, but its precise place is still unknown.

*Cytochrome b₅* is closely related to the better known cytochrome b and presumably has the identical prosthetic group. Cytochrome $b_5$ is a characteristic component of the microsomes, where it probably participates in electron transport or in hydroxylations.

*Cytochrome a.* At one time, a distinction was made on spectroscopic evidence between cytochrome a and $a_3$. It appears very much, however, that there is only *one* substance in different states of binding or oxidation; it is identical with Warburg's *Atmungsferment*. Its prosthetic group, called *cytohemin* or *hemin a*, is one of the green hemins with spectroscopic similarities to the *Spirographis hemin*. The cytohemin was recently separated from the whole structure and its chemical constitution studied. A long side chain, probably a farnesyl residue, is attached to one of the pyrrole nuclei. According to Lynen, the biosynthesis proceeds through the addition of farnesyl pyrophosphate (and $HO^-$) to the vinyl group of nucleus I. On this basis we can construct the following formula for cytohemin:

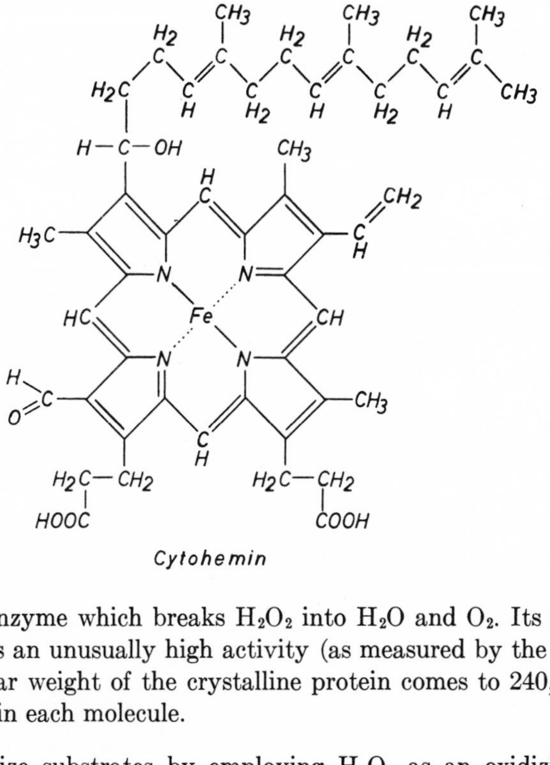

Cytohemin

**Catalase** is an enzyme which breaks $H_2O_2$ into $H_2O$ and $O_2$. Its active group is protohemin. It has an unusually high activity (as measured by the turnover number). The molecular weight of the crystalline protein comes to 240,000. There are four heme groups in each molecule.

**Peroxidases** oxidize substrates by employing $H_2O_2$ as an oxidizing agent. Depending on their origin, they may contain either a red heme (protoheme or closely related ones) or a green heme; if they contain the latter they may be called *verdoperoxidases*. One red enzyme from milk has a molecular weight of 82,000. Horseradish is particularly rich in peroxidase, which has been crystallized (1 heme per molecule). A verdoperoxidase is found in pus; molecular weight 150,000.

**Chlorophyll,** the pigment of green leaves, is a magnesium-containing porphyrin. The main features of the structure are the two "supernumerary" hydrogen atoms in ring IV, the isocyclic ring, and the phytyl side chain, which imparts lipid solu-

bility to the whole molecule. In almost all plants there occur the two closely related pigments, chlorophylls a and b. They differ in the side chain of ring II as
shown in the partial formula:

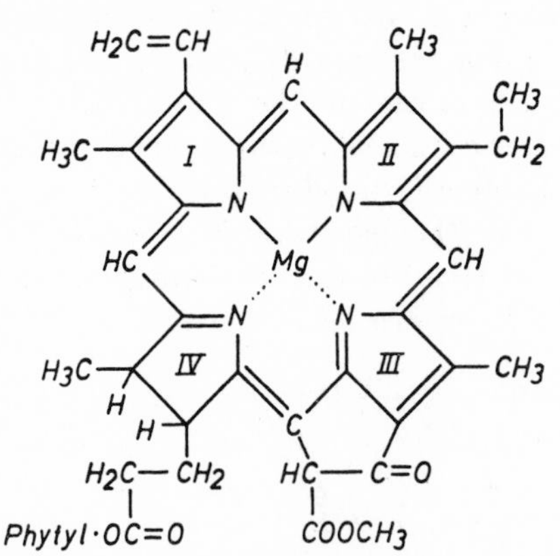

Chlorophyll a 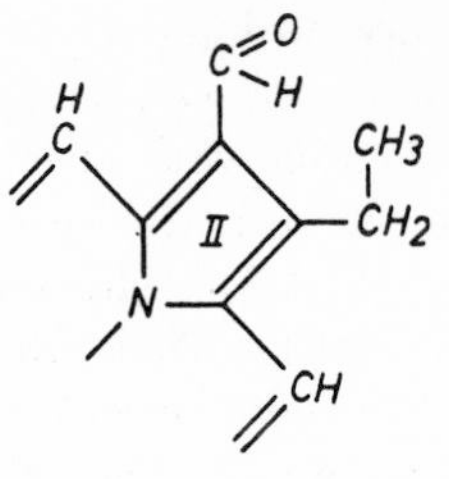                                    Chlorophyll b

Chlorophyll is the photosynthesizing pigment which effects the conversion of
light energy into chemical energy. The significance and mechanism of photosynthesis, and the role of chlorophyll, are discussed in detail in Chap. XVI.

BIBLIOGRAPHY

L. Eales, The porphyrins and porphyrias, *Ann. Rev. Med.*, **12**, 251–270 (1961).
J. E. Falk, R. Lemberg, and R. K. Morton, "Hematin Enzymes," (Symposium International
    Union of Biochemistry), Pergamon Press, New York, 1961.
S. Granick and D. Mauzerall, The metabolism of heme and cholorophyll, *in* "Metabolic Pathways"
    (D. M. Greenberg, editor) Vol. 2, pp. 525–616, Academic Press, New York, 1961.
G. Klatskin, Bile pigment metabolism, *Ann. Rev. Med.*, **12**, 211–250 (1961).
G. S. Marks, The biosynthesis of porphyrins, *Ann. Rept. Chem. Soc., London* **59**, 385–399 (1962).
J. Mathewson and A. Corwin, *J. Am. Chem. Soc.*, **83**, 135–137 (1961).

# CHAPTER X

# Biologic Oxidation—

# Metabolism of Oxygen

## 1. Combustion and Biologic Oxidation

About 1780, Lavoisier concluded that combustion processes must also take place in the animal organism. Since then, biologic oxidation has often been compared to combustion. There is indeed no difference in the net equations, the end products in both cases are $CO_2$ and $H_2O$ and the energy released during combustion and biologic oxidation are equal, at least numerically. For example:

| Glucose | $C_6H_{12}O_6 + 6\ O_2 = 6\ CO_2 + 6\ H_2O$ | $\Delta H = -674$ kcal/mole |
|---|---|---|
| Fatty Acid | $C_{16}H_{32}O_2 + 23\ O_2 = 16\ CO_2 + 16\ H_2O$ | $\Delta H = -2379$ kcal/mole |

($\Delta H$ = heat of combustion at constant pressure.)

The analogy cannot, however, be extended much beyond this. While in technology the oxidation of carbon to $CO_2$ is still the most important source of energy, the same process assumes a rather subordinate role in biochemistry. Furthermore, one characteristic feature of combustion processes is a drastic rise in temperature and an unchecked evolution of heat. In the mammalian body, in contrast, all processes proceed at a constant temperature (around 37°C) and the energy of oxidation appears only in part as heat, the remainder being conserved as chemical energy.

The principles of biologic "combustion" of foodstuffs (carbohydrates, fats, and in part proteins) may be summarized in four sentences:

(1) Complex organic molecules are first broken down to two-carbon fragments[1] (activated acetate).

(2) The further breakdown of the $C_2$ fragments occurs in a series of individual steps, in each of which one $CO_2$ or two H atoms are split off; or, the molecule is altered so as to prepare for such a step.

---

[1] In carbohydrates this step is reached *via* decarboxylation. A $C_6$ compound yields two $CO_2$ and two $C_2$ fragments (Chapt. XV-9).

(3) The end product $CO_2$ arises *without any considerable change in energy* by decarboxylation of organic acids.

(4) The end product $H_2O$ arises from reduced coenzymes of the respiratory chain with concomitant storage of part of the energy produced in the form of an energy-rich compound, adenosine triphosphate.

The most important $CO_2$-yielding processes will be treated in the following chapter. First, however, let us discuss the formation of water (point 4). This is not only the chief energy-producing process, but it also represents the main pathway for utilizing respiratory oxygen and requires the participation of cytochromes as was discussed in Chapt. IX. There are some other reactions, however, by which oxygen is inserted directly into organic molecules. The enzymes catalyzing those reactions are called oxygenases.

## 2. Oxidation as a Loss of Electrons

Oxidation is defined today very generally as a loss of electrons ($e^-$). Oxidation of molecular hydrogen can therefore be formulated as follows:

$$H_2 - 2e^- = 2H^+$$

The electrons must be accepted by an oxidizing agent. If we use, for example, a ferric salt, the equation becomes:

$$H_2 - 2e^- = 2H^+ \tag{1}$$

$$2Fe^{+++} + 2e^- = 2Fe^{++} \tag{2}$$

$$\text{Sum:} \quad \underline{H_2 + 2Fe^{+++} = 2H^+ + 2Fe^{++}}$$

Molecular oxygen can act as an oxidizing agent, in a similar manner, picking up either two or four electrons:

$$O_2 + 2e^- = O_2^{--} \overset{+2H^+}{\rightleftarrows} H_2O_2 \tag{3}$$

$$O_2 + 4e^- = 2O^{--} \overset{+4H^+}{\rightleftarrows} 2H_2O \tag{4}$$

The coupling of reactions 1 and 4 constitutes the formation of water from its elements:

$$2H_2 - 4e^- = 4H^+$$
$$\underline{O_2 + 4e^- = 2O^{--}}$$
$$2H_2 + O_2 = 2H_2O \qquad \Delta F = -57 \text{ kcal/mole } H_2O$$

It will be remembered that the reaction is exergonic.

The application of such concepts to organic chemistry was formerly debated heatedly. But when the chemical bond was finally understood to be a bond of electrons, the definition of oxidation simply as a removal of electrons was accepted in organic chemistry, too. It may be formulated best by the following example:

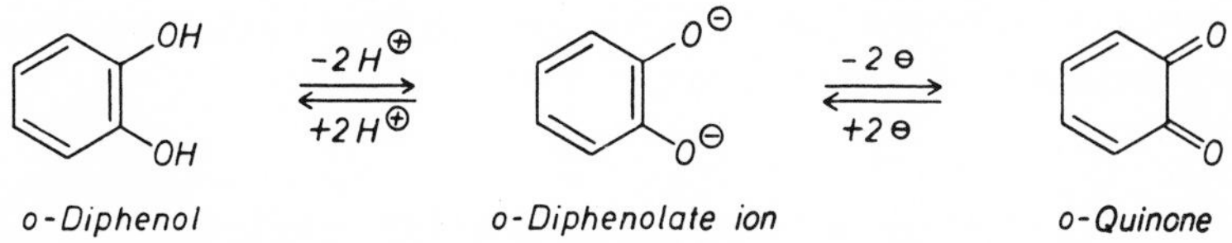

o-Diphenol          o-Diphenolate ion          o-Quinone

Oxidation of hydroquinone consists of the removal of electrons from the quinolate ion which thus becomes quinone.[2] Previously we have similarly formulated the oxidation of glutathione-SH to the disulfide (Chapt. III-3).

Dehydrogenation of a primary alcohol (or oxidation by removal of hydrogen) also can be seen to be a removal of electrons (formulas below). It should be noted that the initial step, the dissociation of a proton with formation of the alcoholate ion, does not involve a change in oxidation level. In the second step, the molecule becomes even more polarized, as symbolized by the wedge-shaped bond, and finally the binding pair of electrons comes off together with the proton.

This last step, the removal of electrons, is the oxidation proper (or dehydrogenation). In the process, a hydride ion[3] $H^-$ is transferred to the dehydrogenating agent, and the remaining molecule stabilizes itself by the formation of the C=O double bond. If a pyridine nucleotide should serve as the dehydrogenating agent, as it is the case in enzymic dehydrogenations, then we have arrived at the mechanism of pyridine nucleotide catalysis, as outlined briefly in Chapt. VI-4. The loss of both $H^+$ and $H^-$ really amounts to nothing more than the dissociation of two protons and the loss of two electrons.

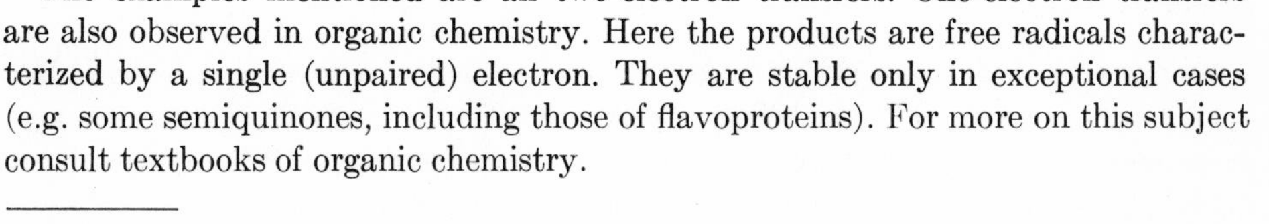

Alcohol          Alcoholate          Aldehyde

The examples mentioned are all two-electron transfers. One-electron transfers are also observed in organic chemistry. Here the products are free radicals characterized by a single (unpaired) electron. They are stable only in exceptional cases (e.g. some semiquinones, including those of flavoproteins). For more on this subject consult textbooks of organic chemistry.

---

[2] We have chosen catechol (o-quinone); p-quinone would exemplify the reaction just as well.

[3] If a proton picks up two electrons, then a negatively charged hydrogen ion, the hydride ion, is formed. Compounds which contain the hydride ion are familiar from inorganic chemistry: the hydrides of alkali and alkaline earth metals. They are decomposed instantly by water, since the $H^-$ ion reacts with the $H^+$ ion to release $H_2$.

In the formation of quinones, oxygen can accept electrons directly, not only in chemical experiments but also biochemically, with the aid of the enzyme phenol oxidase. As far as the reaction of the substrate is concerned, it is immaterial whether the electrons are transferred directly to oxygen or to some prosthetic group. It suffices that they are removed and the substrate thus oxidized.

## 3. The Redox Potential

**Exchange of Electrons through Wires.** Once more we return to the oxidation of molecular hydrogen by $Fe^{+++}$ ions (Section 2). Instead of the electrons being exchanged in a direct interaction between partners, they can also be transported through a wire. This constitutes an electric current. The generation of electricity in galvanic elements (e.g. dry batteries) depends on such processes.

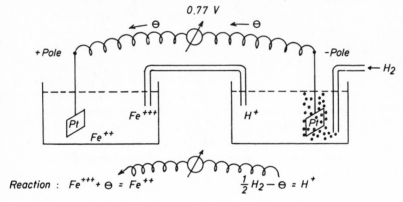

FIG. 37. Electrochemical cell

We may construct two half-cells (Fig. 37). In the left solution are both $Fe^{++}$ and $Fe^{+++}$ salts; in the right half-cell are $H^+$ ions and molecular hydrogen. The electrodes would ordinarily be platinum. The electrons leave the molecular hydrogen and temporarily build up a negative charge, but after closing of the circuit they can travel to the iron salt solution, which is positively charged as compared to the hydrogen half-cell. The electronic potential between the two half-cells can be measured directly.

To permit a comparison of the various half-cells or redox systems with one another —e.g. the pair $Fe^{++}/Fe^{+++}$ with the pair $Ti^{+3}/Ti^{+4}$ or $Sn^{+2}/Sn^{+4}$—the concept of a redox potential was invented. Arbitrarily, the hydrogen half-cell has been chosen as the reference cell for all other systems. The redox potential then is designated simply as that electric potential (in volts or millivolts) which can be measured against the hydrogen reference electrode.[4]

---

[4] The half-cell potentials of metal ions, e.g. $Cu/Cu^{++}$, are of great significance in inorganic chemistry. If metals are arranged according to increasing potentials, the result is the familiar electromotive series.

**Redox Potential and Free Energy.** The concept of redox potential, derived from the above experimental setup, has been an invaluable aid in chemistry. The concept is intimately associated with the free energy of an oxidation-reduction reaction, because the reaction in a galvanic cell is reversible and electric energy is made available for useful work. Thus the redox potential becomes a direct measure of the free energy (cf. Chapt. V–2), except that it is expressed in different units. It must always be remembered, however, that the redox potential invariably refers to the reaction with gaseous hydrogen. That is the zero point of the redox scale.

The reaction with hydrogen is usually less interesting than that with some other oxidant or reductant. The difference in redox potentials determines the change of free energy. To convert one to the other, we use the expression:

$$\Delta F^\circ = -n\,\mathfrak{F}\,\Delta E_0$$

($n$ = number of electrons transferred; $\mathfrak{F}$ = amount of charge per mole = 96,500 coulomb). With the turnover of 1 mole of electrons ( = change in valence by 1, and 1 mole of substance reacted) and a potential difference of 1 volt, 23.07 kcal are developed. In two-electron transfers the available work would be double that, or 46.1 kcal. As another example, the free energy of ATP hydrolysis ($-7.0$ kcal/mole under standard conditions) corresponds to 0.152 volts potential difference with a two-electron change.

The standard values of free energy and also the redox potentials refer to standard concentrations of oxidized and reduced reactants, including the concentration (more precisely, the activity) of $H^+$ = 1, pH = 0. The dependency of half-cell potentials on concentration is given by the following expression:

$$E_n = E_0 - \frac{RT}{n\mathfrak{F}} \ln \frac{C_{\text{oxidized}}}{C_{\text{reduced}}}$$

This equation is entirely analogous to equation (5) of Chapt. V–2.

**Zero Point on the Biochemical Redox Scale.** Since hydrogen ions participate in most biochemical redox reactions, their concentration should also be set at 1 $M$ in order to measure the standard potentials. Of course, this is not feasible because the enzymes are not active at such a low pH. Furthermore, it seems more reasonable to choose "physiological" conditions. In biochemistry, therefore, it is customary to use standard potentials $E_0'$ referring to pH of 7. At that pH, the hydrogen electrode has a potential difference of $-0.42$ volts with respect to the hydrogen electrode of pH 0.

For reactions in living cells the relative amounts of oxidized and reduced substrates or coenzymes obviously are important. A drastic shift in concentration may actually reverse the sign, so that the more powerful oxidizing agent, according to the normal potentials, is in effect oxidized by the weaker one.

**Biologic Redox Systems.** The cytochromes discussed in Chapt. IX are truly the prototypes of biologic redox systems. The iron atoms that they contain change their valence with the release or uptake of electrons. Electron transport is their physiological function (see below). The redox potentials have been measured (cf.

TABLE XIV

REDOX POTENTIALS AT pH 7 $(E_0')$ FOR SOME BIOCHEMICAL REDOX SYSTEMS

| $\Delta F°$ kcal | (a) Coenzymes | | (b) Substrates | |
|---|---|---|---|---|
| | $E_0'$ volt | Substance | $E_0'$ volt | Substance |
| | | | −0.47 | Acetaldehyde/acetate |
| | | | −0.42 | $H_2/2H^+$ |
| | −0.32 | $NADH/NAD^+ + H^+$ | | |
| | | | −0.20 | Ethanol/acetaldehyde |
| −11.5 | −0.185 | Riboflavin-P·$H_2$/riboflavin-P | | |
| | | | −0.18 | Lactate/pyruvate |
| | −0.06 | Flavoproteins | | |
| | −0.05 | Phyllo-hydroquinone/phylloquinone | | |
| | −0.04 | Cytochrome b | | |
| | | | 0.0 | Succinate/fumarate |
| −15.5 | | | +0.01 | Methylene blue/leuko dye |
| | | | +0.20 | Ascorbate/dehydroascorbate (pH 3.3) |
| | +0.26 | Cytochrome c | | |
| −25 | +0.29 | Cytochrome a | | |
| | | | +0.81 | $\frac{1}{2}O_2/O^{--}$ |

Table XIV). It should be noted that the values depend very much on the protein components, the protein-free system heme/hemin having a much more negative potential (−0.115 volts) than the cytochromes.

In Chapt. VI we have discussed the chemical nature of several hydrogen-transferring coenzymes. They are redox systems, because hydrogen transfer is equivalent to electron transfer (Section 2). Other redox systems consist of substrates which react with enzymes and their cosubstrates (= coenzymes); for example, the mixture of alcohol and acetaldehyde (equimolar) can be assigned a standard potential, as can the system succinate-fumarate, and so forth. Redox potentials of this kind are listed in the right-hand half of Table XIV.

## 4. The Respiratory Chain

**Energy of Water Formation.** In Section 1 we have emphasized that the formation of water is the decisive energy-yielding reaction of metabolism. The potential difference between the hydrogen electrode and the oxygen electrode amounts to $0.81 − (−0.42) = 1.23$ volts and is equivalent to a change of free energy of $\Delta F° = −57$ kcal/mole. The cell ordinarily oxidizes $NADH_2$, and not molecular hydrogen, since this coenzyme accepts the hydrogen from substrates. The potential difference compared to $O_2$ is then only 1.13 volts and $\Delta F° = −52$ kcal.

This amount of energy (52 kcal) is very great for a biochemical reaction. It is subdivided into small individual energy parcels, for $NADH_2$ does not react with oxygen directly but rather through a series of intermediate steps. A comparison has been made with a cascade where running water reaches a lower level over several steps. The total potential energy of the water fall is released in parts. The biologic significance of such a chain of redox systems stems from the possibility of coupling each of the steps with other reactions. Part of the free energy of water formation is conserved as chemical energy and is not dissipated as heat. The carrier of chemical energy is again adenosine triphosphate (ATP): *In the respiratory chain ADP and inorganic phosphate are converted to ATP.*

**Localization of the Respiratory Chain in Mitochondria.** We may note here that the enzymes of the respiratory chain and the ATP synthesis linked with it are associated with certain cell structures, the mitochondria (visible by light microscopy). These particles can be isolated from cells, and can be used for the study of cell respiration. But if one wishes to isolate the individual enzymes from mitochondria then the structure must be destroyed, and usually the capacity of mitochondria to respire normally is abolished. This fact has been the source of great difficulties in the experimental study of the participating enzymes. D. E. Green has discussed a multienzyme system which functions normally only as an intact whole (cf. also Chapt. X–5, XIX–3).

**Sequences of Redox Systems in the Respiratory Chain.** A logical arrangement of the component enzymes of the respiratory chain can be devised on the basis of the redox potentials of their prosthetic groups. The most negative potential is that of nicotinamide-adenine dinucleotide, the $NADH/(NAD^+ + H^+)$ system. Reduced nicotinamide nucleotides can deliver hydrogen to flavoproteins. The reduced flavoproteins may be reoxidized by the $Fe^{+++}$ of cytochrome (b or c). Here hydrogen ions are formed and from now on only electrons are transported by the change of valence of iron. The chain of enzymes ends with cytochrome oxidase, which transfers electrons onto oxygen. The resulting $O^{--}$ ion, of course, is not stable (its equilibrium concentration in water is $10^{-32}$ M); it immediately picks up two $H^+$ ions to produce $H_2O$. The formation of water has been accomplished:

Substrate-$H_2$
(e.g. malate) → NADH + H⊕
Substrate-$H_2$ → Flavin Enzyme → Cytochrome system → Cytochrome oxidase → ½$O_2$
(e.g. succinate)
2H⊕ . . . . . . . . . . . . . . . . . . . . . . . . $O^{2\ominus}$

(cf. also the full-page diagram of formulas on page 194).

Experimental investigations have corroborated this arrangement, in principle at least, but numerous obscurities remain.

We now propose to discuss the individual steps of this general scheme, in particular the enzymes, with continual reference to the diagram.

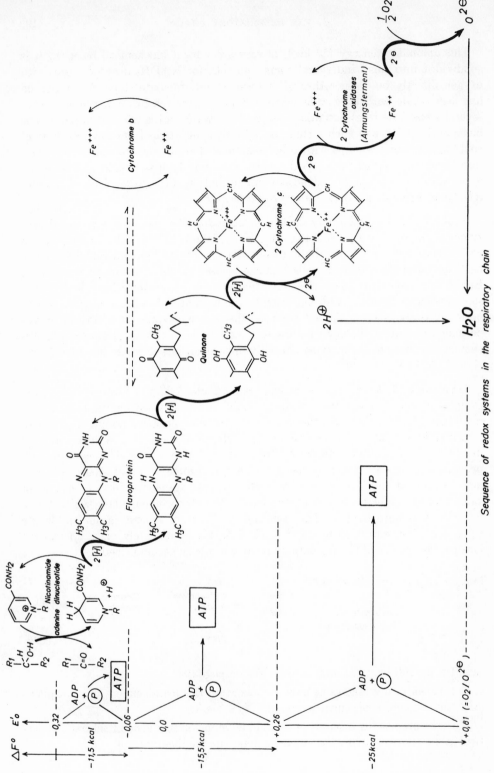

Sequence of redox systems in the respiratory chain

**NAD and NADP Catalysis.**[5] Under the discussion of the individual substrates we shall see numerous examples of enzyme catalyzed reactions dependent on NAD and NADP. Here it suffices to accept the reduced nicotinamide nucleotides, $NADH_2$ and $NADPH_2$ (formulas in Chapt. VI–4), as a common pool for hydrogen, just as ATP is the common pool for active phosphate. Hydrogen bound to NADP is used largely for synthetic purposes (but not entirely); $NADH_2$ relinquishes its hydrogen through the respiratory chain, beginning with the reduction of the flavoproteins.

NAD occurs both in mitochondria and in the cytoplasm. Only the coenzyme reduced within the mitochondria is oxidized by the respiratory chain; extra-mitochondrial $NADH_2$ cannot pass through the mitochondrial membrane. The exchange of hydrogen between cytoplasm and mitochondria appears to be delegated to certain substrates (glycerophosphate, $\beta$-hydroxybutyrate) which function as "transport metabolites" (cf. also Chapt. VI-4).

**Flavin Catalysis.** About 60 different flavin-containing enzymes are known; some have flavin mononucleotide (FMN), but the majority has flavin-adenine dinucleotide (FAD) as the active group (formulas of flavins in Chapt. VI–4). Many flavin enzymes work directly on the substrates, while others in the respiratory chain oxidize (dehydrogenate) the reduced nicotinamide coenzymes. This second group of flavin enzymes, which usually contain FMN as prosthetic group, is commonly termed *$NADH_2$-cytochrome c reductase*, although it seems to be a complex enzyme system (see below). Different groups of workers have obtained preparations of $NADH_2$ dehydrogenases with different properties; certain preparative procedures permit the isolation of various fractions from the multienzyme system, and there probably exist several enzymes.

One very active $NADH_2$-cytochrome c reductase from mitochondria recently was separated into two components, a $NADH_2$-ubiquinone reductase and an ubihydroquinone-cytochrome c reductase (see below under "Quinone Catalysis"). In addition, non-heme-bound iron was found (about 15 moles/mole of flavin). Martius prepared a highly purified phylloquinone reductase, which contains flavin-adenine dinucleotide (FAD) and which reduces ubiquinone besides phylloquinone (= vitamin K). The hydroquinone is assumed to be reoxidized to the quinone by cytochrome b.

It has been observed recently that many flavoproteins contain metals; one particular $NADH_2$—cytochrome c reductase, for example, has 4 atoms Fe per mole flavin, and the iron is not a component of a porphyrin system. The iron is supposed to permit the transition from two-electron transport (or $H_2$ transport) to the one-electron transport characteristic of the cytochromes. The separation of 2H into $2H^+$ and $2e^-$ can take place there. Furthermore, the metal seems to be important for binding the flavin group to the protein.

The redox reaction between $NADH_2$ and the cytochrome system was formerly ascribed to *diaphorase* (v. Euler; F. B. Straub), but diaphorase has actually turned out to be part of the $\alpha$-ketoglutarate oxidase and to transfer hydrogen from dihydrolipoate to NAD (cf. also Chapt. XI-2).

Another flavoprotein is *succinate dehydrogenase* (succinic dehydrogenase,[6] succinate oxidase). It is bound exceptionally tightly to the respiratory chain and acts

---

[5] We remind the reader again that the Committee on Enzymes of the International Union of Biochemistry has suggested the designations NAD (nicotinamide-adenine dinucleotide) and NADP (nicotinamide-adenine dinucleotide phosphate) for what have previously been known as DPN and TPN (di- and triphosphopyridine dinucleotide) (cf. also Chapt. VI-4 and Chapt. XVIII-1, footnote 2).

[6] Since at the pH of the cell (pH $\sim$ 7) succinic acid exists in its salt form, succinate dehydrogenase is the more correct name.

on its substrate, succinate, directly (without the collaboration of the nicotinamide coenzyme[7]). It can also transfer hydrogen even to unphysiological acceptors, such as methylene blue, but this is possible only with partially purified preparations of the succinate oxidase complex which still contain cytochrome b. After butanol treatment, succinate dehydrogenase can be eluted from the complex and purified further; its flavin group is similar to FAD; the isoallaxazine ring, however, is bound to the protein by primary valence bonds. The enzyme system furthermore contains iron ions and ubiquinone. Since succinate is a member of the citric acid cycle (see Chapt. XI–2), the linking of succinate dehydrogenation to the respiratory chain has special physiological significance.

**Quinone Catalysis.** We have already shown that electrons can easily be removed from hydroquinone and that the loss of electrons is equivalent to an oxidation to the quinone. One such quinone-hydroquinone system is in all likelihood interposed as a hydrogen carrier in the respiratory chain between the flavoproteins and the cytochromes.

Ubiquinone                                          Ubihydroquinone

We have formulated the reaction on the example of ubiquinone, also called coenzyme Q, which is particularly abundant in mitochondria. Several workers, furthermore, have proposed the participation of vitamin E quinone, of vitamin K (Martius), and —in plants—of plastoquinone. These quinones are grouped with the fat-soluble vitamins, but they will be discussed in Chapt. XIV because of their isoprenoid side chains. Their formulas will be shown there, too. Being lipids they are bound as mitochondrial lipoproteins or are at least associated with the lipoproteins. The quinones may be thought of as being incorporated in an orderly arrangement in the protein-lipid double layers of mitochondria.

The enzyme which transfers hydrogen from the quinone system to cytochrome c, called ubihydroquinone-cytochrome c reductase, recently was isolated, but the preparation was still contaminated with cytochrome b and $c_1$.

There seem to be enzymes that catalyze a direct reaction of flavin groups with the cytochromes (the real cytochrome reductases). Here the quinone system would be shunted out. Several authors suggest that such a "short circuit" is quite characteristic of the non-phosphorylating respiratory chain.

---

[7] Collaboration of the NAD system in the dehydrogenation of succinate is thermodynamically impossible because the nicotinamide system with a redox potential of $E_0' = -0.32$ volt is too weak an oxidizing agent. The flavoprotein ($E_0' = -0.06$), in contrast, can attain equilibrium with the system succinate/fumarate ($E = 0.00$). It is almost a general rule that the introduction of a C—C double bond into a saturated chain requires flavoproteins.

**Hemin Catalysis (Cytochromes).** As discussed in the preceding chapter, the hemin system is involved in quite a few catalytic functions. In the respiratory chain we find mainly the two cytochromes b and c, and cytochrome oxidase which is equal to cytochrome a (and identical with Warburg's *Atmungsferment*). Cytochromes are distinguishable by their spectra.

*Cytochrome c* is the best studied cytochrome, because it is soluble and relatively easily obtained. For its chemical constitution see Chapt. IX–6. It is responsible for the electron transport[8] from flavin (or a quinone) to cytochrome oxidase. It is noteworthy that neither $CN^-$ nor CO can inhibit cytochrome c. While the soluble cytochrome c has been known for some time now, two closely related cell hemins were discovered recently, a cytochrome c lipoprotein and a cytochrome $c_1$.

*Cytochrome b* is very tightly bound to the flavoproteins and quinones. It is an open question whether it precedes cytochrome c in the main path of electron transport, or whether it is in a sidepath. The prosthetic group seems to be identical with the heme of hemoglobin in blood.

*Cytochromes a and $a_3$* are distinguished by their spectra; recent evidence indicates that they are actually two states of one enzyme, *cytochrome oxidase*. The enzyme has been obtained as a homogeneous protein with the molecular weight of 530,000. Its prosthetic groups are 5 moles of "cytohemin," i.e. an iron porphyrin with altered side chains which is not red, but greenish. In addition, three atoms of copper per mole of porphyrin have appeared in cytochrome oxidase preparations. The Cu might be involved in the catalytic action by changing valence.

This complex is the so-called terminal oxidase, that enzyme of the respiratory chain which reacts directly with respiratory oxygen. Oxygen is charged with electrons while the iron of the cytochrome oxidase porphyrin undergoes a change in valence. Since one molecule of oxygen must take up four electrons and the transition of $Fe^{++}$ to $Fe^{+++}$ yields only one, a question arises concerning the possible cooperation of several hemin groups; it is not yet solved.

The oxidized "respiratory enzyme" is reduced again by cytochrome c. This process requires a lipoprotein which apparently links the cytochrome oxidase ("respiratory enzyme") to cytochrome c.

**The Respiratory Chain as a Dynamic Equilibrium.** The respiratory chain is an excellent example of the fact that in the organism true chemical equilibria do not exist. The respiratory chain fulfills its job only if it continuously accepts hydrogen from the substrates and with it reduces the oxygen supplied by hemoglobin. A steady state is reached, which is a *dynamic equilibrium* and which is influenced much more by the supply of oxygen, the concentration of substrates, and above all by the phosphorylating system (Section 6) coupled to it, than by redox potentials. The nicotinamide nucleotides are present largely in the reduced form, and the successive coenzymes are oxidized to a rising degree. Measurements which indicate this have

---

[8] Some authors consider cytochrome c to be merely an auxiliary substrate of the respiratory chain, and not an enzyme. This is a matter of definition which need not concern us here.

TABLE XV

DYNAMIC EQUILIBRIA IN THE RESPIRATORY CHAIN

| Experimental Conditions | Percentage of Active Groups in Reduced Form | | Cytochromes | | |
|---|---|---|---|---|---|
| | NAD | Flavoprotein | b | c | a |
| "State 4" (resting state): | | | | | |
| Much substrate; ADP limiting | 99% | 40% | 35% | 14% | 0% |
| "State 3" (active state): | | | | | |
| Maximal $O_2$ consumption | 53% | 20% | 16% | 6% | 4% |

been conducted by B. Chance and his co-workers; some of the values found are given in Table XV.

In "state 4," the resting state, ATP arises from ADP and inorganic phosphate through a coupled reaction ("oxidative phosphorylation"; see below); here the small amount of endogenously formed ADP controls the overall reaction. If more ADP is provided, then more electrons are transported to oxygen per unit time, until, with excess of ADP in "state 3," the maximum rate of electron transport is reached. In this last situation the steady concentrations are shifted in favor of the oxidized states. This example of biochemical regulation will be mentioned again in Chap. XIX.

## 5. The Electron-Transport Particles

From the previous section it is evident that our knowledge about the respiratory chain is still quite incomplete. We know which prosthetic groups participate (cf. diagram in Section 4). It remains to be clarified, however, to what proteins they are bound and what role the metals and any new cofactors might play. The reason for this unsatisfactory state of knowledge is that the enzymes under consideration are bound very firmly to the mitochondrial structure (cf. Chapt. XIX–3). Only very recently have techniques been developed to subdivide the mitochondria in such a manner that most of their activity is retained. The subunits thus obtained have been called "electron-transport particles" (Green and co-workers). Some of the catalytic capabilities have been sacrificed (e.g. the enzymes of the citric acid cycle). But they are still able to oxidize $NADH_2$ or succinate with consumption of $O_2$ and formation of ATP (see below). With the further destruction of these subunits, the capacity for oxidative phosphorylation disappears.

The particles can be further broken down in a variety of ways; the smaller fragments, however, can catalyze only partial processes of the respiratory chain. A green hemoprotein has been isolated, for example, which contains the cytochrome c oxidase activity.

*The electron-transport particles* are looked upon by Green as complex giant (or super-) molecules of definite composition. Regardless of whether this is true or whether they are fragments which contain, in addition to the essential components, varying amounts of structural material, the significant feature here is the presence of an orderly system of enzymes working together on one task. To this multi-enzyme system belong the flavoproteins, succinate dehydrogenase, and $NADH_2$—cytochrome c reductase, probably also a flavin-containing quinone reductase, the cytochromes b, c, and a, non-heme-bound iron and copper, as well as various lipids, especially phosphatides. Some preparations lose their activity when the lipids are extracted; lecithins and cephalins can then restore the activity.

On this basis the respiratory chain of the electron-transporting particles may be written as follows:

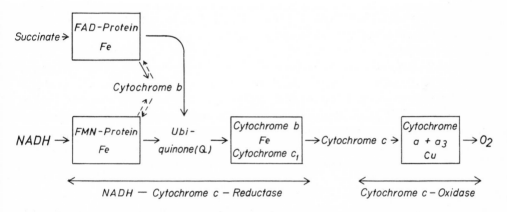

It should be noted that this constitutes a more specific version of the large general diagram in Section 4. Ubiquinone and cytochrome c are represented as auxiliary substrates; the complexes within the frames are the true enzymes of the respiratory chain. Their composition, particularly with regard to prosthetic groups, is not yet fully understood. It is even possible that additional complexes may be involved. Many current controversies will hopefully be decided experimentally in the near future.

Very valuable tools in the study of respiratory-chain enzymes are specific inhibitors: $NADH_2$ dehydrogenase is inhibited specifically by *Amytal* (isoamylethylbarbiturate) and by *rotenone*; the reduction of cytochrome c is blocked by the antibiotic *antimycin A*; and cytochrome oxidase is sensitive to $CN^-$ and CO.


## 6. Oxidative Phosphorylation (Respiratory Chain Phosphorylation)

The importance of the respiratory chain resides in the fact that the free energy of oxidation of each of the individual steps is trapped and stored in the form of

ATP. This process has been termed oxidative phosphorylation (it could just as well have been called "phosphorylative oxidation"). The energy calculations have been outlined in the scheme in Section 4 and in Table XIV: Whenever 1 mole of $NADH_2$ is oxidized by $\frac{1}{2} O_2$, 52 kcal are set free. The synthesis of 3 moles ATP from ADP and orthophosphate (= "inorganic phosphate") requires about 21 kcal; thus, from an energy standpoint, the synthesis is entirely feasible and has an "efficiency quotient" of 40% (i.e. under standard conditions; with physiological concentrations the efficiency would tend to be greater). From the table of energies, evidently 1 ATP can arise for each electron (or hydrogen) transferred between $NADH_2$ and flavoprotein, flavoprotein and cytochrome c, or cytochrome c and oxygen.

Measurements in various laboratories have repeatedly confirmed this value of 3 ATP per $\frac{1}{2} O_2$ (or per 1 mole $H_2O$). The quotient ATP formed/O consumed is called the P/O ratio. A P/O ratio of 3, however, applies only to substrates that are dehydrogenated by NAD. Succinate, oxidized directly by flavoprotein, yields only 2 moles ATP per mole $H_2O$, and cytochrome c only 1 mole.

It was surprising to find that the respiratory chain can run backwards with a consumption of ATP (Klingenberg). NAD is reduced, in other words, and flavin and cytochromes are oxidized. Considering the redox potentials, this reaction must be endergonic and require energy. The necessary energy is supplied by the cleavage of ATP or of some energy-rich intermediate product of the oxidative phosphorylation (see below). But it can hardly be assumed that this process has any significance in the organism. Nevertheless, it has considerable theoretical interest and it could perhaps help to elucidate the mechanism of oxidative phosphorylation.

Various substances inhibit the formation of ATP without interrupting the transport of electrons. This phenomenon is called "*uncoupling of oxidative phosphorylation.*" The most frequently used substance is dinitrophenol. Dicumarol, the antagonist of vitamin K, also is an uncoupling agent. A biologic regulation of coupling is probable; the biologic uncoupler, however, is still not known.

Various theories attempt to explain how orthophosphate is transformed to the energy-rich ATP. According to Lehninger a cycle with the following steps may be written:

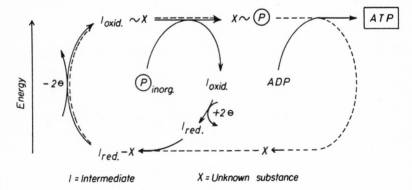

I = Intermediate          X = Unknown substance

This sequence of reactions is based on the idea that initially some substance X with a relatively low energy content is added and that oxidation (removal of electrons) converts the low energy bond to the high energy bond. Models of this are familiar from the metabolism of carbohydrates ("substrate phosphorylation"; Chapt. XV-7). Exchange reactions at a high energy level, probably following the mechanism of phosphorolysis, incorporate inorganic phosphate into energy-rich bonds and transfer it to ADP producing ATP. The initial acceptor X and the intermediate I are regenerated subsequently by a reductive process. Schemes may be proposed in which the energy-bond arises from reduction instead of oxidation. In that case, the positions of "I-red" and "I-ox" would have to be exchanged and the sign of the electron transport reversed.

We still do not know what compound X is. Considerable evidence indicates that the energy-rich compound formed originally is not a phosphate derivative, but rather that phosphate enters subsequently in exchange for some other group with a high-energy bond. Recently the discovery of an energy-rich "primary phosphate" has been reported; it is a protein (Boyer) which has phosphate bound to a histidyl residue.

Several authors have proposed that a hydroquinone-quinone system takes up phosphate directly. But such a hypothesis does not seem to be very probable. Lindberg, Ernster, and Grabe have suggested that the initial phosphorylation step takes place directly on the flavin nucleus. Thioesters involving the SH groups of proteins have even been discussed as possible stores of energy.

# 7. Other Oxygen-Activating Enzymes

In the respiratory chain we have become acquainted with only one enzyme that reacts directly with oxygen, namely cytochrome oxidase. Another name for it is end-oxidase (or terminal oxidase), because it is found at the end of the electron transport chain. Cytochrome oxidase may be the most important enzyme to react with oxygen, but it is not the only one.

**Classification and Nomenclature.** In recent years it has been recognized more and more that oxygen is not only an acceptor of electrons (or hydrogen), but that it can also enter organic molecules directly. Today three groups of enzymes are distinguished; all react with $O_2$ and catalyze the following reactions:

(1) *Oxidases* (electron-transferring oxidases). The general equations are:

$$O_2 + 4e^- \to 2O^{--} \overset{+4H^+}{\rightleftarrows} 2H_2O$$

or

$$O_2 + 2e^- \to O_2^{--} \overset{+2H^+}{\rightleftarrows} H_2O_2$$

(2) *Oxygenases* (oxygen transferases). The general equation is:

$$A + O_2 \to AO_2$$

(3) *Hydroxylases* (oxygenases with mixed functions). General equation:

$$AH + DH_2 + O_2 \rightarrow AOH + D + H_2O$$

(AH = substrate; $DH_2$ = hydrogen donor)

*Further Oxidases.* Several enzymes which contain copper, such as cytochrome oxidase, but which do not contain any porphyrin group are able to transfer electrons from *o*- or *p*-hydroquinones or from ene-diols to oxygen. Water (not $H_2O_2$) is the other product of the reaction. The enzymes therefore transfer 4 electrons to $1O_2$. To this group belong *laccase* (= *p*-hydroquinone oxidase), and *ascorbate oxidase*. The latter is found in plants, and it has often been suggested that it can serve as end-oxidase in cellular respiration. Catecholase will be discussed later (end of this section).

Practically without exception the two-electron-transferring oxidases (= $H_2O_2$-forming enzymes) contain flavin as prosthetic group. It has long been known that yellow enzymes can act as oxidases, i.e. that they dehydrate substrates and transfer the hydrogen (or its electrons) onto oxygen molecules (= "aerobic dehydrogenases") giving rise to $H_2O_2$.[9]

The flavin enzymes also are capable of transferring hydrogen (or its electrons) to acceptors other than oxygen. Methylene blue and other quinonoid dyes in *in vitro* experiments serve as unphysiological acceptors, whereas *in vivo* the soluble cytochrome c generally would seem to assume the role of the redox dye; thus the formation of $H_2O_2$ is avoided. The flavoproteins, often called oxidases (e.g. amino acid oxidase, aldehyde oxidase), are "facultative oxidases" which usually function as dehydrogenases.

**Oxygen Transferases.** The typical reaction of these enzymes is the cleavage of an aromatic ring; the product has two C=O groups at the points left after C=C scission. The mechanism calls for the addition of an oxygen molecule forming, as an intermediate, a cyclic peroxide:

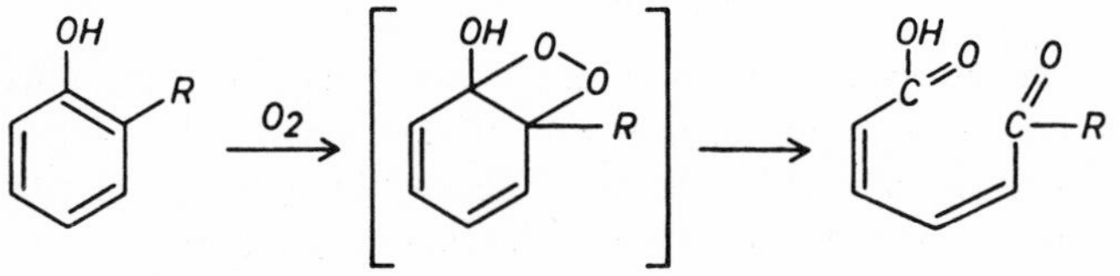

The metabolism of the aromatic amino acids provides examples of this reaction; e.g., the oxidation of homogentisic acid (Chapt. VIII–11), the oxidation of 3-hydroxyanthranilic acid (Chapt. VIII–11), and the oxidation of tryptophan to formylkynurenine (Chapt. VIII–11). The enzyme for this last oxidation, contains a ferroporphyrin system and the oxidation of $Fe^{++}$ to $Fe^{+++}$ inactivates the enzyme. The other iron-containing enzymes have no porphyrin.

---

[9] In 1912, in his theory of dehydrogenation, Wieland had assumed that that was the regular pathway of respiration.

**Enzymic Hydroxylations:** "Oxygenases with mixed function." A distinction must be made between the oxidative ring cleavage above and hydroxylations. The latter almost always require the cooperation of a hydrogen donor, usually $NADPH_2$. The enzymes usually contain iron, copper, or manganese. Through isotopic tagging it was determined that one atom of the oxygen molecule is inserted into the substrate while the second oxygen atom is reduced to form water, thus oxidizing the hydrogen donor. The hydroxylations of aromatic rings follow this principle, as illustrated by the conversion of phenylalanine to tyrosine. The $H_2$ donor in this case is tetrahydrofolate, which is oxidized to dihydrofolate; $NADPH_2$ reduces it back to tetrahydrofolate:

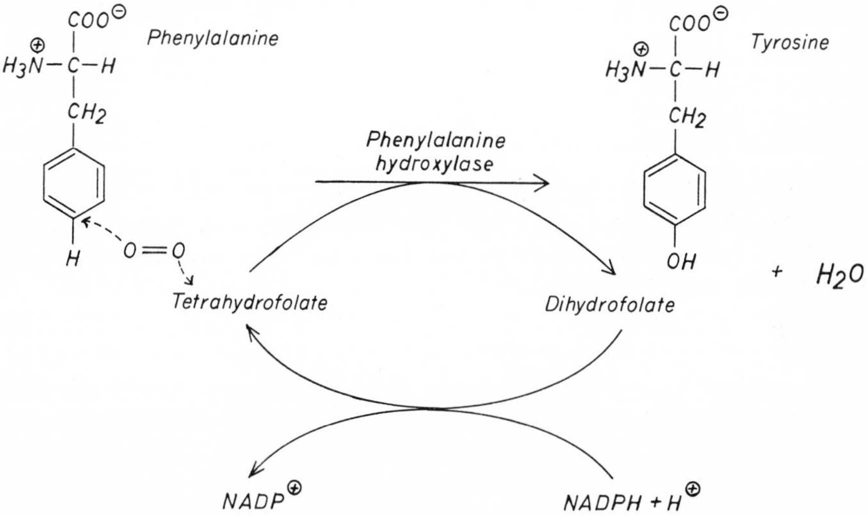

It is easy to imagine that the free energy of water formation facilitates the attack of oxygen on the ring (a coupled reaction). Similar hydroxylation reactions are undergone by aromatic substances foreign to the body, e.g. many drugs. In these cases, the hydroxylation is nonspecific as far as the position of the entering oxygen function is concerned.

Very specific hydroxylases of this type, however, exist for the steroids. Here the hydroxylating enzyme is not only specific for a definite carbon atom, but is stereospecific as well. Enzymic hydroxylation, e.g., in position 11 permits the formation of only the $\beta$-hydroxy compound (cf. Chapt. XIV-6). Most of the hydroxylases are localized on the microsomes (cf. Chapt. XIX–2).

In addition to direct hydroxylation by means of oxygen, a hydroxy group can also be inserted into a molecule by the addition of a molecule of water across a double bond. Actually that is the more common way and in the degradation of carbon chains it is invariably employed.

*Phenolase Complex.* Phenolase (= tyrosinase, or phenol oxidase) converts tyrosine to dopa (= dihydroxyphenylalanine) and oxidizes the dihydroxy derivative further to the quinone stage. Through a series of subsequent reactions, some of which occur spontaneously and without enzymic catalysis, the black or brownish black melanin is finally formed (for a schematic representation of the reactions see Chapt. VIII–11). The phenolase is an oxidase with mixed functions, where the product of oxygenation, the hydroquinone derivative, simultaneously acts as hydrogen donor. The mechanism of reaction can be written as follows:

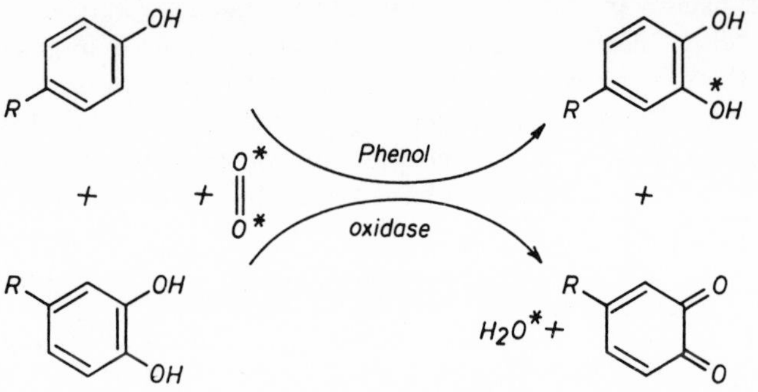

This mechanism has been supported by data from experiments with isotopically labeled oxygen (O*). The majority of phenol oxidases can carry out the oxidation of hydroquinone derivatives (lower line of the diagram above) by themselves without coupling. This is termed the catecholase effect because catechols are oxidized. Here $H_2O$ (and not $H_2O_2$) is formed.

Phenolases (tyrosinases) are widely distributed in the plant kingdom (champignon mushrooms, potatoes, bananas). They are responsible for the darkening of freshly cut surfaces of plants or fruits. For insects, phenolases are important both for melanin formation and for browning and hardening (sclerotization) of the cuticle.

### BIBLIOGRAPHY

B. Chance and G. R. Williams, The respiratory chain and oxidative phosphorylation, *Advances in Enzymol.*, **17**, 65 (1956).

L. Ernster and Chuan-Pu Lee, Biological oxidoreductions, *Ann. Rev. Biochem.*, **33**, 729–788 (1964).

D. E. Green, Electron transport and oxidative phosphorylation, *Advances in Enzymol.*, **21**, 73 (1959).

O. Hayaishi, "Oxygenases," Academic Press, New York, 1962.

A. L. Lehninger and C. L. Wadkins, Oxidative phosphorylation, *Ann. Rev. Biochem.*, **31**, 47–78 (1962).

H. S. Mason, Mechanism of oxygen metabolism, *Advances in Enzymol.*, **19**, 79 (1957).

H. Netter, "Theoretische Biochemie," Springer Verlag, Berlin, 1959.

W. C. Schneider, Mitochondrial metabolism, *Advances in Enzymol.*, **21**, 1–72 (1959).

# CHAPTER XI

# Carbon Dioxide Formation

# in the Citrate Cycle

## 1. Significance of the Citrate Cycle

The end products of aerobic metabolism are chiefly carbon dioxide and water (cf. Chapt. X–1). In metabolism, carbon dioxide arises from carboxylic acids mainly by two pathways of decarboxylation:

(1) Decarboxylation of β-keto acids, a reaction which proceeds spontaneously even *in vitro*.

(2) "Oxidative decarboxylation" of α-keto acids, whose mechanism has already been discussed briefly (Chapt. VI–4, VIII–10).

The ultimate purpose of metabolism[1] may be thought to consist in converting the various foodstuffs into compounds that can undergo one of these two general reactions. It is a welcome simplification that in almost all organisms breakdown invariably follows the same path. The starting material for this final degradation is "activated acetate," in which the acetyl group is bound to *coenzyme A*. The origin of this substance from the amino acid alanine has already been discussed. How fats and carbohydrates are broken down to activated acetate will be described in Chapt. XII and XV.

The breakdown of activated acetate itself takes place in the citric acid cycle (Krebs' cycle; tricarboxylic acid cycle). In this cycle the pathways of protein, fat, and carbohydrate catabolism are united. Furthermore, the cycle provides many of the necessary components for the synthesis of endogenous substances. The citric acid cycle therefore encompasses a large pool of common intermediates, which can be used either for synthesis of new cell material or for degradation to gain energy. The full significance of these interrelationships will be demonstrated later (cf. Chapt. XVIII).

---

[1] Referring to the energy-yielding or catabolic aspect of metabolism.

The net reaction for the breakdown of acetyl-CoA can be written as follows:

$$CH_3\overset{\overset{\displaystyle O}{\|}}{-C}\sim\overline{SCoA} + 3H_2O = 2CO_2 + 8[H] + \overline{HSCoA}$$

No oxygen is taken up in this oxidation; instead, water is added and dehydro-

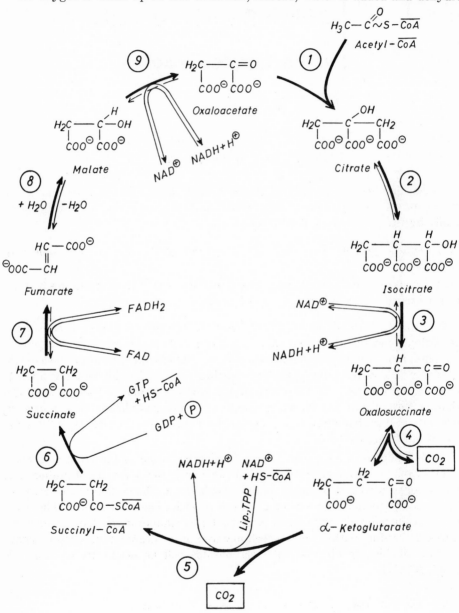

genated several times. The hydrogen is picked up by the appropriate coenzymes and brought to reaction with oxygen in the respiratory chain.

The process, however, is not restricted to $C_2$ and $C_1$ fragments. On the contrary, the condensation of the acetyl-CoA with a $C_4$ compound yields a $C_6$ compound, citric acid (whence the name of the cycle is derived) and by a series of steps the $C_4$ compound is regenerated eventually, whereby the cycle is completed. The whole sequence of reactions is illustrated on page 206. Since, at the pH of the cell, organic acids are ionized, we have drawn the salt forms. The steps have been numbered for more convenient reference.

The citric acid cycle was discovered independently at about the same time in 1937 by Martius and Knoop and by Krebs. The discovery permitted the correlation of many isolated facts.

## 2. The Individual Steps

To initiate the citrate cycle a "spark" is required. Along with *activated acetate*, its reaction partner, *oxaloacetate*, must be present. *Oxaloacetate* can arise from aspartate by transamination (Chapt. VIII–13). The keto group of oxaloacetate can react with acetyl-CoA by a modified aldol condensation:

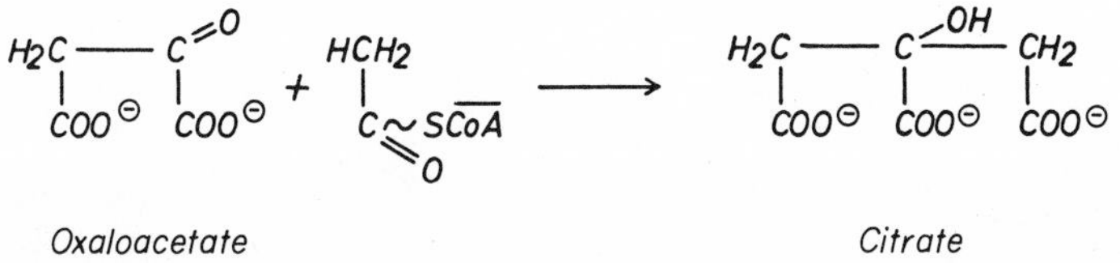

Oxaloacetate                                     Citrate

In this reaction (1) the activating CoA group is split off. The product of the condensation reaction is a monohydroxytricarboxylic acid with the trivial name *citric acid*.

The series of transformations of citrate begins with the isomerization to *isocitrate*. The enzyme aconitase catalyzes the attainment of the equilibrium among citrate (89%), *cis*-aconitate (3%), and isocitrate (8%). It is now believed that the reaction proceeds *via* a carbonium cation as the common intermediate for all three tricarboxylic acids:

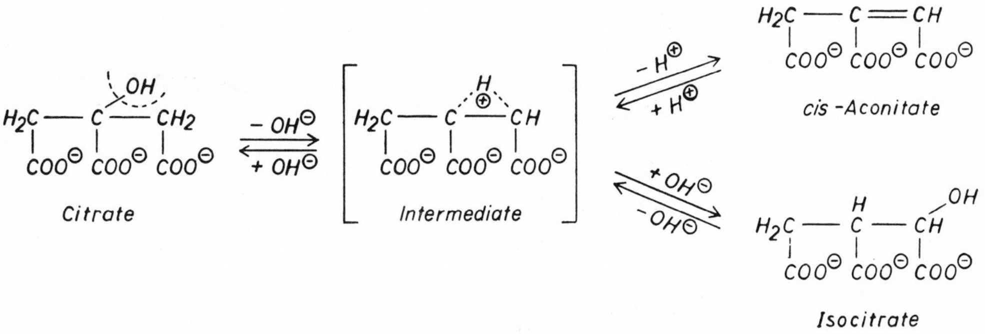

Citrate                        Intermediate

In the further breakdown of isocitrate, the secondary alcohol group is dehydrogenated. Isocitrate dehydrogenase transfers the hydrogen to NAD or[2] NADP and at the same time catalyzes the reversible decarboxylation of the $\beta$-keto acid (oxalosuccinate). The product is $\alpha$-ketoglutarate, with which we have already become acquainted in connection with the degradation of glutamate (reactions 3 and 4).

$\alpha$-Ketoglutarate is an important branching point. In the cycle it is decarboxylated oxidatively; this means that $CO_2$ is split off with a concomitant loss of hydrogen, resulting in a dicarboxylic acid (succinate) shorter by one C atom (reactions 5 and 6). This last step is irreversible and its mechanism is somewhat complicated.

The decarboxylation alone requires the participation of thiamine pyrophosphate and lipoate; the succinyl group is then taken up by coenzyme A as shown:

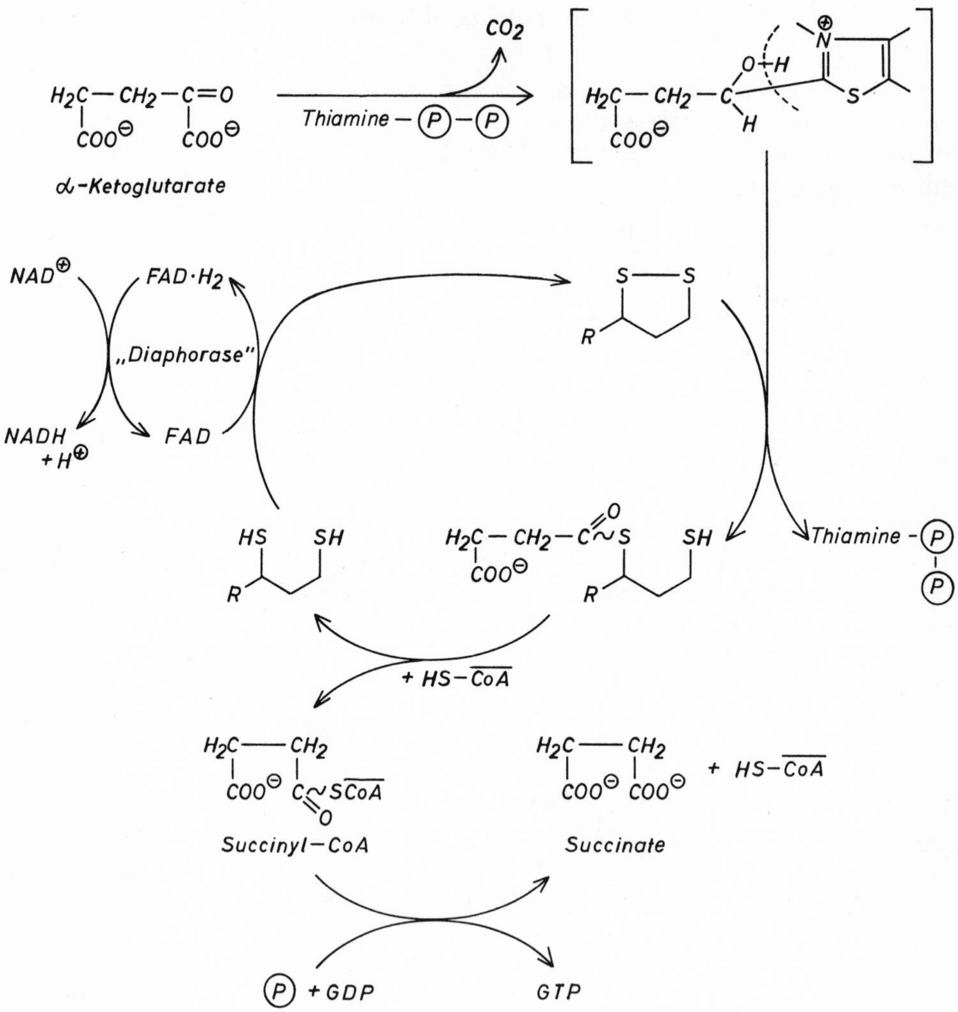

The course of this reaction is analogous to the oxidative decarboxylation of pyruvate (cf. Chapt. VIII–10, XV–9).

---

[2] There are two different enzymes, distinguishable among other things by their coenzymes. The normal terminal breakdown reaction relies chiefly on the NAD-dependent enzyme. Again, we would like to draw attention to the change in nomenclature: The nicotinamide coenzymes formerly were known as diphosphopyridine nucleotide (DPN) and triphosphopyridine nucleotide (TPN).

S-acyl dihydrolipoate is a compound with a high potential for group transfer (a type of thio-ester); the free energy of the aldehyde oxidation has been trapped as chemical energy. The succinyl residue is transferred to CoA, forming succinyl-CoA and dihydrolipoate which must be dehydrogenated again. A flavoprotein, the *diaphorase*, takes care of the hydrogen transfer to NAD, and the resulting $NADH_2$ is reoxidized in the respiratory chain. We can now summarize the train of redox catalysts in the following way:

$$\text{Lipoate} \rightarrow \text{flavoprotein} \rightarrow \text{NAD} \rightarrow \text{flavoprotein} \rightarrow \text{cytochromes} \rightarrow O_2$$

It is remarkable that two flavoproteins with opposite functions—the reduction of NAD and the dehydrogenation of $NADH_2$—should be involved here.

The succinyl-CoA either is used in synthetic reactions (cf. Chapt. IX–1) or is converted to succinate; the energy content is preserved as chemical energy by the coupled transformation of *guanosine diphosphate* (GDP) and orthophosphate to the energy-rich *guanosine triphosphate* (GTP). Evidently, the adenylic acid system does not always have to participate directly; in this case, it is in a secondary equilibrium relation with the GDP-GTP system.

Dehydrogenation of succinate introduces a C—C double bond to give rise to the *trans*-compound *fumarate* (step 7). The enzyme succinate dehydrogenase is a flavoprotein and is a member of the respiratory chain (cf. Chapt. X–4). This reaction is inhibited by malonate—the classical example of competitive inhibition: The "wrong substrate" is attached to the enzyme, but cannot undergo the reaction for simple chemical reasons.

Water is added across the double bond of fumarate in a reaction which is catalyzed by the enzyme fumarase. The reaction is reversible, although slightly exergonic. At equilibrium there is 82% L-*malate*. In the ninth and last step of the cycle, the secondary hydroxyl group of malate is dehydrogenated. The enzyme malate dehydrogenase transfers the hydrogen to NAD. The product of this reaction is *oxaloacetate*, the primer for the whole chain of reactions. The cycle is closed and we have finished one trip around it.

In summary we can see that one $C_2$ fragment, the activated acetate, forms a $C_6$ compound which is then broken down *via* a complicated series of nine steps to the same $C_4$ compound which initially entered the cycle as a carrier. Two carbon atoms are removed in steps 4 and 5. In addition, four times 2 H atoms are taken up by codehydrogenases and oxidized to $H_2O$ in the respiratory chain.

Actually it is not quite correct to say that the same oxaloacetate molecule is introduced merely as a carrier and appears again. It has been found, in fact, that two C atoms of the oxaloacetate are split off and the acetate added originally is retained in the new oxaloacetate molecule. These fine points are of subordinate significance and are interesting only because citrate, a symmetrical molecule, behaves here like an asymmetric compound. Ogston was able to explain this by suggesting that citrate is bound to the enzyme surface at three points and water is removed from one side only.

## 3. Energy Yield of the Citrate Cycle

In the citrate cycle, water is taken up and one molecule of activated acetate is broken down into 2 $CO_2$ and hydrogen which is bound to the coenzymes $(4 \cdot [2\text{ H}])$. The combined steps[3] yield a relatively small decrease of free energy ($\Delta F° = -25$

---

[3] For exhaustive calculations see M. Netter, "Theoretische Biochemie," Springer Verlag, Berlin, 1959.

kcal), essentially explained by the cleavage of the energy-rich CoA bond ($-8$ kcal) and by the two decarboxylation reactions. Thermodynamically, this is an advantage because at equilibrium all the reactants can be present in comparable concentrations.

For the cycle to run in this fashion—i.e., anaerobically—there would always have to be a fresh supply of NAD to enter the cycle as a true substrate. But actually the coenzyme is present only in catalytic amounts and is regenerated continuously. The citrate cycle runs only in conjunction with the respiratory chain, and the calculation of energy yields must be revised. Indeed, of a total of 216 kcal of chemical energy released 191 are due to the respiratory chain. This should make it quite clear that the energy is really derived from the formation of water and not from $CO_2$ production!

The organism utilizes this energy in part as heat—to maintain its body temperature—and partly as chemical energy in the form of ATP gained from oxidative phosphorylation. The net result is:

| | |
|---|---:|
| from steps 3, 5, and 9, three ATP for each $NADH_2$ oxidized, or a total of | 9 ATP |
| from step 7, through flavin oxidation | 2 ATP |
| from step 6, through transfer of the energy-rich bond | 1 ATP |
| Total: | 12 ATP |

Under standard conditions this corresponds to a total amount of energy of $12 \times 7 = 84$ kcal/mole of activated acetate or an efficiency of about 40% of the theoretically available free energy.

In general, the storage of energy in the form of ATP is probably more important for the body than the incidentally produced heat. For most purposes it suffices to know the ATP yield in moles per mole of oxidized acetate (through the cooperation of the citrate cycle and the respiratory chain).

## 4. Relations to Synthetic Tasks. Glyoxylate Cycle

The citrate cycle is not only a degradative scheme, but at the same time furnishes a general pool of intermediate products. It accepts the $C_2$ fragments from carbohydrate, fat, and protein catabolism; it is involved in the synthesis of glucose (which will be discussed in Chapt. XV, the key substance being oxaloacetate); it provides the raw material for the synthesis of several amino acids, aspartate and glutamate, for example. Finally, the blood pigment also arises from succinyl-CoA, another intermediate of the cycle.

On the other hand, the cycle demands for its proper functioning sufficient reserves of oxaloacetate. If oxaloacetate is converted to aspartate, or if some other intermediate is diverted, the cycle falters; acetyl-CoA cannot enter the cycle without the acceptor molecule oxaloacetate. It is highly significant, therefore, that oxaloacetate may also be formed from pyruvate, the key substance of carbohydrate breakdown (*via* malate, cf. Chapt. XV–10).

In some microorganisms an interesting variation of the citrate cycle is realized. There the emphasis is not on the degradation of activated acetate, but rather on the synthesis of succinate, malate, and oxaloacetate (and eventually of carbohydrates) from acetyl-CoA. Two new reactions have been added:

(1) Cleavage of isocitrate into succinate and *glyoxylate*, the reverse of an aldol condensation.

(2) Condensation of glyoxylate with acetyl-CoA, similar to the formation of citrate (which means addition of the methyl group of acetate to the carbonyl group), resulting directly in the formation of malate.

With the addition of some reactions of the citrate cycle, we may draw the following scheme:

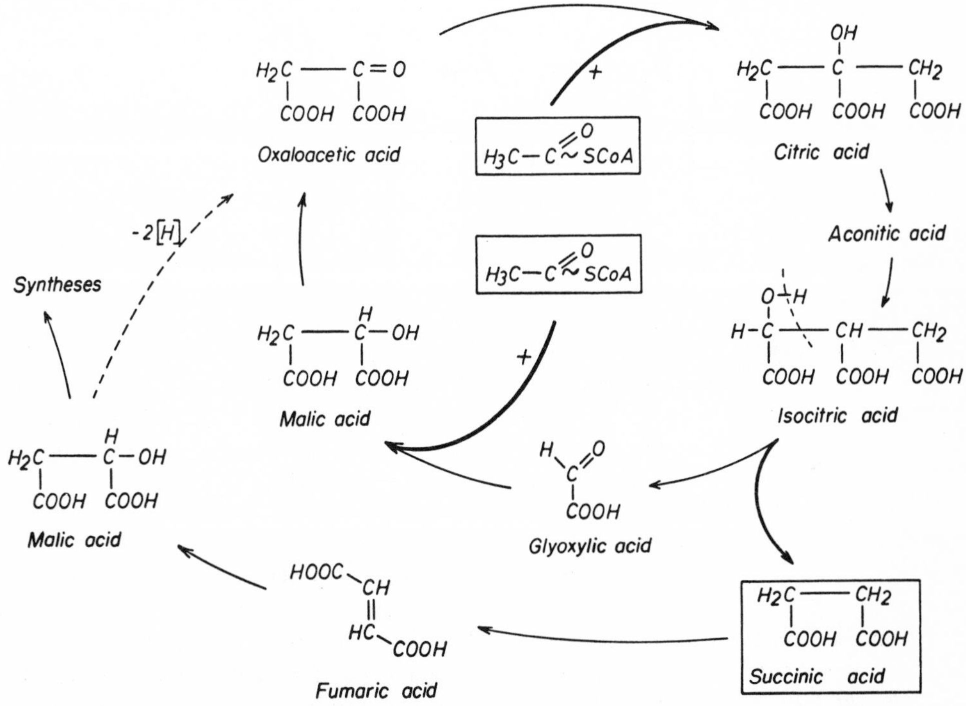

Oxaloacetate can be regenerated from both cleavage products of isocitrate: From glyoxylate by condensation with acetyl-CoA to form malate which is subsequently dehydrogenated, and from succinate through the usual citrate cycle. As a net result, 2 moles of activated acetate have been converted to succinate which can undergo further reactions by familiar pathways. Other synthetic pathways branch off these secondary products.

It is of historical interest that the linkage of 2 moles of acetate with elimination of 2 H to form succinate was already postulated by Wieland and Thunberg around 1920 and had long been considered a central reaction of metabolism.

The *glyoxylate cycle* does not exist in the mammalian organism. The search for the enzymes in question has been fruitless. The cycle plays a dominant role, however, in plant seedlings, which utilize fat reserves in this way for synthetic purposes, and in microorganisms which grow on fatty acids or acetic acid as an exclusive source of carbon.

BIBLIOGRAPHY

S. R. Dickman, Aconitase, *in* "The Enzymes" (P. D. Boyer, H. Lardy, and K. Myrbäck, editors), Vol. 5, pp. 495–510, Academic Press, New York, 1961.

H. L. Kornberg and H. A. Krebs, Synthesis of cell constituents from $C_2$ units by a modified tricarboxylic cycle, *Nature*, **179**, 988 (1957).

E. M. Kosower, "Molecular Biochemistry," pp. 14–17, and pp. 71–90, McGraw-Hill Book Co., New York, 1962.

J. M. Wiame, Le rôle biosynthetique du cycle des acides tricarboxyliques, *Advances in Enzymol.*, **18**, 241 (1957).

# CHAPTER XII

# Fats and Fat
# Metabolism

The fats proper and fat-like materials are classified together as "lipids" mainly because of their similar solubilities. Without exception, they are almost insoluble in water but very soluble in common organic solvents such as benzene, ether, chloroform, or chloroform-methanol mixtures. Fat-like materials will be discussed in subsequent chapters without emphasizing their similarities to fats.

## 1. Chemical Composition of Fats

Neutral fats are composed of several simpler compounds. Chemically they are esters (cf. Chapt. I–2). Their acid components are unbranched monocarboxylic acids, the *fatty acids*. The alcohol component is invariably *glycerol*, which has three hydroxyl groups (a trihydric alcohol):

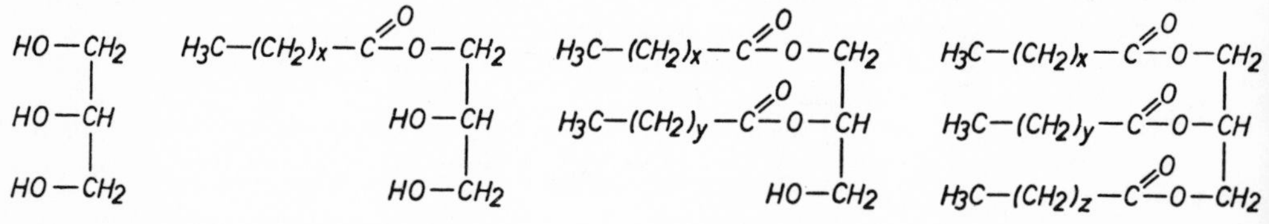

$$HO-CH_2 \qquad H_3C-(CH_2)_x-C\overset{O}{\underset{}{=}}O-CH_2 \qquad H_3C-(CH_2)_x-C\overset{O}{\underset{}{=}}O-CH_2 \qquad H_3C-(CH_2)_x-C\overset{O}{\underset{}{=}}O-CH_2$$

$$HO-CH \qquad\qquad\qquad HO-CH \qquad H_3C-(CH_2)_y-C\overset{O}{\underset{}{=}}O-CH \qquad H_3C-(CH_2)_y-C\overset{O}{\underset{}{=}}O-CH$$

$$HO-CH_2 \qquad\qquad\qquad HO-CH_2 \qquad\qquad HO-CH_2 \qquad H_3C-(CH_2)_z-C\overset{O}{\underset{}{=}}O-CH_2$$

| Glycerol | Monoglyceride | Diglyceride | Triglyceride |

Being a trihydric alcohol, glycerol can form mono-, di-, or triesters. Such esters are designated as mono-, di-, or triglycerides. The triglycerides generally contain two or three different fatty acids.

Naturally occurring fats are always mixtures of numerous triglycerides; hence, the isolation of a pure triglyceride from such a mixture is inordinately laborious.

Upon hydrolyzation of the ester linkages the components are released. This is accomplished quite readily in alkaline solutions, in which case the alkali salts, the so-called *soaps*, rather than the free acids are released. The technic of preparing soaps is a very old one, and the term saponification has been applied in organic chemistry not only to the hydrolysis of fats but also to that of other esters, amides, and so forth.

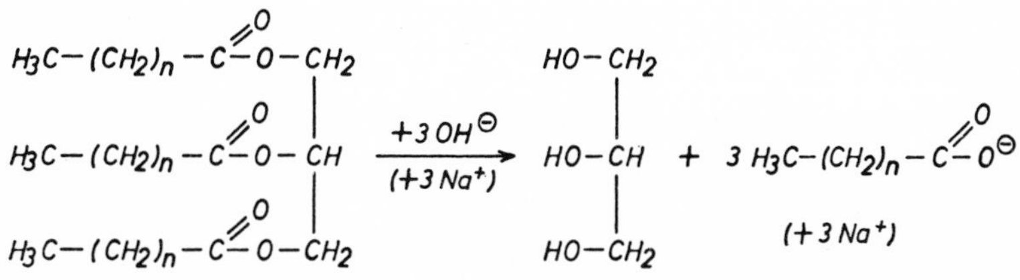

$$H_3C-(CH_2)_n-C\overset{O}{\underset{}{\diagup}}O-CH_2$$
$$H_3C-(CH_2)_n-C\overset{O}{\underset{}{\diagup}}O-CH \quad \xrightarrow[(+3\,Na^+)]{+3\,OH^{\ominus}} \quad HO-CH \quad + \quad 3\,H_3C-(CH_2)_n-C\overset{O}{\underset{}{\diagup}}O^{\ominus}$$
$$H_3C-(CH_2)_n-C\overset{O}{\underset{}{\diagup}}O-CH_2$$

HO-CH_2 ... HO-CH ... HO-CH_2 ... (+3 Na⁺)

**Fatty Acids.** All the acids of the naturally occurring fats have an even number of carbon atoms. This phenomenon is quite understandable in the light of the fact that they are all synthesized from $C_2$ units (acetyl radicals) (cf. Section 6). It is not so clear, however, why acids with 16 or 18 C atoms, e.g., palmitic acid ($C_{16}H_{32}O_2$) and stearic acid ($C_{18}H_{36}O_2$), are most commonly found in nature.

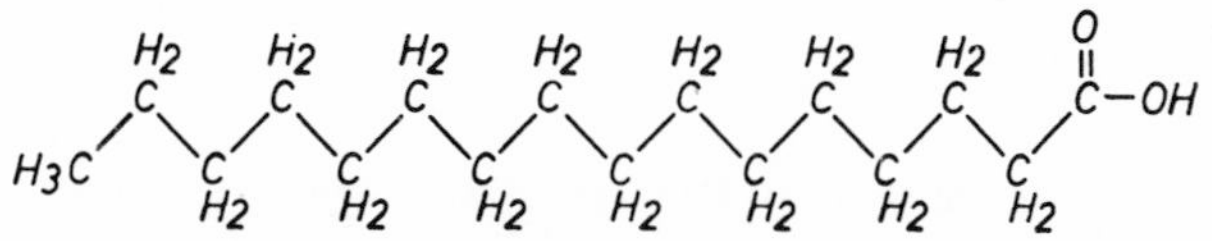

Palmitic acid

(Simplified formula)

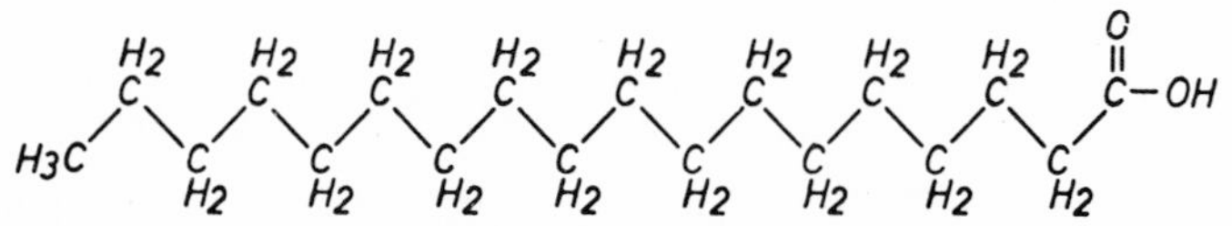

Stearic acid

(Simplified formula)

For the sake of simplicity in this and subsequent chapters we shall represent the long chains of $CH_2$ groups by zigzag lines, in which each corner corresponds to a C atom; the hydrogens are left out. The zigzag line represents the most stable configuration of such carbon chains.

In addition to the saturated fatty acids, *unsaturated fatty acids* are frequently found, especially with the double bond between C atoms 9 and 10 (the carboxyl C atom is number 1). This makes oleic acid almost symmetrical because the double bond is located exactly in the middle of the chain. It should be recalled (Chapt. I-4) that double bonds give rise to stereo-isomerism: The substituents of the two C atoms linked by the double bond can be arranged either *cis* or *trans* to each other. *Oleic acid* is a *cis*-compound; the *trans*-form may be prepared by reactions involving chemical rearrangement; it is called *elaidic acid*.

Some more highly unsaturated fatty acids are *linoleic, linolenic,* and *arachidonic acids.* It should be noted that the double bonds are always separated by *two* C—C single bonds; they are "isolated" as the chemist would say. Double bonds separated by only one single bond have special properties, notably in their UV-absorption spectra (cf. Chapt. XIV-7, carotenoids).

*Linoleic* and *linolenic acids* abound in certain vegetable oils, e.g. linseed oil. Mammals evidently are unable to synthesize them and therefore depend on them as essential food components (also called "vitamin F"; see Chapt. XXII). Fish livers contain even more highly unsaturated fatty acids. Polyunsaturated fatty acids with 20–24 C atoms and 4–6 double bonds are synthesized in the mammalian organism from linolenic acid. They are components of several phosphatides (Klenk).

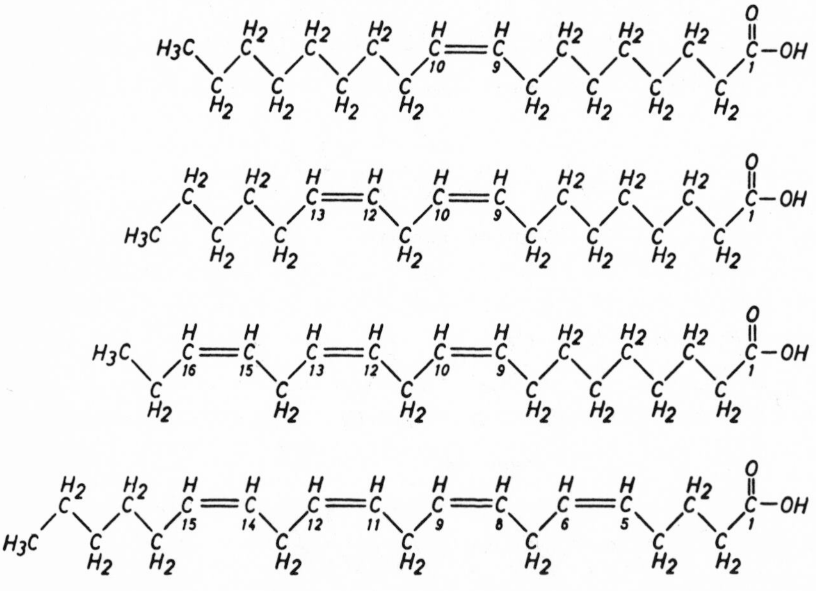

Oleic acid $C_{18}H_{34}O_2$

Linoleic acid $C_{18}H_{32}O_2$

Linolenic acid $C_{18}H_{30}O_2$

Arachidonic acid $C_{20}H_{32}O_2$

**Hardening of Fats.** Fats that contain a large proportion of saturated fatty acids (there is always a variety of fatty acids in a fat) have a higher melting point and are solid at room temperature, whereas those fats with a high content of unsaturated fatty acids are liquid or oily (the term *oil* denotes consistency and not a chemical structure). The unsaturated bonds can be hydrogenated by adding catalytically activated hydrogen to the double bonds. The melting point of the fats is raised by this procedure so that previously oily fats become solid at room temperature; hence, the term "hardening" of fats. The process plays a significant role in the production of shortening and consequently in the nutrition of man.

**Waxes,** too, are esters; but in this case glycerol is replaced by higher aliphatic monohydroxy alcohols. From beeswax, myricin, an ester of palmitic acid and myricyl alcohol, $C_{30}H_{61}OH$, has been isolated; from spermaceti (or "head oil" of the sperm whale), cetyl palmitate, $CH_3(CH_2)_{14}COOC_{16}H_{33}$. Natural waxes are not homogeneous substances, of course, but are mixtures which are difficult to separate; besides the esters, they contain hydrocarbons, esters of sterols, free fatty acids, and hydroxy fatty acids.

## 2. Fats as Depot Material

The fats play a major role in human nutrition (and in the nutrition of many animals). Fats are nutrients of high caloric value (cf. also Chapt. XXII–1), but their real biologic significance lies in the fact that they constitute reserve stores for the organism. Any foodstuffs ingested beyond the normal requirements are largely converted to fat and deposited in appropriate tissues. Then in times of need the fat is again made available. The fat of the liver has a much more rapid turnover than that of the adipose tissue. In the rat the biologic half-life for liver fat is 1–2 days; for depot fat it is 15–20 days.

In certain tissues, fats are also structural components, although in relatively small amounts compared to the more important fat-like phosphatides, sterols, etc. And in most membrane material they participate in the construction of the protein-lipid double layers (Chapt. XIX–3).

Whenever the organism utilizes dietary fats or calls on its fat reserves, it must first degrade them. The initial step is the hydrolytic cleavage catalyzed by lipases to release glycerol and fatty acids.

**Lipases.** These enzymes are hydrolases, subgroup esterases. They split ester bonds; with the uptake of one molecule of water a free fatty acid and a diglyceride are produced; with continued action the second and third acid residues are also removed.

Lipases are widely distributed. Unusually high concentrations are found in the pancreas, in the intestinal wall, and the liver. The pancreatic lipase hydrolyzes only fatty acids in $\alpha$- or $\alpha'$-position, whereas the enzyme of the intestinal wall attacks the $\beta$-position as well. The true lipases act only on emulsified fats, and not on soluble fats.

Lipases are often cited as examples of synthetic enzymes. With the proper choice of concentrations *in vitro* (very high proportion of glycerol) appreciable amounts of esters are found at equilibrium. Within the cell or in the intestine, however, the reactant water is present in great excess and, therefore, biosynthesis by lipases is impossible. The equilibrium under *in vivo* conditions is entirely on the side of cleavage (for fat synthesis see Section 6).

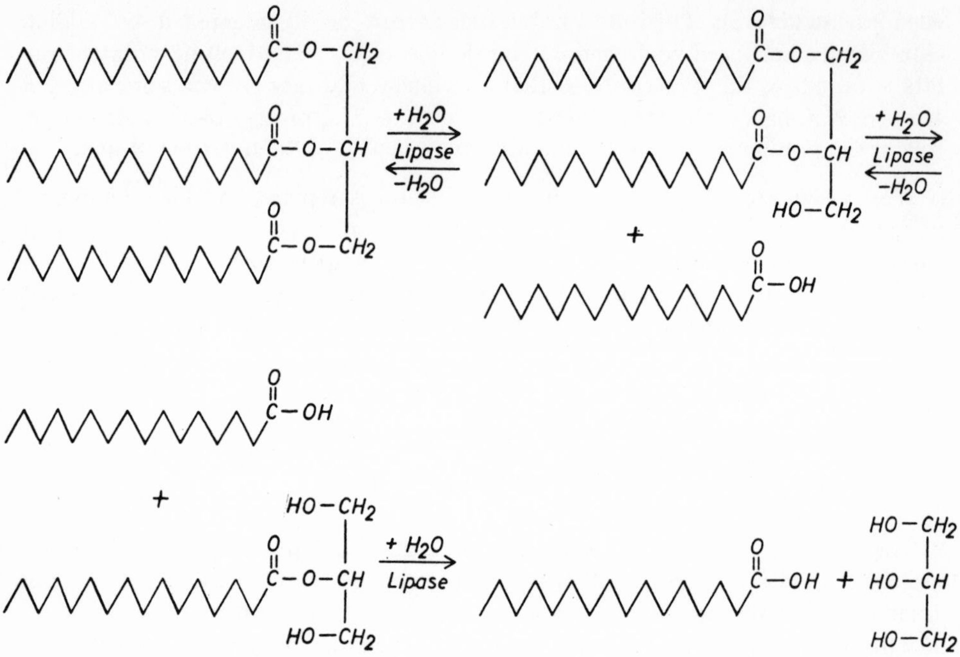

The cleavage products follow separate pathways of metabolism. Glycerol, closely related to carbohydrates, is either utilized for the biosynthesis of fructose and glucose or, after phosphorylation, is broken down in the same way as the carbohydrates (Chapt. XVIII–1). Fatty acids are decomposed according to the rules of $\beta$-oxidation to $C_2$ units (activated acetate) which may then either be used for biosynthesis or be oxidized to $CO_2$ and $H_2O$ through the citrate cycle (Chapt. XI) and the respiratory chain.

## 3. $\beta$-Oxidation of Fatty Acids

Fatty acids are relatively inert chemically. Their reactivity is raised when they become converted to thioesters. Thioesters have a great potential for group transfer; they are "energy-rich." The thiol group is provided by coenzyme A, which contains $\beta$-mercaptoethylamine (formula Chapt. VI–5). The formation of the energy-rich bond requires an expenditure of 1 ATP:

$$CH_3\!-\!(CH_2)_n\!-\!COOH + ATP + HS\!-\!\overline{CoA} \rightarrow CH_3\!-\!(CH_2)_n\!-\!CO\!-\!S\overline{CoA} + AMP + PP$$

This net equation can be rewritten in two parts. Initially the fatty acid reacts with ATP and an enzyme and by loss of pyrophosphate forms the intermediate acyl adenylate (Chapt. VI–5) which is then transformed by $\overline{CoA}$—SH to acyl-$\overline{SCoA}$ and AMP.

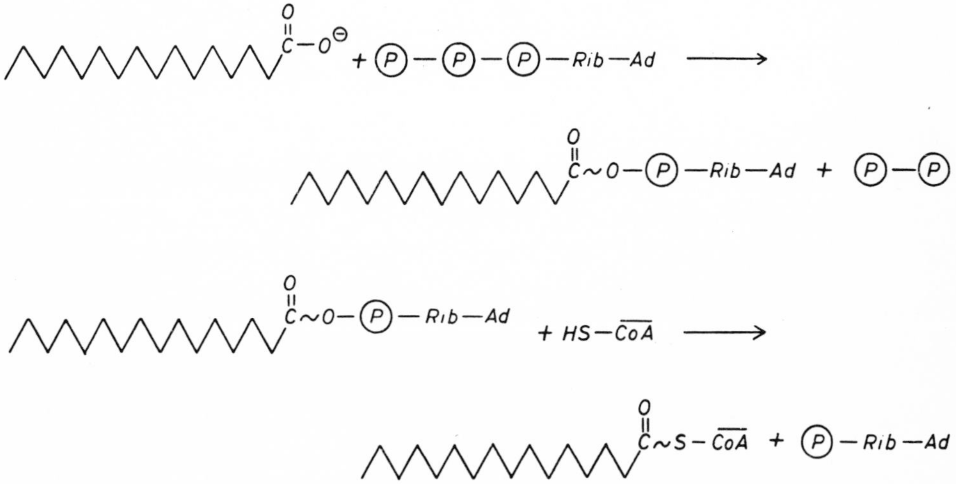

$$\text{/\!\!\!/\!\!\!/\!\!\!/}\overset{O}{\underset{||}{C}}-O^{\ominus} \; + \; \textcircled{P}-\textcircled{P}-\textcircled{P}-Rib-Ad \; \longrightarrow$$

$$\text{/\!\!\!/\!\!\!/\!\!\!/}\overset{O}{\underset{||}{C}}\sim O-\textcircled{P}-Rib-Ad \; + \; \textcircled{P}-\textcircled{P}$$

$$\text{/\!\!\!/\!\!\!/\!\!\!/}\overset{O}{\underset{||}{C}}\sim O-\textcircled{P}-Rib-Ad \; + \; HS-\overline{CoA} \; \longrightarrow$$

$$\text{/\!\!\!/\!\!\!/\!\!\!/}\overset{O}{\underset{||}{C}}\sim S-\overline{CoA} \; + \; \textcircled{P}-Rib-Ad$$

All further reactions of the β-oxidation take place on the fatty acyl-CoA compound (see diagram below). The activated compound is first dehydrogenated by a dehydrogenase (a flavoprotein); the product is the corresponding $\alpha,\beta$-unsaturated acyl-CoA compound. The enzyme *acyl dehydrogenase* contains flavin-adenine dinucleotide (FAD, cf. Chapt. VI–4) as the active group. There is a whole series of such enzymes, not just one, with differing substrate specificities; some prefer to act on long-chain fatty acids. ($C_{18}$, $C_{16}$, $C_{14}$), others on those of medium length or on short ones. The enzymes of the respiratory chain reoxidize the flavoproteins (Chapt. X–4) in order to permit them to dehydrogenate more fatty acids.

Water is then added across the double bond of the unsaturated fatty acyl-CoA compound to yield a β-hydroxy acid. Reaction 2 is catalyzed by *crotonase*. In the next step, the β-hydroxy group is dehydrogenated to the keto group (reaction 3). The enzyme for this step, called *β-hydroxyacyl dehydrogenase*, transfers hydrogen to NAD, whence it is transported along the respiratory chain to become oxidized to water. The dehydrogenated compound, the β-keto acid, is not very stable; with another molecule of $\overline{CoA}$—SH it is cleaved in the manner indicated below. The process is termed *thioclastic cleavage*, and the enzyme involved is *β-keto thiolase*. The prominent feature of the whole degradation is this reaction 4, the cleavage of a C—C bond. The two scission products are acetyl-CoA (called activated acetate because of its high potential for group transfer) and the remaining acyl-CoA molecule. Since the latter is bound to CoA it need not be activated by ATP according to the scheme presented before. The free energy of the cleavage reaction (4) has been preserved as chemical energy in the enzymic reaction with CoA (instead of water).

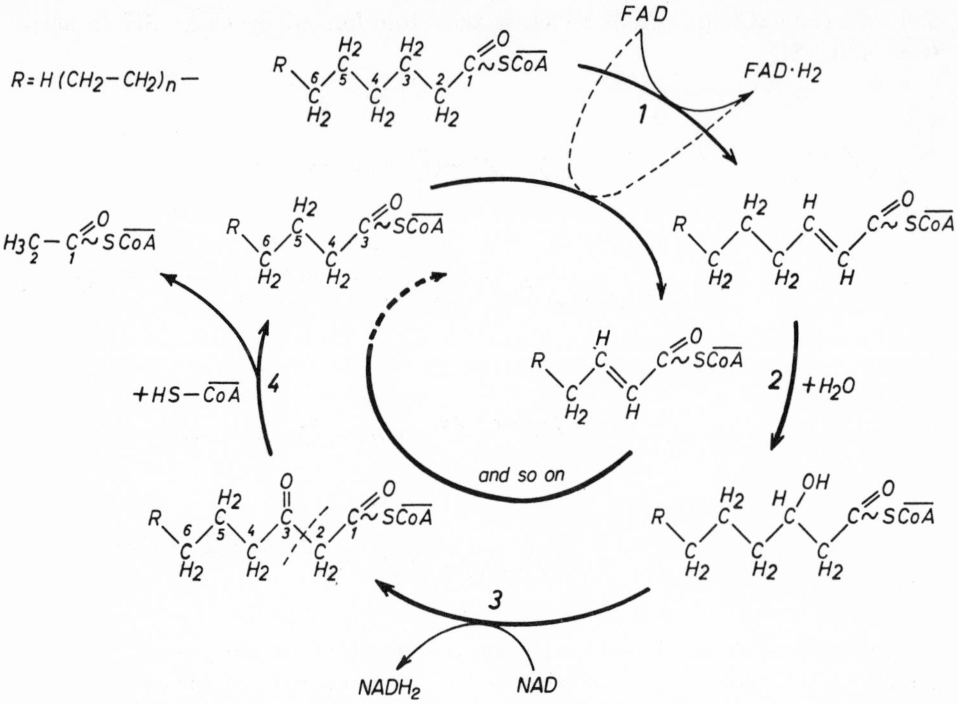

$R = H(CH_2-CH_2)_n-$

FAD

FAD·H$_2$

1

$R$ ... $C\sim SCoA$

$H_3C - C\sim SCoA$

$+HS-CoA$   4

and so on

2   $+H_2O$

3

NADH$_2$     NAD

Note that the newly formed acyl-CoA compound can again undergo reaction 1 and can run through the whole series of subsequent reactions without the need for another molecule of ATP. It suffices to have a fatty acid, be it 12, or 16, or 22 C atoms long, activated once with CoA (with consumption of 1 ATP) in order for it to be broken down step by step into $C_2$ units (acetyl-CoA units). Since without exception the chain is shortened by two C atoms at a time, and the dehydrogenation, hydration, and further dehydrogenation afford $\beta$-hydroxy and $\beta$-keto acids, the entire course of reactions is called simply $\beta$-oxidation.[1]

We should stop and ask ourselves what has been achieved up to this point. Energy has been gained first of all by funneling a number of hydrogen atoms through the respiratory chain: From each $C_2$ fragment two H atoms release 2 ATP *via* flavoprotein, and the other 2 H release 3 ATP *via* NAD, presuming complete phosphorylation, of course. But at this point we have not yet seen the production of $CO_2$; instead the organism has been flooded with activated acetate. Normally, acetyl-CoA is put to excellent use, either for synthesis (cf. Section 6 and Chapt. XIV–1, and summary in Chapt. XVIII–2) or for further breakdown through the citrate cycle (see Chap. XI). In pathologic conditions (e.g. in diabetes mellitus), however, this overproduction of acetyl-CoA is critical, because it gives rise to acetoacetate and acetone in urine.

---

[1] The principle of $\beta$-oxidation (degradation by two C atoms) was discovered more than 50 years ago by F. Knoop. The individual steps have been elucidated only very recently, chiefly by F. Lynen, F. Lipmann, D. E. Green, and others.

## 4. Formation of Acetoacetate—"Ketogenesis"

When a long-chain fatty acid has finally been degraded to the $C_4$ compound, butyrate (in the activated form), the next oxidation cycle in the $\beta$-position produces acetoacetate—or more correctly, acetoacetyl-CoA. The reaction is reversible as many others are; when acetyl-CoA is available in superabundance (e.g. during fasting, which causes the mobilization of fat reserves; or in diabetes, where due to pathologically elevated production of acetyl-CoA not all of it is used up), then acetoacetyl-CoA is formed from 2 acetyl-CoA.[2]

The activating group, coenzyme A, may be lost from acetoacetyl-CoA. Hydrolysis was formerly assumed, but now it seems more probable that the CoA moiety is transferred onto succinate, forming succinyl-CoA. Actually, however, the liberation of free acetoacetic acid appears to proceed primarily *via* a detour, an attempt at synthesis:

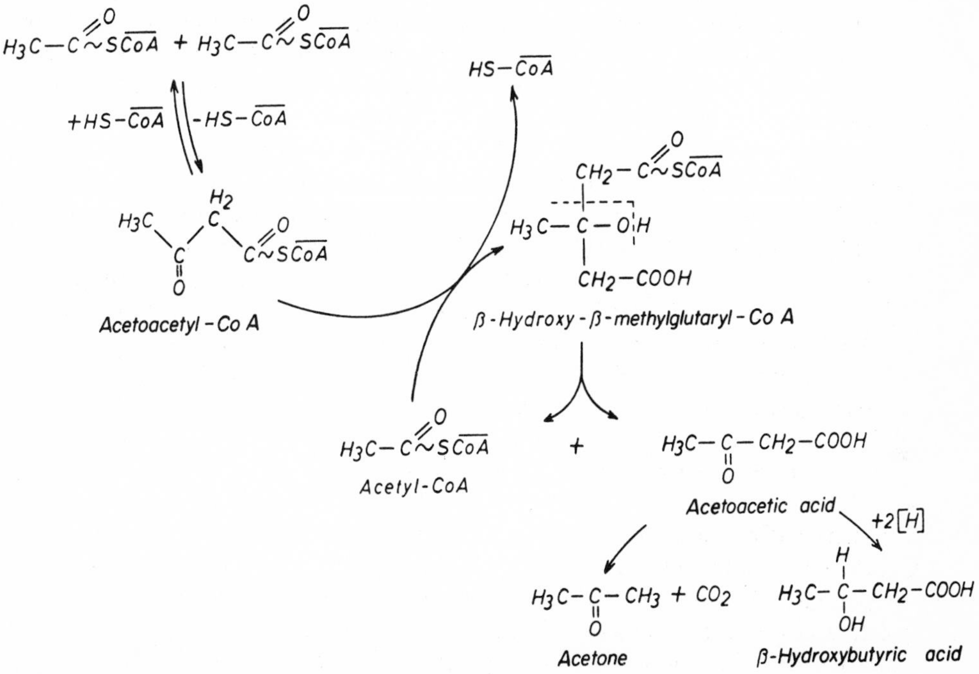

$$H_3C-C\overset{O}{\diagup}{\sim}S\overline{CoA} + H_3C-C\overset{O}{\diagup}{\sim}S\overline{CoA}$$

$$+HS-\overline{CoA} \quad\rightleftarrows\quad -HS-\overline{CoA}$$

$$H_3C-\underset{\underset{O}{\|}}{C}-\overset{H_2}{\underset{}{C}}-C{\sim}S\overline{CoA}$$

**Acetoacetyl-CoA**

$$HS-\overline{CoA}$$

$$\begin{aligned}&CH_2-C\overset{O}{\diagup}{\sim}S\overline{CoA}\\&\ \ |\\&H_3C-C-O\!H\\&\ \ |\\&CH_2-COOH\end{aligned}$$

**β-Hydroxy-β-methylglutaryl-CoA**

$$H_3C-C\overset{O}{\diagup}{\sim}S\overline{CoA} \quad + \quad H_3C-\underset{\underset{O}{\|}}{C}-CH_2-COOH$$

**Acetyl-CoA**      **Acetoacetic acid**   $+2[H]$

$$H_3C-\underset{\underset{O}{\|}}{C}-CH_3 + CO_2 \qquad H_3C-\underset{\underset{OH}{|}}{\overset{\overset{H}{|}}{C}}-CH_2-COOH$$

**Acetone**      **β-Hydroxybutyric acid**

Acetoacetyl-CoA condenses with one more molecule of acetyl-CoA at its carbonyl group. The C=O double bond is opened and a new C—C bond is formed. By the hydrolytic loss of one molecule of CoA, $\beta$-hydroxy-$\beta$-methylglutaryl-CoA is produced. This branched-chain acid is a precursor of cholesterol (cf. Chapt. XIV–1). But in our context, $\beta$-hydroxy-$\beta$-methylglutaryl-CoA is split again to release acetyl-CoA and free acetoacetate. The cleavage is very similar to the reverse of the synthesis. In this cycle a total of two molecules of acetyl-CoA are

---

[2] Malonyl—CoA is an intermediate.

converted to free acetoacetate and two molecules of CoA. The cycle is a mechanism for regenerating the coenzyme. Acetoacetate diffuses into the blood and eventually into the urine. Being a β-keto acid it can decarboxylate spontaneously to form acetone, but it can also be reduced enzymically to form β-hydroxybutyrate.

## 5. Metabolism of Branched-Chain Fatty Acids

In addition to the fatty acids with straight (unbranched) chains and an even number of C atoms, small amounts of acids with branched methyl groups or with an odd number of C atoms are also found in nature. Their metabolic fate in β-oxidation is of considerable interest and can best be studied on the examples of the methyl branched $C_4$- and the $C_5$-carboxylic acids. These two acids arise from the catabolism of the amino acids leucine, isoleucine, and valine by transamination and oxidative decarboxylation, as described in Chapt. VIII–10. Basically only two situations need to be discussed: one with a methyl group in the α-position, or potentially in α-position (i.e. by repeated shortening of the chain by two C atoms the methyl group eventually ends up in α-position); the other with a methyl group in the β-position, or at least potentially in β-position.

α-**Branching.** Isoleucine is initially broken down to α-methylbutyryl-CoA (Chapt. VIII–10). The methyl group does not impede the action of the acyl dehydrogenase; indeed, the breakdown continues to proceed normally through the stage of the unsaturated acid, the β-hydroxyl acid, and the β-keto acid. The specificity of the enzymes evidently is not strict enough to permit a methyl group to inhibit the reactions. Thioclastic cleavage yields two products: acetyl-CoA and propionyl-CoA. The methyl group was responsible for the formation of the next higher homolog (formulas below). Propionyl-CoA is carboxylated (with the cooperation of a biotin enzyme and ATP; cf. Chapt. VI–5) and converted to methylmalonyl-CoA. This derivative of a $C_4$-dicarboxylic acid can be isomerized (with the aid of vitamin $B_{12}$) to form succinic acid. The problem of this type of methyl branching is solved for the organism with this last step, because succinic acid can be metabolized along pathways discussed earlier (cf. citric acid cycle, Chapt. XI–1).

Unbranched fatty acids with an odd number of carbon atoms similarly end up as propionyl-CoA (instead of acetyl-CoA) after β-oxidation. They are oxidized completely in the same way as the branched-chain acids.

Oxidative decarboxylation of *valine* produces isobutyryl-CoA, which is then subjected to a modified fatty acid degradation: Dehydrogenation is followed by addition of water to the double bond. The product is not a secondary, but a primary alcohol group which apparently is not attacked by the enzyme β-hydroxyacyl dehydrogenase. After the hydrolytic removal of the CoA group, dehydrogenation to methylmalonate semialdehyde can take place. This β-aldehyde acid is easily decarboxylated to yield propionic aldehyde, which subsequently is oxidized to the acid. Propionic acid reacts in the manner indicated above. This scheme points out that, although the degradative pathway is the same in principle, certain detours are followed occasionally. In this case, methylmalonate semialdehyde first is decarboxylated and propionate is carboxylated to give back methylmalonate. The explanation is probably found in the specificity of the participating enzymes.

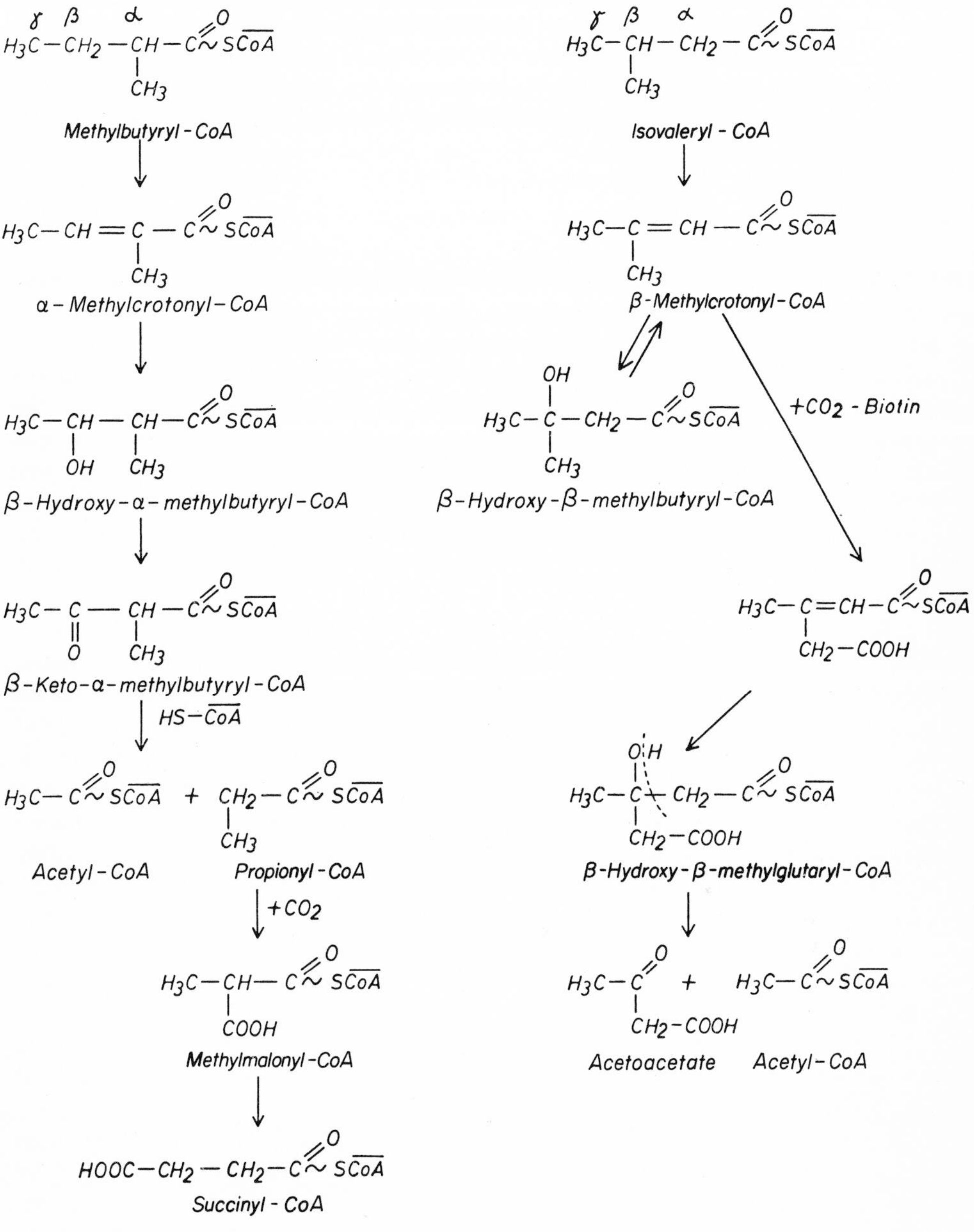

$$\overset{\gamma}{H_3C}-\overset{\beta}{CH_2}-\overset{\alpha}{CH}-C\!\!\overset{O}{\underset{\sim}{\diagup}}\,S\overline{CoA}$$
$$|$$
$$CH_3$$

Methylbutyryl-CoA

↓

$$H_3C-CH=C-C\!\!\overset{O}{\underset{\sim}{\diagup}}\,S\overline{CoA}$$
$$|$$
$$CH_3$$

α-Methylcrotonyl-CoA

↓

$$H_3C-CH-CH-C\!\!\overset{O}{\underset{\sim}{\diagup}}\,S\overline{CoA}$$
$$|\qquad|$$
$$OH\quad CH_3$$

β-Hydroxy-α-methylbutyryl-CoA

↓

$$H_3C-C-CH-C\!\!\overset{O}{\underset{\sim}{\diagup}}\,S\overline{CoA}$$
$$\|\qquad|$$
$$O\quad CH_3$$

β-Keto-α-methylbutyryl-CoA

↓ HS—$\overline{CoA}$

$$H_3C-C\!\!\overset{O}{\underset{\sim}{\diagup}}\,S\overline{CoA}\;+\;CH_2-C\!\!\overset{O}{\underset{\sim}{\diagup}}\,S\overline{CoA}$$
$$|$$
$$CH_3$$

Acetyl-CoA    Propionyl-CoA

↓ +CO₂

$$H_3C-CH-C\!\!\overset{O}{\underset{\sim}{\diagup}}\,S\overline{CoA}$$
$$|$$
$$COOH$$

Methylmalonyl-CoA

↓

$$HOOC-CH_2-CH_2-C\!\!\overset{O}{\underset{\sim}{\diagup}}\,S\overline{CoA}$$

Succinyl-CoA

---

$$\overset{\gamma}{H_3C}-\overset{\beta}{CH}-\overset{\alpha}{CH_2}-C\!\!\overset{O}{\underset{\sim}{\diagup}}\,S\overline{CoA}$$
$$|$$
$$CH_3$$

Isovaleryl-CoA

↓

$$H_3C-C=CH-C\!\!\overset{O}{\underset{\sim}{\diagup}}\,S\overline{CoA}$$
$$|$$
$$CH_3$$

β-Methylcrotonyl-CoA

↙    ↘ +CO₂ - Biotin

$$OH$$
$$|$$
$$H_3C-C-CH_2-C\!\!\overset{O}{\underset{\sim}{\diagup}}\,S\overline{CoA}$$
$$|$$
$$CH_3$$

β-Hydroxy-β-methylbutyryl-CoA

$$H_3C-C=CH-C\!\!\overset{O}{\underset{\sim}{\diagup}}\,S\overline{CoA}$$
$$|$$
$$CH_2-COOH$$

↙

$$O\!H$$
$$|$$
$$H_3C-C\!\!\!\!\not\,\,-CH_2-C\!\!\overset{O}{\underset{\sim}{\diagup}}\,S\overline{CoA}$$
$$|$$
$$CH_2-COOH$$

β-Hydroxy-β-methylglutaryl-CoA

↓

$$H_3C-C\!\!\overset{O}{\diagup}\;+\;H_3C-C\!\!\overset{O}{\underset{\sim}{\diagup}}\,S\overline{CoA}$$
$$|$$
$$CH_2-COOH$$

Acetoacetate    Acetyl-CoA

**β-Branching.** Branching in the form of a methyl group in β-position, for example isovaleryl-CoA, the degradation product of leucine, poses a more formidable problem. The sequence of formulas shown above reveals that by dehydrogenation the unsaturated compound can be formed and water can be added to it, but the resulting tertiary alcohol cannot be further dehydrogenated to form the keto compound. The regular pathway of breakdown is blocked there.

Carboxylation of the unsaturated compound again turns out to be the escape route from the impasse; a biotin-activated carbon dioxide is involved in the reaction. Addition of water to the new compound results in hydroxymethylglutarate (in the CoA form) which in turn—as already seen—breaks into acetoacetate and acetyl-CoA, or which can undergo further reactions to form the "active isoprene unit" (cf. Chapt. XIV–1). Thus the acids with $\beta$-methyl branches have also been brought back to common metabolic reactions. We can now appreciate why leucine is particularly ketogenic; it is degraded directly to acetoacetate (and not to aceto-acetyl-CoA).

## 6. Biosynthesis of Fatty Acids

Fat can be synthesized in the mammalian organism from various other food-stuffs, as is amply demonstrated by the hog; when fed with potatoes or bran (i.e. a diet rich in carbohydrates) it puts on much fat.

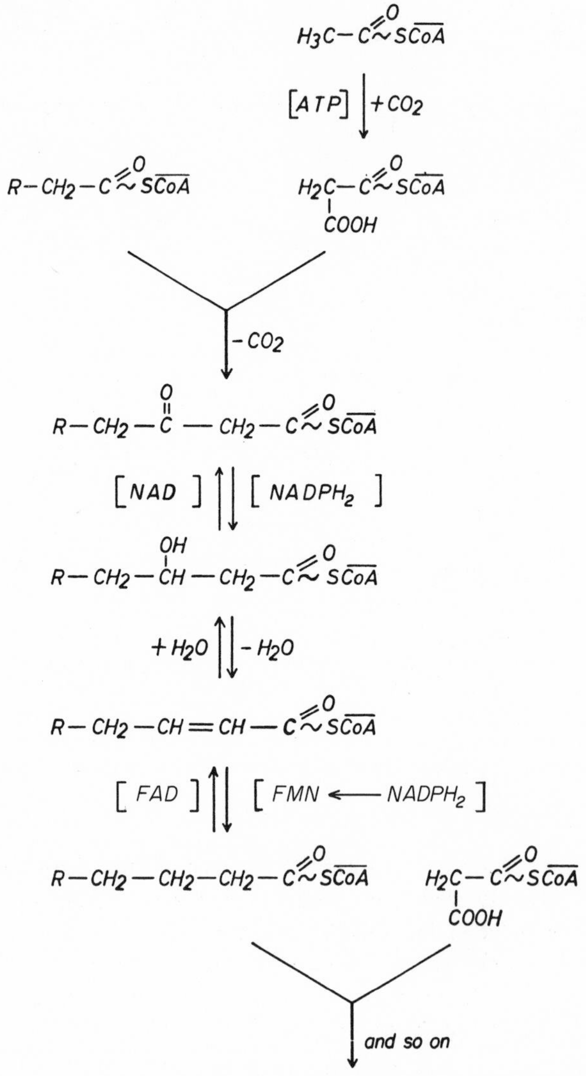

The biosynthesis begins with acetyl-CoA, which is the most important intermediate in the breakdown of carbohydrates as well as fats and which has already occupied our attention. Since all reactions of β-oxidation are reversible, it was thought at first that the catabolic reactions would be reversed by an excessive supply of reduced coenzymes and energy in the form of ATP (or acetyl-thioester). The organism, however, does not appear to use this possibility, except perhaps to a minor extent, and instead prefers to follow an alternate route for synthesis.

Acetyl-CoA was found to add $CO_2$ with the aid of a specific, biotin-containing enzyme to form *malonyl-CoA*. The reaction is ATP-dependent and passes through the intermediate "active carboxyl," the carboxy-biotin (cf. Chapt. VI–5). Malonyl-CoA contains an unusually reactive $CH_2$ group that combines easily with acyl-CoA (acetyl-CoA or higher activated fatty acids). The result is, with loss of $CO_2$, a β-keto acid (as shown on page 222):

The subsequent conversions essentially parallel the reverse of the β-oxidation. They differ, however, in that the reductions of both the β-keto acid and the unsaturated acyl-CoA derivative require $NADPH_2$. The whole process can now be repeated.

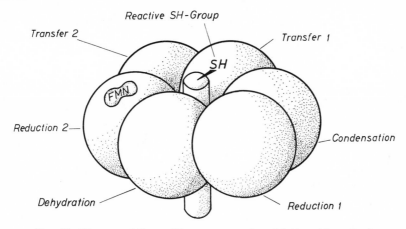

FIG. 38. Diagram of the multi-enzyme complex of fatty acid synthesis.

Lynen has isolated from yeast a multi-enzyme complex (see Fig. 38) which carries out the entire synthesis of long-chain fatty acids at one swoop. The reaction series commences with the transfer of a malonyl residue to a reactive SH group of one protein (transfer 1 in the figure). Acetyl-CoA (or a longer chain acyl-CoA) then condenses with the malonyl residue to yield the β-keto derivative, which remains bound to the SH group of the complex. Now, in succession, follow reduction to the hydroxyl group, elimination of a molecule of water, and the second reduction (of the C—C double bond) with the participation of a flavin group (FMN) firmly fixed to the protein molecule. The FMN group takes over the hydrogen of $NADPH_2$. The elongated acyl molecule is returned to CoA in a second transfer and thus is ready to undergo another condensation in a new cycle; a new malonyl residue is attached to the central SH group and the reaction continues. Only when the final length of $C_{16}$ (or $C_{18}$) is reached is palmityl-CoA (or stearyl-CoA) set free.

It is remarkable that fatty acid synthesis for a long stretch runs in common with the reverse of β-oxidation, but deviates in one significant step. A very similar situation will be found with the carbohydrates. The detour is more favorable thermodynamically (synthesis is favored by the equilibrium) but does require one extra ATP per $C_2$ unit. Note also that the detour permits separate regulation of synthesis and degradation.

**Synthesis of Fats from Fatty Acids.** The above biosynthesis releases fatty acids in the form of the acyl-CoA derivatives. They are then stored as glycerol esters, i.e. as neutral fats. Esterification does not take place on the glycerol molecule itself, but rather on glycerol phosphate, which could have arisen, e.g., from reduction of dihydroxyacetone phosphate (cf. Chapt. XVIII–2). There is an enzyme which is responsible for the formation of diglyceride phosphate (also called phosphatidic acid) from glycerol phosphate and 2 moles of activated fatty acid. CoA—SH is released in the process. It is important for the organism to have the coenzyme A available for other reactions.

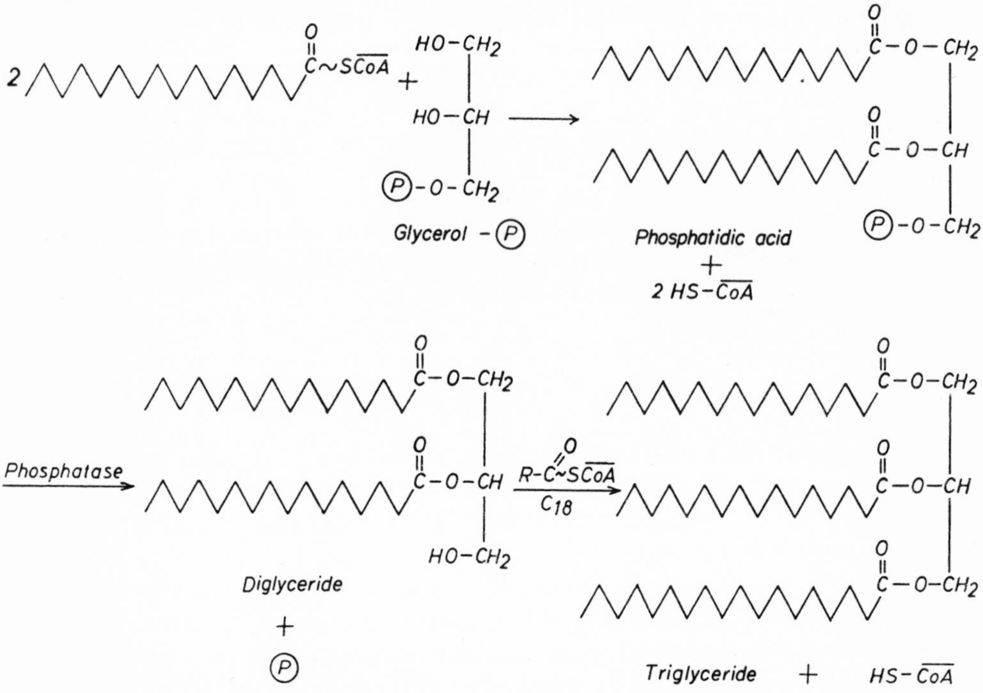

Glycerol – (P)          Phosphatidic acid
                              +
                          2 HS–CoA

Diglyceride          Triglyceride   +   HS–CoA
      +
    (P)

The enzyme is not very specific for definite chain lengths of the activated acids; it reacts more swiftly, however, with $C_{16}$-, $C_{17}$-, and $C_{18}$-fatty acids. This fact provides one possible explanation for the predominance of $C_{16}$- and $C_{18}$-fatty acids in neutral fats.

In the last step, the diglyceride phosphate is dephosphorylated by the action of a phosphatase and is brought to reaction with another mole of acyl-CoA. So-called neutral fat has been formed and can be stored as depot fat (or organ fat).

### BIBLIOGRAPHY

K. Bloch, "Lipide Metabolism," Wiley, New York, 1960.

J. K. Grant (editor), "The Control of Lipid Metabolism," 191 pp., Academic Press, New York 1963; *Biochem. Soc. Symposium (Cambridge, Engl.) No. 42* held at Oxford, 19 July, 1963.

T. P. Hilditch, "The Chemical Composition of Natural Fats," 3rd ed., Chapman and Hall, London, 1956.

H. P. Kaufmann, "Analyse der Fette und Fettprodukte," Vol. 1, Springer Verlag, Berlin, 1958.

F. Lynen, Participation of acyl—CoA in carbon chain biosynthesis, *J. Comp. Physiol.*, **54**, Suppl. 1, 33 (1959).

F. Lynen and M. Tada, The biochemical basis of the "polyacetate rule," *Angew. Chem.* **73**, 513 (1961).

H. M. Sinclair, "Essential Fatty Acids," Butterworths, London, 1958.

P. R. Vagelos, Lipid metabolism, *Ann. Rev. Biochem.*, **33**, 139–172 (1964).

# CHAPTER XIII

# Phosphatides, Cerebrosides,

# Gangliosides

These substances, together with the sterols (Chapt. XIV), are called lipoid (fat-like) because of their solubility properties. Lipoid substances serve primarily as structural components; they form hydrophobic (water-repelling) layers. Membranes frequently contain protein-lipoid double layers.

## 1. Occurrence and Classification

Phosphatides, often called phospholipids, are present in all cells; usually they are components of cell membranes. Nerve tissue in particular is rich in phosphatides, cerebrosides, and gangliosides. Egg yolk is another excellent source of phosphatides (especially lecithins).

Chemically, *phosphatides* are diesters of phosphoric acid, which is esterified both with glycerol or sphingosine and with choline, ethanolamine, serine, or inositol. The *cerebrosides* do not contain phosphate, but are structurally very similar to the sphingosine phosphatides. The *gangliosides* are analogous to the sphingosine cerebrosides, but generally are more complicated and have higher molecular weights, and for these reasons have been placed in a separate classification by Klenk. The above names are taken from a now obsolete system of classifying fat-like material. It appears to be more logical to classify them according to the main alcohol component, as shown in Table XVI.

The list probably is not complete. Structural lipids can by no means be considered to have been studied exhaustively. Their fractionation is extraordinarily difficult, since tissue always contains mixtures from which individual homogeneous components can be extracted only by much tedious effort. Modern techniques of separation have given new stimulus to this line of investigation.

**General Significance of Phosphatides and Glycolipids.** We have pointed out that nerve tissue characteristically is rich in lipid material. The fine structure of nerves, particularly of the myelin sheath, can be understood only if one understands

Table XVI

Classification of Phosphatides and Glycolipids

| Name | Main Alcohol Component | Other Alcohol Components | P:N Ratio |
|---|---|---|---|
| **I. Glycerophosphatides** | | | |
| 1. Phosphatidic acids | Diglyceride ( = glycerol diester) | | 1:0 |
| 2. Lecithins | Diglyceride ( = glycerol diester) | Choline | 1:1 |
| 3. Cephalins | Diglyceride ( = glycerol diester) | Ethanolamine, serine | 1:1 |
| 4. Inositides | Diglyceride ( = glycerol diester) | Inositol | 1:0 |
| 5. Plasmalogens ("acetal phosphatides") | Glycerol ester and enol ether | Ethanolamine, choline | 1:1 |
| **II. Sphingolipids** | | | |
| 1. Sphingomyelins | N-Acylsphingosine | Choline | 1:2 |
| 2. Cerebrosides | N-Acylsphingosine | Galactose,[a] glucose[a] | 0:1 |
| 3. Sulfatides | N-Acylsphingosine | Galactose[a] | (1 $H_2SO_4$) |
| 4. Gangliosides | N-Acylsphingosine | Hexoses,[a] hexosamine,[a] neuraminic acid[a] | no P |

[a] These components are not present as phosphoric esters, but rather in glycosidic linkage: For this reason, group II, 2–4, are called glycolipids.

phosphatides, for these substances are the hydrophobic components of membranes and provide electrically insulated layers; the protein layers, being hydrophilic, conduct electricity. However, this is not the full extent of the significance of the lipids. Generally speaking, they are involved in the formation of membrane structures. More attention will have to be devoted to them in the future. (For the structure of membranes and the participation of membranes in biochemical processes, cf. also Chapt. XIX.)

## 2. Glycerophosphatides

The basic component common to all glycerophosphatides is L-α-glycerophosphate, which arises from dihydroxyacetone phosphate by enzymic reduction. Esterification of the two free hydroxyl groups with two long-chain fatty acids results in a phosphatidic acid.

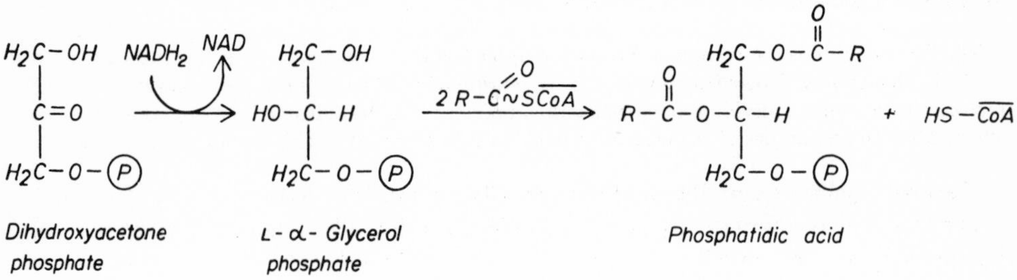

Dihydroxyacetone phosphate     L - α - Glycerol phosphate               Phosphatidic acid

We have already seen phosphatidic acid as the intermediate in the formation of neutral fats. Only small amounts of free phosphatidic acids occur in the mammalian organism; they are abundant, however, in plants (cabbage).

**In Lecithins** the second acidic group of phosphoric acid is esterified with the amino-alcohol *choline*, $HO-CH_2-CH_2-N^{\oplus}(CH_3)_3$.

Choline is a quaternary ammonium base (cf. Chapt. I–2) bearing a positive charge. Since a negative charge may appear on the phosphate, depending on the pH, lecithin may be a zwitterion.

Lecithins contain the same fatty acids which also abound in the neutral fats; as a general rule, the fatty acid in the $\beta$-position is unsaturated (oleic or linolenic acid) while that in the $\alpha$-position is saturated (palmitic or stearic acid). Occasionally, saturated and unsaturated fatty acids with 20 or 22 C atoms are found. Extraction of phosphatides from biologic material always results in complex mixtures.

**The Cephalins** differ from lecithins in their low solubility in alcohol. They consist of two main fractions, the *ethanolamine cephalins* and the *serine cephalins*. As is evident from the partial formulas, the base *ethanolamine*, $HO-CH_2-CH_2-NH_2$, or the amino acid *serine*, $HO-CH_2-CH(COOH)-NH_2$, replaces choline. Serine is the biochemical precursor of ethanolamine and ethanolamine cephalins can be methylated (with active methionine) to form lecithins (cf. Chapt. VIII–12). The three phosphatides are therefore closely related biogenetically.

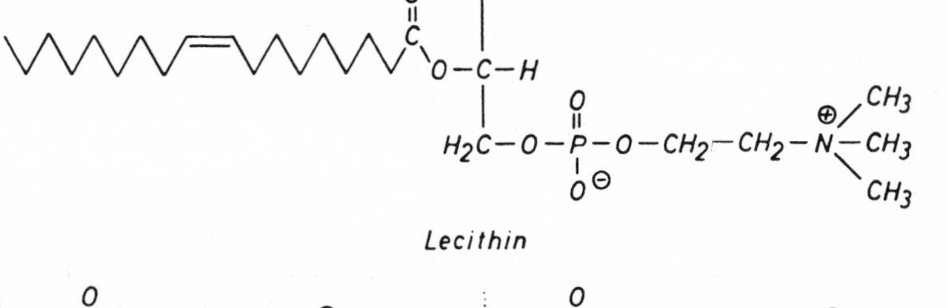

*Lecithin*

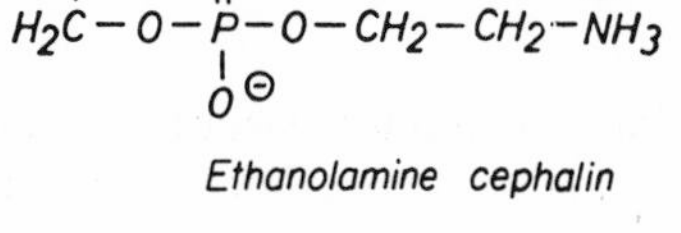

*Ethanolamine cephalin*

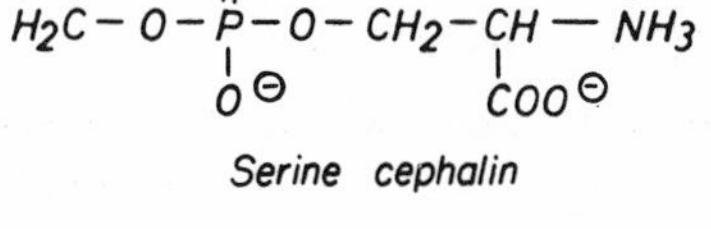

*Serine cephalin*

The hydrolysis of lecithins and cephalins always produces, in addition to the $\alpha$-glycerophosphoric acid, some of the $\beta$-isomer, which has the phosphoric acid at the middle C atom. This observation led to the belief that there are both $\alpha$- and $\beta$-lecithins (and cephalins), but it is now recognized that the $\beta$-form is an artifact, a rearrangement product, and that the natural glycerophosphatides are derived without exception from the $\alpha$-glycerophosphoric acid.

*Lysolecithins* and *lysocephalins* are produced by the hydrolytic action of snake-venom enzymes (cf. Section 3). These products have only one fatty acid residue left; the hydroxyl group in $\beta$-position is free.

**Inositol Phosphatides** (or *inositides*) contain inositol, a cyclic hexahydroxy alcohol, instead of a nitrogenous alcohol. In inositol, the six hydroxyl groups may be arranged either "above" or "below" the plane of the six-membered C ring.[1] Fully nine isomers are possible; the formula shows *myo*-inositol, which occurs free in muscle tissue and which happens to be a symmetric, optically inactive meso-form.[2]

In one group of inositides, the 1-hydroxyl of inositol is simply esterified with phosphatidic acid (see formula below). Another group contains 2 moles of phosphate and upon hydrolysis yields a *meta*-diphosphate of inositol, 1 mole of glycerol, and one of a fatty acid. There are also higher molecular and more complex inositides which contain in addition ethanolamine, galactose, and tartaric acid. Details of their structure are not known; the difficulty in studying these substances again centers around the purification procedures; in other words, the fractionation of the naturally occurring mixtures. Tissues often contain considerable amounts of these inositol phosphatides; according to Claude, they make up about one-fourth of the microsomal lipids.

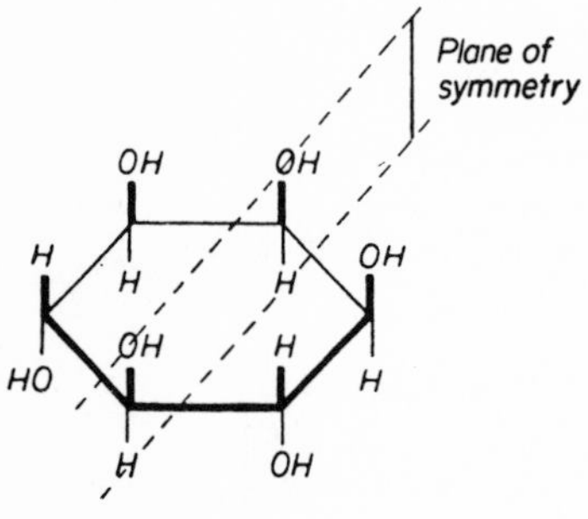

myo - Inositol

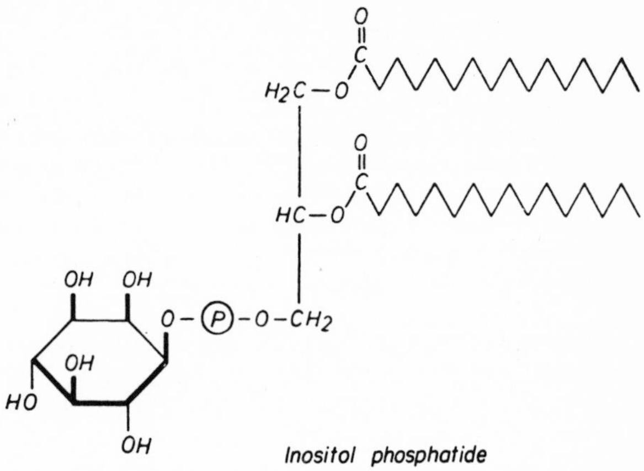

Inositol phosphatide

*Cardiolipin*, a phospholipid originally isolated from heart muscle, has a similar structure. Inositol is replaced by glycerol which is esterified with phosphatidic acids in its $\alpha$- and $\gamma$-positions.

**Plasmalogens** are lipids which release some aldehyde under certain conditions and thus are responsible for the histochemical aldehyde reaction of cytoplasm

---

[1] "Above" and "below" are oversimplified concepts. The molecular model reveals that the C—O bonds protrude either nearly in the plane of the ring, called *equatorial*, or more perpendicular to the plane of the ring (above or below), called *axial*. Here, the ring is represented as planar for greater clarity; for a more correct representation see conformation of steroids, Chapt. XIV-2.

[2] For this reason *myo*-inositol was formerly called *meso*-inositol. That designation is vague, however, since seven of the nine isomers are *meso*-forms.

("plasmal reaction"). Long-chain aldehydes, corresponding to stearic and palmitic acid, are bound as enol ethers to the $CH_2OH$ group of glycerophosphate; the middle C atom of glycerophosphate is esterified with a fatty acid, as shown here.

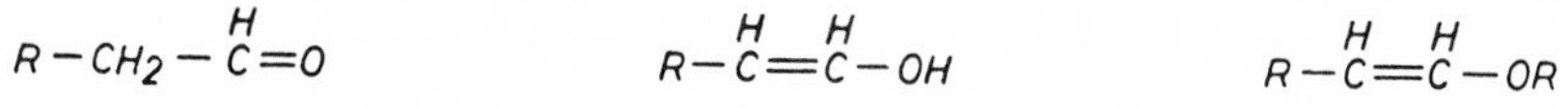

| Aldehyde | Enol form | Enol ether |

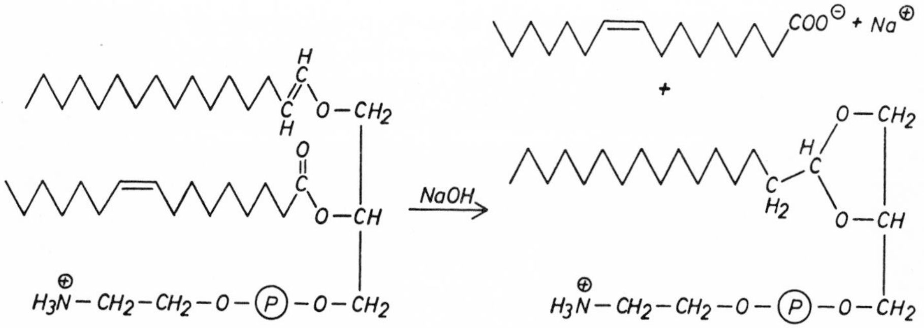

$R-CH_2-\overset{H}{C}=O$   $R-\overset{H}{C}=\overset{H}{C}-OH$   $R-\overset{H}{C}=\overset{H}{C}-OR$

Plasmalogen          Acetal phosphatide
                           (artifact)

The procedure formerly used for isolating plasmalogens consisted in destroying the lecithins and cephalins by alkaline hydrolysis. The ester bond on the $\beta$-hydroxyl group of glycerol is, of course, also hydrolyzed. The free hydroxyl then adds across the double bond of the enol; the result is an acetal. Feulgen first isolated such acetals, and for a long time these artifacts were considered to be naturally occurring substances and the entire class of substances received the name acetal phosphatides for that reason.

Besides the fatty aldehydes, the enol-ether phosphatides contain only unsaturated fatty acids and the base ethanolamine or choline.

## 3. Biosynthesis and Degradation of Glycerophosphatides

The synthesis of phosphatides proceeds for some distance over the same pathway as that of the neutral fats. Glycerophosphate is esterified by long-chain activated fatty acids (i.e. by acyl-CoA compounds) to form phosphatidic acids. A mono-phosphodiesterase then frees the $\alpha$-hydroxyl group to make room for the phospho-choline residue (see diagram Chapt. XII–6).

Phosphate diester bonds are produced by a specific, group-transferring co-enzyme, *cytidine diphosphate* (cf. Chapt. VI–5). A hydroxyl compound, here in our diagram it is choline, is phosphorylated initially and then raised to a high potential for group transfer by the reaction with cytidine triphosphate (CTP); pyrophosphate is split off in the process.

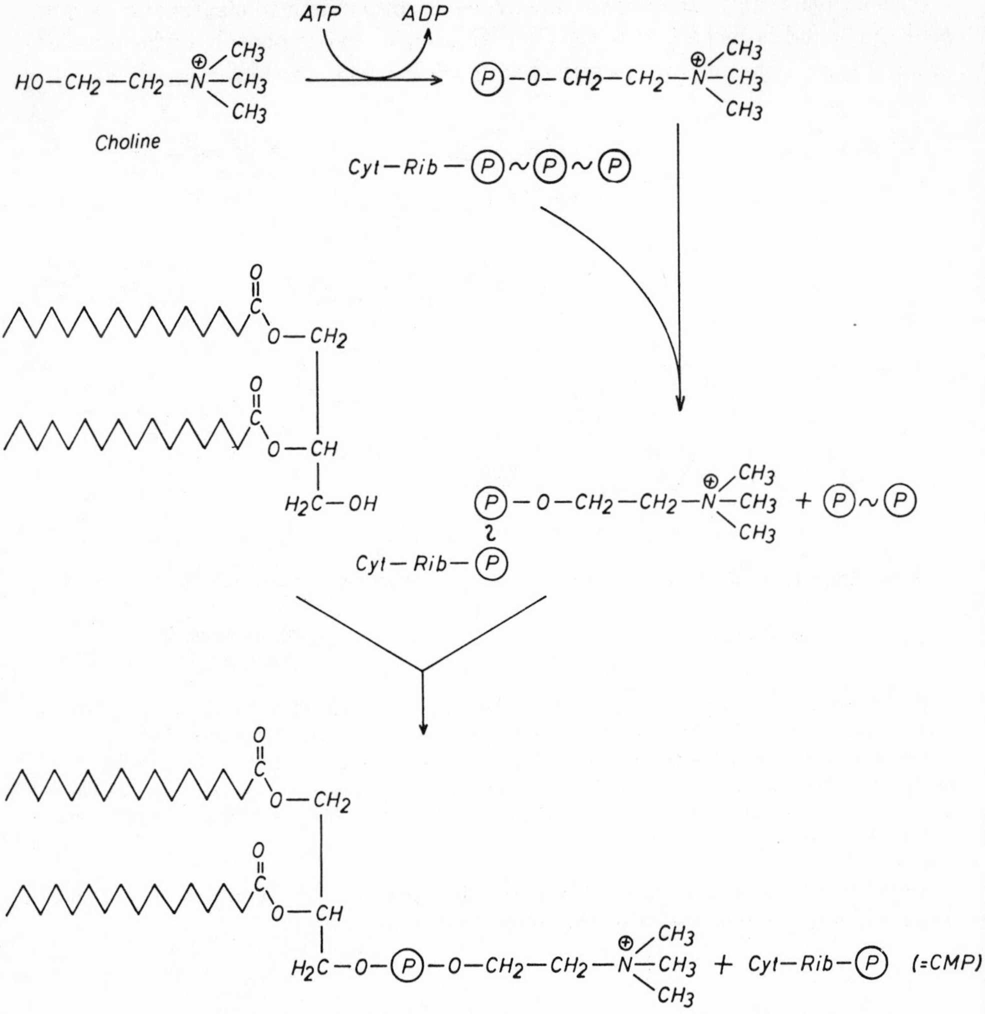

*Cytidine diphosphate choline* now is able to transfer phosphocholine onto the other alcohol components, the diglyceride; cytidine monophosphate (CMP) is released and rephosphorylated to CTP by ATP. The formation of lecithin thus demands relatively much ATP; at times the organism seems to waste its energy-rich phosphates.

*Ethanolamine cephalins* are formed in the same way, i.e. ethanolamine is activated with CDP and transferred onto a diglyceride. Cephalins may be methylated to produce lecithins with adenosylmethionine as methyl group donor. This methylation apparently is the main biosynthetic pathway of lecithin and is an important source of choline from ethanolamine (Greenberg and Bremer).

It is noteworthy that diglyceride residues can also be linked with CDP. The product is an active derivative capable of reacting with inositol to give an inositol phosphatide. Cardiolipin, a bisphosphatidylglycerol, also might arise by a transfer of phosphatide groups.

**Phosphatide-Cleaving Enzymes (Phosphatidases).** Both the carboxy- and phospho-esters of phosphatides can be cleaved hydrolytically (the hydrolyses are exergonic). The appropriate enzymes are, in part, highly specific. The following diagram illustrates the points of attack of several phosphatidases, using a lecithin as an example.

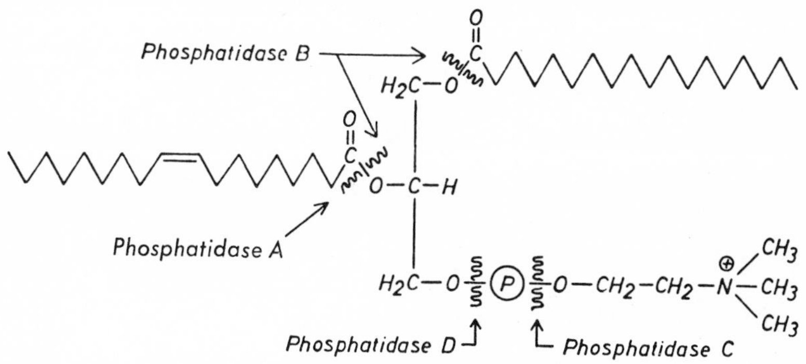

The phosphatidases A are carboxy-esterases by their specificity: They are mainly found in the venom of snakes and bees. The products of the enzymic action are the *lysolecithins*, so called because they hemolyze erythrocytes. It was once believed that the poisonous quality of the venoms could be traced to that effect, but snake venom also contains other toxic substances without phosphatidase activity. Phosphatidase B splits off both fatty acids. Both phosphatidase C (from plants) and D (from gas-gangrene bacilli) are classified as *phosphodiesterases*.

Phosphatidases of type A and B were discovered in the pancreas and other animal organs; nerve tissue contains a specific glycerophosphorylcholine diesterase, which further breaks down the cleavage products of the action of phosphatidase B.

# 4. Sphingolipids

It is characteristic of all these substances that the trihydroxy alcohol glycerol is replaced by the amino dialcohol *sphingosine*. Sphingosine is a long-chain $C_{18}$ compound that contains a *trans* double bond, an $NH_2$ group on C atom 2, and two OH groups (on C-1 and C-3). The steric configurations at the centers of asymmetry are indicated in the projection formula shown below.

Sphingosine often is accompanied by the saturated *dihydrosphingosine*, and in plants by *phytosphingosine*, with an additional hydroxy group (formally derived by addition of a molecule of water across the double bond of sphingosine). The biosynthesis begins with serine and a $C_{16}$ compound, probably a fatty aldehyde; palmitic aldehyde would produce dihydrosphingosine directly by a condensation with the $\alpha$-C atom of serine and subsequent decarboxylation.

Sphingolipids are especially abundant in the brain. Some storage diseases are characterized biochemically by the accumulation of certain sphingolipids. In Niemann-Pick's disease sphingo-myelins are stored; in Gaucher's disease, glucocerebrosides (Klenk). In leucodystrophy of the Scholz type, sulfatides are greatly increased (Jatzkewitz); in amaurotic idiocy of the Tay-Sachs type, gangliosides (Klenk).

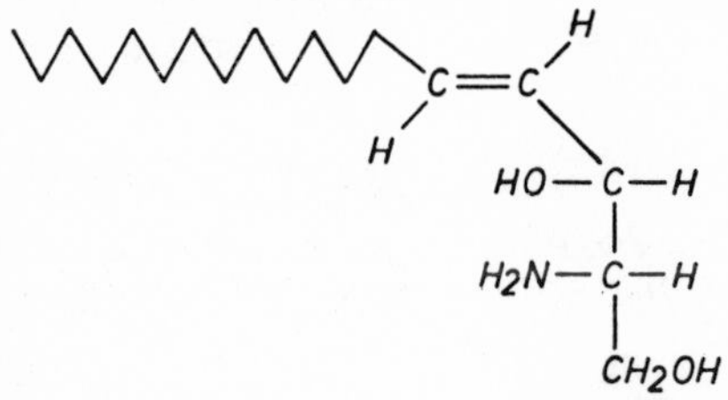

*Sphingosine*

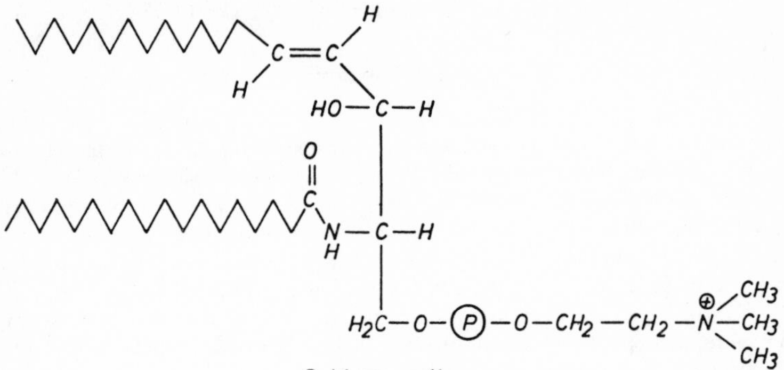

*Sphingomyelin*

**The Sphingosine Phosphatides** are called *sphingomyelins*, because of their occurrence in the myelin sheaths of nerves. Sphingomyelin has a fatty acid residue in amide linkage with its nitrogen and phosphorylcholine on its terminal hydroxyl group. The formula is shown above. It has an obvious similarity to the glycerophosphatides. Since sphingosine, which replaces glycerol, itself contains one N atom, there are two N atoms for each P atom; these substances, therefore, are sometimes called diaminophosphatides.

Sphingomyelins are also isolated as mixtures because of the different fatty acid components. Predominant among these are the acids with 24 C atoms, lignoceric acid (saturated) and nervonic acid (one double bond).

The large group of *glycolipids* is still inadequately studied. The name refers to the content of sugars (galactose, rarely glucose). The cerebrosides and gangliosides are glycolipids and are associated with the phosphatides, especially in the brain, although they do not contain any phosphoric acid.

**Cerebrosides** are structurally closely related to sphingomyelins. They differ in that the phosphorylcholine (of the sphingomyelins) is replaced by a molecule of sugar, usually galactose, in glycosidic linkage (cf. Chapt. XVII–1) at C atom 1. The formula is shown below.

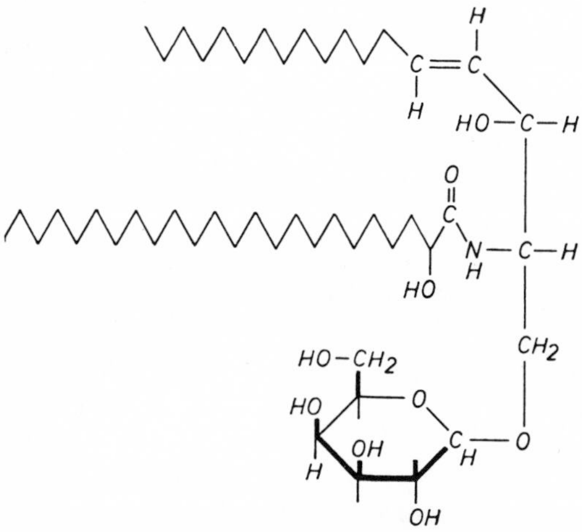

Cerebroside (Cerebron)

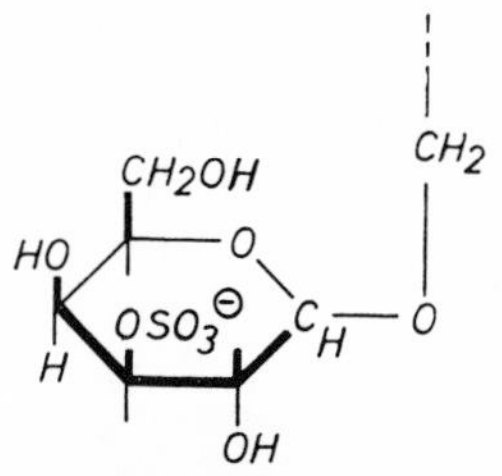

Sulfatide
(partial formula)

The fatty acid constituents are $C_{24}$ acids with a double bond or a hydroxyl group (in $\alpha$-position). The cerebrosides do not always lack acidic groups, for some contain sulfuric acid in ester linkage to C atom 3 of galactose, as is illustrated in the partial formula. They are called *sulfatides*.

**Gangliosides.** The name implies occurrence in ganglionic cells. The main components are sphingosine, fatty acids, and carbohydrates: hexoses, aminohexoses, and neuraminic acid. The latter is a product of condensation between mannosamine and pyruvic acid (formula, Chapt. XV–4). The construction of gangliosides is very similar to that of cerebrosides; only the carbohydrate moiety is far more complex. The various gangliosides differ primarily in the number of sugar residues. On page 234 is the tentative formula of a typical ganglioside frequently found. Enzymic cleavage of the terminal N-acetylneuraminic acid residue frees another ganglioside, often called the "main ganglioside" of the brain.

Neuraminic acid-containing components of cellular membranes have acquired considerable interest recently, because they play a role in the attachment and penetration of virus particles. The virus receptors of the cellular membrane can be destroyed by an enzyme from *V. cholerae* (receptor destroying enzyme). This enzyme has proved to be very specific for neuraminic acid.

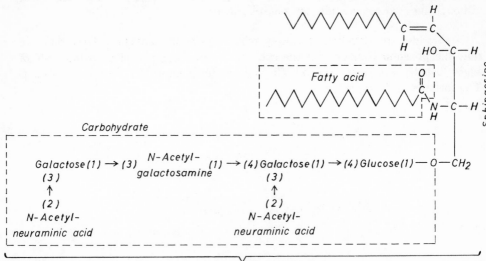

Ganglioside GIV

BIBLIOGRAPHY

D. M. Greenberg, Biological methylation. *Advances in Enzymol.*, **25,** 395–431 (1963); specifically pp. 417–420.

J. Kennedy, "Cytidine Diphosphate and Phosphatide Biosynthesis," 11th Mosbach Colloquium der Gesellschaft für physiologische Chemie, Springer Verlag, Berlin, 1961.

J. A. Lovern, "The Chemistry of Lipids of Biochemical Significance," Methuen, London, 1955.

R. J. Rossiter, Metabolism of phosphatides, *in* "Metabolic Pathways" (D. M. Greenberg, editor), Vol. I, pp. 357–388, Academic Press, New York, 1961.

# CHAPTER XIV

# Isoprenoid Lipids:

# Steroids and Carotenoids

*Isoprene* is a branched-chain, unsaturated hydrocarbon of five C atoms. This same carbon skeleton

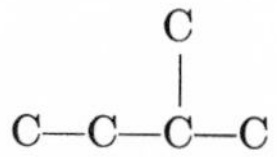

$$
\begin{array}{c}
\text{C} \\
| \\
\text{C--C--C--C}
\end{array}
$$

is the basis of a great many plant and animal products (terpenes, camphor; carotenoids; steroids, etc.). In 1922, Ruzicka suggested that all these natural products are derived from one common precursor. His *"isoprene rule"* has proved very useful; the nature of the biologic isoprene, however, has been elucidated only in comparatively recent years through the efforts of Lynen, Bloch, Popjak, and Folkers. The biosynthesis of cholesterol, the most important steroid for the animal organism, will be described here.

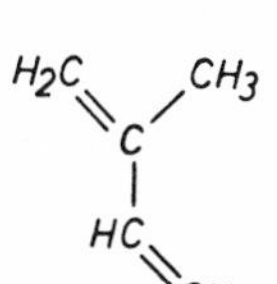

| Isoprene | Terpinolene (2 Isoprene residues) | biologic Isoprene precursor |

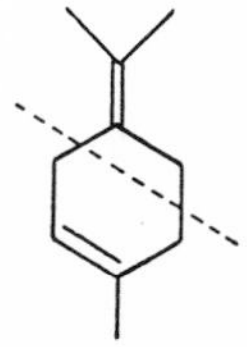

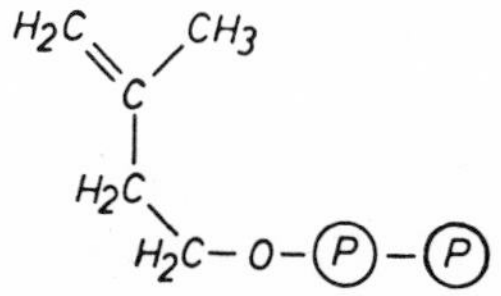

## 1. Biosynthesis of Cholesterol

**Formation of Mevalonic Acid.** The starting material for the formation of isoprene and hence of cholesterol is activated acetate, *acetyl-CoA*, which we have already met several times. We have also seen that two molecules of activated acetate condense to form *acetoacetyl-CoA* and a third acetyl-CoA may condense on to it

235

as a side chain. This reaction, formulated in Chapt. XII–4, is entirely analogous to the formation of citrate from oxaloacetate and acetyl-CoA (cf. citrate cycle, Chapt. XI–1).

The acid produced in this condensation reaction, *β-hydroxy-β-methylglutaric acid*, still bears a CoA group, which is split off reductively. The carboxyl group is converted to an alcohol group with the consumption of 2 $NADPH_2$. In this way the key substance for the synthesis of isoprenoids, *mevalonic acid*, is produced.

**Isopentenyl Pyrophosphate, the "Active Isoprene Unit."** Mevalonic acid is subjected to several changes before it can condense to form larger compounds. First it is phosphorylated, the pyrophosphate being formed with the consumption of 2 ATP. In a complex reaction, whose detailed mechanism is not understood, $H_2O$ and $CO_2$

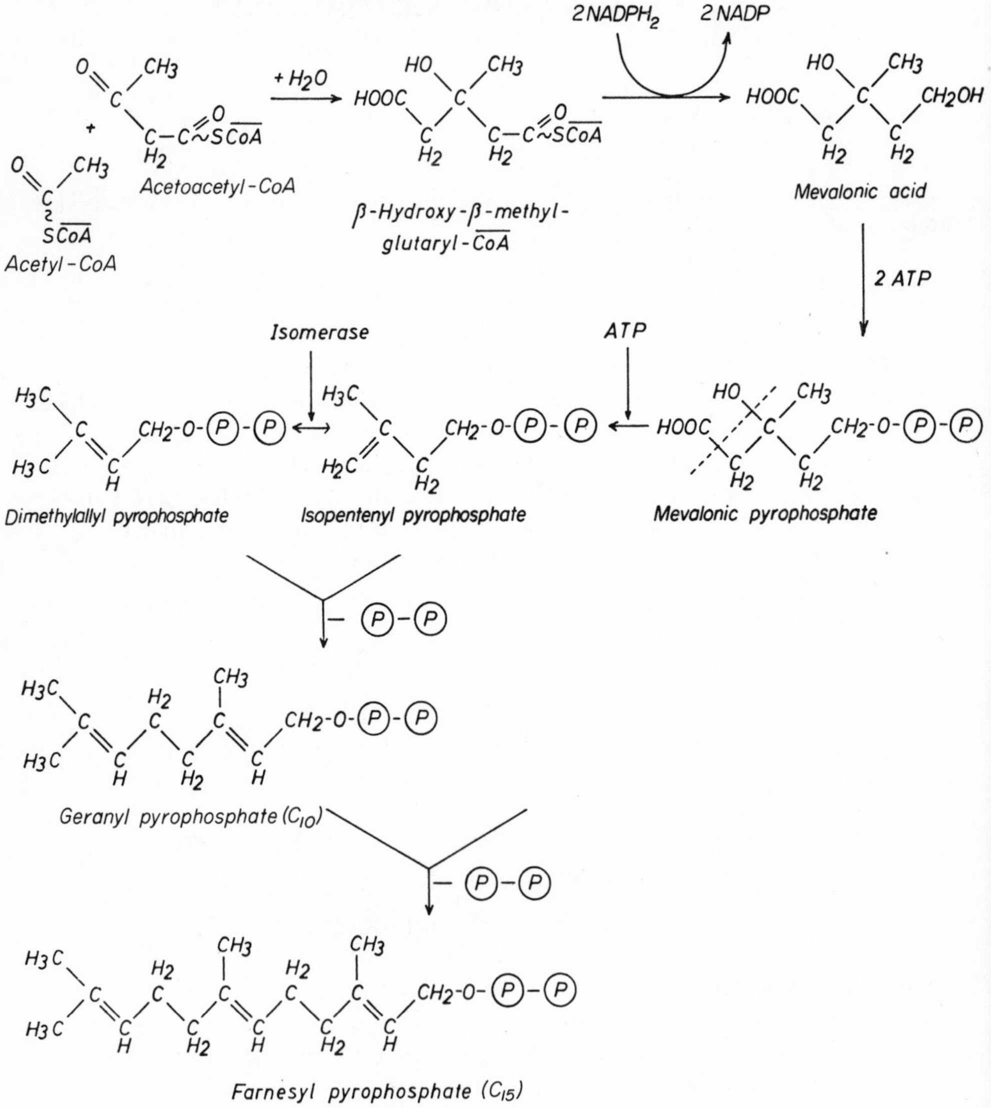

Acetoacetyl-CoA

Acetyl-CoA

β-Hydroxy-β-methyl-glutaryl-CoA

Mevalonic acid

2 ATP

Isomerase

ATP

Dimethylallyl pyrophosphate

Isopentenyl pyrophosphate

Mevalonic pyrophosphate

Geranyl pyrophosphate (C₁₀)

Farnesyl pyrophosphate (C₁₅)

are split off, ATP again being required. The product is *isopentenyl pyrophosphate* (Lynen), which is very similar to isoprene, as can be seen from the formula (the loss of pyrophosphoric acid would yield isoprene). The active isoprene unit (isopentenyl pyrophosphate) now undergoes a chain of reactions that begins with an enzyme-catalyzed double bond migration (from $\Delta^3$ to $\Delta^2$) in one molecule giving *dimethylallyl pyrophosphate*. A pyrophosphate anion is eliminated easily from the allyl derivative, and the remaining carbonium cation attaches itself to the double bond of an isopentenyl pyrophosphate. The loss of a proton stabilizes the molecule yielding *geranyl pyrophosphate*. A repeat of this condensation reaction finally produces the $C_{15}$ compound *farnesyl pyrophosphate*.

From this compound, the series of reactions proceeds to form either the $C_{20}$ compound (see Section 7) or the highly polymeric natural rubber (see Section 9), or it is terminated by a head to head condensation of two $C_{15}$ units. The mechanism again includes an allylic rearrangement, farnesyl pyrophosphate to a nerolidol derivative, and an attack by a carbonium ion. A reduction step with $NADPH_2$ finally forms *squalene*.

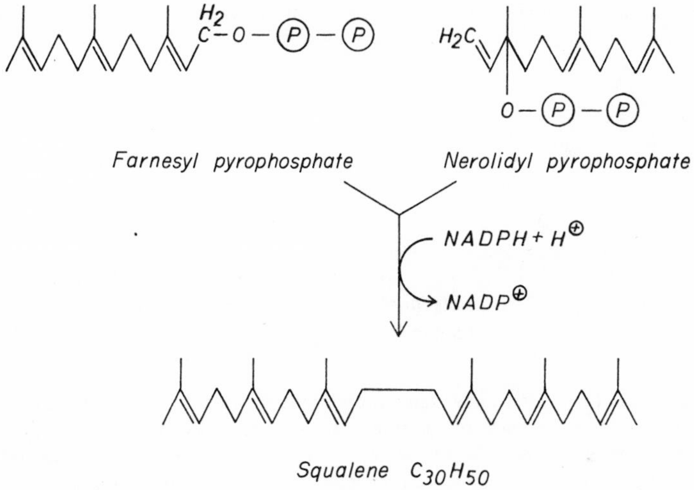

Farnesyl pyrophosphate    Nerolidyl pyrophosphate

$- NADPH + H^{\oplus}$

$\rightarrow NADP^{\oplus}$

Squalene $C_{30}H_{50}$

**Squalene**, a hydrocarbon $C_{30}H_{50}$, was first isolated from shark liver and is found in small amounts also in mammals. As is evident from the biosynthesis just discussed, squalene is an isoprenoid composed of two symmetrical halves. Among the formulas shown here, two ways of writing the same molecule are presented. The spatial arrangement indicated in the second formula permits cyclization to the steroid skeleton, after a preliminary hydroxylation. The first isolable product is *lanosterol*:

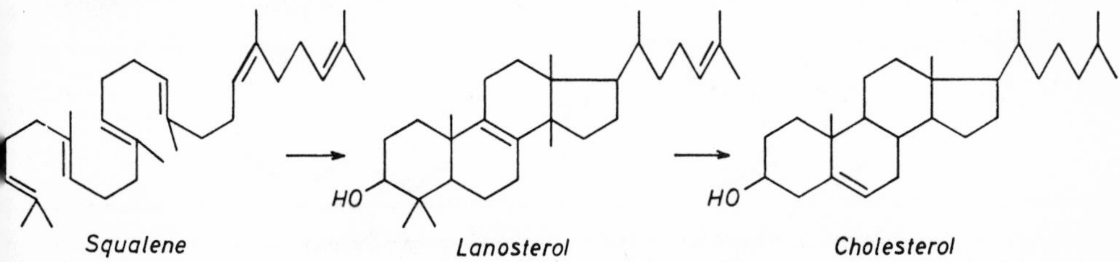

Squalene          Lanosterol          Cholesterol

During cyclization two methyl groups migrate; they are the two methyl groups that end up between rings C and D. How this happens, why this particular possibility of folding is realized, and why just this system of rings is formed is not yet known. The squalene molecule presumably is held in this arrangement by the surface of the enzyme protein.

Before we reach cholesterol, three methyl groups must be removed oxidatively (as $CO_2$), one double bond in the ring system shifted, and the other in the side chain reduced. Though these reactions occur in steps, we have merely written down the final product *cholesterol* (the principal zoosterol).

## 2. Nomenclature and Stereochemistry of the Steroids

We must concern ourselves briefly with the chemistry of steroids before we can discuss their biologic significance.

**The Ring System and Its Possibilities for Isomerism.** According to systematic chemical nomenclature, cholesterol is a derivative of cyclopentanoperhydrophenanthrene. This alicyclic, saturated hydrocarbon (without double bonds or aromatic character) bears the trivial name *sterane*. The C atoms are numbered in the manner indicated.

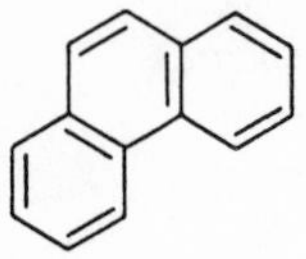

Phenanthrene          Sterane                    Cholestane
(aromatic)          (alicyclic)

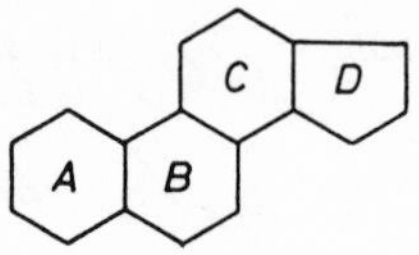

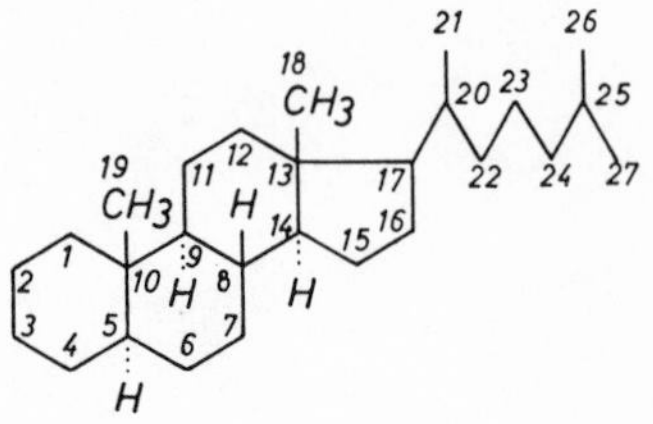

Two substituents of a cyclohexane ring (in *ortho*-position in the formulas below) can be either both on the same side of the plane of the ring (*cis*) or on opposite sides (*trans*). The possibility of isomerism is retained even when the two substituents are connected by C atoms (see formula) to form a second ring. If this second ring is a six-membered ring then the compound is decalin, whose two isomers have been isolated (Hückel).

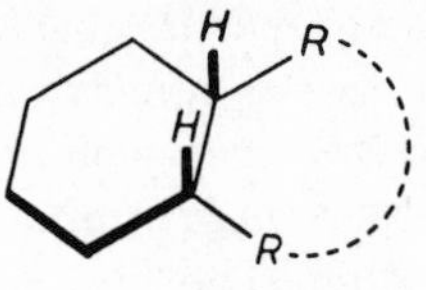

cis - Configuration 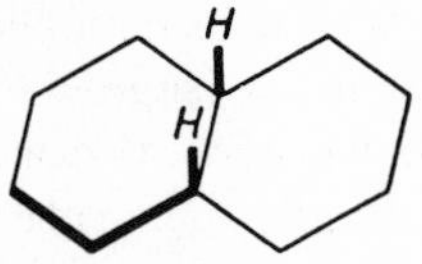          cis - Decalin

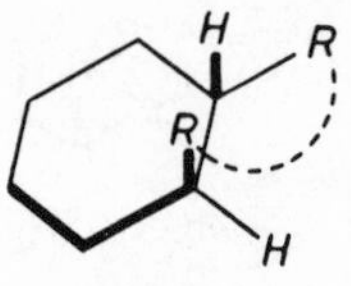

trans - Configuration 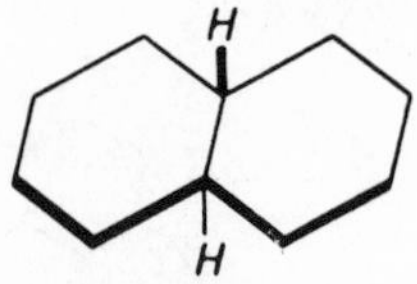          trans - Decalin

Two saturated rings, therefore, can be fused in two ways: *cis* or *trans*. The sterane system has four fused rings which have been designated A, B, C, and D. It is easy to remember that in all naturally occurring steroids rings B and C as well as rings C and D are attached *trans*; only in the attachment of rings A and B are both isomers found. The fundamental hydrocarbon with *trans*-connection is called androstane; with *cis*-connection, etiocholane. Recently the more systematic designations 5α-*androstane* and 5β-*androstane* have come into use. As can be seen from the formulas, in 5α-androstane (and in *cholestane*) the hydrogen atoms and the methyl groups are alternatively above or below the plane of the rings. In cholesterol itself the isomerism of the ring attachment A/B is abolished, since there is a double bond at C–5.

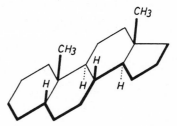

5α-*Androstane (Androstane)*                 5β-*Androstane (Etiocholane)*

**The Position of Other Groups.** By convention, the spatial orientation of hydrogen at the points of ring juncture, of hydroxyl groups, or side chains, i.e. of every substituent, is *referred to the methyl group at C atom 10*. In the formulas above, this particular methyl group sticks out above the flat ring system.[1] For example, one talks about the β-position of a OH group if it is *cis* to the methyl group on C atom 10; the β—OH group sticks out above the ring system. In formulas this orientation of the bond is represented by a solid or heavy line.

If a substituent is oriented *trans* to the 10-methyl group and points down in the flat model, then such a substituent is said to be in α-position, symbolized in formulas by a dotted line as valence bond. Androstane, with *trans*-fused rings, has its hydrogen on C atom 5 in *trans*-position and therefore is called the 5α-compound. The same convention holds for hydroxyl groups. Cholesterol is a 3β-hydroxy compound. These designations will be very important in the field of steroid hormones, where isomers are frequently found together.

**Conformation.** For a better explanation of chemical properties, especially of reactivity, the concept of conformation has recently proved more valuable than the assignment to the α- or β-series. One must realize that cyclohexane rings actually are not planar, but exist rather in the so-called *chair form*, in which C atoms *para* to each other are pushed out of the plane above and below. (The *boat form* of cyclohexane does not exist normally.[2]) All substituents are either

[1] The convention had been agreed upon before the absolute configuration was determined. This arbitrary choice later turned out to be the correct one.

[2] In some textbooks it is stated that in *cis*-decalin the boat form is realized. That is not so; *cis*-decalin has two different double chair forms.

*equatorial*, i.e. away from the center of the ring and approximately in the plane of the ring, or they are *axial*, i.e. approximately perpendicular to the plane of the ring (see drawing). In this way, *trans*-oriented substituents (in the drawing the hydroxyls on C-2 and C-3) can come together much closer than *cis*-oriented groups (e.g., those on C-1 and C-2).

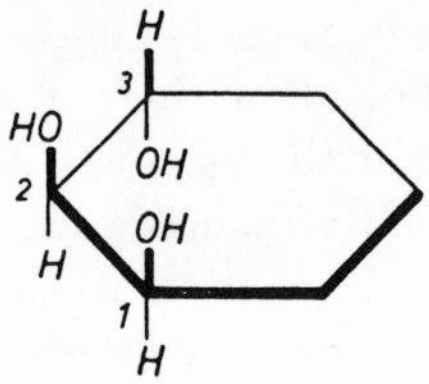

Simplified representation 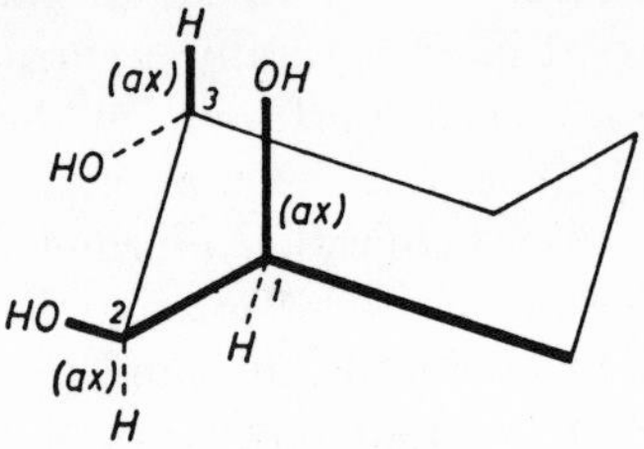        Chair form

Such considerations are pertinent to the "molecular anatomy" of membranes. The formulas of cholestanol and coprostanol (below) illustrate how very differently space is filled when at one time rings A and B are fused *trans* and at another *cis* (respectively). But a clear concept of these relationships can only be acquired by using molecular models.[3]

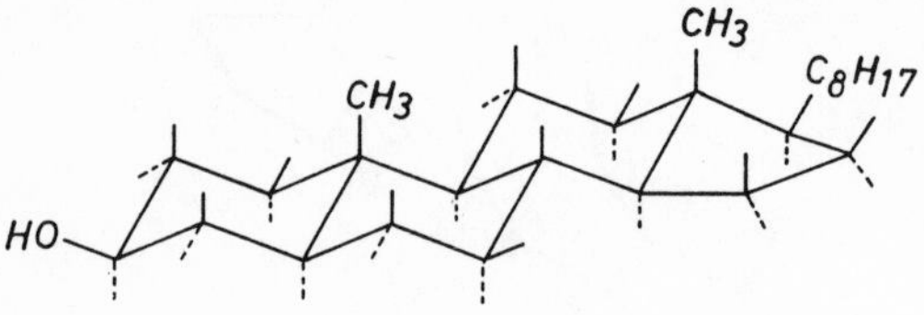

Cholestanol 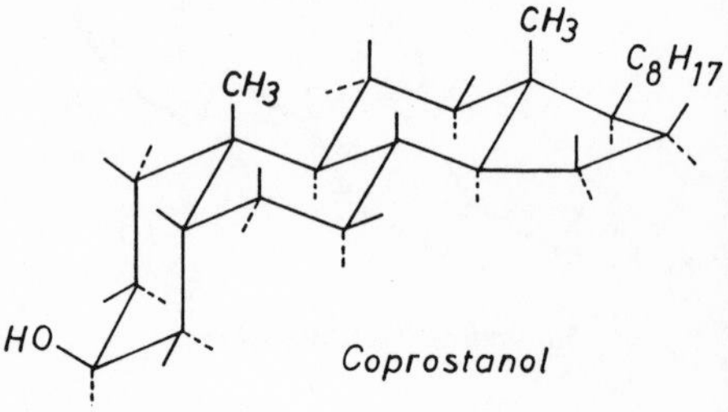                 Coprostanol

**The Great Variety of Steroids.** In nature, the steroids are converted to substances that execute the most varied tasks. An outline of some of these functions is provided by Table XVII.

TABLE XVII

STEROIDS AND THEIR BIOLOGIC ROLE

| Group | Representative | Formula | Occurrence and Function |
|---|---|---|---|
| **Sterols** | | | |
| $C_{27}$–$C_{30}$ $3\beta$—OH | Cholesterol | $C_{27}H_{46}O$ | Ubiquitous; structural component |
| | $\Delta^7$-Dehydrocholesterol | $C_{27}H_{44}O$ | Skin; provitamin D |
| | Ergosterol | $C_{28}H_{44}O$ | Yeast; provitamin D |
| **Bile Acids** | | | |
| $C_{24}$ | Cholic acid | $C_{24}H_{40}O_5$ | Gall bladder and intestines; absorption of fats |
| **Hormones** | | | |
| $C_{21}$ | Progesterone | $C_{21}H_{30}O_2$ | Corpus luteum hormone |
| | Deoxycorticosterone | $C_{21}H_{30}O_3$ | Adrenocortical hormone |
| | Cortisol | $C_{21}H_{30}O_5$ | Adrenocortical hormone |
| $C_{19}$ | Testosterone | $C_{19}H_{28}O_2$ | Testicular hormone |
| $C_{18}$ | Estradiol | $C_{18}H_{24}O_2$ | Follicular hormone |

[3] For a more extensive treatment of conformational analysis see L. F. Fieser and M. Fieser, "Steroids," Reinhold, New York, 1959.

## 3. Sterols and Plant Steroids

*Sterols* are characterized by a hydroxyl group on C atom 3. The sterol of the vertebrates is cholesterol, which is distributed among all cells. It participates, in conjunction with phospholipids, in the construction of membranes; the shape of the molecule, a small flat disk, seems to be particularly suited to this purpose. In nerve tissue, cholesterol is a component of the myelin sheath (cf. Chapt. XXIII–7). Its appearance in vascular walls (atherosclerosis) and in gallstones (where it was discovered as early as 1769) is pathological.

Besides being a structural component, cholesterol also serves the organism as a starting material for the synthesis of numerous other steroids such as bile acids, the steroid hormones of the adrenal cortex, sex hormones, and vitamin D. Intestinal bacteria reduce cholesterol to *coprostanol*, in which rings A and B are *cis*.

*Cholesterol*          *Coprostanol*          *Ergosterol*

In addition to cholesterol, a whole series of other sterols has been found in plants and lower animals—but the higher in the animal kingdom, the more uniform the pattern of sterols.

*Lanosterol* has already been mentioned as a biosynthetic intermediate; it is abundant in the wool fat of sheep. The related *zymosterol*, which lacks the three extra methyl groups, was first isolated from yeast. The most important yeast sterol, however, is *ergosterol*, a $C_{28}$-steroid with three double bonds; it is a provitamin D (see below). Plants contain several sterols with additional C substituents in the side chain, such as ergosterol has; examples are stigmasterol and sitosterol. Insects are incapable of synthesizing the sterane skeleton; they require sterols as essential food components.

**Saponins, Digitaloids, and Steroid Alkaloids.** These substances are plant products. They are characterized by numerous hydroxyl groups, ether and lactone linkages, and, in the case of alkaloids, by the content of nitrogen. Many of them exist as glycosides. They are secondary plant products with greater pharmacologic than physiological interest. The formulas are presented to demonstrate the great variety of steroids rather than to point out or catalog individual substances (see formulas below).

*Saponins* in solution foam strongly. One typical saponin is *digitonin* (from digitalis seeds). With 3β-hydroxy steroids (e.g. cholesterol) digitonin forms insoluble addition compounds; the reagent is useful for the determination of cholesterol. The reaction with cholesterol is probably the cause of its hemolytic (erythrocyte-disrupting) action. Digitonin is a glycoside consisting of a pentasaccharide and the steroid digitogenin. The formula is shown below.

As an example of a cardiac glycoside we mention *strophanthin*, a glycoside with therapeutic applications. Noteworthy features of the formula are that the methyl group on C-10 is oxidized to the aldehyde (the methyl group is intact in the digitalis compounds) and that the side chain is in the form of a five-membered, unsaturated lactone ring. The lactone ring is common to all glycosides with cardiac activity. In glycosides from *squill* and from *toad poisons* the ring is six-membered.

From the vast number of steroid alkaloids we have chosen *solanine* as a representative. As the formula shows, it also is a glycoside. It occurs in potato shoots. The steroid alkaloids cannot all be derived from one common structure, as is possible with the cardiac drugs. For other representatives, see special reference works.

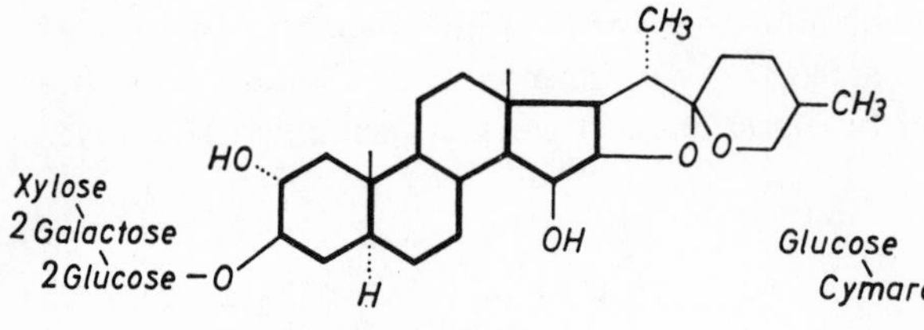

Digitonin

(a Saponin)

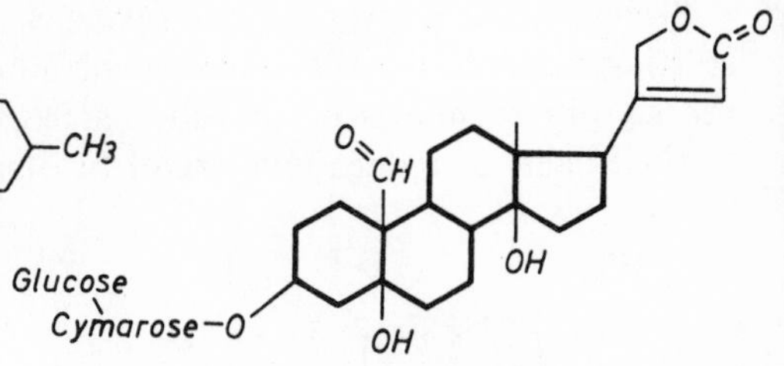

Strophanthin

(a cardiac stimulant)

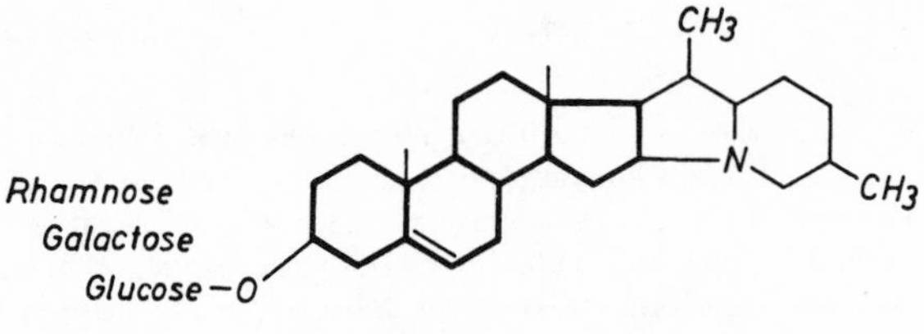

Solanine

(a sterol alkaloid)

## 4. Vitamin D

The letter D was used to designate the antirachitic vitamin of liver oil (for its physiological action see Chapt. XXII–4). Windaus first prepared vitamin D by irradiating ergosterol and determined its constitution.

Several active substances are known (vitamin $D_2$, $D_3$, etc.[4]) and one correctly speaks of the vitamins of the D group. Although they are not really steroids themselves (they do not possess the four-ring system), they are nevertheless closely related to the steroids: The immediate precursors, the provitamins D, are ergosterol and 7-dehydrocholesterol. With ultraviolet light these substances, having two conjugated double bonds in ring B, undergo a characteristic change which breaks open ring B.

---

[4] $D_1$ was the designation for the first crystalline material, which later turned out to be a mixture.

Windaus had assumed a series of intermediate steps, but Velluz could show that the photochemical reaction produces precalciferol (*pre-vitamin D₂*), which is in equilibrium with Vitamin D₂ through a thermal rearrangement reaction; vitamin D₂ is the major component of the equilibrium. Both *lumisterol* and *tachysterol* are side products and not intermediates. As can be seen from the formulas, the transition to precalciferol entails the opening of ring B with the consequent formation of a new double bond. The rearrangement to vitamin D₂ consists in a shift of the double bonds by one place.

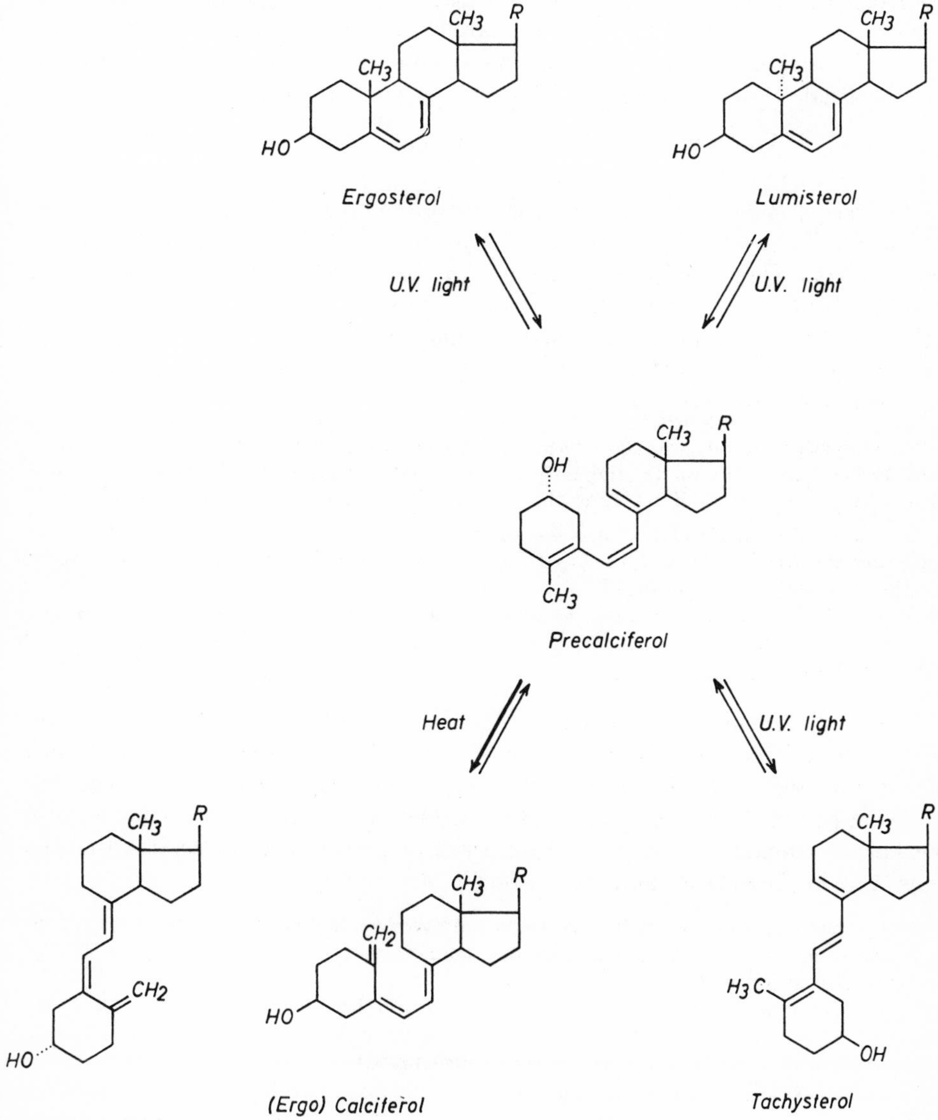

Ergosterol

Lumisterol

U.V. light

U.V. light

Precalciferol

Heat

U.V. light

(Ergo) Calciferol

Tachysterol

The temptation is great to represent vitamin $D_2$ in a way which emphasizes its relationship with the steroids, but such a representation does not correspond to the true configuration. In writing such formulas it can be noticed that the methylene group really has not enough room. The representation at the far left corresponds much better with the true situation. The two formulas stand for the same substance, and not for isomers.

The photochemical reaction is not limited to ergosterol. Other steroids with $\Delta^{5,7}$-double bonds undergo the conversion. Of physiological significance are vitamin $D_2$, *ergocalciferol*, derived from ergosterol, and vitamin $D_3$, *cholecalciferol*, derived from dehydrocholesterol. The latter is found in liver oil and arises also in the human organism in the skin during exposure to direct sunlight. 7-Dehydrocholesterol is present in relatively high concentration in the skin; this fact explains the beneficial effect of sunlight or UV-radiation on rachitis (rickets).

## 5. Bile Acids

The *salts of the bile acids* are the digestion-promoting constituents of bile. They are surface active agents; this means that they lower surface tension and thus can emulsify fats. They also activate lipases. The bile acids, for these reasons, play a leading role in the digestion and absorption of fats.

Without exception, in all bile acids, the juncture of rings A and B is *cis*, and the hydroxyl groups are $\alpha$-oriented. The side chain is usually made up of five C atoms and bears the carboxyl group.

The biosynthesis of bile acids takes place in the liver. It begins with the insertion of a 7$\alpha$-hydroxyl group into cholesterol; the ring is then reduced and epimerized at C-3 (the ketone must be assumed to be the intermediate). After these changes in the ring system, and occasionally after hydroxylation at C-12, the side chain is shortened oxidatively: One methyl group is hydroxylated and oxidized further to the acid; the $C_{27}$ carboxylic acid is then broken down by $\beta$-oxidation (as are the fatty acids). The splitting-off of propionic acid produces the "specific bile acids," which are activated with ATP and CoA and connected to the amino group of *glycine* or *taurine* in amide linkage. Deoxycholic acid (3$\alpha$,12$\alpha$-dihydroxycholanic acid) arises from cholic acid by the action of intestinal bacteria.

The chief bile acids are the taurine and glycine derivates of *cholic acid* (3$\alpha$,7$\alpha$,12$\alpha$-trihydroxycholanic acid), of *deoxycholic acid* (3$\alpha$,12$\alpha$-dihydroxycholanic acid), and of the isomeric *chenodeoxycholic acid* (3$\alpha$,7$\alpha$-dihydroxycholanic acid). The bile acids are one of the end products of the metabolism of cholesterol; however, over 90% of the amount secreted (20–30 gm per day) is reabsorbed in the intestine and thus stays in the enterohepatic circulation.

Deoxycholic acid can join with fatty acids and other lipids (cholesterol, carotene) to form molecular compounds. In the case of stearic or palmitic acid, eight molecules of bile acid are joined to each molecule of fatty acid.

## 6. Steroid Hormones

Many of the hormones are steroids. The organism synthesizes them from cho-

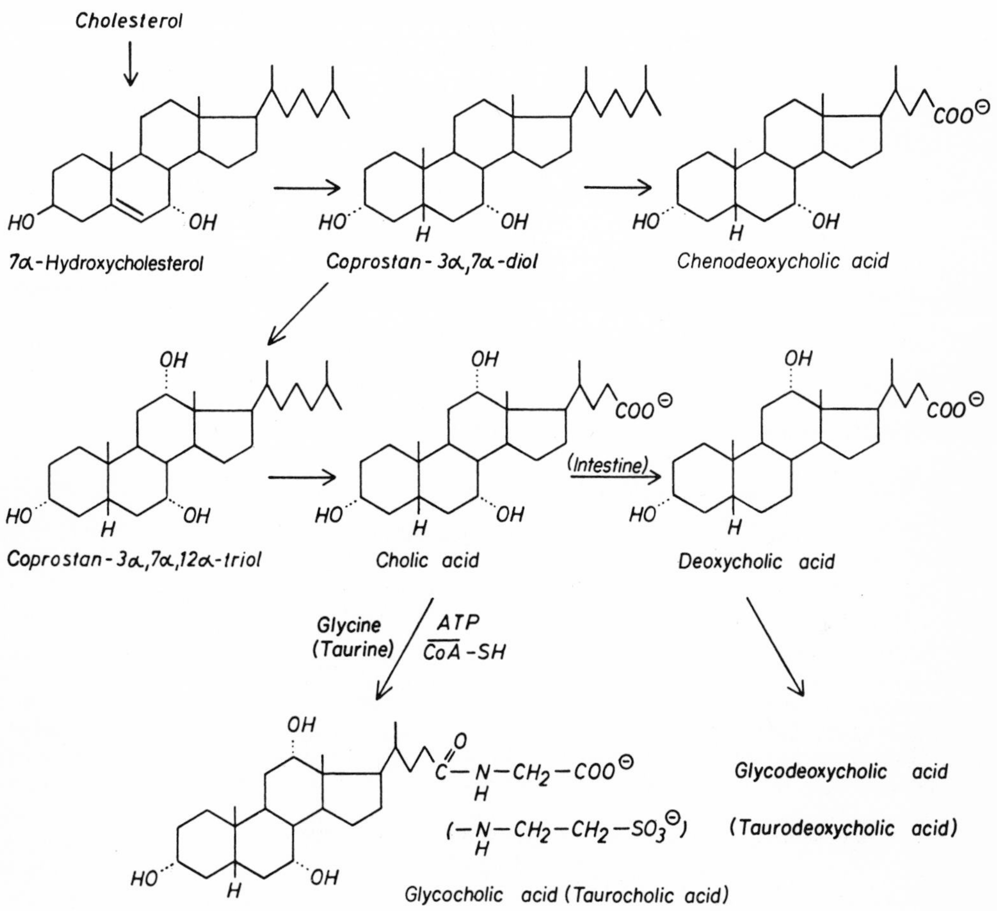

Cholesterol

7α-Hydroxycholesterol → Coprostan-3α,7α-diol → Chenodeoxycholic acid

Coprostan-3α,7α,12α-triol → Cholic acid —(Intestine)→ Deoxycholic acid

Glycine (Taurine) / ATP, CoA-SH

Glycodeoxycholic acid
(Taurodeoxycholic acid)

Glycocholic acid (Taurocholic acid)

lesterol (or cholesterol derivatives) in special glands—the adrenal cortex, ovaries, corpus luteum, placenta, and testes. The hormone production in the adrenal cortex has been studied best and actually is the most versatile. In this chapter, structure and biogenesis of the hormones will be discussed; physiological properties will be treated later in Chapt. XX.

The C$_{21}$-Steroids, consisting of the corpus luteum hormone progesterone and most of the adrenal cortical hormones (see Table XVII), are formally derived from *pregnane*, a hydrocarbon with a β-oriented side chain of two C atoms. The biosynthesis starts with cholesterol, and the first isolable conversion product is *pregnene-3β-ol-20-one*. The oxidative shortening of the side chain of cholesterol probably proceeds by hydroxylations at C-20 and C-22 and cleavage to form isocaproic acid. The resulting pregnenolone is then dehydrogenated to form *progesterone*, one of the fundamental biologic key substances.

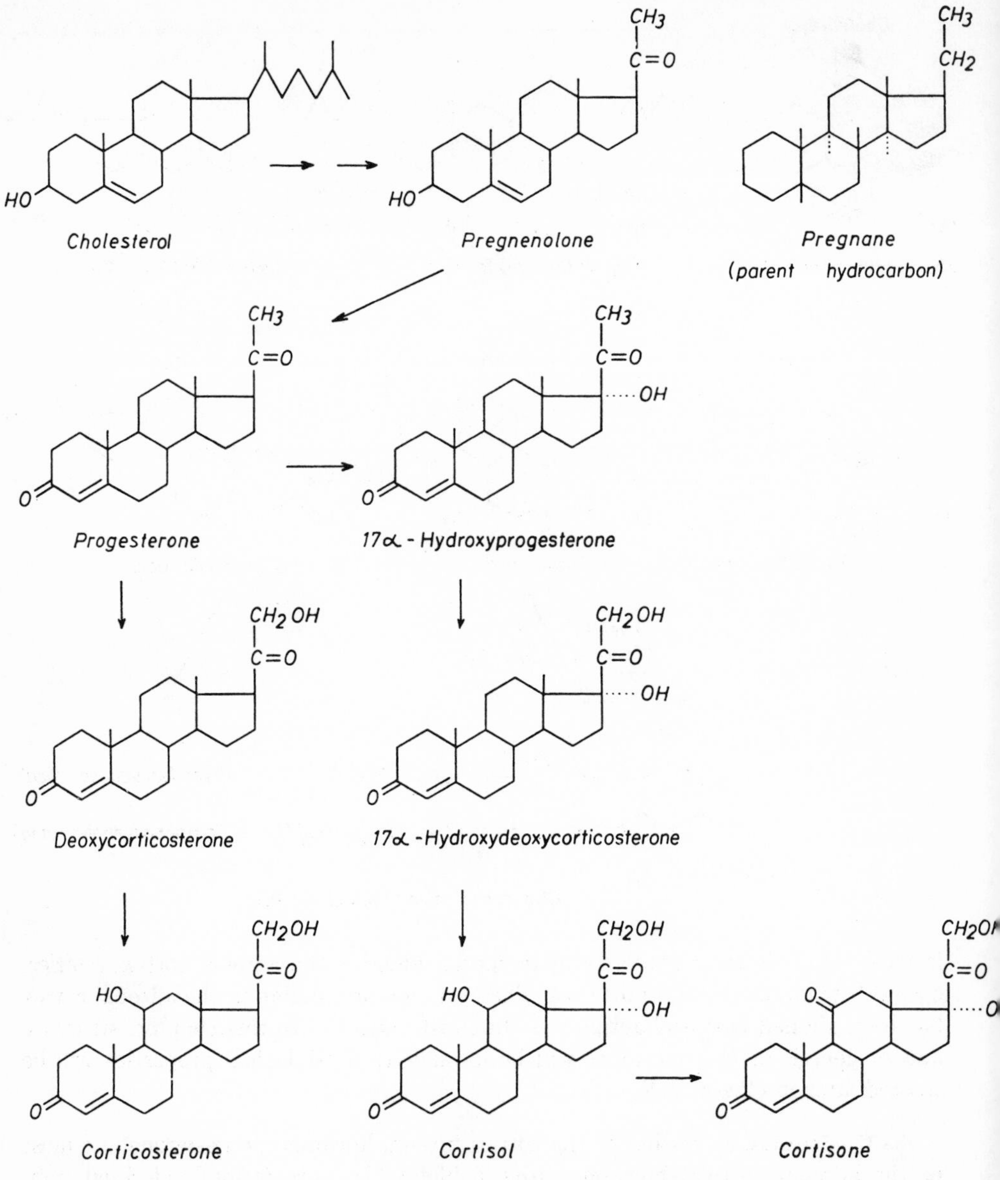

Cholesterol  Pregnenolone  Pregnane
(parent hydrocarbon)

Progesterone  17α - Hydroxyprogesterone

Deoxycorticosterone  17α -Hydroxydeoxycorticosterone

Corticosterone  Cortisol  Cortisone

Progesterone, the hormone of corpus luteum, is at the same time a precursor of the *corticoids*, which contain additional hydroxyl groups. The introduction of these hydroxyl groups follows the principle of oxygenation with $O_2$ + NADPH$_2$ (cf. Chapt. X–7). The *steroid oxygenases (hydroxylases)* are highly specific with regard to the position of the hydroxyl group introduced into the steroid skeleton. We know a *17-oxygenase*, a *21-oxygenase*, and an *11-oxygenase*; if they act one after another, they produce cortisol *via* 17-hydroxyprogesterone (cf. formulas above).

It is interesting that the 17-oxygenase will not attack a C-21 hydroxy compound. If a hydroxyl is first introduced at C–21, then further conversion stops at corticosterone and cortisol will not be produced (diagram of formulas above). The 11-hydroxy compounds can be dehydrogenated reversibly to the 11-keto compounds.

*Aldosterone.* Another adrenal cortical hormone with very high activity is aldosterone, with an aldehyde function at C-18. During its biosynthesis the methyl group apparently is oxidized. The aldehyde group very easily forms a hemiacetal ring with the OH group on C-11, as is shown by the formula on the right.

**Aldosterone**

**Inactivation and Excretion of C$_{21}$-Steroid Hormones.** As explained in more detail in Chapt. XX–1, the inactivation and excretion of hormones is an essential link in the chain of hormonal regulation. Degradation occurs mostly in the liver; by reduction of the unsaturated ketone grouping complete or nearly complete inactivation is achieved. A C-3 hydroxyl and a new asymmetric center at C-5 (the point of ring juncture) are also created thereby. The majority of the excretion products are 3$\alpha$-hydroxy-5$\beta$-compounds, i.e. the hydroxyl group usually has the opposite steric configuration to that of the starting materials cholesterol and pregnenolone, and rings A and B are *cis*. However, some 5$\alpha$-compounds (allopregnane derivatives) are formed, too.

The saturated C$_{21}$ compounds are then either conjugated with glucuronic acid and appear in urine as the glucuronides, or they are further broken down. The side chain is split off particularly easily from 17-hydroxy compounds. The products are *17-keto steroids, androsterone, etiocholanolone,* and others, which are also excreted as glucuronides (more rarely as sulfates). The amount of 17-keto steroids in urine can be estimated easily with Zimmermann's color reaction; it is useful for the diagnosis of adrenal cortical activity. One should be aware, however, that only a part of the corticosteroid excretion is measured, together with testosterone inactivation products. Normally, about 10–20 mg per day of 17-keto steroids are excreted.

**Biosynthesis of C$_{19}$-Steroids.** The principal C$_{19}$-steroid is the male sex hormone *testosterone* ($\Delta^4$-androstene-17$\beta$-ol-3-one). Its biosynthesis in the testes proceeds essentially through the intermediates already discussed, progesterone and *17$\alpha$-hydroxyprogesterone.* Loss of the side chain yields *androstene-3,17-dione* and finally testosterone by reduction at C-17.

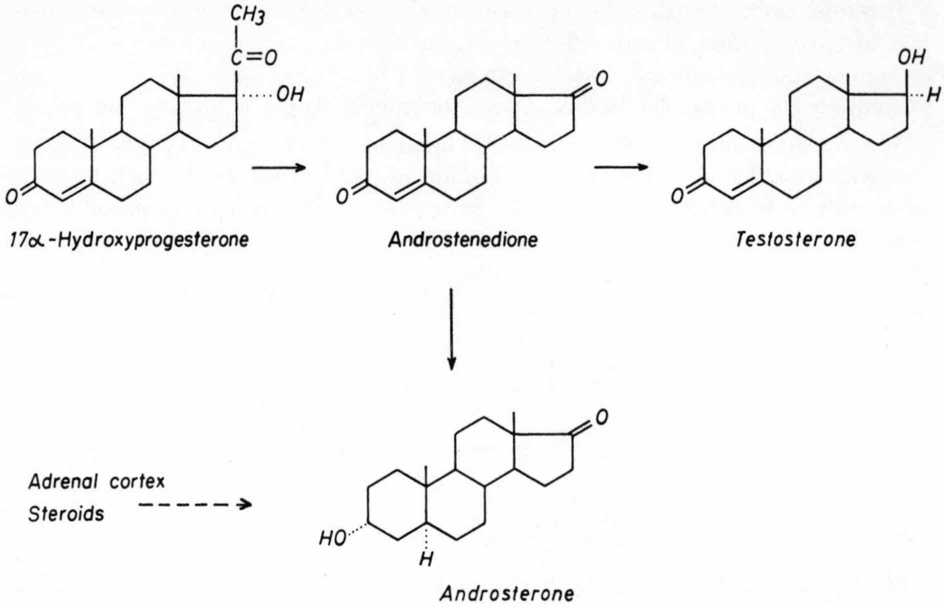

17α-Hydroxyprogesterone     Androstenedione     Testosterone

Adrenal cortex
Steroids  - - - - →

Androsterone

The elimination of the side chain, which here leads to the synthesis of a hormone, is on the other hand a catabolic reaction for the adrenal cortical hormone 17-hydroxy-11-deoxycorticosterone. As we have mentioned, the hormones are inactivated by reduction in ring A. The urinary excretion product *androsterone* is formed by the oxidative loss of the side chain at C-17 and reduction of ring A.

**Biosynthesis of Estrogens.** Estrogens ($C_{18}$-steroids) differ from the previously discussed steroids in one important respect: ring A is aromatic. There can be no methyl group at C-10. The aromatization of ring A, therefore, implies loss of the angular methyl group at C-10 and the alcohol group at C-3 has phenolic character. The biosynthesis starts with testosterone, whose angular methyl group, i.e. C-19 (cf. formula of cholestane in Section 2, for the numbering), is hydroxylated and possibly further dehydrogenated to the aldehyde. C-19 could then be removed as formaldehyde, and ring A would be aromatized.

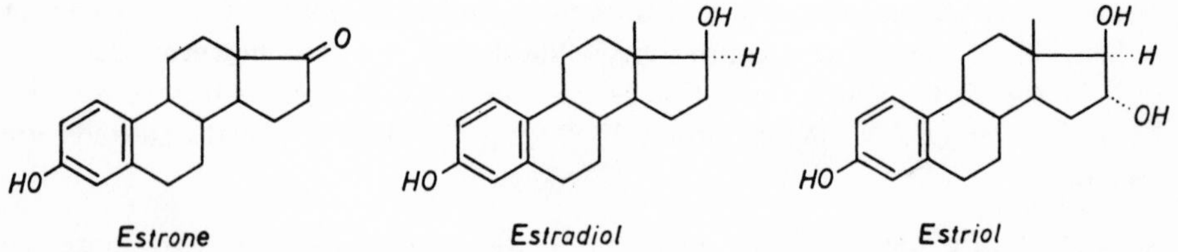

Estrone     Estradiol     Estriol

Important estrogens are *estrone*, *17β-estradiol*, and *3,16α,17β-estriol*. Estrone easily converts to estradiol, which is considered to be the true female sex hormone. For physiological properties see Chapt. XX.

# 7. Carotenoids

Carotenoids enjoy wide distribution both in the animal and plant kingdoms, but are exclusively of plant origin. They are isoprene derivatives with a high degree of unsaturation. Because of the very many conjugated bonds they are colored reddish or yellow: The pigments of the tomato (lycopene) and of the carrot ($\alpha$- and $\beta$-carotene) are red; many oxygen-containing carotenoids are yellow (xanthophylls). Since the double bonds permit *cis-trans*-isomerism, numerous forms are possible. Most carotenoids, however, exist in the all-*trans*-form. The long hydrocarbon chains make them lipid soluble, so that they may also be called "lipochromes."

The true carotenoids and xanthophylls have 40 carbon atoms; this corresponds to 8 isoprene residues. Like squalene, they are constructed symmetrically and it is assumed that they arise by head-to-head condensation of two $C_{20}$ precursors. It has been found that *mevalonic acid* is one important precursor; the appropriate enzyme systems from plants can convert mevalonate to carotenoids. The tetra-

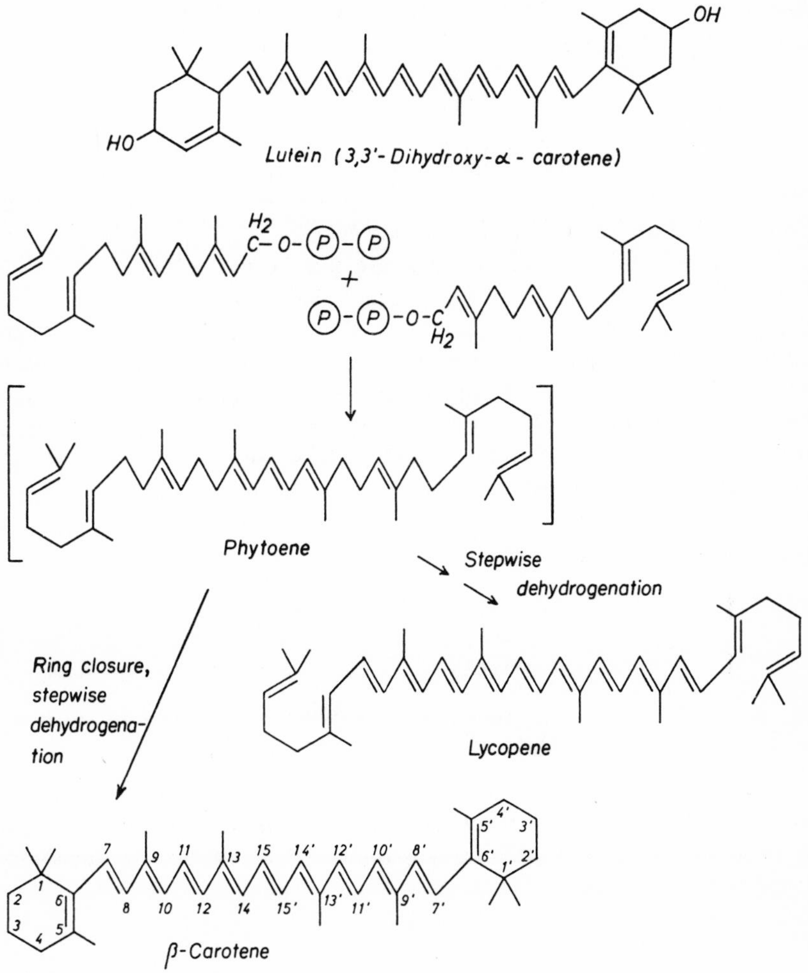

Lutein ( 3,3'- Dihydroxy-$\alpha$- carotene)

Phytoene

Stepwise dehydrogenation

Ring closure, stepwise dehydrogenation

Lycopene

$\beta$-Carotene

isoprenoid geranylgeranyl pyrophosphate may perhaps be dimerized in analogy to farnesyl pyrophosphate, to yield a $C_{40}$-hydrocarbon with eight or nine double bonds.

The precursors of the carotenoids, according to this scheme, are more hydrogenated than later products. The initial isolable product is still colorless *phytoene*; of its 9 double bonds only 3 are conjugated. The conjugated system grows by gradual dehydrogenation (2H with each step), producing successively *phytofluene, ζ-carotene, neurosporene,* and *lycopene.* In some mutants the biogenesis is interrupted at certain points; larger quantities of hydrogenated and colorless carotenoids are accumulated. From one *Neurospora* mutant, e.g., the pale yellow carotenoid neurosporene was obtained.

*Lycopene and the Carotenes.* The formula reveals that lycopene is a long-chain hydrocarbon with 13 double bonds, 11 of which are in conjugation.

Lycopene is the main pigment of the tomato, paprika, and other fruits. We have indicated in the schematic formula that the ends of the chain can easily close up to form rings, with the disappearance of terminal double bonds. Ring closure on only one end results in *γ-carotene*; with ring closure on both ends, *β-* and *α-carotene* are produced. These two carotenes differ in the position of the double bonds in the rings: In *β-carotene* both annular double bonds are in conjugation with the system of double bonds of the long chain (*β-ionone* structure); in *α-carotene* one of the annular double bonds is removed from the system of conjugation by one position (*α-ionone* structure). These details have physiological significance, because vitamin A can only arise from the *β-ionone* structure (see below).

*Xanthophylls* are characterized by hydroxyl groups in the ionone rings, *para* to the long chain of carotenes. Leaf xanthophyll (*lutein*) is derived from *α*-carotene; the pigment in corn *zeaxanthine*, from *β*-carotene. Even more oxygen is present in *astaxanthine* (3,3'-dihydroxy-4,4'-dioxo-*β*-carotene) which is found among crustaceans and is responsible for the appetizing redness of boiled lobsters. Astaxanthene is present in the shells as a chromoprotein (dark green) and is liberated upon denaturation of the protein component (hence the change in color).

γ - Carotene
(partial formula)

α - Carotene
(partial formula)

Carboxylic acids also occur among the carotenes, e.g. saffron yellow or *crocetin*, $C_{20}H_{24}O_4$, and *norbixin*, $C_{24}H_{28}O_4$. They should be regarded as biologic degradation products of the xanthophylls.

**Biologic Significance.** Besides being pigments, the carotenoids also participate in photosynthesis. Along with chlorophyll, they are structural and functional components of the *chloroplasts* (the photosynthesizing organelles of plant cells), and light absorbed by carotenoids is used for photosynthesis.

For mammals, the carotenes (especially β-carotene) are *provitamins A*.

## 8. Vitamin A and Visual Purple

The mammalian organism oxidatively splits carotene at the plane of symmetry between C-15 and C-15′. The initial cleavage product is assumed to be vitamin A aldehyde (retinene), which then is reduced to the alcohol. The alcohol, simply called *vitamin A₁*, can be esterified for storage. Another active substance, *vitamin A₂*, differs from A₁ by an additional double bond in the ring, in conjugation with the entire system.

Vitamin A is a growth factor. In addition to the alcohols A₁ and A₂ and the aldehyde, vitamin A acid is also active in biologic assays. Perhaps the latter is the active form of the vitamin. But in the visual process the acid does not fill the role of vitamin.

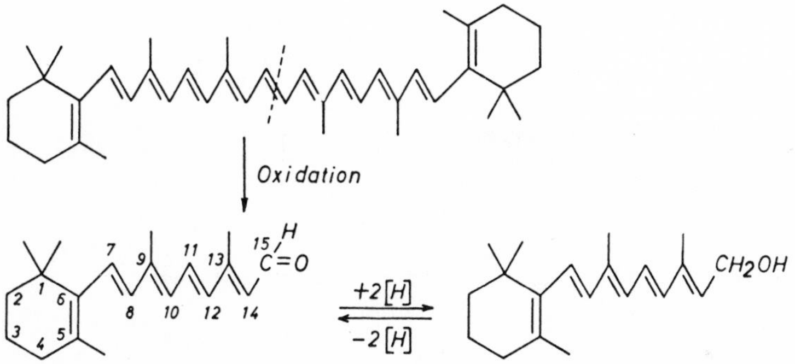

Oxidation

+2[H]
⇌
−2[H]

*Vitamin A₁ Aldehyde*
*(all-trans-Retinene I)*

*Vitamin A₁*

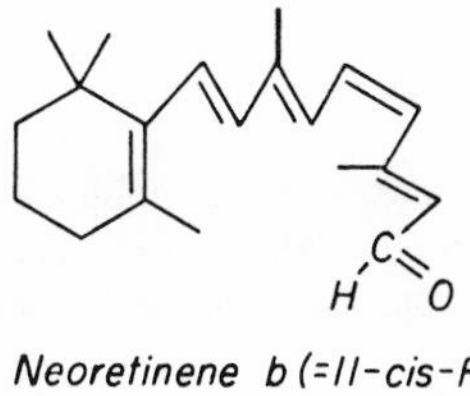

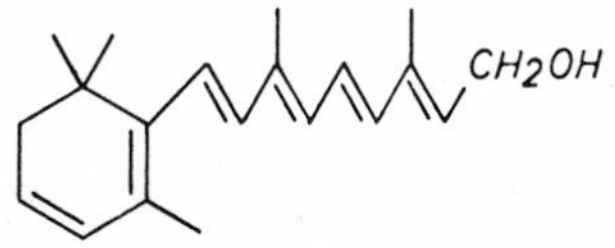

*Neoretinene b (=II-cis-Retinene)*

*Vitamin A₂*

**Biochemistry of the Visual Process.** The photosensitive pigment of the eye is visual purple or *rhodopsin*. It consists of the protein *opsin* and *neoretinene b*, a stereo isomer of the all-*trans*-retinene (vitamin A aldehyde). The protein opsin attaches only to this *cis*-isomer to form the chromoprotein.

During the visual process—the conversion of light to nerve impulses—neo-retinene b is first arranged to the more stable all-*trans*-configuration. Light only initiates the process. The altered molecular shape interferes with the bond to the protein. Probably the tertiary structure of the protein is affected and the all-*trans*-retinene dissociates. In what way the photochemical changes are translated to neural excitation is wholly unknown.

The action of light bleaches visual purple, which means the dissociation to opsin and retinene. Visual purple can only be regenerated after retinene is rearranged to the 11-*cis*-form, the neoretinene b. The rearrangement is possible both as a photochemical reaction and as an oxygen-dependent dark reaction. An appreciable portion of retinene is reduced by alcohol dehydrogenase with the aid of $NADH_2$ to form vitamin A alcohol which then exchanges with vitamin A of the blood circulation. These processes have been represented schematically:

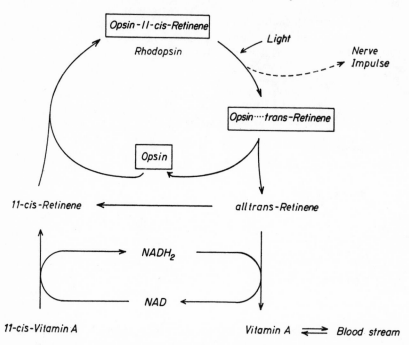

Besides opsin, there is another protein, scotopsin. Either protein can combine either with neoretinene₁ b or with neoretinene₂ b, the 11-*cis*-form of vitamin A₂ aldehyde. Consequently there are four visual pigments, which cover a broad area of the spectrum. These interrelationships have been elucidated chiefly in the laboratory of G. Wald.

## 9. Tocopherol, Phylloquinone, Ubiquinone, and Plastoquinone

These substances are probably synthesized *in vivo* from two components, an aromatic nucleus and an isoprenoid chain, although they have a C—C bond between the isoprene part and the aromatic part. Being vitamins, they must be supplied to the organism in the food. The vertebrate animal, however, is capable of executing a partial synthesis: The isoprenoid side chain is formed in the body (according to the principle of farnesol synthesis, extended by several $C_5$ units) and is attached to the aromatic nucleus. Thus it was found by isotopic labeling that 2-methylnaphthoquinone is converted to vitamin $K_2$ by addition of the difarnesyl side chains (see below).

Phytyl chains often take the place of farnesyl side chains. The alcohol *phytol* has already been mentioned in connection with chlorophyll, where it is esterified to one of the carboxyl groups. Phytol is linearly composed of four isoprene units and is hydrogenated extensively; in fact, it retains only one double bond near the primary alcohol group.

$\alpha$-Tocopherol (vitamin E), the "antisterility vitamin," contains a chromane ring (cf. Chapt. I-1, Table I). The close kinship with other substances of this group is brought out best with *tocohydroquinone*, which arises from hydrolytic cleavage of the O-containing ring. Careful oxidation converts it to a quinone, *tocoquinone* (see formula on p. 255). The reversible transition of quinone $\rightleftharpoons$ hydroquinone has been suggested to be of biologic significance. The open form was thought to be either the hydroxyl derivative obtainable *in vitro* with the phytyl side chain (i.e. the intact double bond) or a corresponding compound.

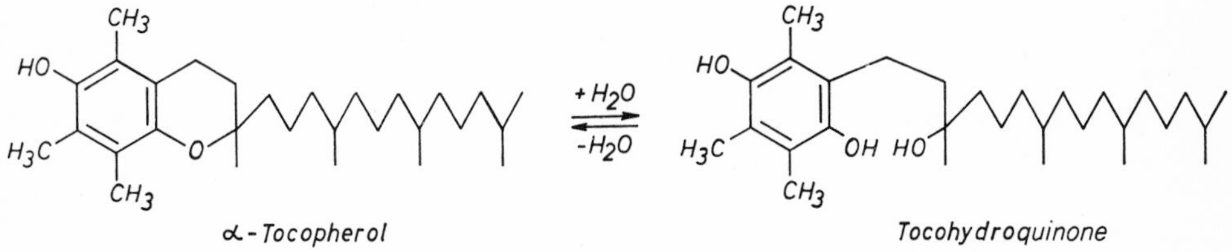

α-Tocopherol          +H₂O / -H₂O          Tocohydroquinone

Other naturally occurring tocopherols are the $\beta$-, $\gamma$-, and $\delta$-tocopherols; they are short one or two methyl groups on the aromatic ring. Concerning tocopherol deficiency, see Table XIX, Chapt. XXII-4.

**Phylloquinone** (vitamin K), the antihemorrhagic vitamin, is composed of a naphthoquinone with an isoprenoid side chain. Besides phylloquinone (vitamin

K$_1$, phytyl side chain) two vitamins K$_2$ with six and seven isoprene residues in the side chains (and six or seven double bonds) have also been discovered. The chain is built analogously to the condensation, forming farnesyl phosphate. In the bioassay, *menadione* (2-methylnaphthoquinone) is also active, presumably because it is converted to vitamin K$_2$ in the organism (proof with C$^{14}$-menadione).

**Ubiquinone** (coenzyme Q), the third member of this group, was discovered relatively recently (Morton; Crane et al.). The name refers to its distribution in nature. It has been found nearly everywhere, in the animal and plant kingdom. It is also called coenzyme Q because of a presumed function in the respiratory chain (cf. Chapt. X). Its vitamin nature is still debated, since nothing is known about the origin of the aromatic, or better the quinonoid, part of the molecule. It is established, however, that the side chain is formed in the organisms from mevalonic acid. Besides, the methyl group in *ortho*-position in tocoquinone, phylloquinone, and ubiquinone, ubiquinone contains two methoxyl groups. The length of the side chain varies. From pig hearts, an ubiquinone-50 (50 C atoms in the side chain = 10 isoprene units) has been isolated. An ubiquinone-30 was found in yeast.

In the equally ubiquitous, isomeric *ubichromenol* the side chain is added to the quinone system. As in the case of the ubiquinones, there is a whole series of related substances. Their function is not yet known.

**Plastoquinone,** isolated from chloroplasts, chemically falls between ubiquinone and γ-tocoquinone. The quinone ring is substituted with methyl groups, save for one position, just as in the tocopherol series. The side chain is an unsaturated polyisoprenoid with 45 carbon atoms.

The similarity of the four quinones is conspicuous. It has been proposed frequently that they participate in oxidative phosphorylation of the respiratory chain. They could do this in two ways: Either they are additional redox systems in the transport of hydrogens (or electrons) or they are intermediate carriers of the energy-rich phosphate. These roles have already been discussed in Chapt. X–4. It should be mentioned that ubiquinone is found in relative abundance in the *mitochondria*, while the other quinones have not been found there with equal certainty. Plastoquinone presumably is involved in the electron-transport system of chloroplasts connected with photosynthesis (cf. Chapt. XVI–2).

**Natural Rubber.** In Section 1 we have discussed the condensation of isoprene units (isopentenyl pyrophosphate). Farnesyl pyrophosphate is the precursor of squalene, but longer chains are also formed and then attached as side chains to quinones. If such a condensation process is imagined to continue until thousands of isoprene units are linked together, the natural rubber molecule is obtained. It is virtually certain that the biosynthesis actually proceeds in such a fashion; it has been carried out even *in vitro* using enzymes of tree sap. The milky sap of the rubber tree (*Hevea*) contains high molecular weight natural rubber (mol. weight about 350,000) in the form of minute spheres. Chemically, it is noteworthy that all the double bonds are exclusively in the *cis*-configuration. The elasticity very probably depends on the shape of the molecule which results from this configuration.

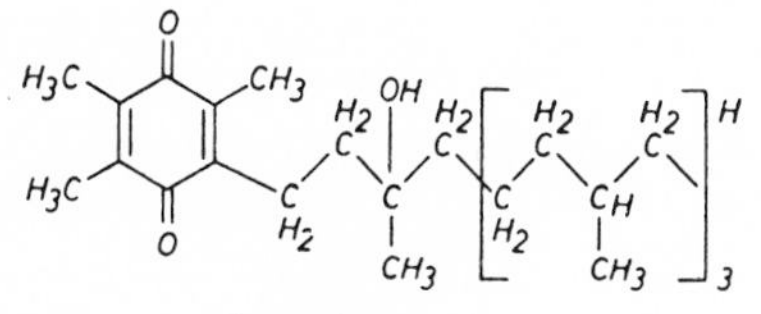

*Tocoquinone*

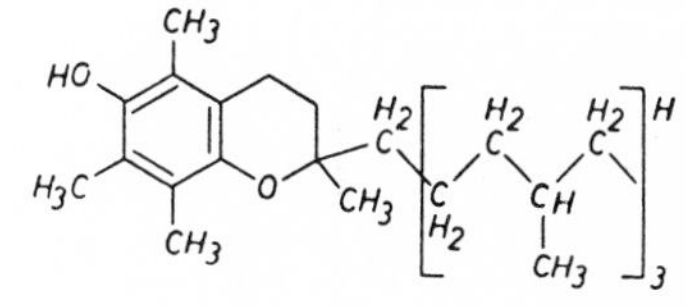

*Tocopherol*

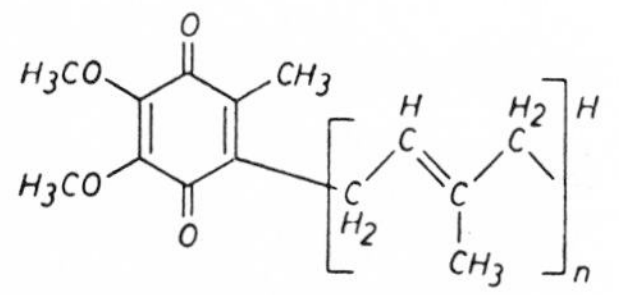

*Ubiquinone (n = 6 – 10)*

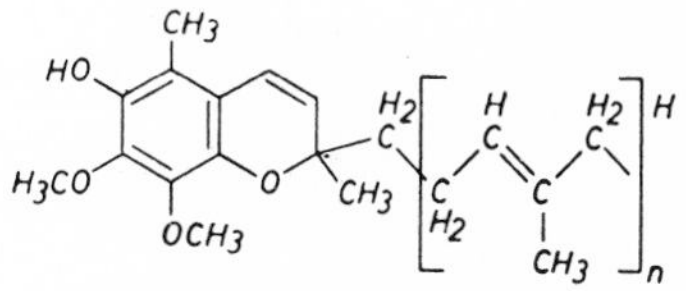

*Ubichromenol*

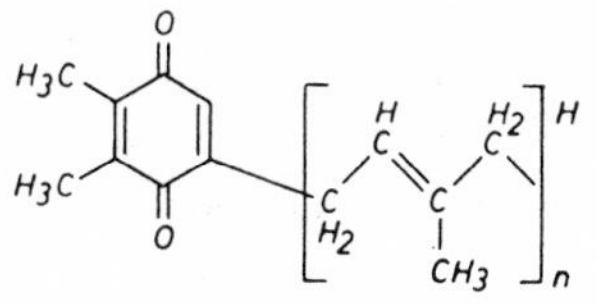

*Plastoquinone (n = 9)*

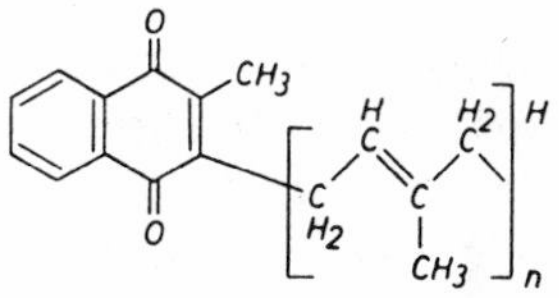

*Vitamin K$_2$ (n = 6 - 9)*

## BIBLIOGRAPHY

L. L. Engel and L. J. Langer, Biochemistry of steroid hormones, *Ann. Rev. Biochem.*, **30**, 499–524 (1961).

L. F. Fieser and M. Fieser, "Steroids," Reinhold, New York, 1959.

K. Folkers, C. H. Shunk, B. O. Linn, F. M. Robinson, P. E. Wittreich, J. W. Huff, J. L. Gilfillan, and H. R. Skeggs, *in* "Biosynthesis of Terpenes and Sterols," Ciba Foundation Symposium, Little, Brown, Boston, Massachusetts, 1959.

T. W. Goodwin, Biosynthesis and function of carotenoids, *Ann. Rev. Plant Physiol.*, **12**, 219–244 (1961).

V. H. T. James, Metabolism of steroid hormones, *Ann. Rept. Chem. Soc., London* **59**, 426–435 (1962).

Lettré-Inhoffen-Tschesche, "Über Sterine, Gallensäuren und verwandte Naturstoffe," 2 vols., Ferd. Enke Verlag, Stuttgart, 1954, 1959.

J. W. Porter and D. G. Anderson, The biosynthesis of carotenes, *Arch. Biochem. Biophys.* **97**, 520–528 (1962).

J. H. Richards and J. B. Hendrickson, "The Biosynthesis of Steroids, Triterpenes, and Acetogenins," W. A. Benjamin, Inc., New York, 1964.

L. D. Wright, Biosynthesis of isoprenoid compounds, *Ann. Rev. Biochem.* **30**, 499–524 (1961).

"Quinones in Electron Transport," Ciba Foundation Symposium, Churchill, London, 1961.

# CHAPTER XV

# Simple Sugars, Monosaccharides

The simple sugars constitute a subclass of the great class of natural substances, the carbohydrates. In sheer amount, the carbohydrates make up the bulk of organic substance on this earth. Though predominantly of plant origin, they constitute the principal component of the food of many animals and of man. Of the customary divisions of foodstuffs—protein, fats and carbohydrates—the carbohydrates rank highest as energy suppliers.

Many simple sugars contain carbon and the elements of water in the ratio of 1:1; this fact has caused the name *carbohydrate* to be given to this class of compounds.

The designation originated at a time when real significance was attached to the empirical formula $C_x(H_2O)_n$, which represents these substances as hydrates of the element carbon. Today we are no longer bound by the empirical formula; we call deoxyribose $C_5H_{10}O_4$ and glucosamine $C_6H_{13}O_5N$ "carbohydrates," but not lactic acid $C_3H_6O_3$.

The simple sugars are either polyhydroxy aldehydes or polyhydroxy ketones. The carbohydrates ordinarily also encompass all substances that are closely related to sugars, e.g., simple derivatives (amino sugars, carboxylic acids, etc.) and polymers of them (oligo- and polysaccharides), which will be discussed in Chapt. XVII.

## 1. Nomenclature and Definitions

**Aldoses and Ketoses.** Carbohydrates differ from ordinary polyalcohols in that one of the alcohol groups is oxidized to a carbonyl group. We use glycerol as an example:

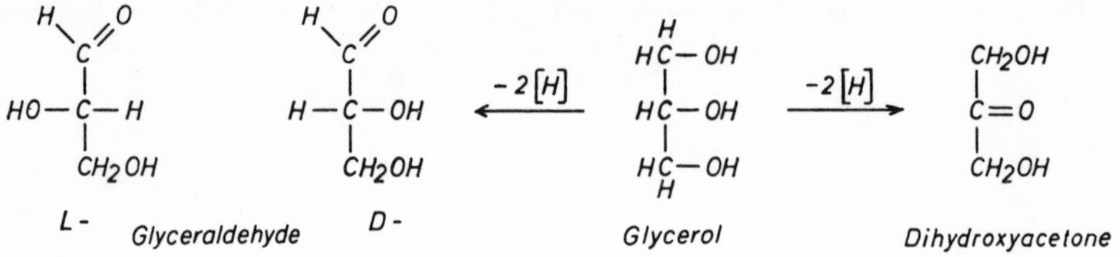

L- Glyceraldehyde    D-        Glycerol        Dihydroxyacetone

Obviously, two dehydrogenation products are possible, either the aldehyde or the ketone. Sugars with a keto group (e.g. dihydroxyacetone) are called *ketoses*, while those with an aldehyde group (e.g. glyceraldehyde) are called *aldoses*. The two formulas for glyceraldehyde shown above represent mirror-image isomers (cf. Chapt. I-3); they are the two optically active forms, D-glyceraldehyde and L-glyceraldehyde.

By convention, D-glyceraldehyde, in whose projection formula the OH group points to the right, is taken as the basis of the entire D-series. This convention is very important for the carbohydrates. Assignment to a steric series is independent of the direction of rotation of light (cf. Chapt. I-3, II-1).

**Structure of Aldoses.** Mentally, the carbon chain of glyceraldehyde may be lengthened most easily by condensation with formaldehyde (the synthetic chemist has better methods available). Two compounds can arise thereby, with the following projection formulas:

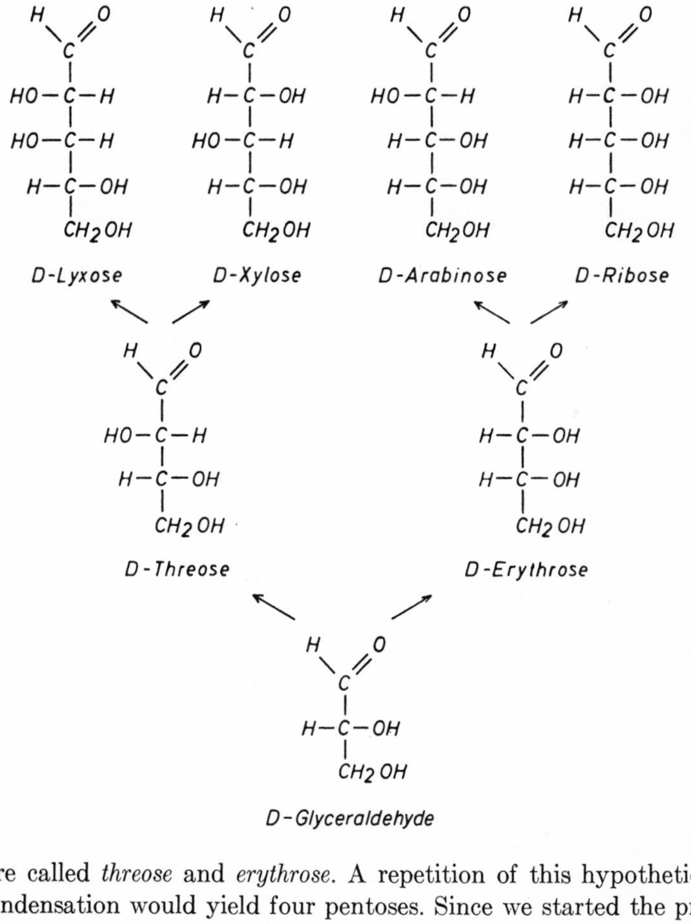

They are called *threose* and *erythrose*. A repetition of this hypothetical formaldehyde condensation would yield four pentoses. Since we started the process with

D-glyceraldehyde, they would all belong to the D-series. Chain elongation of D-glyc-eraldehyde produces only D-sugars; the same procedure starting with L-glyceral-dehyde yields exclusively L-sugars. The latter are mirror images of the former. Since by definition the aldehyde group, or more generally the most highly oxidized group, is written on top, the bottom-most asymmetric C atom determines the as-signment to either the D- or L-series. It is also the asymmetric carbon with the highest number, because numbering starts with the aldehyde carbon.

The symbols D- and L- denote only membership in the corresponding configurational series; nothing is said about optical rotation, which may be either + (to the right) or − (to the left). Rotation is measured easily, whereas assignment to a steric series is usually difficult. The sugar must be broken down stepwise, converted to a compound whose configuration is already known, and then identified. The configuration of most sugars is known. For more on configurational determinations see textbooks of organic chemistry.

The number of possible aldoses grows by a factor of 2 with each additional C atom. Hence there are two glyceraldehydes (D- and L-), four sugars with four C atoms, called *tetroses*, eight *pentoses* with five C atoms (they are called D- and L-ribose, D- and L-arabinose, D- and L-xylose, and D- and L-lyxose), 16 *hexoses*[1] and so fourth. Furthermore, there is a similar series of ketoses. The large number of asymmetric C atoms and the consequent number of isomers complicates the chemis-try of carbohydrates considerably.

We have employed Fischer's projection formulas for our discourse on isomerism. In the transition from projection formula to the spatial model and back, it should be noted that the projection rule (cf. Chapt. I-3) applies to each individual C atom: Neighboring C atoms must be behind, while H and OH groups are in front of the plane of projection. For a pentose (D-ribose) the correct three-dimensional model is shown in Fig. 39.

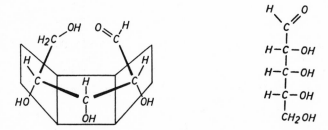

Fig. 39. Projection formula of a sugar. In the model the C—C—C bonds form an angle of 110°; the planes of projection (framed in the left figure), therefore, are at an angle to each other. In writing the formula (as at right), the planes are forced into the plane of the paper.

---

[1] Formerly, sugars were classified by the number of O atoms and not by C atoms. Fucose, $C_6H_{12}O_5$, for example, was called methylpentose; in modern nomenclature it is called a deoxy-hexose. Compare the rules for nomenclature in *J. Chem. Soc.* pp. 5108–5121 (1952).

## 2. Hemiacetal Formulas

Figure 39 illustrates that the aldehyde group at C-1 and the hydroxyl group at C-5 come rather close together. This proximity facilitates the reaction leading to hemiacetal formation. Aldehydes in general can add hydroxyl compounds to the C=O bond (cf. Chapt. I-2). If H—O—H is added, the product is the hydrate of the aldehyde; if an alcohol is added the hemiacetal is formed. Full acetals (or simply "acetals") arise from hemiacetals plus alcohols by elimination of water. This reaction is the basis for glycoside formation by carbohydrates (see formulas below).

Whenever hemiacetal formation proceeds intramolecularly, a ring is produced; it is either a five-membered ring with one O atom, or a six-membered ring with one O atom. In reference to the model compounds furan and pyran (see Table I, Chapt. I-1) the corresponding forms of the sugars are called *furanose* or *pyranose*. The sugars of interest to us usually exist in the pyranose form; in some polysaccharides, however, the furanose form may appear too.

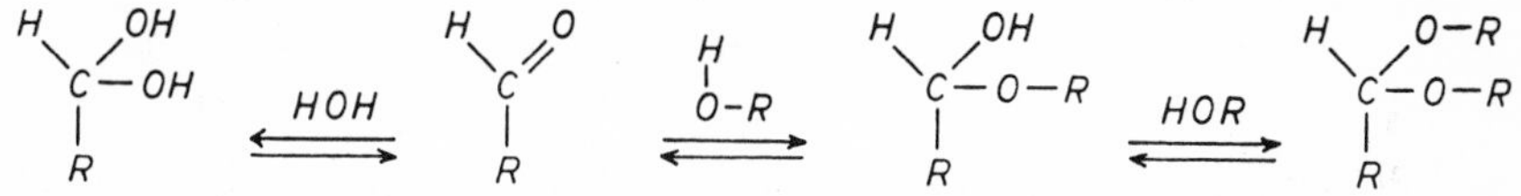

Aldehyde hydrate        Aldehyde        Hemiacetal        (Full) Acetal

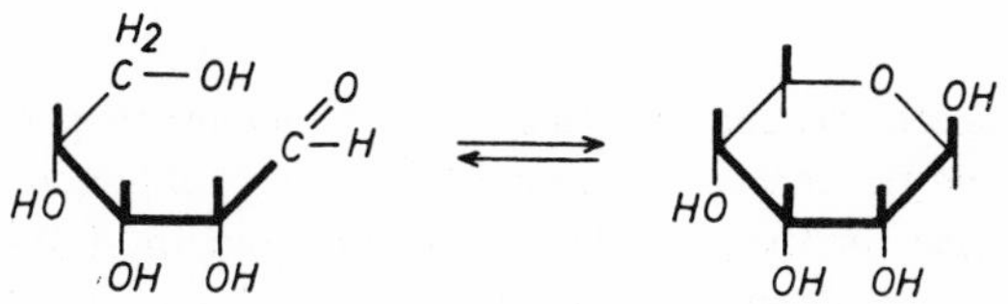

Pyranose

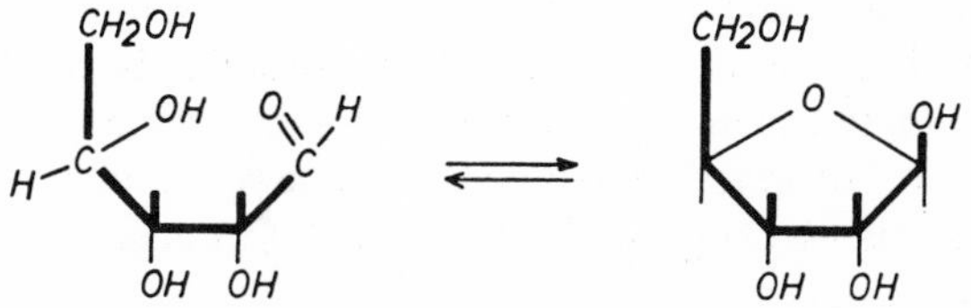

Furanose

In using the Fischer projection formulas, it is customary to indicate the ring by a long line between C-1 and C-5 (representation b for D-glucose, Fig. 40). An error is thereby commited: As can be seen in the figure, ring closure becomes possible only after the OH group at C-5 is rotated to a suitable position (transition d → e → f); the corresponding projection formula is shown in c. Compared to the Fischer projection formula, the H atom seems to have changed its position, a consequence of the altered projection rule.

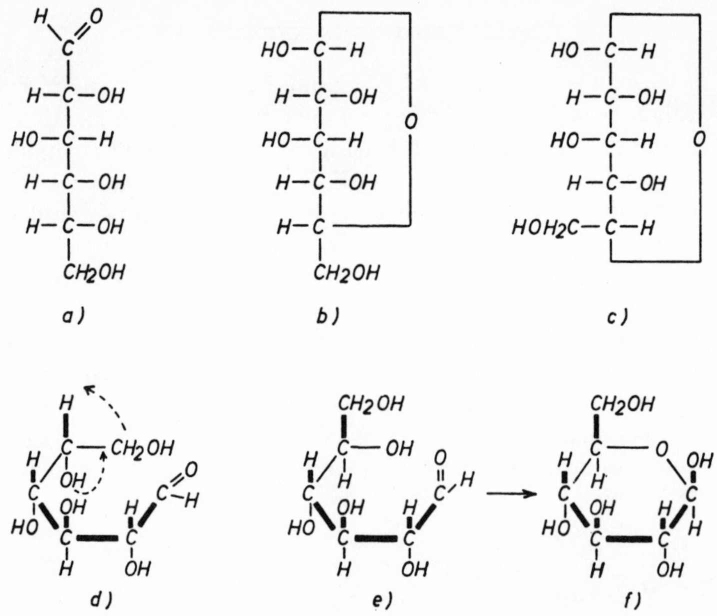

FIG. 40. Different ways of representing glucose. Formulas a, d, and e show the aldehyde form, which is practically nonexistent; in b, c, and f, $\beta$-D-glucose is shown. The series d → r → f clarifies the transition to the ring form, during which the $CH_2OH$ group reaches the top.

Haworth proposed writing the ring form of sugars in perspective as shown by formula f: Imagine the molecular model to lie on a table and draw the model looking down on it with the oxygen toward the rear and the $CH_2OH$ group protruding on top as a side chain. (This arrangement is typical of all D-sugars in this manner of representation.) The C atoms are usually not written out. We have already used this type of representation on other occasions (inositol, Chapt. XIII–2; sterols, Chapt. XIV–2). The use of such perspective formulas is governed by other rules than the projection formulas; for one thing, the drawing may not be rotated in the plane of the paper, but must be redrawn in the new position.

Whenever possible we shall use these Haworth formulas. The following two rules should be remembered:

(1) When oxygen is in back and C-1 at right—the most usual form—then in all D-sugars[2] the $CH_2OH$ group is up.

(2) In $\beta$-D-glucose all hydrogens are *trans*, i.e. they are alternately up and down.

$\alpha$- and $\beta$-**Forms.** During ring closure a new asymmetric C atom is created; there are now four different substituents on the former carbonyl carbon. Therefore, two different forms are possible; they are called the $\alpha$- and the $\beta$-forms. They are easily

---

[2] Presuming that the hydroxyl which determines the D-series is a member of the ring. This is most often the case. Exceptions are aldohexoses in the rare furanose form, and heptoses.

interconvertible, probably through the aldehyde form, which is however present only in infinitesimal amounts in the equilibrium mixture. The $\alpha$- and $\beta$-forms differ in their physical constants, including their optical rotation; they are not mirror-image isomers. Example:

| Glucose | Rotation | Melting Point | Crystallized from |
|---|---|---|---|
| $\alpha$-D-Glucose | +112° | 146° | Water |
| $\beta$-D-Glucose | +19° | 148–150° | Glacial acetic acid; Pyridine |

| $\alpha$-D-Glucose | al-D-Glucose (Aldehyde form) | $\beta$-D-Glucose |

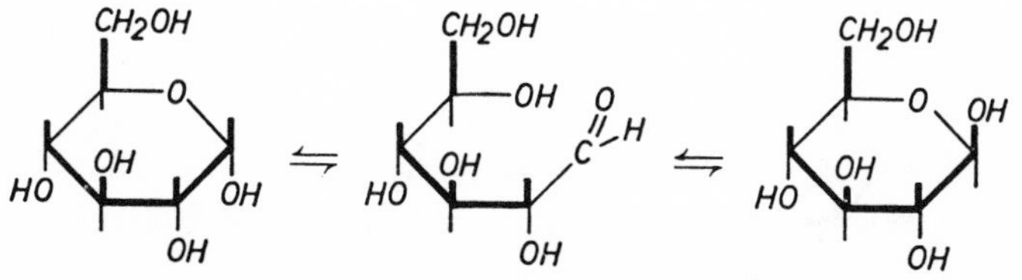

Immediately after $\alpha$-D-glucose is dissolved in water, the degree of rotation recorded above can be observed. However, the rotation gradually diminishes and a few hours later comes to rest at $\alpha_D = +52°$, which corresponds to the equilibrium mixture. This same final value of rotation is observed when one starts with a solution of $\beta$-glucose. This phenomenon of a shift in rotation is called *"mutarotation,"* and the discovery of the $\alpha,\beta$-isomers confirmed the correctness of the ring formulas.

The assignment of the rotational isomers to the two formulas which can be written for them has been a difficult stereochemical problem. At first, in all sugars of the D-series the more strongly dextrorotatory form[3] was called the $\alpha$-form. Later it was noticed that the $\alpha$-form in the projection formula invariably has the hydroxyl group on the same side as the hydroxyl group determining the D-series (i.e. to the right in the D-series; to the left in the L-series). The reason for this is that each C atom contributes a definite amount to the optical rotation (Hudson's rule of superimposition). In the Haworth formulas, this means that, if the OH at C-1 is down, we have the $\alpha$-form; if the OH is up, the $\beta$-form.

## 3. General Reactions of Monosaccharides

The chemical properties of sugars are determined primarily by the many hydroxyl groups. Being polyhydroxy compounds they dissolve readily in water, are insoluble in lipid solvents and in fats, and taste sweet (even glycerol is sweet). The aldehyde groups (or ketone groups in ketoses) are not manifest; simple color reactions for aldehydes are negative, because in solution there is practically no aldehyde present, but rather the hemiacetal.

---

[3] In the L-series, the $\alpha$-form is the more levorotatory form.

**Functional Derivatives of Hydroxyl Groups.** Alcohol groups can be esterified. This reaction is used frequently in organic chemistry for the purpose of characterizing sugars or for blocking certain hydroxyl groups. Acetate or benzoate esters often serve in syntheses with carbohydrates.

In biochemistry, the esters of phosphoric acid have special significance; the organism metabolizes almost exclusively phosphorylated sugars. We symbolize the phosphate group by P. Different phosphates of the very same sugar (e.g. glucose 1-phosphate and glucose 6-phosphate; see formulas) behave entirely differently in biochemical reactions.

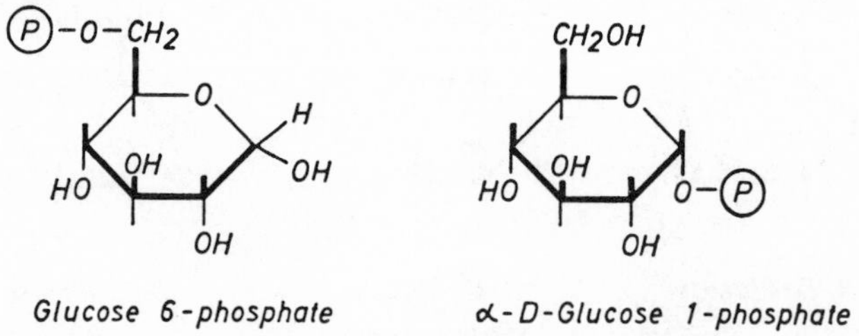

Glucose 6-phosphate          α-D-Glucose 1-phosphate

Alcoholic groups are also able to form ethers. The hemiacetal hydroxyl group on C-1 is unusually reactive; compounds derived from it are called glycosides. A separate chapter is devoted to them (Chapt. XVII). Ether formation (e.g. methylation with dimethylsulfate and alkali) is also important for the constitutional determination of oligosaccharides.

**Derivatives of the Carbonyl Group.** Not many reactions of the aldehyde or keto group of sugars are observed, because the carbonyl forms of sugars comprise only a fraction of one percent in the equilibrium mixture. They can be trapped, however, in a few reactions, e.g. by oxime formation. Important for the identification of sugars is the reaction with phenylhydrazine or with substituted phenylhydrazines (E. Fischer), which involves two carbon atoms and results in *osazones*:

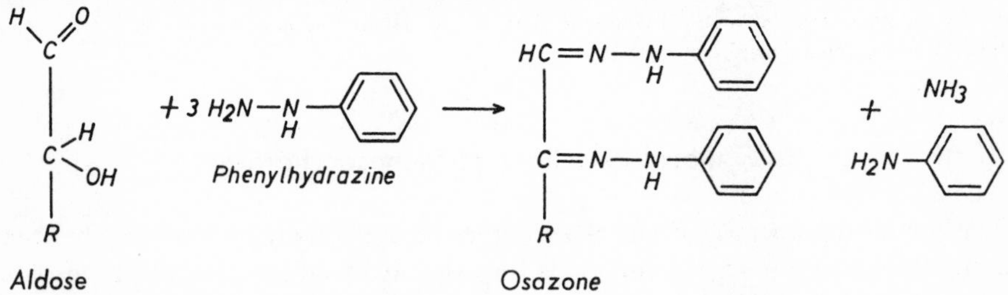

Aldose          Phenylhydrazine          Osazone

The course of the reaction was recognized correctly by Weygand (1941) as a series of rearrangements (cf. textbooks of organic chemistry).

Sugars possess only limited stability toward acids and alkali. In strongly acid solution, water molecules are split out; pentoses are thereby converted to furfural, while hexoses become hydroxymethylfurfural, which decomposes further to the smaller hydroxy aldehydes that are responsible for certain color reactions of the sugars (see below).

Alkali augments the formation of enols; the asymmetry at C-2 is lost thereby, and glucose becomes fructose or mannose (or the reverse). Sugars that differ only at C-2 are called epimeric sugars; as can be seen clearly, they form identical osazones. Continued heating with more concentrated alkali destroys the molecule, and strongly reducing fragments (reductones) are generated.

Reduction of the carbonyl group produces the corresponding polyalcohol; for example, mannitol is obtained from mannose.

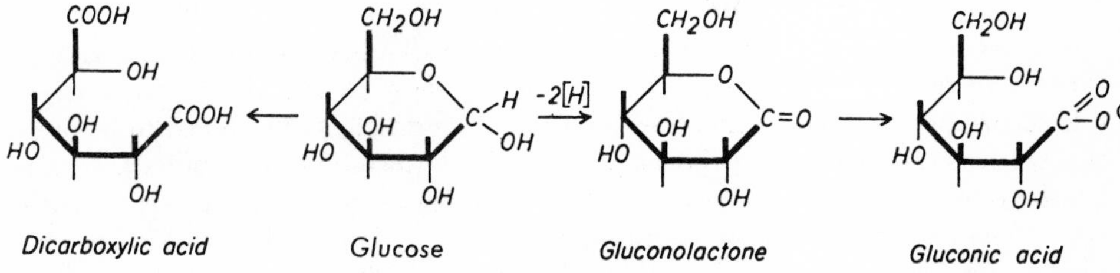

Dicarboxylic acid    Glucose    Gluconolactone    Gluconic acid

Cautious oxidation dehydrogenates the hemiacetal to form the lactone of an acid (in alkaline solution, the salt of that acid). The lactone may be reduced again to reform the hemiacetal. More vigorous oxidation forms the dicarboxylic acid by oxidizing the terminal $CH_2OH$.

**Color Reactions of Carbohydrates.** There are a few color reactions of sugars with phenols ($\alpha$-naphthol, anthrone, resorcinol, orcinol, etc.) and concentrated mineral acids. The acids effect loss of water, resulting in furfural derivatives, some of which break down further to form lower aldehydes. The aldehydes then condense with the phenols to produce the colored substances. The reaction mechanisms are not completely understood.

General color reactions of this type include the Molisch test with $\alpha$-naphthol and concentrated sulfuric acid and the *anthrone reaction* with anthrone and sulfuric acid. The latter is used for quantitive colorimetric determinations. Reaction conditions can be chosen so that only ketoses react (HCl + resorcinol, Seliwanoff's test) or only pentoses (HCl + orcinol, Bial's test). These reactions help to distinguish the various sugars.

All mono- and some oligosaccharides are reducing sugars; this property is due to the $\alpha$-ketol grouping (carbonyl group adjacent to a hydroxyl group). Although tests for reducing sugars are nonspecific, they are used frequently to detect and to determine sugars. The reduction of $Cu^{++}$ ions in alkaline solution is the basis of Benedict's and Fehling's reactions. Aldoses are initially oxidized to the carboxylic acids, but may undergo further cleavage (especially in more concentrated alkali). Ketoses are split to glycolaldehyde and a tetrose that can be further oxidized.

## 4. The Individual Sugars

**Trioses.** D-*Glyceraldehyde* (formula in Section 1) is the dehydrogenation product of glycerol. More important, however, is 3-phosphoglyceraldehyde, an intermediate in the degradation of carbohydrates (Chapt. XVII–6), which is in equilibrium with dihydroxyacetone phosphate; the attainment of equilibrium is catalyzed by the enzyme triose phosphate isomerase (cf. Section 7).

**Tetroses.** Both *threose* and *erythrose* have already been mentioned (formulas in Section 1). The ketose *erythrulose* should be mentioned because it appears as an · intermediate in several biochemical transformations (among others in photosynthesis) in the form of its phosphate.

**Pentoses.** The names and formulas of the aldopentoses may be found in Section 1. *Ribose* and ribose phosphates are components of the nucleic acids and the nucleotide coenzymes. In these derivatives the furanose form has been proved to be present, whereas free ribose exists in the pyranose form (formulas in Section 2). *Deoxyribose* (formula in Chapt. VII) is responsible for the name of the deoxyribonucleic acids. The free sugars are in equilibrium with the aldehyde form, which in this case can be demonstrated with fuchsin sulfurous acid. The lack of a hydroxyl group on C-2 is the basis of this reaction (used in Feulgen's nuclear staining technique).

Besides the 3-phosphate and the 5-phosphate of ribose, there is also the 5-phosphate-1-pyrophosphate (phosphoribosyl pyrophosphate), an intermediate in the biosynthesis of nucleosides (cf. Chapt. VII-2).

*Arabinose* is a component of gum arabic and otherwise widely distributed in the plant kingdom.

*Ribulose* is the ketose corresponding to ribose. In general, the ketoses are designated by the ending *-ulose* (unless they have trivial names, such as fructose). *Xylulose* is an epimer to ribulose at C-3. Ribulose phosphate and diphosphate play a role in biologic interconversions of the sugars and in photosynthesis (Chapt. XVI-4).

**Hexoses.** The most important and most widely distributed carbohydrate is D-*glucose* (also called "grape sugar" or "dextrose"). The β-form has already been introduced with its formula; it is easy to remember that all its hydrogen atoms are *trans* (in the Haworth formula or corresponding simplifications). Common grape sugar actually consists chiefly of α-glucose; the initial specific optical rotation of +112° decreases to the final value of +52° in solution (mutarotation; for explanation see end of Section 2). Free glucose occurs primarily in sweet fruits; smaller amounts are found in blood (between 0.06 and 0.10% in human blood) of the animal organism.

The more important phosphate esters of glucose (formulas in Section 3) are glucose 1-phosphate (also called Cori ester), which is in equilibrium with the storage form glycogen (Chapt. XVII-6), and the 6-phosphate (also called Robison ester), which is formed enzymically from glucose and ATP (hexokinase reaction, Section 7). Glucose 1-phosphate can be converted to glucose 6-phosphate *via* the intermediate "coenzyme" glucose 1,6-diphosphate.

Glucose, mannose, and the ketose, fructose, form the same osazone. In alkaline solution the three are interconvertible through a common enol form, but further degradation and breakdown into smaller fragments occurs easily.

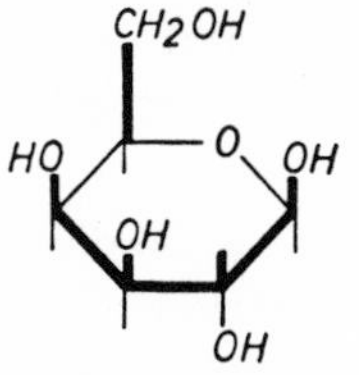

CH₂OH ... (structural formulas)

β-D-Galactose 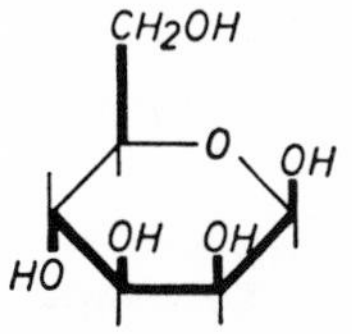          β-D-Mannose 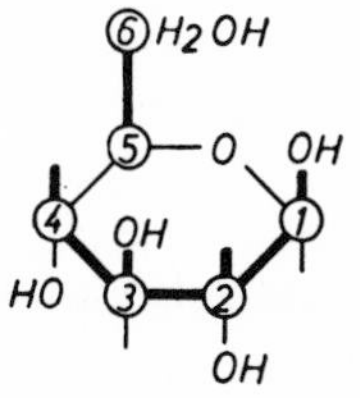          β-D-Glucose

D-(+)-*Mannose* is an epimer of glucose; the two sugars differ only at C-2. Mannose occurs freely at times in plants, but is more often bound. In the animal organism, it is a component of glycolipids (Chapt. XIII-4), glycoproteins, and blood group substances.

D-(+)-*Galactose* is a component of milk sugar (lactose) and other oligosaccharides and of a few other more complicated compounds. It differs from glucose in the steric configuration at C-4; as a consequence, three hydroxyls in the ring form are *cis*. An enzyme is able to convert galactose to glucose, i.e. it performs a Walden inversion at C-4 (galactowaldenase; coenzyme: uridine diphosphate). Nitric acid oxidation of galactose produces mucic acid (tetrahydroxyadipic acid) in its meso form. This reaction was important in the determination of its constitution. Besides the common D-isomer, L-galactose also occurs naturally (in agar agar and elsewhere).

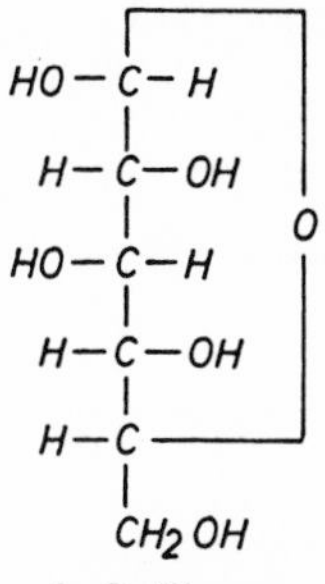

β-D-Glucose 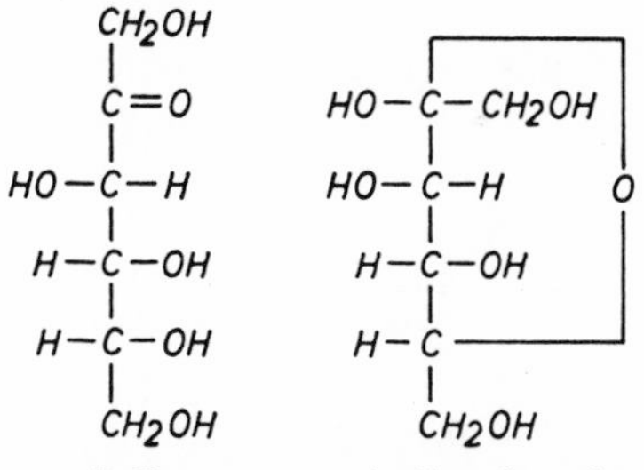          D-Fructose, projection formulas

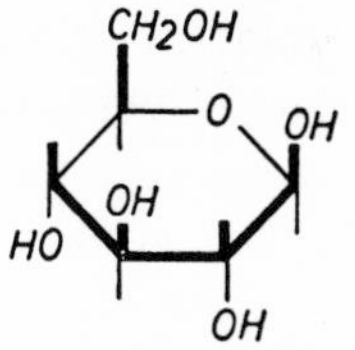

β-D-Glucose 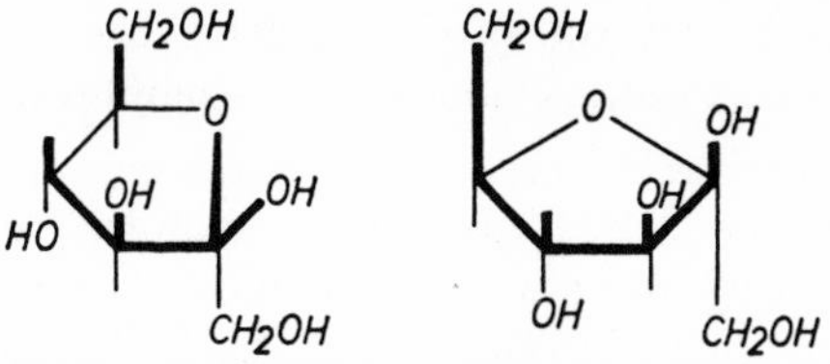          β-D-Fructofuranose

D-(−)-*Fructose*, a keto hexose, was discovered as a cleavage product of cane sugar and called levulose, because it rotates polarized light to the left. Nevertheless, it belongs to the D-series and is closely related to D-glucose (see formulas above). *Free* fructose prefers to exist in the pyranose form (six-membered ring); only in oligosaccharides (cane sugar), in polysaccharides (inulin), and in several phosphate esters is the furanose form realized. Fructose occurs mainly in the plant kingdom and in honey.

Two phosphate esters, fructose 6-phosphate and fructose 1,6-diphosphate (the Harden-Young ester) are biochemically significant because they are intermediates in the breakdown of glucose according to the Embden-Meyerhof pathway (Section 7); this pathway is actually the route of breakdown of fructose 1,6-diphosphate.

*Deoxyhexoses.* A component of a few oligosaccharides of milk and of blood group substances (see Chapt. XVII-7) is L-*fucose* (6-deoxy-L-galactose). *Rhamnose* (6-deoxy-L-mannose) occurs in glycosides, e.g. in strophanthin. Note that both deoxyhexoses belong to the L-series.

**Heptoses.** Only *sedoheptulose* is of interest to us. It is a ketose with the same structure as ribose between C-4 and C-6. Its phosphate is formed from ribose 5-phosphate during the interconversion of the monosaccharides (Section 5).

**Cyclitols** have the same formula as hexoses, $C_6H_{12}O_6$, but are not carbohydrates. Instead they are carbocyclic homologs of glycerol; for this reason they have been discussed under the lipids, of which they are components (inositol, Chapt. XIII-2).

**Amino Sugars** are formed formally by the replacement of a hydroxyl group with an amino group. In biochemistry three such compounds are important: glucosamine (chitosamine), galactosamine (chondrosamine) and neuraminic acid.

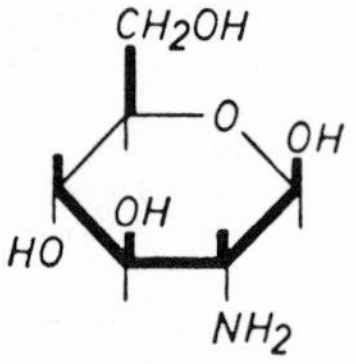

β-D-Glucosamine 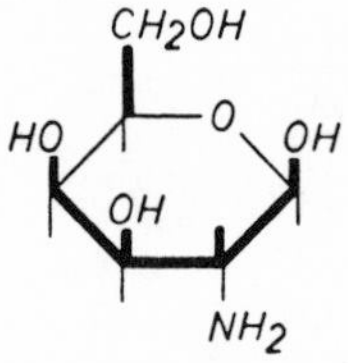          β-D-Galactosamine

*Glucosamine* in its structure resembles D-glucose; the amino group is at C-2. It occurs only bound, e.g. in chitin (hence the name chitosamine), in glycolipids, in blood group substances, and in other complex polysaccharides. The amino group is frequently acetylated.

*Galactosamine* (chondrosamine) resembles galactose; the OH group in position 2 is replaced by an amino group which is usually acetylated. Acetylgalactosamine occurs in complex glycolipids and polysaccharides.

*Neuraminic acid* has a somewhat more complicated structure, which has been elucidated very recently. The structure may be derived from the product of an aldol condensation between mannosamine (an epimer to glucosamine at C-2) and pyruvate. The newly formed hydroxyl group is oriented *trans* to the amino group, and the keto group of pyruvate forms a pyranose hemiacetal ring.

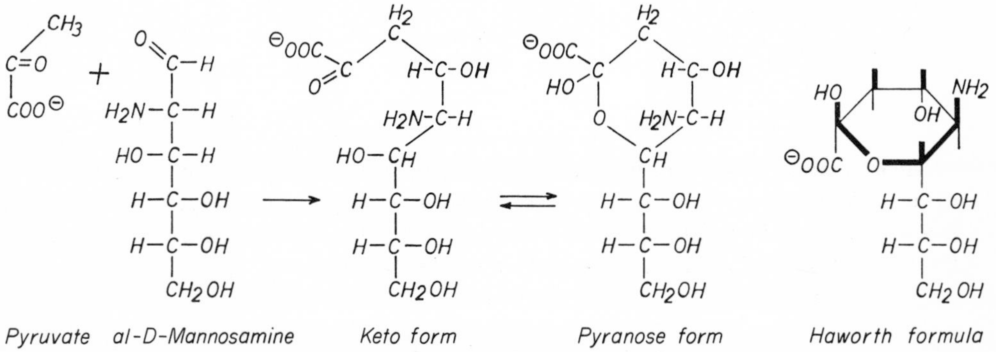

| Pyruvate | al-D-Mannosamine | Keto form | Pyranose form | Haworth formula |

Neuraminate

Neuraminic acid has received much attention recently. In its acetylated form, it is a component of membrane-forming glycolipids (cf. Chapt. XIII–4) and of the "bifidus factors." The latter are oligosaccharides of human milk, important for the nutrition of infants.

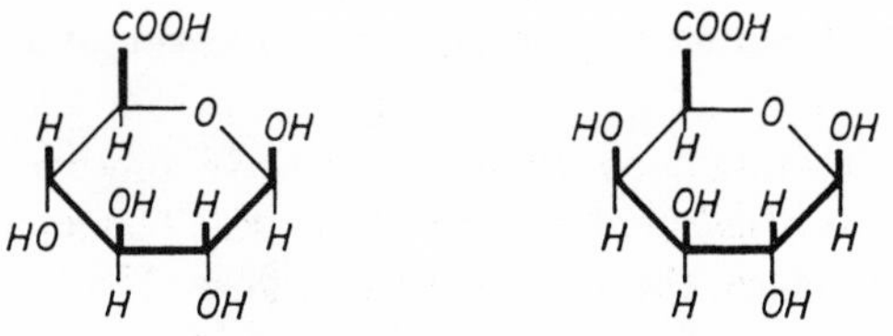

β-D-Glucuronic acid      β-D-Galacturonic acid

**Uronic Acids.** Oxidation of sugars at the $CH_2OH$ group, but not at the aldehyde group, yields uronic acids. This reaction can be carried out chemically only by indirect means; the organism, however, performs the step directly (cf. Chapt. XVII–4). *Glucuronic acid*, the prototype of the uronic acids, is important because it forms glycosides rather easily; they are called *glucuronides*. Many substances are excreted in the urine after coupling with glucuronic acid (cf. Chapt. XVII–1). *Galacturonic acid* is found in pectin.

**Ascorbic Acid** (*vitamin C*) was discovered and isolated as the anti-scurvy vitamin (for physiological properties cf. Chapt. XXII–5). Ascorbic acid is the lactone of 2-keto-L-gulonic acid. It contains an en-diol group (a double bond between two adjacent hydroxyl groups) and is a strong reducing agent, as are all en-diols. By loss of hydrogen, it is converted to dehydroascorbic acid (formula at right). The reaction is reversible, and ascorbic acid presumably acts as a redox catalyst in the cell.

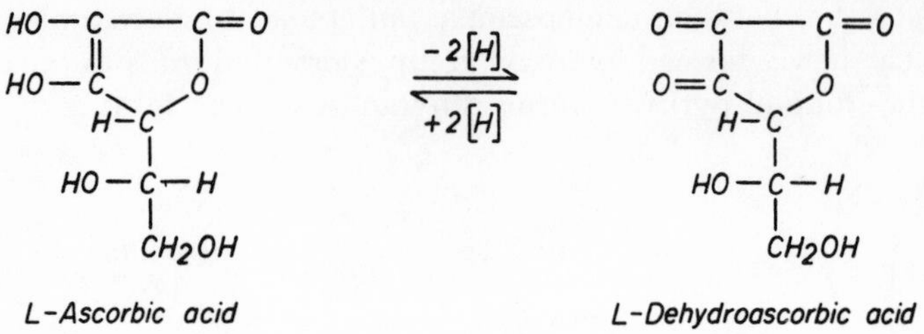

$$
\begin{array}{ccc}
HO-C & C=O \\
\| & \\
HO-C & O \\
H-C & \\
| & \\
HO-C-H & \\
| & \\
CH_2OH &
\end{array}
\qquad
\underset{+2[H]}{\overset{-2[H]}{\rightleftharpoons}}
\qquad
\begin{array}{ccc}
O=C & C=O \\
& \\
O=C & O \\
H-C & \\
| & \\
HO-C-H & \\
| & \\
CH_2OH &
\end{array}
$$

L-Ascorbic acid            L-Dehydroascorbic acid

Ascorbic acid is distributed primarily in the plant kingdom, where ascorbic oxidase, a copper-containing, four-electron-transferring oxidase (cf. Chapt. X–7), is also found. Rats and many other mammals are able to synthesize ascorbic acid; they do not depend on a supplementation of the "vitamin."

## 5. Interconversion of Sugars

Most organisms can interconvert sugars; e.g. they can form ribose out of glucose whenever ribose is required, as it is for the synthesis of nucleic acids. Several types of reactions are available for such interconversions.

(1) Epimerization (the inversion of steric configuration at a C atom) and isomerization (the conversion of aldose $\rightleftharpoons$ ketose). The number of C atoms does not change.

(2) Transfer of $C_3$ or $C_2$ fragments from one sugar to another; thus hexoses can be converted to trioses, tetroses, pentoses, and heptoses. The donor of the $C_3$ or $C_2$ fragment is invariably a ketose; the acceptor is an aldose. The *sum* of carbohydrate C atoms remains constant.

(3) Oxidative removal of one C atom by dehydrogenation of the aldehyde to form the acid and subsequent decarboxylation. Hexoses become pentoses (see below); the chain is shortened by one C atom.

Biochemical *epimerization* at certain asymmetric centers has been discovered relatively recently. An example is glucose $\rightleftharpoons$ galactose; the coenzyme is uridine diphosphate, whose reactions will be discussed in another context (cf. Chapt. XVII–4). Among the pentoses, there is the conversion of ribulose 5-phosphate to xylulose 5-phosphate (epimerization at C-3).

Isomerization at a carbon atom adjacent to a carbonyl group can be achieved *in vitro* in a basic solution. The simplest example of an enzymic isomerization is the one of triose phosphate (cf. Section 7). The conversion of glucose to fructose and the reverse is also catalyzed by an isomerase.

$C_3$ *fragments* can arise in the simplest manner from cleavage of a ketose. Fructose 1,6-diphosphate is in equilibrium with dihydroxyacetone phosphate and glyceraldehyde 3-phosphate; in this case, the keto form (or open-ring form) undergoes the reaction (cf. also Section 7).

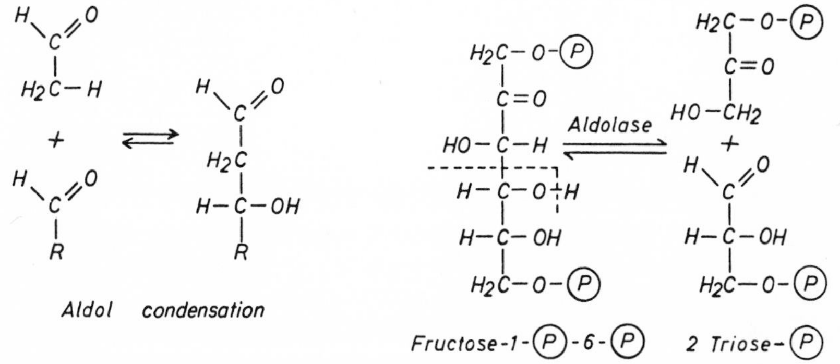

$$
\begin{array}{ccc}
\underset{\text{H}_2\text{C}-\text{H}}{\overset{\displaystyle H\!\!\diagdown_{\!\!C}\!\!\diagup\!\!O}{|}} \;+\; \underset{R}{\overset{\displaystyle H\!\!\diagdown_{\!\!C}\!\!\diagup\!\!O}{|}} & \rightleftarrows & \underset{\underset{R}{H-\overset{|}{C}-OH}}{\overset{H\!\!\diagdown_{\!C}\!\!\diagup O}{\underset{|}{H_2C}}}
\end{array}
$$

*Aldol condensation*

$$
\underset{\underset{H_2C-O-\text{(P)}}{\underset{|}{H-C-OH}}}{\overset{\overset{H_2C-O-\text{(P)}}{|}}{\underset{\underset{|}{H-C-O \vdots H}}{\underset{|}{HO-C-H}}}}\overset{\overset{\displaystyle C=O}{|}}{} \quad\underset{\text{Aldolase}}{\rightleftarrows}\quad
$$

*Fructose-1-(P)-6-(P)    2 Triose-(P)*

The aldolase reaction is the biochemical version of a reaction well-known in organic chemistry, the aldol condensation. An aldehyde is attached to an active CH₂ group, whereby a new C—C bond is formed and hydrogen is accepted by the aldehyde oxygen (left part of the diagram of formulas).

**Transaldolase.** While aldolase produces only trioses from hexoses (and the reverse) the analogous enzyme transaldolase transfers the dihydroxyacetone residue onto other aldoses. The enzyme is highly specific: Transaldolase splits only fructose and sedoheptulose (reverse of aldol condensation) and transfers the C₃ residue (a dihydroxyacetone, which remains bound to the ε-amino group of a lysine residue on the enzyme surface) to a corresponding aldehyde, i.e. to glyceraldehyde phosphate or erythrose 4-phosphate, or possibly to ribose 5-phosphate:

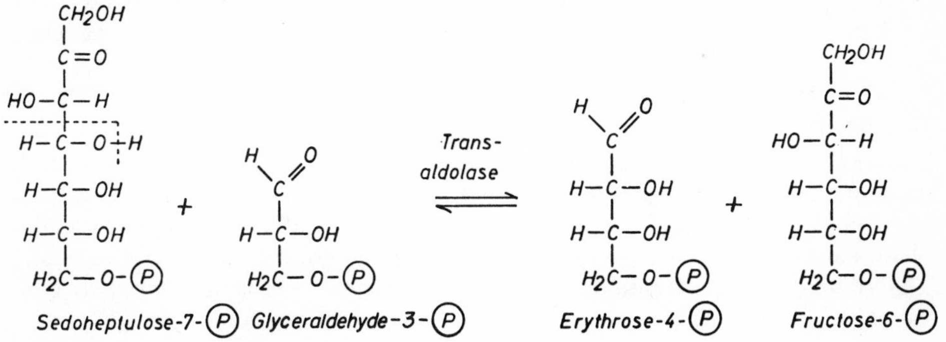

*Sedoheptulose-7-(P)    Glyceraldehyde-3-(P)    Erythrose-4-(P)    Fructose-6-(P)*

Transaldolase does not seem to require any coenzyme. It has been found in yeast, plants, and mammals.

**Transketolase.** A C₂ *fragment, active glycolaldehyde,* is transferred during the *transketolase* reaction. This is an equilibrium reaction similar to the acyloin condensation of organic chemistry, in which two moles of aldehyde yield a hydroxy-ketone:

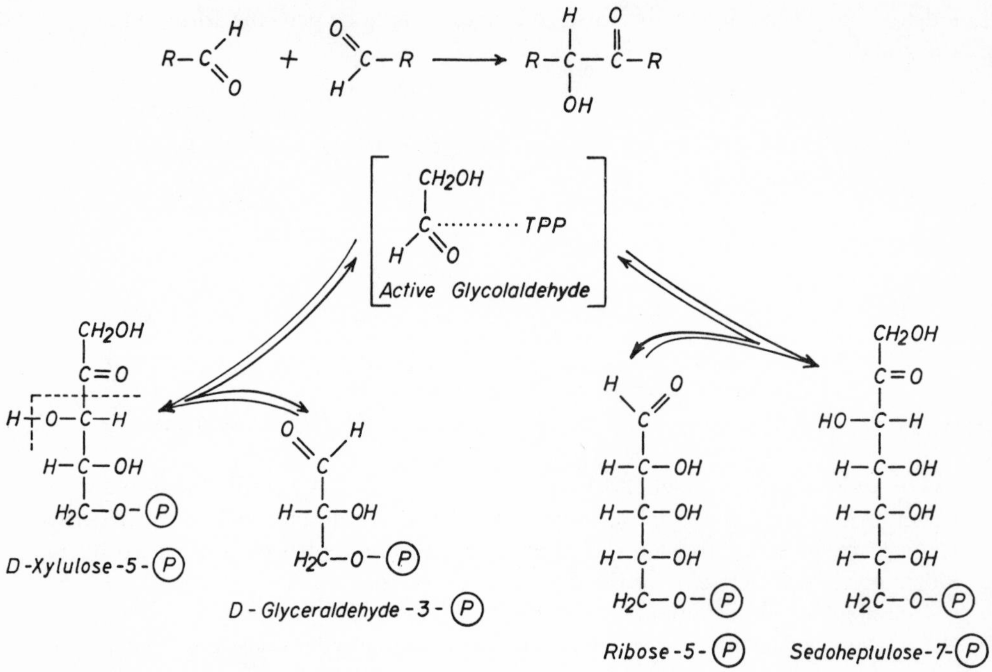

$$R-C\overset{H}{\underset{O}{\diagdown}} \;+\; \overset{O}{\underset{H}{\diagup}}C-R \longrightarrow R-\overset{\overset{\displaystyle H}{|}}{\underset{\underset{\displaystyle OH}{|}}{C}}-\overset{\overset{\displaystyle O}{\|}}{C}-R$$

$$\left[\; \begin{array}{c} CH_2OH \\ | \\ C \cdots\cdots TPP \\ H\diagup \quad \diagdown O \end{array} \;\right]$$

Active Glycolaldehyde

CH_2OH
|
C=O
|
H┼O—C—H
|
H—C—OH
|
H_2C—O—(P)

D-Xylulose-5-(P)

$$O\overset{\diagdown}{\underset{\diagup}{}}\overset{H}{\underset{C}{}}$$
H—C—OH
|
H_2C—O—(P)

D-Glyceraldehyde-3-(P)

H
\
C=O
|
H—C—OH
|
H—C—OH
|
H—C—OH
|
H_2C—O—(P)

Ribose-5-(P)

CH_2OH
|
C=O
|
HO—C—H
|
H—C—OH
|
H—C—OH
|
H_2C—O—(P)

Sedoheptulose-7-(P)

In biochemistry, the transketolase reaction has been discovered to be the cleavage mechanism of ketopentoses. Xylulose 5-phosphate is broken down to a $C_3$ fragment (glyceraldehyde phosphate) and a $C_2$ fragment. Active glycolaldehyde does not appear in its free form, but remains bound to the coenzyme thiamine pyrophosphate (TPP), probably in the same way as acetaldehyde does during the decarboxylation of pyruvate. In this form, glycolaldehyde is able to react with other sugars, e.g. ribose or erythrose. In the first case, sedoheptulose is formed. The donor of the $C_2$ fragment evidently must be a ketose phosphate, or more precisely (due to the enzyme specificity) a ketose phosphate whose steric configuration at C-3 corresponds to that of fructose. Ribulose 5-phosphate, for this reason, can become a $C_2$ donor only after epimerization to xylulose 5-phosphate. There is the further possibility of obtaining active glycolaldehyde by decarboxylation (thiamine pyrophosphate assisted) of hydroxypyruvate. The acceptor molecule is always an aldose. The combination of transaldolase and transketolase reactions permits a great variety of interconversions among the sugars (cf. Section 6, and Chapt. XVI-4).

*Oxidation and Decarboxylation of Glucose.* We have seen above that careful oxidation of glucose produces gluconolactone. The same reaction occurs *in vivo* with glucose 6-phosphate as the substrate. Hydrogen is accepted by nicotinamide-adenine dinucleotide phosphate.

Warburg discovered this reaction in 1931 as one of the first reactions involving a pyridine coenzyme. The apoenzyme was called "Zwischenferment" at that time, but now the name has historical interest only.

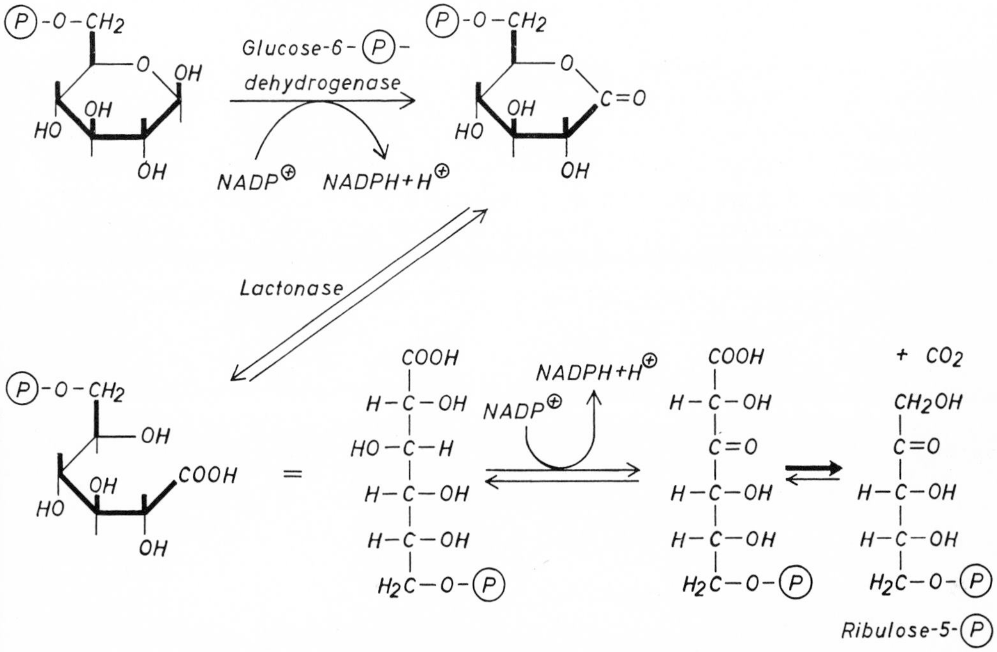

$(P)-O-CH_2$ ... (glucose-6-phosphate structure) 

Glucose-6-$(P)$-
dehydrogenase

$NADP^{\oplus}$    $NADPH+H^{\oplus}$

$(P)-O-CH_2$ ... $C=0$ (gluconolactone structure)

Lactonase

$(P)-O-CH_2$ ... $COOH$ (gluconate 6-phosphate, ring form) $=$

$$
\begin{array}{ccc}
COOH & & COOH & + CO_2 \\
H-C-OH & NADPH+H^{\oplus} & H-C-OH & CH_2OH \\
HO-C-H & NADP^{\oplus} & C=O & C=O \\
H-C-OH & \rightleftharpoons & H-C-OH & \rightleftharpoons & H-C-OH \\
H-C-OH & & H-C-OH & H-C-OH \\
H_2C-O-(P) & & H_2C-O-(P) & H_2C-O-(P)
\end{array}
$$

Ribulose-5-$(P)$

Gluconolactone is easily hydrolyzed to gluconate (the reaction is catalyzed by a lactonase but can also proceed spontaneously). Gluconate 6-phosphate can be dehydrogenated by another enzyme, with the simultaneous loss of $CO_2$. The pentose ribulose 5-phosphate arises from gluconate 6-phosphate presumably *via* the intermediate 3-keto-gluconate 6-phosphate, which, being a $\beta$-keto acid, decarboxylates easily. The product ribulose 5-phosphate is in equilibrium with the aldose ribose 5-phosphate (the equilibrium reaction is catalyzed by ribose-5-phosphate isomerase). In this fashion several pentoses are formed from glucose.

## 6. Glucose Oxidation Through the Pentose Phosphate Cycle

By a proper arrangement of the reactions already discussed, the complete breakdown of glucose to $CO_2$ and $NADPH_2$ may be formulated. The scheme is generally known as the Warburg-Dickens-Horecker pathway or the *pentose phosphate cycle*. The cycle begins with the direct oxidation of glucose, discovered by Warburg, which is really a dehydrogenation. The reaction can proceed at an appreciable rate only if $NADPH_2$, the reducing coenzyme, is reoxidized through some synthetic activity (fatty acid synthesis, Chapt. XII–6) or by $NADPH_2$-cytochrome c reductase and cytochrome c and thus made available for the renewed uptake of hydrogen (coenzymes are present only in catalytic amounts). The second step, dehydrogenation of gluconate-6-P, also produces $NADPH_2$ and again requires some H acceptor to regenerate the coenzyme. The process of oxidation is completed by the conversion of glucose-6-P to pentose phosphate. The entire oxidation is limited to one C atom which is eliminated as $CO_2$; in addition, 2 $NADPH_2$ are produced.

Pentose phosphates, however, do not accumulate to any extent. They react with one another: Through a complicated mechanism catalyzed by transketolase and transaldolase, they are converted back to hexoses (fructose-6-P and glucose-6-P). This interaction starts with the isomerization of ribulose-5-P to xylulose-5-P; the rest of the pathway can be illustrated schematically as follows (for simplicity, only the number of sugar C atoms and the fragments transferred are indicated):

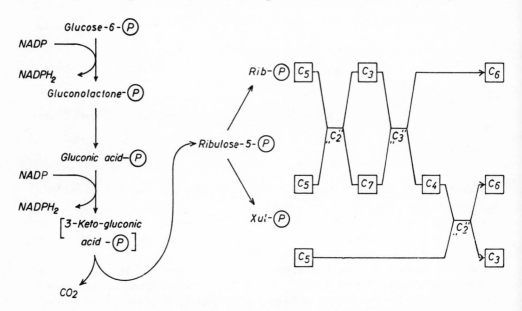

At first, xylulose-5-P (xul-P) and ribose-5-P (rib-P) by a $C_2$ transfer form sedoheptulose-7-P and triose-P: $C_5 + C_5 = C_7 + C_3$. The subsequent transfer of a $C_3$ fragment from sedoheptulose to triose forms hexose; erythrose-4-P remains: $C_7 + C_3 = C_4 + C_6$. Finally, another $C_2$ fragment is transferred from a third molecule of pentose (xylulose-5-P) onto erythrose-4-P; the result is again a hexose (fructose-6-P) and a triose-P.

In summation, three pentose molecules $(3 \times 5 = 15C)$ produce two hexoses and one triose $(2 \times 6 + 1 \times 3 = 15C)$. The hexoses can reenter the direct glucose oxidation reaction (fructose-6-P must first be isomerized to glucose-6-P).

Triose can enter one of two pathways: Either it is broken down further according to the Embden-Meyerhof scheme (see below), or two molecules of triose condense to form a new molecule of hexose (fructose diphosphate) which may reenter the cycle. It is possible, therefore, to decompose hexose completely to $CO_2$ and coenzyme-bound hydrogen ($NADPH_2$). Unlike $NADH_2$, $NADPH_2$ cannot produce

ATP directly through oxidative phosphorylation. Hydrogen can go through the respiratory chain only after it is transferred from $NADPH_2$ to NAD. (In this way, one would obtain 6 moles of ATP per mole of $CO_2$ or 36 moles of ATP for each mole of glucose 6-phosphate). "Transhydrogenation" is, however, of minor importance, and as a result, glucose breakdown *via* the pentose phosphate cycle is *not* a source of energy.

The pathway just discussed is not the main degradative path of glucose in the organism. Its real significance is based on the variety of intermediates produced and also on the amount of $NADPH_2$ produced, since synthetic activity demands this coenzyme. The glycolytic breakdown of glucose, on the other hand, which consumes the lion's share of the glucose, produces exclusively $NADH_2$.

The conversion of pentoses to hexoses by the reversal of the cycle constitutes, in essence, the pathway of carbon in photosynthesis of green plants. The primary acceptor of $CO_2$, ribulose diphosphate, is regenerated according to that scheme (cf. Chapt. XVI-4).

## 7. Glycolysis and Alcoholic Fermentation

Glycolysis is usually defined as the anaerobic breakdown of carbohydrates in the organism. It turns out, however, that aerobic catabolism also follows many of the steps of glycolysis. Actually, the only difference between aerobic and anaerobic breakdown is found in the utilization of the reduced coenzymes and of pyruvate. Alcoholic fermentation also branches off at the step of pyruvate utilization. It is not surprising that the different lines of research on these processes profited from each other.

**Some History.** Knowledge of alcoholic fermentation and particularly of its products, the intoxicating beverages, is very old. The history of the scientific investigation of alcohol fermentation is that of biochemistry itself from its inception, at the time of Lavoisier, to the present. Gay-Lussac first presented the correct overall equation for the fermentation reaction (1815). Around 1840 it was noted that fermentation is caused by cellular organisms, the yeast cells. The question arose then whether fermentation depended on some "vital force" or could also take place outside living cells. Pasteur, who had accumulated much experimental data on the metabolism of yeast and other microorganisms and who had described lactic acid fermentation, citric acid fermentation, and other types of fermentation, considered fermentation an expression of life. Some of his contemporaries (around 1870), however, differed with Pasteur and pointed to pepsin, already known at that time, and the digestion of protein, among other things. Traube wrote: "... ferments[4] are chemical substances, akin to proteins ... they possess definite chemical structure and evoke changes in other substances depending on their specific chemical affinities. ..." This opinion is almost completely valid even today.

The arguments centering around Pasteur's ideas were settled finally in 1897, when Buchner prepared a cell-free extract of compressed yeast ("yeast press juice") that could carry out alcoholic

---

[4] At that time the German word *"Ferment"* was often used synonymously with yeast cell ( = "formed ferments"), and to avoid these connotations Kühne introduced the term *"enzyme"* (cf. Chapt. V-1).

fermentation. This fundamental discovery removed the grounds for much useless speculation and greatly stimulated further experimentation. Some of the authors who studied reactions in yeast extracts and comparable extracts of muscle and who contributed so much to our present knowledge are Harden and Young, C. Neuberg, N. V. Euler, G. Embden, O. Meyerhof, Parnas, O. Warburg, K. Lohmann, C. and G. Cori. The names of some of these workers have been applied to "their" phosphate esters. In honor of the principal workers, the glycolytic degradative pathway is also called the *Embden-Meyerhof pathway* or *Embden-Meyerhof-Parnas pathway*.

**Principles of the Glycolytic Breakdown.** One essential characteristic of glycolysis is that it can proceed anaerobically and still provide energy (36 kcal are produced per mole of glucose, enough to convert 2 moles of phosphate into energy-rich ATP). Although the net equation

$$C_6H_{12}O_6 = 2 \ C_3H_6O_3$$

glucose = 2 lactic acid

corresponds to an isomerization reaction, a dehydrogenation step is nonetheless inserted; the coenzyme is regenerated, however, in a separate hydrogenation reaction.

While in the direct oxidation of glucose the dehydrogenation reaction occurs right in the beginning of the reaction chain, in the Embden-Meyerhof pathway this reaction takes place at a much later step. Four phases may be distinguished:

(1) The conversion of hexose to 2 moles of triose phosphate; this occurs at the oxidation level of the carbohydrate and requires ATP for phosphorylation.

(2) The dehydrogenation of triose phosphate with NAD to form phosphoglycerate with a concomitant yield of energy, which is conserved partially as chemical energy in the form of ATP (1 mole per mole of triose).

(3) The conversion of phosphoglycerate to pyruvate, which raises the phosphate to a high energy level and allows the regeneration of another ATP (from ADP).

(4) The metabolism of pyruvate, which may be either an anaerobic or an aerobic breakdown. The aerobic breakdown leads into the citric acid cycle and the respiratory chain; in the anaerobic breakdown the coenzyme NAD is regenerated in a hydrogenation step which produces lactate in the muscle, and ethyl alcohol in yeast.

**Phosphorylation and Conversion to Triose Phosphate.** Glucose circulating in blood must first be absorbed by cells. In most cases, there is a selective transport mechanism that is as yet little understood. Inside the cell, glucose is phosphorylated in the 6-position; ATP donates the phosphate and the enzyme is called *hexokinase*.[5] *Glucose-6-P* very generally is the metabolically active form of glucose. The intracellular form of storage is glycogen, which through phosphorolysis can be transformed to glucose-1-P and thence by isomerization to glucose-6-P without the consumption of ATP (cf. Chapt. XVII–6).

---

[5] *"Kinase"* is the general term for any enzyme that transfers a phosphate group from ATP to some other substrate.

Glucose-6-P is then isomerized by phosphohexose isomerase to *fructose-6-P* (making up 30% of the equilibrium mixture). Another kinase phosphorylates the 1-position and the resulting *fructose diphosphate* is cleaved in an equilibrium reaction to two trioses, namely *dihydroxyacetone phosphate* (C-1 to C-3) and *glyceraldehyde phosphate* (C-4 to C-6). The equilibrium mixture is composed of 89% hexose and 11% triose (under the conditions of Meyerhof's measurements); condensation, therefore, is the preferred (= exergonic) reaction. The reaction is analogous to the aldol condensation described in organic chemistry (Chapt. I-2, XV-5). Catalysis of the reverse reaction by the enzyme aldolase is explained by the fact that enzymes always catalyze "up to the equilibrium."

Aldolase is found in relatively high concentrations in muscle. It has been prepared in crystalline form, and its molecular weight is 150,000. It is activated by bivalent ions.

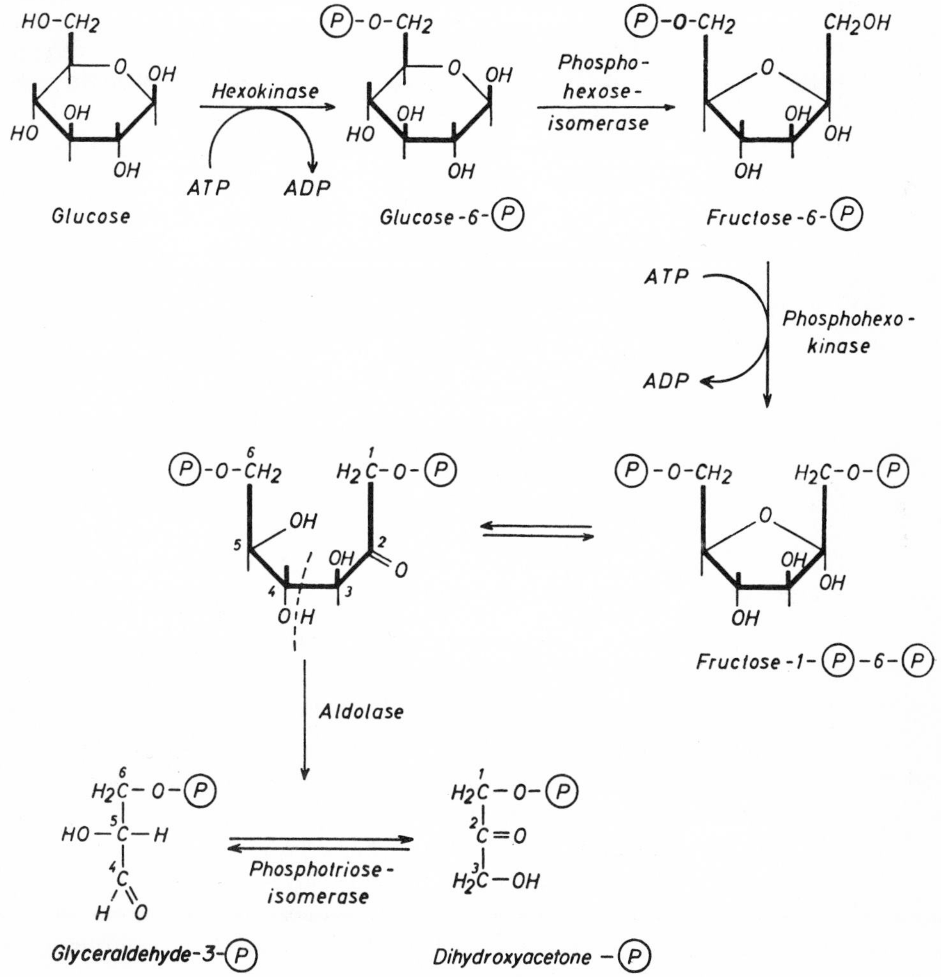

The keto-triose and the aldo-triose are in equilibrium through the enol form common to both of them; 96% is in the keto-form, dihydroxyacetone phosphate. The attainment of equilibrium is accelerated by the enzyme *triose-phosphate isomerase* which possesses an astoundingly high turnover number (several hundred thousand molecules per minute). Hence, the small amounts of gyceraldehyde phosphate present are replenished as soon as they are used up in the subsequent reaction.

**Dehydrogenation of Glyceraldehyde Phosphate.** Next, the aldehyde group of the triose is dehydrogenated to yield the carboxylic acid. This reaction could proceed in the simplest possible way, since it is strongly exergonic:

$$R—CHO + H_2O + NAD \rightleftharpoons R—COOH + NADH_2 \qquad \Delta F° = -16 \text{ kcal}$$

But since alcoholic fermentation and glycolysis are anaerobic, *energy-yielding*, metabolic processes, little would be gained if the reaction ran in this way and all the energy were dissipated as heat. Actually, 7 kcal are stored as chemical energy—in the form of 1 mole of ATP. This is accomplished by conducting the dehydrogenation by way of the following detour:

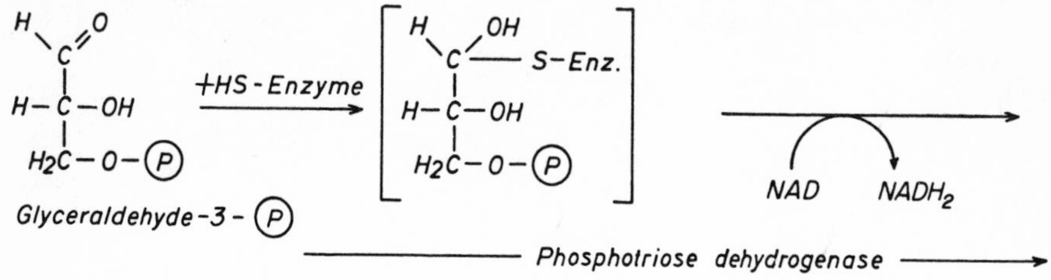

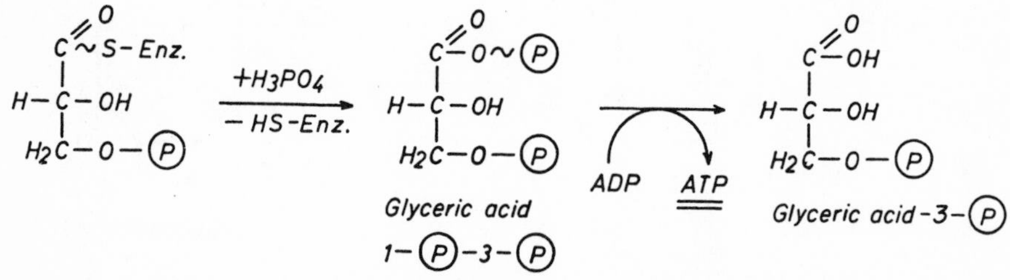

The aldehyde group is attached to the SH group of the enzyme; the dehydrogenation is then carried out by transferring hydrogen to NAD. An acyl-S-enzyme complex analogous to "active acetate" is thus formed. Hydrolysis would release the energy of the thioester as heat; phosphorolysis, however, conserves it as chemical energy in the acyl phosphate bond (1,3-diphosphoglycerate). The energy-rich phosphate group is then transferred by the enzyme phosphoglycerate kinase onto ADP. The result is *3-phosphoglycerate* and ATP; this type of ATP formation is termed substrate-linked phosphorylation.

**Pyruvate Formation.** 3-Phosphoglycerate is now rearranged by phosphoglyceromutase to 2-*phosphoglycerate*; the participating coenzyme is 2,3-diphosphoglycerate. One must visualize that the 3-phosphate is phosphorylated by the enzyme-diphosphate complex and that the dephosphorylated coenzyme (2-phosphoglycerate) dissociates off the enzyme while the product of phosphorylation becomes the new coenzyme. After this, water is split off by the action of enolase; the resulting compound is the phosphorylated enol form of pyruvate (see formulas below).

Phosphate is again present in an energy-rich form (namely the enol ester). It can be transferred by phosphopyruvate kinase to ADP; this transfer affords *pyruvic acid*, which is the most important metabolite of both anaerobic and aerobic carbohydrate metabolism.

The sequence of reactions from phosphoglycerate to pyruvate is equivalent in essence to the cleavage of the phosphate group and its transfer to the adenylic acid system; it is the phosphate which originally—during phosphorylation of the hexose—was supplied by ATP. The ATP invested originally is reclaimed here.

$$
\begin{array}{c}
COO^{\ominus} \\
| \\
H-C-OH \\
| \\
H_2C-O-\textcircled{P}
\end{array}
\quad + \quad
\begin{array}{c}
\textit{Enzyme} \\
COO^{\ominus} \\
| \\
H-C-O-\textcircled{P} \\
| \\
H_2C-O-\textcircled{P}
\end{array}
\quad \rightleftharpoons \quad
\begin{array}{c}
\textit{Enzyme} \\
COO^{\ominus} \\
| \\
H-C-OH \\
| \\
H_2C-O-\textcircled{P}
\end{array}
\quad
\begin{array}{c}
COO^{\ominus} \\
| \\
H-C-O-\textcircled{P} \\
| \\
H_2C-O-\textcircled{P}
\end{array}
\quad
\begin{array}{c}
COO^{\ominus} \\
| \\
H-C-O-\textcircled{P} \\
| \\
H_2C-OH
\end{array}
$$

Glyceric acid 3-\textcircled{P}        *Phosphoglyceromutase*        Glyceric acid -2-\textcircled{P}

$$
\begin{array}{c}
COO^{\ominus} \\
| \\
H-C-O-\textcircled{P} \\
| \\
H_2C-OH
\end{array}
\quad \xrightarrow{\textit{Enolase}} \quad
\begin{array}{c}
COO^{\ominus} \\
| \\
C-O\sim\textcircled{P} \\
\| \\
CH_2
\end{array}
\quad \xrightarrow[\text{ADP} \quad \text{ATP}]{\textit{Pyruvate kinase}} \quad
\begin{array}{c}
COO^{\ominus} \\
| \\
C-OH \\
\| \\
CH_2
\end{array}
\quad \rightleftharpoons \quad
\begin{array}{c}
COO^{\ominus} \\
| \\
C=O \\
| \\
CH_3
\end{array}
$$

Enol-pyruvate-\textcircled{P}        Pyruvate

**The Pathway of NAD and Pyruvate.** In order to formulate a continuous process, the reduced pyridine nucleotide $NADH_2$ must be reoxidized and made available again. The reoxidation could be achieved, e.g. through the respiratory chain, if oxygen were available at the site of carbohydrate breakdown. In the absence of oxygen, however, another solution must be found. In the metabolism of vertebrates, in anaerobic glycolysis of muscle, pyruvate is reduced to lactate; in yeast the reduction is preceded by a decarboxylation to form acetaldehyde, and the product of the reduction is the much desired ethyl alcohol.

In glycolysis the chain of reactions is terminated by lactate dehydrogenase which reduces pyruvate (the reverse of what the name indicates) and which makes the pyridine nucleotide available again in its oxidized form to catalyze the dehydrogenation of more triose.

In summary, one hexose is converted to the diphosphate with the uptake of 2 ATP; the diphosphate is cleaved; it traverses a series of equilibrium reactions and releases hydrogen to the pyridine nucleotide. The breakdown is coupled at two places with the adenylic acid system in order to trap and store chemical energy. For formulas see the diagram:

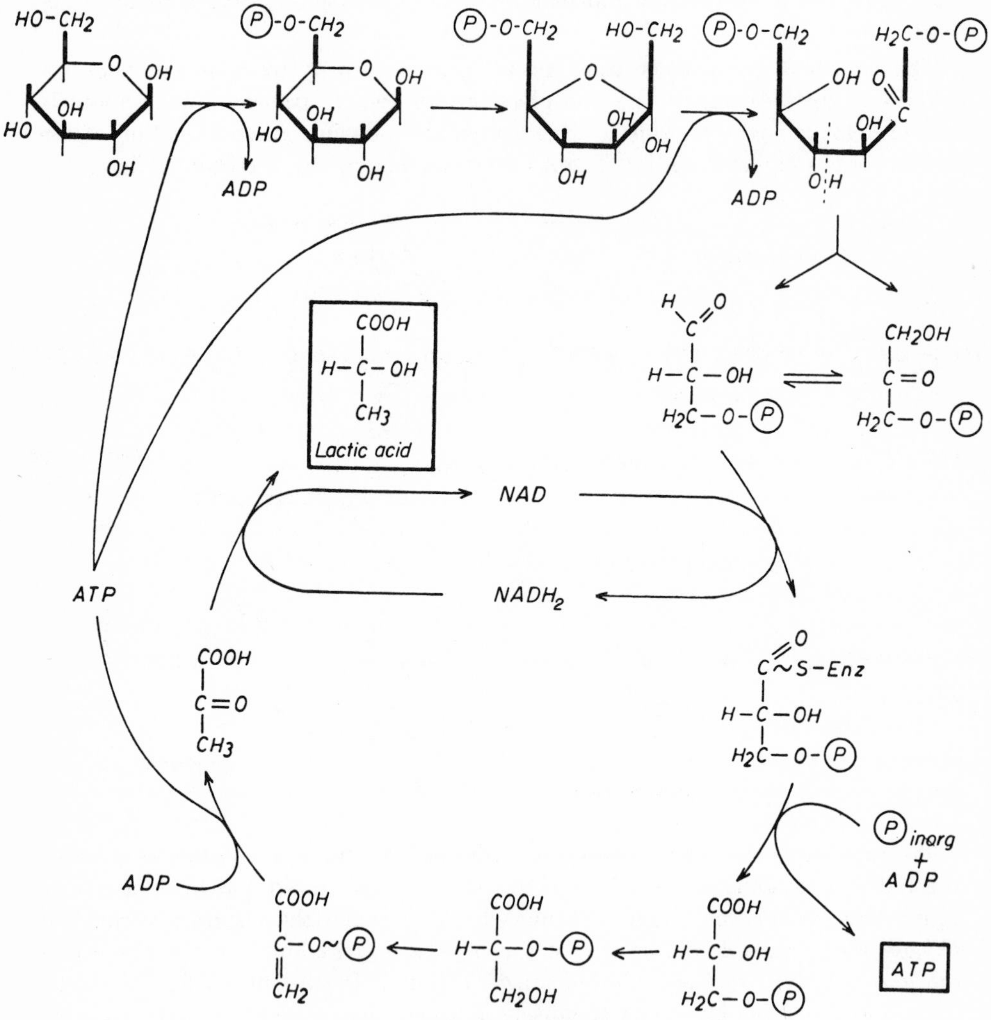

Diagram of anaerobic glycolysis

The net yield is only 2 ATP per mole of glucose; the conversion to lactate is unable to provide more energy than that. But the relatively energy-rich substrate, lactate, can be broken down further in the presence of oxygen. Lactate is transported from skeletal muscle to the liver, a highly vascular organ well supplied with oxygen.

In fermentation, as we have pointed out, pyruvate is decarboxylated to form *acetaldehyde*. The enzyme pyruvate decarboxylase, or simply carboxylase, requires $Mg^{++}$ and thiamine pyrophosphate[6] as cofactors. Acetaldehyde is probably bound in its activated form at first, because it can undergo several reactions. Under certain conditions, two molecules can combine to form acetoin. Pyruvate decarboxylase is found only in plants.

In microorganisms acetaldehyde is then reduced by alcohol dehydrogenase and $NADH_2$ to form ethyl alcohol. At the same time the coenzyme is returned to its oxidized form. The coenzyme, therefore, is an auxiliary substrate for hydrogen, passing through a cyclic process, just as phosphate when it is removed from ATP and later transferred back to ATP.

## 8. The Metabolism of Fructose

Cane sugar is composed of glucose and fructose, as will be explained in Chapt. XVII–2, and is decomposed to these constituents in the intestines. Thus, fructose is one of the regular components of our diet. In some circumstances, fructose can make up a considerable part of all the carbohydrates ingested.

Fructose phosphates are intermediates in the breakdown of glucose according to the Embden-Meyerhof pathway, but free fructose is broken down in a different fashion. At first it is phosphorylated by a fructokinase and ATP to produce *fructose 1-phosphate*.[7] The phosphate is split by a specific enzyme, 1-phosphofructoaldolase, to *dihydroxyacetone phosphate* and *glyceraldehyde*. This last step corresponds to the aldolase reaction of glycolysis except that the resulting glyceraldehyde is unphosphorylated.

Free glyceraldehyde is dehydrogenated by an aldehyde dehydrogenase to become *glycerate*. This dehydrogenation, proceeding from the hydrated form, does not appear to be coupled with a phosphorylation. Glycerate is then phosphorylated in the 2-position. *2-Phosphoglycerate* is the connecting link to the glycolytic pathway.

---

[6] Cocarboxylase ( = thiamine pyrophosphate) was one of the first coenzymes that was prepared pure and whose structure was determined. Its relationship to vitamin $B_1$ was then recognized and it was later found that most (if not all) vitamins are active as components of coenzymes.

[7] Phosphorylation in the 1-position is favored probably because free fructose occurs predominantly in its pyranose form (the oxygen bridges between C-2 and C-6). The 6-hydroxyl group is thus blocked and cannot be phosphorylated.

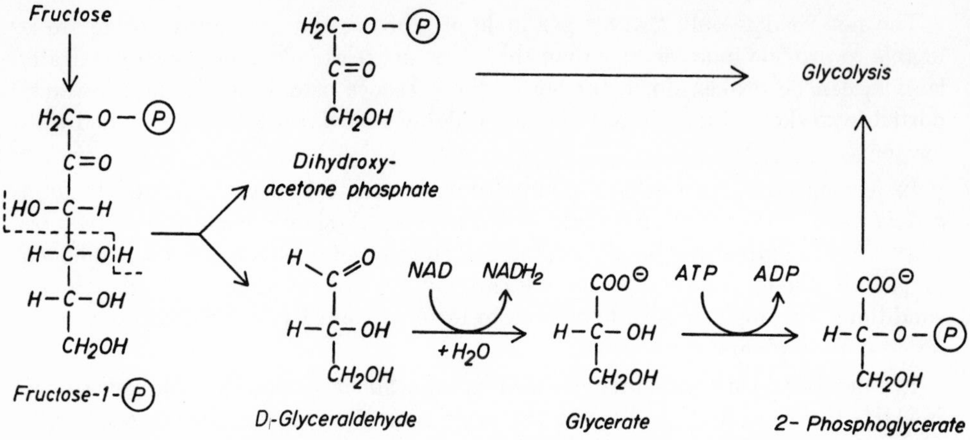

(Dihydroxyacetone phosphate, of course, enters the Embden-Meyerhof pathway immediately.)

As a side path, we should mention the reduction of glyceraldehyde to free glycerol, by alcohol dehydrogenase and the coenzyme $NADH_2$. And finally, glucose can be resynthesized by a reversal of glycolysis starting with dihydroxyacetone phosphate.

## 9. Aerobic Carbohydrate Breakdown

In general, carbohydrates are broken down aerobically, i.e. with a supply of oxygen. Anaerobic glycolysis seems to be more of a bypass for cells with a poor oxygen supply. The Embden-Meyerhof pathway is significant primarily because it operates not only under anaerobic conditions but, up to the step of pyruvate, under aerobic conditions as well (at least to the extent that glucose is not oxidized directly to pentose (Section 6, Chapt. XVIII-1). Reduced nicotinamide-adenine dinucleotide is reoxidized through the respiratory chain, and pyruvate can be metabolized further in a variety of ways.

*Oxidative decarboxylation* is very significant from a quantitative standpoint and is also important because it links the different metabolic pathways. The mechanism of this reaction, requiring the participation of lipoate, coenzyme A, and NAD, has already been discussed in detail (Chapt. VI-6, VIII-10, XI-1). According to the equation shown below, the end-product is "activated acetate" or acetyl-CoA. The greater part of the acetyl-CoA is consumed in the citrate cycle (see Chapt. XI), but any excess can be converted to fat (cf. Chapt. XII-6), provided that there is sufficient $NADPH_2$.

$$CH_3-CO-COOH + HS\overline{CoA} + NAD \rightarrow CO_2 + H_3C-CO \sim S\overline{CoA} + NADH_2$$

**Carboxylation.** Another reaction of pyruvate closely connected with the citrate cycle is the carboxylation to form oxaloacetate. Wood and Werkman discovered it originally as a sum of reactions in microorganisms, and it is often called the

Wood–Werkman reaction. On close study it became clear that it is possible to obtain oxaloacetate from pyruvate by two different routes. In the first route, activated carbon dioxide is added with the aid of a biotin-containing enzyme:

$$CH_3—CO—COO^- + {}^-OOC \sim \text{biotin enzyme} \rightleftharpoons {}^-OOC—CH_2—CO—COO^- + \text{biotin enzyme}$$

The formation of $^-OOC$—biotin enzyme consumes one ATP; the formation of oxaloacetate by this route therefore takes place at the expense of a good deal of energy.

The second $CO_2$-fixation reaction is a reductive carboxylation (Ochoa). The reaction is catalyzed by the "malic enzyme," as follows:

$$CH_3—CO—COOH + CO_2 + NADPH_2 = HOOC—CH_2—CHOH—COOH + NADP$$

It is not yet clear whether biotin is a cofactor; no biotin was detected in highly purified preparations of the enzyme. Malate easily converts to oxaloacetate. The formation of oxaloacetate by one of these two pathways is significant, because it provides the "initial spark" for the citrate cycle, since oxaloacetate is needed as partner for the condensation reaction with acetyl-CoA. Furthermore, oxaloacetate mediates the resynthesis of glucose (see below). It should be pointed out, finally, that pyruvate can be transformed to alanine (Chapt. VIII-10) by transamination so that pyruvate also represents a link to the metabolism of protein.

**Energy Balance of the Aerobic Carbohydrate Breakdown.** Up to the formation of pyruvate 1 mole of ATP and 1 of $NADH_2$ arise from each triose. Another mole of NAD is reduced during the oxidative decarboxylation of pyruvate to acetyl-CoA. Up to the formation of acetyl-CoA (employing the respiratory chain) $1 + 2 \times 3 = 7$ ATP are stored. Complete oxidation of active acetate in the citrate cycle yields another 12 moles of ATP per triose, i.e. a total of 19 ATP per mole of triose or 38 per mole of glucose.

## 10. Resynthesis of Glucose: Gluconeogenesis

During anaerobic glycolysis a lot of lactate is produced, and it has been known for some time that part of this lactate is used for the resynthesis of glucose, though not in the muscle, the place of its origin, but rather in the liver. In theory, the synthesis might be a simple reversal of the Embden-Meyerhof pathway, but the equilibria of some of the reactions are too unfavorable. This is true particularly of the reaction of pyruvate kinase; the phosphorylation of pyruvate by this reaction would require very high concentrations of ATP.

The key reaction was recognized by Utter to be the phosphorylation of oxaloacetate. Formation of the enol is facilitated in this compound and phosphoenolpyruvate is then formed by phosphorylation with inosine triphosphate (ITP) (decarboxylation occurs at the same time). Oxaloacetate itself is provided by the direct carboxylation discussed above *via* a biotin enzyme. Alternately, the reductive carboxylation yields malate which is converted to oxaloacetate. The first reaction, although requiring additional ATP, appears to be the more important one, and, of course, the equilibrium favors $CO_2$-fixation more strongly in this way. The following pathway can now be pieced together for the formation of phosphoglycerate and then (by a reversal of glycolysis) of triose phosphate:

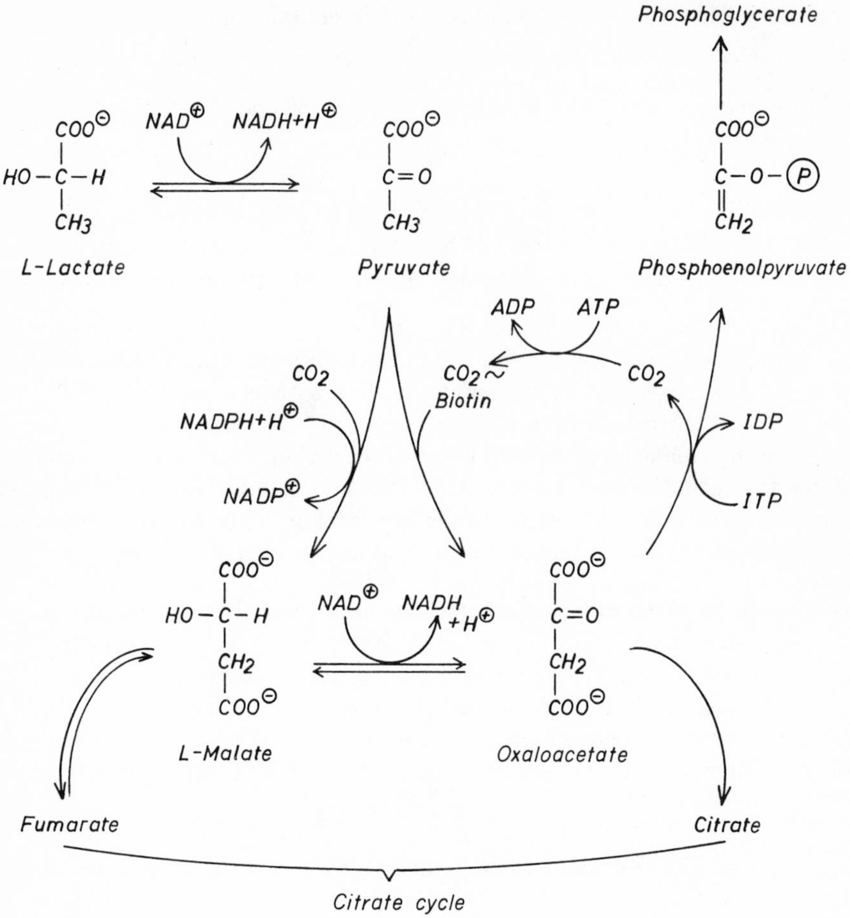

Phosphoglycerate

$$
\begin{array}{ccccc}
COO^{\ominus} & \xrightarrow{NAD^{\oplus}\quad NADH+H^{\oplus}} & COO^{\ominus} & & COO^{\ominus} \\
| & & | & & | \\
HO-C-H & & C=O & & C-O-\text{(P)} \\
| & & | & & \| \\
CH_3 & & CH_3 & & CH_2
\end{array}
$$

L-Lactate       Pyruvate       Phosphoenolpyruvate

ADP   ATP

$CO_2$     $CO_2 \sim$     $CO_2$

$NADPH+H^{\oplus}$    Biotin     IDP

$NADP^{\oplus}$     ITP

$$
\begin{array}{ccc}
COO^{\ominus} & & COO^{\ominus} \\
| & \xrightarrow{NAD^{\oplus}\quad NADH+H^{\oplus}} & | \\
HO-C-H & & C=O \\
| & & | \\
CH_2 & & CH_2 \\
| & & | \\
COO^{\ominus} & & COO^{\ominus}
\end{array}
$$

L-Malate       Oxaloacetate

Fumarate           Citrate

Citrate cycle

Evidently at least 2 moles of energy-rich phosphate are required: One for the formation of phosphoenolpyruvate, and the second for the reduction of 3-phosphoglycerate, which proceeds as a reversal of the glycolytic reaction (see above). The reversal of the breakdown must, of course, be endergonic. It has long been known that 20–30% of lactate is combusted completely in order to allow the resynthesis of glucose.

**Gluconeogenesis from Amino Acids.** The pathway described above has a general significance beyond the utilization of lactate. We have mentioned previously that many amino acids can be converted to glucose, provided that they give rise to $C_4$-dicarboxylic acids. These acids are members of the citrate cycle and thus can easily produce oxaloacetate and then phosphoenolpyruvate by Utter's reaction.

From that point on, the synthesis of glucose is easy, being simply the reverse of glycolysis. Only the phosphorylation reactions of hexose by ATP are not reversible, but phosphate can be split off the hexose diphosphate by specific phosphatases. Furthermore, the synthesis of carbohydrates does not end with free glucose but usually with the polymer glycogen. The polymerization, however, proceeds through phosphorylated intermediates.

It may appear peculiar that build-up and breakdown proceed largely *via* the same route; merely a few key reactions differ. These key reactions are probably the targets of the cell's regulatory mechanism, which must determine the direction that the processes are to take. Gluconeogenesis from amino acids (i.e. ultimately out of proteins), for example, is strongly stimulated by the hormone cortisol (cf. Chapt. XX-2). Such regulation is of decisive importance for the organism's over-all metabolism.

The preceding paragraphs undoubtedly have revealed the complicated and diverse nature of carbohydrate metabolism, both on the level of interconversions among the carbohydrates and on that of degradative reactions for the production of energy. Part of the energy is derived anaerobically by substrate-linked phosphorylation; the major part, however, is liberated in the respiratory chain. The situation is further complicated by the obvious fact that carbohydrate metabolism is not an isolated system of reactions, but is closely tied to other pathways and reaction cycles through common intermediates. A separate chapter (Chapt. XVIII) is devoted to such interrelationships.

BIBLIOGRAPHY

G. Ashwell, Carbohydrate Metabolism, *Ann. Rev. Biochem.* **33,** 101–138 (1964).
B. Axelrod, Glycolysis, *in* "Metabolic Pathways," (D. M. Greenberg, editor), Vol. I, pp. 97–129, Academic Press, New York, 1961; Other pathways of carbohydrate metabolism, *ibid.* pp. 205–250.
S. Hollmann, "Nicht-glykolytische Stoffwechselwege der Glucose," G. Thieme Verlag, Stuttgart, 1961.
W. Pigman, "The Carbohydrates. Chemistry, Biochemistry, Physiology." Academic Press, New York, 1957.

## CHAPTER XVI

# Photosynthesis[1]

## 1. Importance of Photosynthesis

Photosynthesis, the assimilation of carbon dioxide in green plants, is the most important process on this planet, from both a qualitative and a quantitative standpoint. This is evident if we recall that all forms of life which are unable to photosynthesize depend either directly or indirectly[2] on the assimilation by the plants. In fact, present forms of life cannot exist without photosynthesis. The energy for this process is in the form of light, which is trapped by chlorophyll, a leaf pigment, and is utilized through a complicated mechanism. All the organic substances which arise from this one process serve the other forms of life as starting materials for the diverse metabolic interconversions, which we have already studied (cf. Chapt. XVIII). These substances are finally oxidized to $CO_2$, which can again be incorporated into new organic compounds by way of photosynthesis.

The equilibrium between $CO_2$ in the air and organically bound carbon (having remained static for hundreds of thousands or even millions of years) has been disturbed noticeably since the second half of the last century by man's progressing civilization. Fixed forms of carbon, fossil fuel (coal, petroleum) and inorganic carbonates, have been mobilized to a considerable extent and have been allowed to enter the carbon cycle.[3]

In summary, the photosynthetic process appears to be a reversal of the combustion of glucose:

$$6 \ CO_2 + 6 \ H_2O \xrightarrow{h\nu} C_6H_{12}O_6 + 6 \ O_2$$

(Light quanta, i.e. radiant energy, are designated by $h\nu$.)

---

[1] This chapter addresses itself more to students of science than students of medicine.

[2] Strictly speaking, we have to exclude those few types of bacteria that can fill all of their energy requirements from chemical work alone; they gain energy by oxidizing inorganic substances, like sulfur or $H_2S$.

[3] The extent of this process can be calculated from the content of the radioactive isotope [14] C (half-life $5.5 \times 10^3$ years). The same concept is used in "radio-carbon dating" of archaeological or geological objects.

Formerly, the "assimilation of carbon dioxide," as expressed in the above equation, was thought to be characteristic of plants. When isotope techniques were applied to biochemistry, it was realized, however, that even mammalian organisms assimilate measurable amounts of $CO_2$. Metabolically, $CO_2$ is not as inert as had been assumed; we have already seen examples of this (cf. Chapt VI–4, VII–2, XII–6). It is the employment of light for chemical reactions which is peculiar to plants; essentially this is the conversion of light energy to chemical energy. Recognition of this fact has helped to popularize the appropriate term *photosynthesis*.

An arbitrary distinction has been made between *light reactions* and *dark reactions*. The primary light reaction is the absorption of a light quantum by a pigment molecule, such as chlorophyll, which at first merely accepts the energy. All subsequent reactions are actually dark reactions, although some of them cannot be differentiated experimentally from the true light reactions because they proceed so very rapidly.

It is expedient to consider photosynthesis as three reactions:

1. Photophosphorylation, the formation of ATP from inorganic phosphate and ADP.
2. Photolysis of water which produces the "reduction equivalents."
3. $CO_2$ fixation and conversion to carbohydrate.

## 2. Photophosphorylation

We have emphasized that the essence of photosynthesis is the conversion of light energy to chemical energy. We also know that the most important storage form of chemical energy is the adenylic acid system. It should not be surprising that the grana of chloroplasts synthesize ATP by means of light energy, although experimental support for this has been obtained only recently by Arnon and his co-workers (1954).

The discovery of photophosphorylation is perhaps the most important advance in our knowledge of photosynthesis, because here the change of light energy to chemical energy becomes immediately evident. The detailed mechanism of the change is currently under intensive study.

Light is accepted by chlorophyll, the green pigment of leaves (formula Chapt. IX–6). From other photochemical reactions it is known that when a light quantum is absorbed, it excites an electron, i.e. it raises the electron to a higher energy level (see Fig. 41). Arnon proposes that this "energy-rich electron" is then transferred to the special redox system *ferredoxin*. It is an iron-containing protein with the unusually negative redox potential of $-0.432$ volt (this is about 100 millivolts less than that of the nicotinamide coenzymes). Ferredoxin occurs not only in green plants but also in those bacteria that metabolize elemental hydrogen (either release hydrogen gas or consume it). The redox potential is also similar to that of the hydrogen electrode at pH 7 ($H_2/2H^+$; $-0.42$ volt).

From ferredoxin the electron pair returns to chlorophyll over a chain of redox catalysts (see left half of the diagram, Fig. 41). One of these redox catalysts—perhaps the first one—is the system *plastoquinone/plastohydroquinone* with a redox potential of 0.00 volt; furthermore, *cytochrome f* is interposed here. The transport of electrons from plastoquinone to chlorophyll a ($E_0' = +0.45$ volt) is coupled to a phosphorylation step: just as in the respiratory chain, one inorganic phosphate is taken up and stored as ATP.

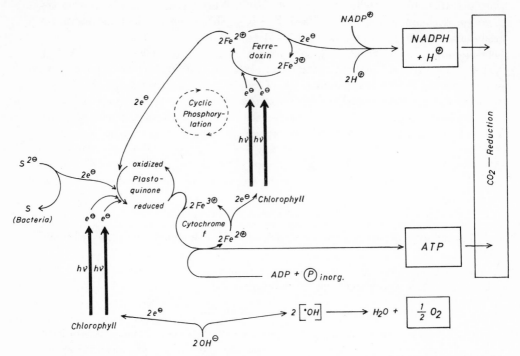

Fig. 41. Photosynthesis. The bold arrows represent the energy rise of the electrons by light absorbtion. See text for further explanation.

The analogy between respiratory-chain phosphorylation and photosynthetic phosphorylation is not entirely accidental. Both the mitochondria and the chloroplasts contain highly ordered enzyme systems which permit an exergonic process (the electron transport through a cytochrome chain) to be coupled with the strongly endergonic formation of ATP from ADP and inorganic phosphate. The two reaction chains possess many characteristics in common; presumably the respiratory chain evolved gradually from the chloroplast structure. The only significant additions have been cytochrome oxidase and the $NADH_2$-dehydrogenase system.

Whereas the respiratory chain requires a continuous supply of substrate and oxygen for its operation, the phosphorylation just discussed does not. In the latter, the electrons are driven around their circuit by the light reaction. In addition to this "cyclic photophosphorylation" there is also a noncyclic photophosphorylation (the right half of the diagram), which includes the production of the "reduction equivalent" and of oxygen. This, however, is part of the second photosynthetic reaction.

## 3. Photolysis of Water

According to the overall formula (Section 1), assimilation appears to consist of a photolytic cleavage of $CO_2$. Indeed, this theory had been taught for a long time before the 1930's. Since then, the opinion that it is actually water, which is cleaved photolytically, became more widely accepted. This theory is able to explain the origin of the "reduction equivalents," i.e. bound hydrogen, as well as of oxygen:

$$H_2O + X \xrightarrow{h\nu} XH_2 + \tfrac{1}{2} O_2$$

As experimental evidence, Van Niel first noted that many bacteria use substances other than water as hydrogen donors, for example:

$$H_2S + X = S + X \cdot H_2$$

or

$$CH_3—CHOH—CH_3 + X = CH_3—CO—CH_3 + X \cdot H_2$$

The photochemical apparatus of chloroplasts can be used under certain conditions to generate gaseous hydrogen, a direct proof of the photolysis of water. For this demonstration, the primary redox system ferredoxin has to be coupled with a bacterial hydrogenase, which transfers electrons from $Fe^{++}$ onto $H^+$ leaving ferredoxin-$Fe^{+++}$ and $\frac{1}{2} H_2$.

Proof of the true origin of elemental oxygen generated in photosynthesis was presented some time ago by Kamen in experiments with isotopically labeled water, $H_2^{18}O$.

The photolysis of water entails initially the transfer of the excited electron to the ferredoxin system; reduced ferredoxin then in turn reduces nicotinamide-adenine dinucleotide phosphate (NADP), whereby $H^+$ ions are taken up (cf. upper right of Fig. 41). The "reduction equivalents" mentioned in the literature so often are nothing more than reduced nicotinamide-adenine dinucleotide phosphate.

While the $H^+$ ion is reduced by accepting an electron, some other substance must be oxidized by losing an electron in order to maintain an electron balance. In the bacteria mentioned before that do not produce any oxygen, the electrons are supplied by some other organic or inorganic substance; for instance, the electrons could be derived from the reaction $S^{2-} \rightarrow S + 2e^-$. In all higher plants, however, the electron donor invariably is the $OH^-$ ion, undergoing the following reaction:

$$2\,OH^- - 2e^- = 2[OH] = \tfrac{1}{2}\,O_2 + H_2O$$

The oxidation of two $OH^-$ ions by the removal of electrons is equivalent to the evolution of $\frac{1}{2}O_2$. Oxygen appears as an unusable by-product which is eliminated by the plant.

The oxidation of $OH^-$ ions also requires light energy. The electrons of a pigment system containing chlorophyll are excited, and the resulting radical is a sufficiently strong oxidizing agent to be able to pull an electron away from the $OH^-$ (see Fig. 41, bottom). The excited electrons reduce the redox catalyst Y, while the subsequent electron transport through a cytochrome permits the storage of energy as ATP. In conjunction with this process, the other light reaction already discussed takes place on the chlorophyll and produces either $NADPH_2$ or, as cyclic photo-phosphorylation, another ATP.

The evolution of $O_2$ from water obviously requires energy since it is but the reverse of the formation of water, which is itself exergonic to the extent of 57 kcal/mole; the reverse is of course correspondingly endergonic. The energy is supplied by 4 moles of light quanta[4] according to Fig. 41 (in the case of red light this amounts to 168 kcal); at the same time 1 mole of ATP per mole of $NADPH_2$ is produced. This phosphorylation step is probably identical with "cyclic phosphorylation."

----

[4] "One mole quantum" is defined as $6 \times 10^{23}$ light quanta. This number corresponds to the number of molecules present in 1 mole.

The theoretical quantum requirement for these events is 4 to 5, or rather 8 to 10 quanta[5] per molecule of $O_2$. This requirement has been determined repeatedly by experiment. A lively controversy is maintained by Warburg, on one hand, who found a requirement of 3 or 4 quanta, and by various other laboratories who have determined the need for at least 6 to 8 quanta, or even more, for evolving 1 $O_2$. At this stage of knowledge, the most probable value is 8 quanta per oxygen molecule. This would correspond to a rather respectable energy yield of 20 to 40%.

## 4. Binding of $CO_2$ and Reduction to Carbohydrate

The other part of photosynthesis, the conversion of $CO_2$ to carbohydrate, is purely a biochemical change, a dark reaction. Calvin and his associates were responsible for shedding light on the very confusing array of these dark reactions.

The use of radioactive carbon ($^{14}CO_2$) made it possible to elucidate the reaction sequence. The old hypotheses postulating formaldehyde as an intermediate were refuted quickly. It took longer, however, to establish the true state of affairs. Some of the intermediate products are exceedingly short-lived; they can be demonstrated only if the reaction is stopped a few seconds after adding labeled $CO_2$.

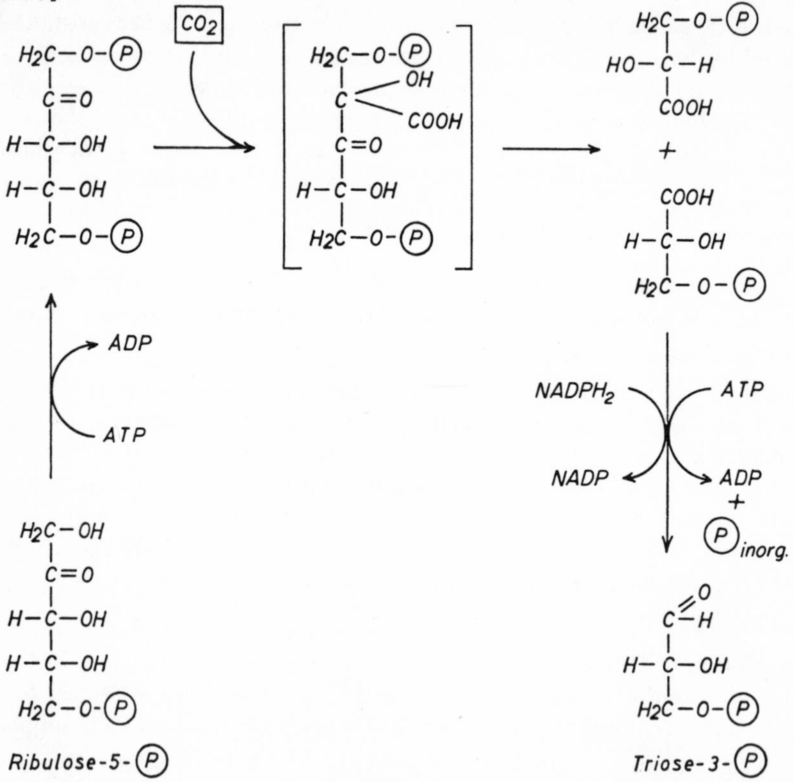

---

[5] According to Arnon, the theoretical quantum requirement for photolysis is 8 quanta per $O_2$ (i.e. 1 quantum per electron). But cyclic phosphorylation operates simultaneously and uses quanta without evolving $O_2$; instead it produces ATP which is vital for the formation of sugars (cf. the sum of reactions below). Hence, the theoretical yield is lowered; about 9–10 quanta are needed for the conversion of 1 $CO_2$ to sugar (and release of 1 $O_2$).

The acceptor for $CO_2$ is *ribulose diphosphate*, which arises from *ribulose 5-phosphate* and ATP by the action of a kinase. In drawing the formulas on p. 288 it was assumed that ribulose diphosphate rearranges to the 3-keto derivative and that a $\beta$-keto acid arises with the addition of $CO_2$. This ephemeral intermediate, however, is still hypothetical; it is presumed to decompose rapidly to 2 moles of *phosphoglycerate*, which is the first isolable photosynthetic product.

Phosphoglycerate is then reduced to *triose phosphate* by reversal of a reaction known from glycolysis (cf. Chapt. XV–7). Both ATP and NADPH₂ are required, involving the following steps: *3-Phosphoglycerate* combines with ATP; a transfer of phosphate then forms *1,3-diphosphoglycerate* and leaves ADP. A HS group of the enzyme binds the "activated" acid through a thioester bond, which can then be split reductively. Hydrogen for this reduction is provided by the nicotinamide co-enzyme, which itself is continually recharged with hydrogen derived from the photolysis of water.

This somewhat complicated and energy-consuming reductive step actually fulfills our task. We have reduced carbon from the oxidation level of $CO_2$ to that of carbohydrate. For the sake of completeness, we must allow this reaction sequence to operate on both molecules of phosphoglycerate. That means we require 2 NADPH₂ and 2 ATP per mole $CO_2$. It should be noted that by cleavage of the acceptor molecule into two molecules of a carboxylic acid, the energy required for further reaction is distributed between two molecules and consequently, is easier to provide.

**Formation of Ribulose Diphosphate.** Up to this point the situation has remained relatively simple. But now ribulose diphosphate has to be regenerated so that it may accept another $CO_2$. Otherwise, photosynthesis would soon come to a halt. The pathway is analogous to the regeneration of hexose by the reverse of the pentose phosphate cycle. Here is a simplified schematic diagram:

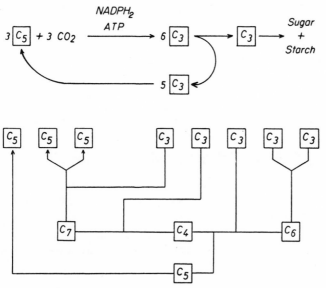

At first two molecules of triose phosphate combine to form hexose diphosphate (*fructose diphosphate*), which is then hydrolyzed by a specific phosphatase to *fructose 6-phosphate* and phosphate. Hexose phosphate and triose phosphate interact in a transketolase reaction to produce *erythrose 4-phosphate* and *xylulose 5-phosphate*, which then rearranges to *ribulose 5-phosphate* (the first pentose molecule). In a type of aldol condensation, erythrose phosphate and triose phosphate combine to form *sedoheptulose diphosphate* ($C_4 + C_3 = C_7$), which is subsequently dephosphorylated. The enzyme transketolase then transfers a $C_2$ fragment from heptulose to triose phosphate yielding 2 moles of pentose (*xylulose 5-phosphate* and *ribose 5-phosphate*); both must be rearranged to *ribulose 5-phosphate*. Having ribulose 5-phosphate available, the cycle can commence again: first, phosphorylation with ATP to the diphosphate, then acceptance of $CO_2$ by the diphosphate, and production of 2 moles of phosphoglyceric acid.

**Summary of Photosynthetic Reactions.** Carbon dioxide assimilation can actually be separated from the photosynthetic apparatus. One need only add ATP and $NADPH_2$, which are usually supplied by the chloroplast. The enzymic reactions[6] may be summarized as follows:

$$3 \ CO_2 + 3 \ C_5{-}P + 9 \ ATP + 6 \ NADPH_2 \rightarrow 6 \ C_3{-}P + 9 \ ADP + 6 \ NADP + 6 \ P + 3 \ H_2O$$

$$5 \ C_3{-}P \rightarrow 3 \ C_5{-}P + 2 \ P$$

$$\overline{3 \ CO_2 + 6 \ NADPH_2 + 9 \ ATP \rightarrow C_3{-}P + 6 \ NADP + 9 \ ADP + 8 \ P + 3 \ H_2O}$$

The following, we recognize to be the true light reactions:

$$ADP + P \xrightarrow{h\nu} ATP$$

$$H_2O + NADP + ADP + P \xrightarrow{h\nu} NADPH_2 + ATP + \tfrac{1}{2} O_2$$

If we now add the dark and light reactions (multiplying the light reactions by 3 and 6, respectively), we approximate the original equation:

$$3 \ CO_2 + 3 \ H_2O + P \rightarrow \text{triose phosphate} + 3 \ O_2$$

Phosphate is removed again in the course of synthesis of sucrose and the polysaccharides.

## 5. Further Synthetic Activities of Plants

The assimilation of carbon dioxide and its conversion to carbohydrate is undoubtedly the most important biologic achievement of the plant. However, there are countless other biosynthetic reactions which cannot take place in the animal

---

[6] Water involved either in cleavage or synthesis of phosphate derivatives is not considered in these equations.

organism and are reserved exclusively for the plant. Typical examples are the syntheses of the many substances which we call vitamins and essential amino acids, and the formation of aromatic compounds.

**Biosynthesis of Aromatic Compounds.** Compounds containing the benzene ring, in general, are not synthesized by the animal organism.[7] In plants and microorganisms, such substances can at times be formed in huge amounts, as exemplified by lignin, a major component of woody material.

The manner of formation of the aromatic ring has been studied mainly in microorganisms using the techniques of biochemical genetics. A determined search provided mutants in which the chain of synthetic steps was interrupted and which required—in contrast to the wild strains—a supplement of aromatic compounds (phenylalanine, tyrosine; cf. also Chapt. VII-6). One mutant of *E. coli* was found to need five different aromatic acids: tyrosine, phenylalanine, tryptophan, *p*-aminobenzoic acid, and *p*-hydroxybenzoic acid. All the requirements of this particular strain, however, were met by a single substance, *shikimic acid*. Evidently all five synthetic pathways begin with this common precursor.

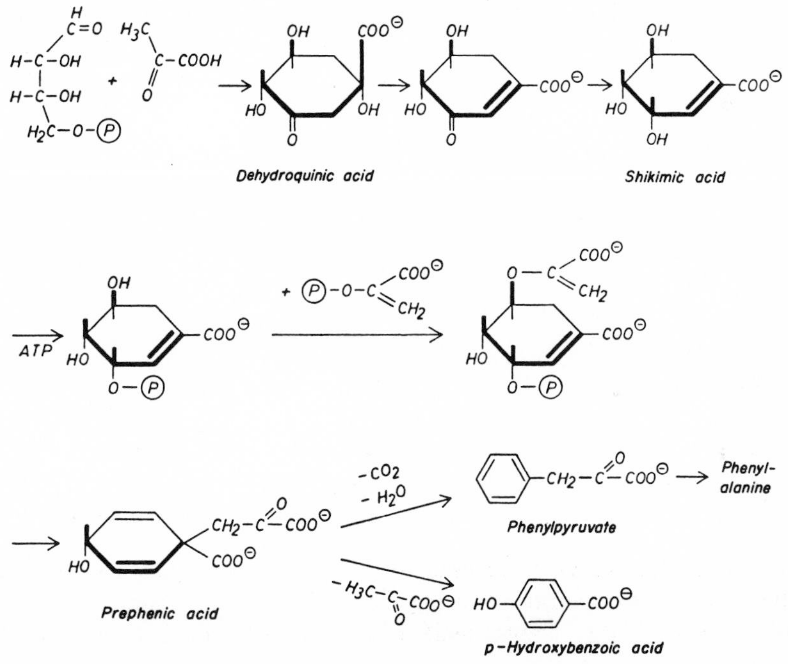

Dehydroquinic acid          Shikimic acid

Phenylpyruvate

Phenyl-alanine

Prephenic acid

p-Hydroxybenzoic acid

The first isolable precursor of the aromatic amino acids is *dehydroquinic acid*, a cyclohexane derivative arising probably from erythrose 4-phosphate and pyruvate. The initial condensation step is similar to the formation of neuraminic acid. By

---

[7] An exception is made by the follicular hormone estradiol, which appears to be formed from cholesterol (cf. Chapt. XIV-6).

elimination of water, dehydroquinic acid changes to dehydroshikimic acid and then to *shikimic acid*, which is phosphorylated in its 5-position. The hydroxyl group in the 3-position then forms an enol ether with phosphoenolpyruvate, which in turn easily rearranges to *prephenic acid* (the phosphate group is split off in the process). Prephenic acid is very labile; merely upon acidification of its solution it loses $CO_2$ and $H_2O$ and is transformed to *phenylpyruvic acid*. Transamination readily yields *phenylalanine*.

*Tryptophan* is formed from anthranilic acid, which supplies the aromatic ring and the nitrogen for the indole ring.

**Lignin.** Although aromatic amino acids are ubiquitous and are essential as food components, in sheer amount, lignin takes first place among the aromatic plant products.

Lignin is a highly polymeric compound. Its structure is not known exactly. It arises from coniferyl alcohol, which has been isolated from wood in its glycosidic form, coniferin. By dehydration and polymerization, coniferyl alcohol is converted to a multiply cross-linked structure. The accompanying figure shows a segment of the molecule with several typical cross links. The molecular weight lies around 10,000.

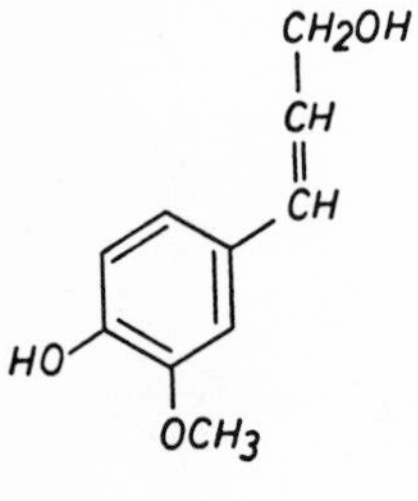

Coniferyl alcohol

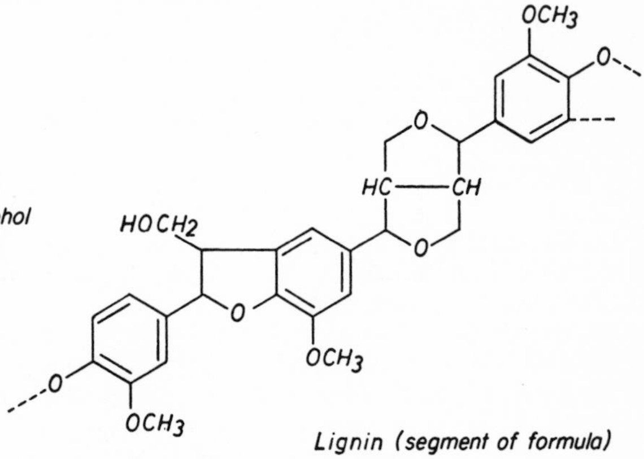

Lignin (segment of formula)

**Biosynthesis of a Vitamin: Pantothenic Acid.** Vitamins are substances that cannot be synthesized by the organism requiring them. Most of the vitamins essential to man are provided by plants. Pantothenic acid, as an example, is formed as shown on page 291.

"Active formaldehyde" (hydroxymethyltetrahydrofolic acid, cf. Chapt. VI–5) is attached to *α-keto-isovaleric acid* (arising from valine by transamination); reduction of the keto group affords pantoic acid. ATP activates the carboxyl group, and the resulting pantoyl-AMP compound condenses with β-alanine to yield pantothenic acid.

Only a few examples of the synthetic capabilities of plants have been presented. The many alkaloids and other secondary plant products cannot be discussed here.

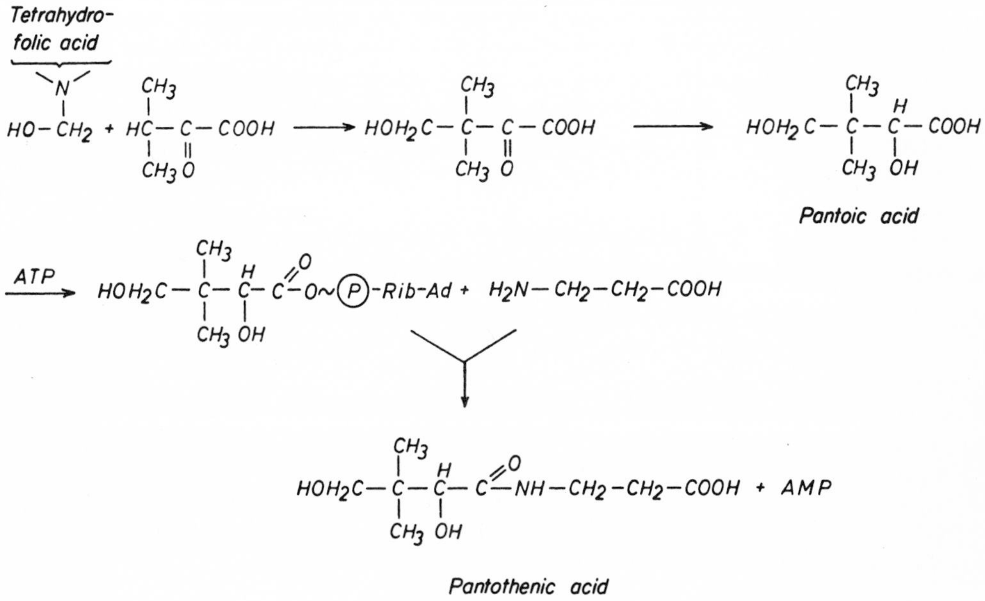

*Tetrahydro-*
*folic acid*

$$\overset{\diagdown}{N}\diagup \quad CH_3 \qquad\qquad\qquad CH_3 \qquad\qquad\qquad\qquad CH_3$$

$$HO-CH_2 \;+\; HC-\overset{|}{\underset{|}{C}}-COOH \;\longrightarrow\; HOH_2C-\overset{|}{\underset{|}{C}}-\overset{}{C}-COOH \;\longrightarrow\; HOH_2C-\overset{|}{\underset{|}{C}}-\overset{H}{\underset{|}{C}}-COOH$$

(with $CH_3$ and $O$ groups on the carbons, $OH$ on the final)

*Pantoic acid*

$$\overset{ATP}{\longrightarrow}\; HOH_2C-\overset{CH_3}{\underset{CH_3}{\overset{|}{\underset{|}{C}}}}-\overset{H}{\underset{OH}{\overset{|}{\underset{|}{C}}}}-C\overset{O}{\diagup}\!\!-O\!\sim\!\textcircled{P}\text{-}Rib\text{-}Ad \;+\; H_2N-CH_2-CH_2-COOH$$

$$HOH_2C-\overset{CH_3}{\underset{CH_3}{\overset{|}{\underset{|}{C}}}}-\overset{H}{\underset{OH}{\overset{|}{\underset{|}{C}}}}-C\overset{O}{\diagup}\!\!-NH-CH_2-CH_2-COOH \;+\; AMP$$

*Pantothenic acid*

## BIBLIOGRAPHY

D. I. Arnon, Conversion of light into chemical energy in photosynthesis, *Nature,* **184,** 10–21 (1959).

D. I. Arnon and co-workers, Photosynthetic phosphorylation and molecular oxygen, *Proc. Natl. Acad. Sci. U.S.,* **47,** 1314–1334 (1961).

√ J. A. Bassham, The path of carbon in photosynthesis, *Sci. American,* **206,** 88–100 (1962). ✓

J. A. Bassham and M. Calvin, "The Photosynthesis of Carbon Compounds," W. A. Benjamin, Inc., New York, 1962.

✓ M. Calvin, The path of carbon in photosynthesis, *Science,* **135,** 879–889 (1962). ✓

R. Hill and C. P. Wittingham, "Photosynthesis," Methuen, London, 1957.

G. Hoch and B. Kok, Photosynthesis, *Ann. Rev. Plant Physiol.,* **12,** 155–194 (1961).

M. D. Kamen, "Primary Processes in Photosynthesis," 182 pp., Academic Press, New York, 1964.

W. D. McElroy and B. Glass (editors), "Light and Life," Johns Hopkins Univ. Press, Baltimore, Maryland, 1961.

K. Mothes and H. R. Schütte, The biosynthesis of alkaloids, *Angew. Chem.,* **75,** 265 and 357 (1963).

√ E. I. Rabinowitch, "Photosynthesis and Related Processes," 3 Vols., Interscience, New York, 1945–1956.

K. Tagawa and D. I. Arnon, Ferredoxins as electron carriers in photosynthesis, *Nature,* **195,** 537–543 (1962).

# Glycosides, Oligosaccharides, Polysaccharides

## 1. The Glycoside Bond

The substances named above have the glycosidic bond as a common structural feature. Warming a solution of glucose with methyl alcohol and HCl produces a mixture of two new substances, $\alpha$- and $\beta$-methylglucosides, with the following structures:

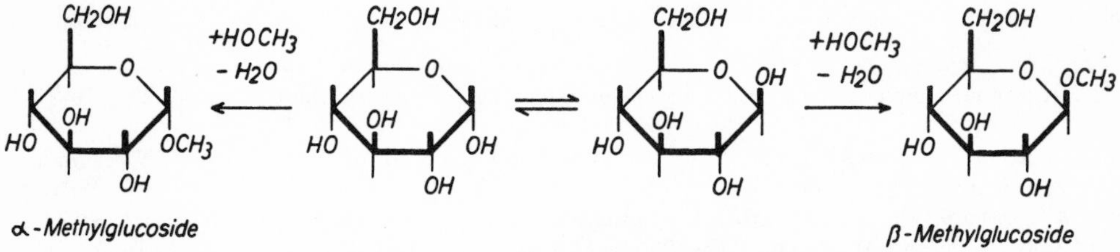

$\alpha$-*Methylglucoside*                                                      $\beta$-*Methylglucoside*

Compounds of this type have the general name of glycosides. They are analogous to the acetals (not the hemiacetals) of the aldehydes (cf. Chapt. I–2, XV–2). These substances are formed from smaller compounds according to our definition (Chapt. I–3), and they decompose to their component parts by hydrolysis. "*Glycoside*" is a generic term for this entire class of substances. Those members of the class that are derived from glucose are called *glucosides*; derivatives of galactose are *galactosides*, etc., and the bond between the sugar and some alcohol (or other sugar) is called the glycosidic bond. The method of forming glycosides from sugar and methanol by acid catalysis is similar to that of acetal formation from aldehydes. The living cell, of course, does not employ methanolic hydrochloric acid.

Isomerism between $\alpha$- and $\beta$-glucosides corresponds to the isomerism between $\alpha$- and $\beta$-glucose discussed previously (Chapt. XV–2). But, while the two forms of glucose in solution are in equilibrium (mutarotation), the corresponding glucosides cannot interconvert. This is understandable, because glycosides cannot equilibrate by passing through the carbonyl form; the hydroxyl group at C-1 is kept from reaction by the substituent R.

A glycosidic bond can be formed with alcohols, with phenolic hydroxyl groups, and even with carboxylic acids (to give the so-called ester glycosides). In glycosidic natural products the alcoholic (or phenolic) component is frequently called the *aglycon* (the sugarless moiety).

Besides O-glycosides there also exist N-glycosides, formed by elimination of water between the hemiacetal hydroxyl and an HN group. The N-glycosides include primarily the nucleosides (Chapt. VI–5) and the polynucleotides (nucleic acids, Chapt. VII–3). They constitute a very important group in biochemistry.

The glycosides occur predominantly in the plant kingdom. Several typical examples are presented here:

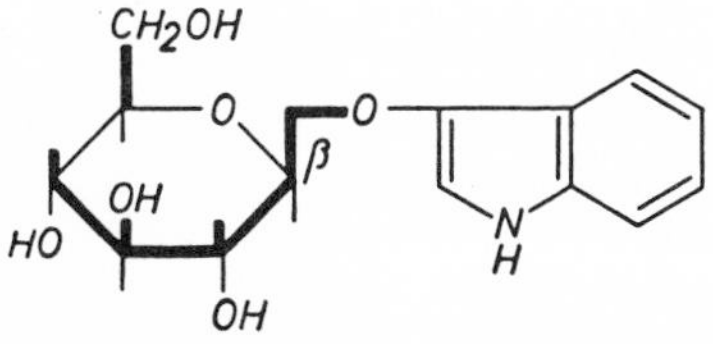

Indican

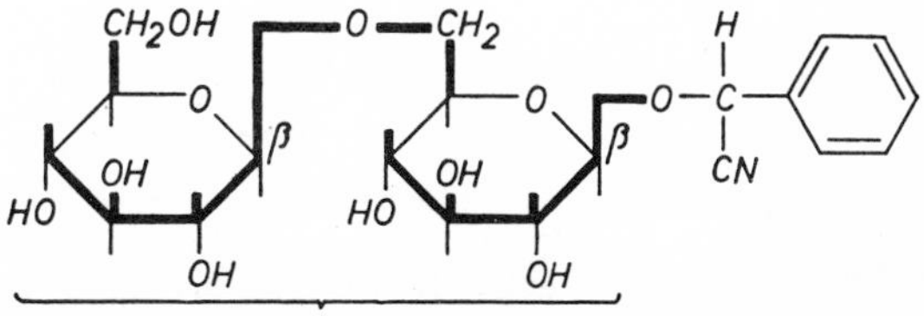

Gentiobiose

Amygdalin

*Plant indican* (from Indigofera species), a glucoside of indoxyl, which used to be important in the isolation of indigo; *amygdalin* from bitter almonds, which upon hydrolysis releases 2 moles of glucose, 1 mole of benzaldehyde, and 1 mole of HCN; *hesperidin*, a flavanone glycoside, formerly assumed to possess vitamin character; and lastly, *streptomycin*, which contains a N-containing inositol (diguanidino-scyllo-inositol) as the alcohol, the branched-chain streptose and N-methyl-L-glucosamine as the sugars.

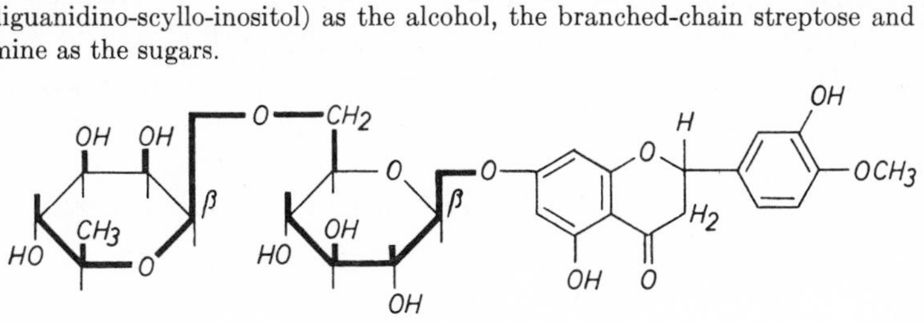

Hesperidin

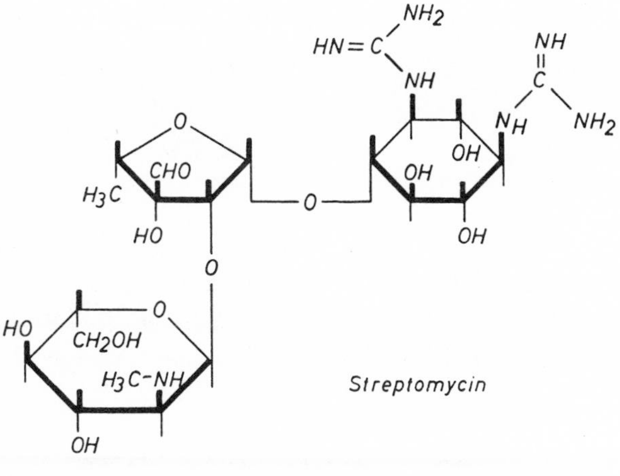

Streptomycin

This group also includes *digitonin* and *digitalin* (Chapt. XIV-3), and the glycolipids discussed in Chapt. XIII-4.

Glycosides are found also in lower animals; in insects, e.g., 4-glycosido-proto-catechuic acid. In the mammalian organism they are found rarely and are replaced by the *glucuronides*, which play an important role as detoxication and excretion products of numerous phenols, alcohols, and carboxylic acids. Steroid glucuronides for example are found regularly in urine, e.g. pregnanediol glucuronide (cf. Chapt. XIV–6).

The glycosidic bond of the glucuronides is completely analogous to that of the plant glycosides described above, but the carbohydrate is glucuronic acid (for bio-synthesis see Section 4).

## 2. Disaccharides

If sugars can combine with any alcohol to form glycosides, then they should also be able to react with the alcohol group of another sugar molecule. This is indeed possible, and the product of two sugar molecules is called a disaccharide. Like other glycosides, the disaccharides break down to their components during hydrolysis. A combination of three (or four) units is called a trisaccharide (or tetrasaccharide); *oligosaccharide* is the term for combinations up to about eight carbohydrate groups; beyond that, they are called polysaccharides.

Many chemical characteristics of the monosaccharide (e.g. reducing properties) depend on the free hydroxyl group of the hemiacetal (at C-1 of the aldoses or C-2 of the ketoses). If one of the other hydroxyl groups of the parent sugar is occupied by a glycoside bond, the resulting disaccharide retains the reducing properties of the parent sugar: it still shows mutarotation, and it can form still another glycoside bond with another alcohol. Such oligosaccharides are of the *maltose type* because maltose is their prototype (4α-glucosido-glucose).

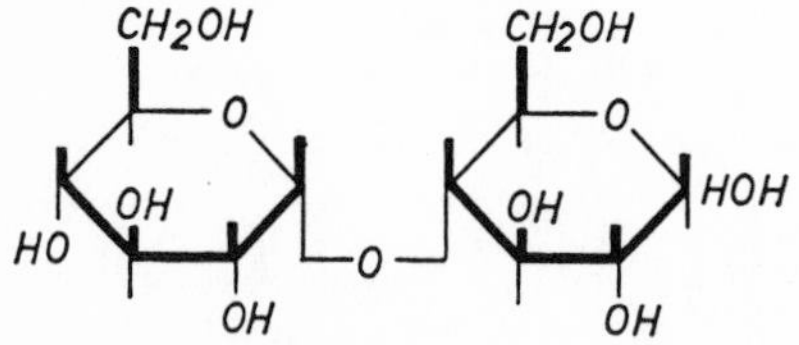

Maltose 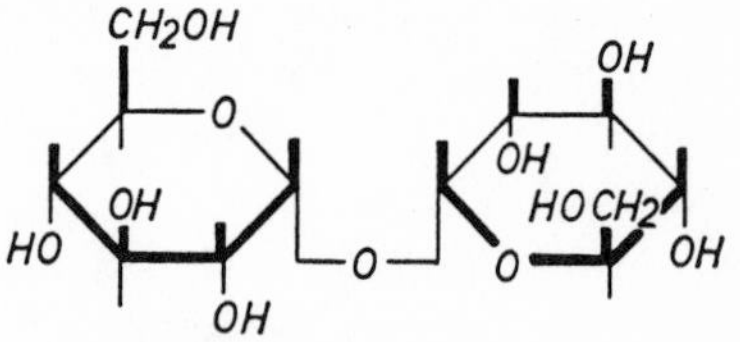          α,α′ - Trehalose

Disaccharides in which both hemiacetal hydroxyls have reacted with one another possess entirely different properties. Both sugar components exist in their full acetal form. Such oligosaccharides are not reducing, show no mutarotation, and form no osazones. Since the simplest natural representative is *trehalose* (1-α-glucosido-1-α-glucoside), the type of linkage in the nonreducing disaccharides is called the *"trehalose type."*

Systematic names indicate the location (number of C atom) of the linkage and the sugar bound at that location.[1] If for example β-D-glucose reacts with glucose, all of the following disaccharides are possible:

| | |
|---|---|
| 1-β-Glucosido-1-β-glucoside | iso-trehalose (made synthetically) |
| 1-β-Glucosido-1-α-glucoside | neo-trehalose (made synthetically) |
| 2-β-Glucosido-glucose | (found in plants) |
| 3-β-Glucosido-glucose | (found in plants) |
| 4-β-Glucosido-glucose | cellobiose (component of cellulose) |
| 6-β-Glucosido-glucose | gentiobiose (e.g. in amygdalin) |

In addition, the corresponding isomers with the α-glycosidic linkage are possible. The free hydroxyl group of the hemiacetal of a disaccharide cannot be assigned to a configuration; the α- and β-form are in equilibrium. The first two disaccharides listed are of the trehalose type; the rest, of the maltose type.

**Some Important Disaccharides.** Natural trehalose is the $\alpha,\alpha'$-compound occurring in plants and recently has been identified as the "blood sugar" of insects.

By far the most important compound of the trehalose type is sucrose (α-gluco-pyranosido-β-fructofuranoside), also known as saccharose, cane sugar, or beet sugar. It is probably the only foodstuff used in the crystalline form. Though sucrose is widely distributed in the plant kingdom, only sugar cane and sugar beets are used for the industrial preparation. Chemically, it is remarkable that fructose is present in its furanose form, the less stable ring form. For this reason, even dilute acids split cane sugar to glucose and fructose. The process is called inversion because the direction of optical rotation is reversed (cane sugar has $\alpha_D = +66°$; the cleavage mixture, $\alpha_D = -20°$, since fructose is strongly levorotatory). The cleavage mixture (*invert sugar*) is the principal component of honey, besides sucrose.

**Disaccharides of the Maltose Type.**[2] *Maltose* (4-α-glucopyranosido-glucose) is a product of the breakdown of starch and occurs in malt (malt sugar). As we have mentioned, it is reducing.

*Cellobiose* (4-β-glucopyranosido-glucose) also features the 1:4 linkage of the glucose groups, but in β-linkage. While in maltose (α-linkage) the two six-membered rings are at an angle in the molecular model, the β-linkage imparts a rather planar shape to the molecule; this becomes clearer in the formula at the right, in which one ring is turned around.

---

[1] In place of the designation *"glucosido,"* *"glucosyl"* is sometimes used.

[2] Since it is meaningless to assign a configuration to the unbound hemiacetal hydroxyl group (the two forms are in equilibrium with one another), the two substituents at C-1 are written as HOH in the formulas.

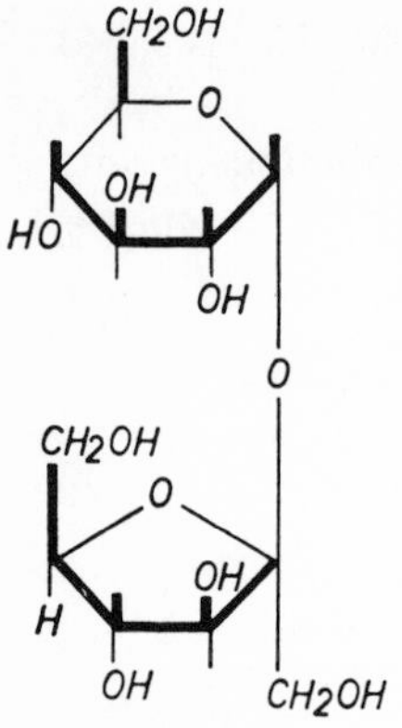

*Isomaltose*

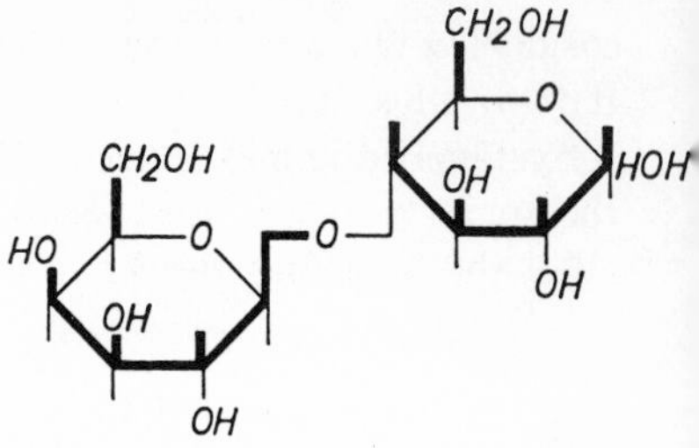

*Lactose*

*Sucrose*

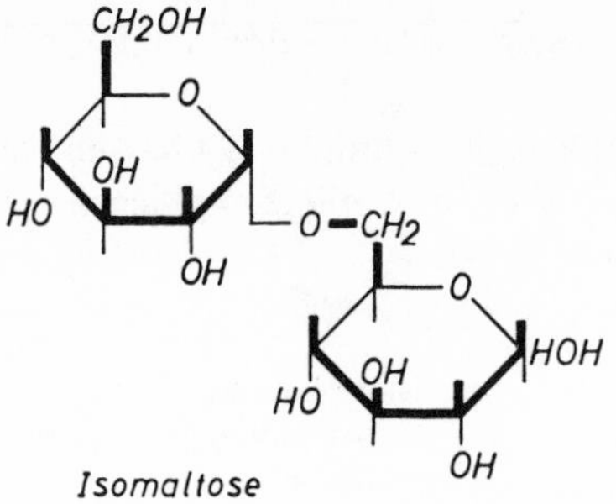

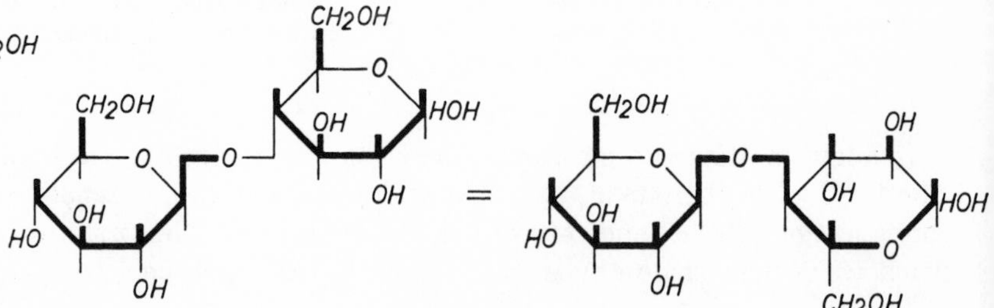

*Cellobiose*

*Isomaltose.* This name was given to 6-α-glucosido-glucose, because it is obtained by hydrolysis of starch. It corresponds to the branch points (cf. Section 5) in starch; the free disaccharide is not important.

*Lactose,* or milk sugar (4-β-galactosido-glucose), is the most important carbohydrate of the milk of all mammals. Human milk contains about 6% (and 0.3% of higher oligosaccharides); cows' milk, about 4.5%.

**Higher Oligosaccharides** are found in many plants. One example is the trisaccharide *raffinose,* α-D-galactosido-(1 → 6)-α-D-glucosido-(1 → 2)-β-D-fructofuranoside.[3] Raffinose can be considered as the galactoside of sucrose.

## 3. Enzymic Cleavage of Oligosaccharides

The hydrolysis of oligosaccharides and glycosides proceeds as shown by the following example:

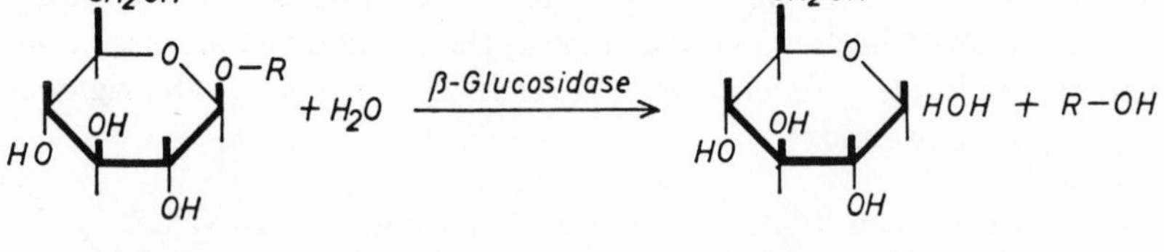

*β-D-Glucoside*                     *Glucose*

[3] The small arrow shows the direction of the glycosidic bond (always from the hemiacetal hydroxyl to some alcohol or hemiacetal group of the following sugar).

This hydrolysis is one of the longest-known enzyme-catalyzed reactions. The equilibrium greatly favors cleavage. The enzymes responsible for establishing the equilibrium are called *glycosidases*; they are a subgroup of the hydrolases. They are usually group specific, and their specificity is aimed at the nature of the *glycosidically* bound sugar and at the kind of glycosidic linkage.

Accordingly, we can distinguish:

| | |
|---|---|
| α-Galactosidases | α-Glucosidases |
| β-Galactosidases | β-Glucosidases |
| β-Fructofuranosidases, etc. | |

*Emulsin* from bitter almonds, one of the longest-known enzymes, is a mixture of glycosidases whose chief component is β-D-glucosidase. It hydrolyzes both natural and synthetic β-glucosides, e.g. β-methylglucoside, amygdalin, cellobiose, and others.

*α-Glucosidases* are also called *maltases*, because they split maltose. They are frequently found together with the starch-hydrolyzing amylase (Section 5). α-Glucosidases can also cleave cane sugar. The cane-sugar-cleaving enzyme of yeast, however, is a β-fructofuranosidase. Since this cleavage involves an inversion of the direction of optical rotation, the enzyme is also known as *invertase*.

Another important group of glycosidases is comprised of the *β-glucuronidases*, which are distributed widely among plants and animals. The substrates are the glucuronides, including not only excretion products but also the *mucoids* (Section 7).

Most glycosidases are really *transglycosidases*, which transfer the glycosidically bound sugar residue to other appropriate molecules with OH groups. Since water is always present in especially high concentrations it is a suitable acceptor molecule, the transfer to water being equivalent to hydrolysis. It has been observed, however, that galactosidase transfers the galactosido residue of lactose onto glucose (preferably at the 6-OH) or onto another lactose molecule; in the latter case, a trisaccharide would be formed (as shown on page 300).

Transglycosidation is important in the synthesis of polysaccharides by plants (see below).

## 4. Biosynthesis of Glycosides and Oligosaccharides

In principle, glycosidases are also able to promote synthesis. Synthesis from monosaccharides is severely limited by the positive free energy of the reaction; when disaccharides are available, however, longer chains can be formed by transglycosidation. Plants perform transglycosidation to a considerable extent, mainly in the formation of polyfructoside from sucrose (Schlubach). A side product of the reaction is glucose, which can be converted back to sucrose *via* some detours.

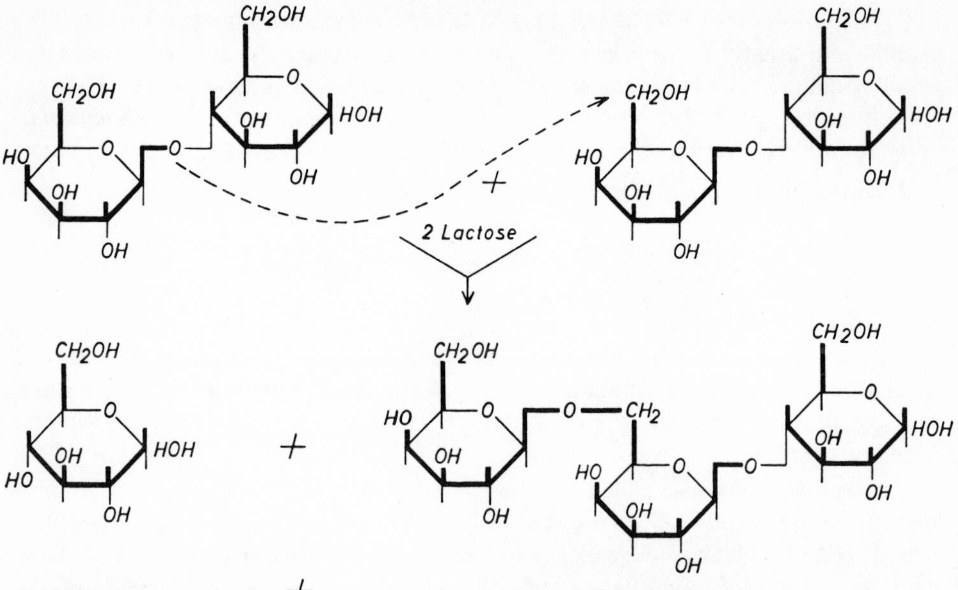

Glucose          +          6-Galactosido-lactose

Monosaccharides must first be activated so that they contain an energy-rich bond. The activating group is usually uridine diphosphate (coenzyme of glycosidation; cf. Chapt. VI–5).

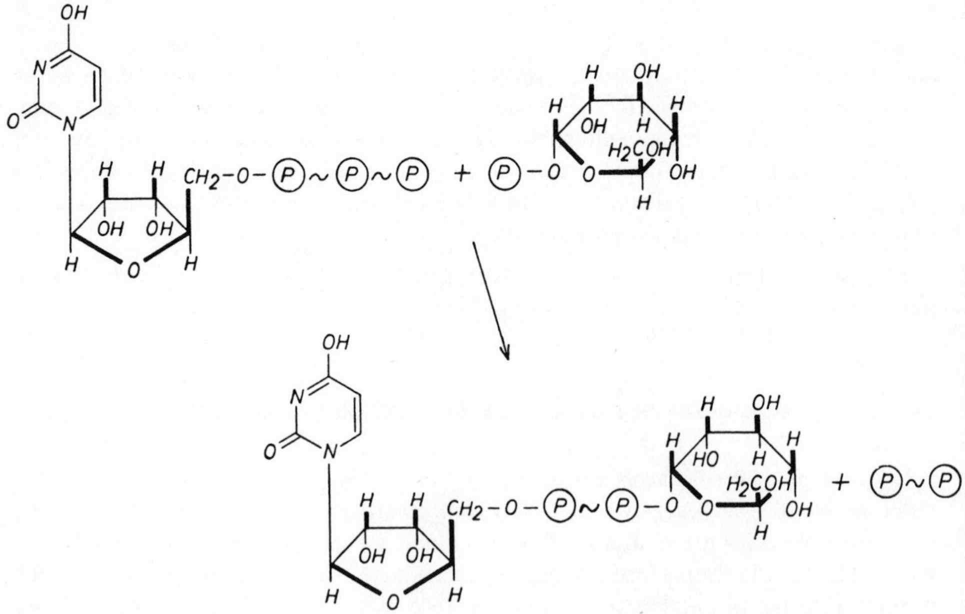

Uridine diphosphate glucose

The binding of glucose to the coenzyme is a complicated process. Initially, a kinase converts glucose to glucose 1-phosphate with the aid of ATP. The 1-phosphate reacts enzymically with uridine triphosphate (UTP) to form uridine diphosphate glucose (see formula below) and inorganic pyrophosphate. The phosphate of glucose 1-phosphate is retained in the UDP-glucose bond.

The glucose molecule activated in this way has various possibilities for further reaction:

**a. Epimerization at C-4** to produce the *galactose derivative*, catalyzed by 4-epimerase (formerly called galactowaldenase). At equilibrium, the ratio is about 1 glucose : 3 galactose. The mechanism of this steric rearrangement is not clear. The supposition is that the rearrangement proceeds *via* the keto compound. This is supported by the observation that the enzyme contains firmly bound NAD.

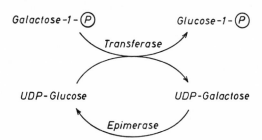

**b. Exchange Between Galactose and Glucose,** according to the equation:

$$\text{UDP–galactose} + \text{glucose-1-P} \rightleftharpoons \text{UDP–glucose} + \text{galactose-1-P}$$

The enzyme is called *glucose-phosphate uridyl transferase.* By this reaction, galactose is bound to the coenzyme; no enzyme is known for the direct reaction between galactose-1-P and UTP. Galactose-1-P is converted to glucose-1-P by the cooperation of the transferase and the epimerase:

*Glucose-1-phosphate uridyl transferase* is important in the human organism for the metabolism of galactose; galactose is apparently introduced into the path of glucose breakdown by reversal of the reaction above. In galactosemia, a hereditary disease, the transferase is lacking. As a result, galactose is not utilized and accumulates in blood. This is a good example of how a change in hereditary characteristics eliminates one enzyme and consequently causes a metabolic anomaly (Kalckar). Under normal nutritional conditions the effects of galactosemia are fatal; complete elimination of galactose (and lactose) from the diet improves the prognosis considerably.

**c. Disaccharide Synthesis:** Active glucose (UDP-glucose) can also combine with a second monosaccharide molecule (in the form of the 6-phosphate) to give a disaccharide. If combined with glucose-6-P, trehalose-6-P results; if combined with fructofuranose-6-P, sucrose-6-P is formed. Free sucrose is released through a separate hydrolysis reaction catalyzed by a phosphatase. The reaction is important especially in plants and explains the biosynthesis of cane sugar.

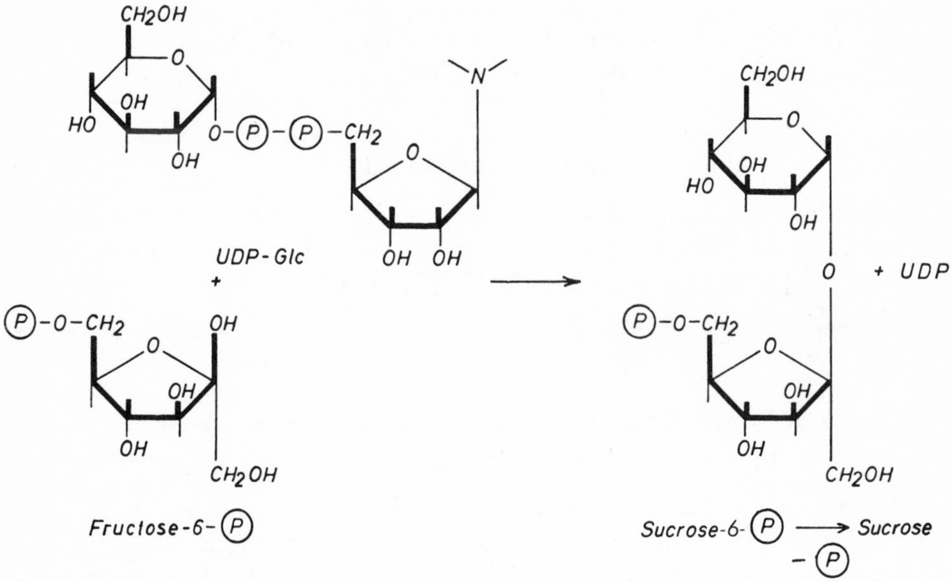

The mammary gland of mammals synthesizes *lactose* in a similar manner. Uridine diphosphate galactose combines with glucose-1-P; the galactose group is transferred to glucose phosphate in $\beta$-glycosidic linkage with the 4-hydroxyl of glucose. The product lactose-1-P is hydrolyzed by a phosphatase to yield free lactose. Polysaccharides seem to be synthesized by an entirely analogous mechanism (Section 6).

**d. Glucuronide Formation:** Uridine diphosphate glucose can be oxidized enzymically (with NAD as the H acceptor) to give glucuronyl diphosphate uridine, i.e. activated glucuronic acid.

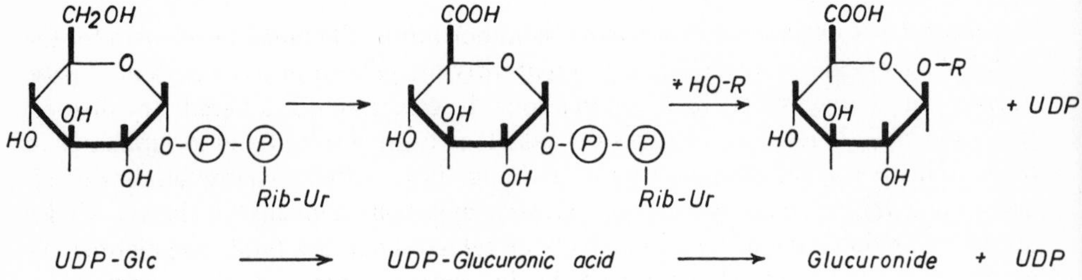

The oxidation is performed on a derivative of glucose in which C-1 is protected. Whereas the great specificity of enzymic reactions would allow the direct oxidation of the $CH_2OH$ group with the preservation of the labile hemiacetal group, the chemist is put at ease by the somewhat less spectacular reaction sequence.

With the aid of appropriate transferases, active glucuronate can form glucuronides with hydroxyl compounds that occur naturally in the body or that have been administered to it (drugs).

The reaction takes place in the liver and is called "detoxication." This word would imply that the enzymes have a definite "purpose." It is more likely that this mechanism simply exists, and that very many substances—both endogenous ones, like hormones or bilirubin, and exogenous ones, like drugs and poisons—are bound in this fashion and are excreted, independent of their "toxicity" and any "intentions" of the organism.

**Metabolism of Mannose.** This sugar is not activated by uridine diphosphate but by guanosine diphosphate instead. There appears to be a certain specificity on the part of the activating coenzyme. The reactions otherwise are largely analogous.

## 5. Polysaccharides: Homoglycanes

A combination of very many monosaccharides, linked by glycosidic bonds and analogous to the structure of oligosaccharides, is called a polysaccharide or "glycane." Polysaccharides are widely distributed in nature, with a greater variety in plants. Some possess low molecular weights, corresponding to 30–90 monosaccharides; but the majority (especially the more important ones) contain several hundred or even thousands of monosaccharide units.

Polysaccharides have various functions. In plants they serve both as structural support (example: *cellulose*, the polysaccharide present in the greatest amount by far) and as storage compounds in seeds and tubers (*starch*). In animals they rarely serve as structural substances (cellulose is found only in tunicates; *chitin* occurs in insects and crabs). *Glycogen* is accumulated by animals as a storage substance.

The chemical structure of polysaccharides permits the following classification: (1) Homoglycanes (analogous to homopolymers), which contain only a single kind of monosaccharide component; (2) heteroglycanes (analogous to copolymers), which consist of different components (usually only two or three); (3) conjugated compounds (glycoproteins and glycolipids). The "glucanes" cellulose, starch, and glycogen are composed of glucose alone; they will be discussed first.

**Cellulose** occurs in plants, usually associated with other structural substances (lignin). The cotton fiber and related fibers are almost pure cellulose (seminal threads of the *Gossypium* species). Industrial cellulose is usually obtained from wood and purified in various ways, i.e. it is freed from lignin and other contaminants. In cellulose, the glucose units are linked between C-1 and C-4 by β-glycoside bonds. The simplest component is therefore *cellobiose* (see formula below). Native cellulose consists of several thousand (in cotton about 1500) cellobiose units.

CH₂OH ... CH₂OH ... CH₂OH

*Segment of formula of cellulose*

Since each cellobiose unit is 10.4 Å long, as found by X-ray analysis of crystals, the entire cellulose molecule has the respectable length of 15,600 Å or 1.5μ. It would be visible in the light microscope if it were more than 7 Å (0.7 mμ) thick. The thread-like molecule need not be absolutely straight and could be bunched up. The chain of glucose units, however, is relatively rigid. In wood, the thread-like molecules are arranged so that highly ordered "crystalline" regions, called *"micelles,"* alternate with less ordered networks (Fig. 42). Furthermore, cellulose is cemented together with lignin.

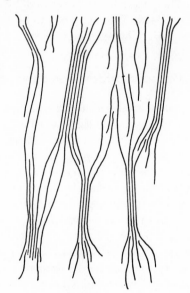

FIG. 42. Diagram of the micellar structure of cellulose.

**Chitin** is a structural substance similar to cellulose. It is a linear molecule with β-1→4 linkages between the individual units, which in this case consists of N-acetylglucosamine. The molecular size is not known, but probably is large. Chitin is found in fungi, but principally among the arthropods (crabs and insects). The armor of crabs and the exoskeleton (or cuticula) of insects consists mostly of chitin and some protein. The excellent mechanical properties of insect cuticula are due to chitin.

The repeating unit of chitin, *chitobiose*, is shown in the formula. It has been isolated from hydrolysates. Chitinases (from the gastric juice of snails or from bacteria) decompose the polysaccharide to N-acetylglucosamine.

**Starch** is a storage substance of plants and is deposited abundantly in seeds (grain) and tubers (potatoes, etc.) in the form of granules. Two types of compounds can be distinguished by chemical methods.

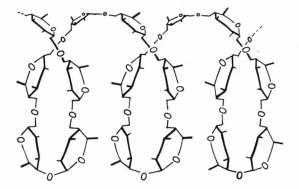

Chitobiose

**a. Amylose** makes up 20–30% of most native starches and consists of 250–300 glucose residues linked by 1 → 4-α-glycoside bonds. The repeating unit is maltose (α-glucosido-4-glucose, formula in Section 2), which is linked to itself in the same way. Because of the α-glycoside bonds the molecule does not appear long and straight, but rather coiled up like a spring (Fig. 43, 45).

FIG. 43. Amylose. The molecular shape of amylose explains some of its chemical and biochemical properties. With iodine, amylose turns intensely blue. This venerable reaction has been explained only recently. It was found that iodine molecules enter the hollow center of the coil created by the glucose units. In such "enclosure compounds" iodine exhibits changed physical characteristics, such as the strong absorption of light. There are enzymes that slit open this tube and free fragments, each of which contains six glucose units (Section 6).

**b. Amylopectin,** the other component of natural starch, is also built up of glucose units in α-glycosidic linkage. But besides the predominating 1 → 4 bonds some 1 → 6 bonds must also be present, because after enzymic cleavage both maltose and isomaltose (6-α-glucosido-glucose) can be isolated. Chemical evidence indicates that in amylopectin the chain is branched. The main chain has side chains, and the latter branch again. The whole molecule is composed of over a thousand glucose residues, and on the average there is one branch point for every 25 glucose residues. A diagram of the molecule is provided in Fig. 44; of course, only a segment of the whole molecule is shown. The solid circle symbolizes the free hemiacetal hydroxyl group at the chain end. The chains and side chains, here represented linearly, are actually coiled helically.

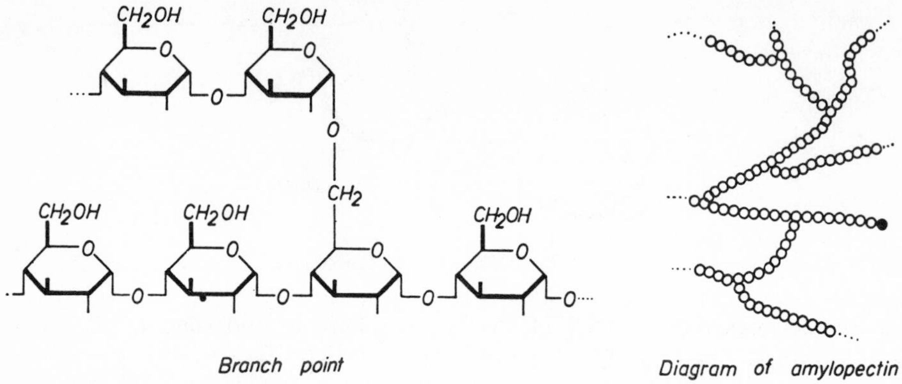

Branch point                                      Diagram of amylopectin

FIG. 44. Segment of the formula and diagram of amylopectin. Glycogen is built similarly, but is even more highly branched.

**Inulin and Pectins.** Besides the plant polysaccharides built up of glucose, there are those that are made up of *fructose*, and others. *Inulin* is a polyfructosan consisting of fructose residues in the furanose form with $2 \rightarrow 1$ linkage. The water solubility of inulin is due to the relatively small number of fructose units in the molecule (fewer than 100). Possibly, the chain is terminated by glucose in a sucrose-type bond. *Agar-agar*, a polysaccharide derived from sea algae, consists of D- and L-galactose, predominantly with $1 \rightarrow 3$ bonds, and always contains some amount of sulfuric acid. Agar-agar forms highly viscous gels and is used extensively for the preparation of bacterial culture media. The various plant gums and *pectins* have more complicated structures. Pectins contain the important gel-forming component, polygalacturonic acid ($\alpha\text{-}1 \rightarrow 4$ linkage); the acid groups are esterified extensively with methanol.

**Glycogen,** sometimes called "animal starch," occurs in liver, muscle, and many other cells as a storage substance.[4] The chemical structure of glycogen is very similar to that of amylopectin (see Fig. 44), but glycogen is much more branched and of higher molecular weight than amylopectin. For muscle glycogen the molecular weight has been estimated to be $10^6$; for liver glycogen, about $5 \times 10^6$ (corresponding to about 30,000 glucose residues). The glycogens are nevertheless water-soluble; the molecules have the shape of a flattened ellipsoid. Insoluble glycogens are of still higher molecular weight and are bound to protein. The molecule is built very irregularly (bushy). The chain length between branch points is usually 10–14 glucose residues; in the center of the molecule, branching is found at every third to fifth glucose residue. Preparations from different sources show different degrees of branching.

## 6. Enzymic Breakdown of Polysaccharides

A distinction must be made between the fate of polysaccharides in digestion and the metabolism of glycogen in liver and muscle, which follows another pathway.

---

[4] Highly polymeric substances are stored better than low molecular ones for two reasons: They are usually insoluble, and even when they are in solution their osmolarity is so low that the accumulation in a cell does not result in hypertonicity.

We shall discuss digestion first and then take up the intracellular metabolism (phosphorolysis).

**Hydrolytic Cleavage.** The principal enzymes, the amylases, break starch (and glycogen) down to maltose units. These enzymes are widely distributed. The term amylase is now used as a generic term; α-amylase (dextrinogenic amylase) and β-amylase (saccharogenic amylase) are distinguished.

*α-Amylases* occur in saliva, pancreas, and malt. In their point of attack they resemble the endopeptidases (Chapt. VIII–1); they cleave in the middle of the macromolecule. The initial cleavage products are oligosaccharides of six or seven glucose units. The assumption is that the enzyme attacks the spiral structure (Fig. 45)

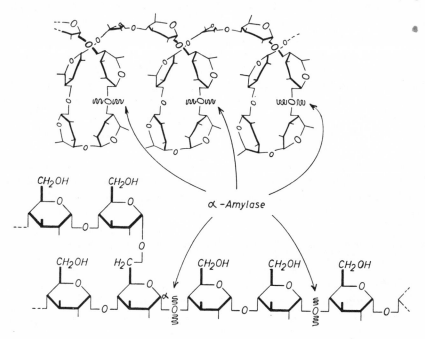

FIG. 45. Schematic diagram of hydrolysis of starch by α-amylase.

and splits neighboring glycoside bonds that are one whole turn of the spiral apart. This also explains the observation that the branch points of the side chains (the 1 → 6 linkages) are skipped and that they present no obstacle to α-amylase, which cannot cleave the 1 → 6 linkages. After prolonged action of the enzyme, the fragments are degraded largely to maltose; hydrolysis stops with the disaccharides.

Endo-amylase (α-amylase) has a liquefying effect, since the viscosity of a colloidal starch solution decreases rapidly and the iodine color reaction disappears without the appearance of reducing sugars. The reducing effect develops later, in a second phase, when the fragments have been broken down further. Maltose is released in the α-form (the optical rotation drops, however, due to mutarotation); hence the name of the enzyme.

*β-Amylases* occur predominantly, if not exclusively, in plants. They are exoglycosidases because they attack the ends and always split off two terminal glucose residues as maltose in its β-form (mutarotation increases). During hydrolysis, a Walden inversion at C-1 takes place.

The terminal cleavage explains the early appearance of reducing sugars ("saccharogenic amylase"). Though amylose is hydrolyzed almost completely, only about half of amylopectin is, since the enzymic reaction stops even before a branch point is reached. Phosphoric acid, an occasional component of starch, also is an inhibitor of the enzyme. Eventually, a relatively high molecular "limit dextrin" is left, and the breakdown continues only if α-amylase or a special $1 \rightarrow 6$-linkage-splitting enzyme is active at the same time.

The end product of the degradation of polysaccharides by amylases is maltose (and isomaltose); glucose arises to a minor extent by the cleavage of maltotriose into two fragments. In the intestinal tract, an α-glucosidase (= maltase) splits maltose to glucose and thus ends the digestion. Maltase can also split sucrose.

*Cellulases* are commonly found in microorganisms, but rarely in animals. The utilization of cellulose almost invariably requires the participation of the microbial flora (e.g. in the rumen of ruminants).

**Phosphorolysis of Starch and Glycogen.** Within cells, the storage carbohydrate is broken down by a different route, involving phosphorolysis. This holds true both for the breakdown of starch in plant cells and for that of glycogen in muscle and liver.

The term phosphorolysis (coined in analogy to hydrolysis) describes the cleavage of a (glycoside) bond by inorganic phosphoric acid. It may be more correct to conceive of the process as a transfer of the terminal glucose residue onto phosphoric acid (as the acceptor molecule) and to classify the enzyme as a transglycosidase. The net result is the same for the two mechanisms (as shown on page 309).

The terminal[5] glucose group of the polysaccharide chain is removed during phosphorolysis and attached to an inorganic phosphate group. The long chain is thus shortened, and glucose-1-P is formed. The enzyme can then repeat its action on the new end group of the polysaccharide. By this process, amylose is converted completely into glucose-1-P; amylopectin is degraded only to dextrin, since the $1 \rightarrow 6$ linkages are not attacked by the enzyme. Phosphorylase is very specific for glucose-$1 \rightarrow 4$ bonds.

---

[5] The nonreducing end of the chains with the free 4-OH group is meant.

CH$_2$OH   CH$_2$OH   CH$_2$OH   CH$_2$OH

HO—                              —O—        —O—        —O—        —O···

HPO$_4^{2-}$

CH$_2$OH                 CH$_2$OH   CH$_2$OH   CH$_2$OH

HO—        —O—$(P)$   +   HO—        —O—        —O—        —O···

Glucose-1- $(P)$

Phosphorylase occurs in muscle and liver. Two forms of the enzyme are distinguished, the relatively inactive *phosphorylase b* and the highly active *phosphorylase a*. The transition from phosphorylase b to a is accomplished by phosphorylation of serine residues in the enzyme protein. This activation reaction requires ATP as phosphate donor, a specific kinase, and a special cofactor, cyclic adenosine-3′,5′-monophosphate (compare reaction scheme below). The initial step in this sequence of reactions, the formation of cyclic adenosine monophosphate from ATP by a certain (structure-bound) enzyme, is stimulated by the two hormones *epinephrine* and *glucagon*. The effect of these hormones in raising blood sugar levels is based on this mechanism (cf. Chapt. XX-10). In certain glycogen storage diseases the phosphorylase is absent while the glycogen-forming enzyme system (see p. 310) is intact; consequently, high molecular polysaccharides are accumulated.

Phosphorolysis of polysaccharides is energetically advantagous to the cell since glucose is always broken down in its phosphorylated form—either through the Embden-Meyerhof pathway or through the pentose phosphate cycle. The cell thereby saves itself the initial phosphorylation step.[6] In the subsequent step, *phosphoglucomutase* changes glucose-1-P to glucose-6-P. "Cofactor" for this enzyme is glucose-1,6-diphosphate whose 1-phosphate group is transferred to the 6-position of the substrate glucose-1-P. In this way, a new molecule of the cofactor is formed

*Enzyme*                                                              *Enzyme*

$(P)$-O-CH$_2$       HO-CH$_2$              $(P)$-O-CH$_2$       $(P)$-O-CH$_2$

                                    Phospho-
                                    gluco-
                                    mutase

HO—    OH    O—$(P)$   +   HO—    OH    O—$(P)$          HO—    OH    OH   +   HO—    OH    O—$(P)$

OH                    OH                              OH                     OH

"Cofactor"            Substrate                      Product               "Cofactor"

---

[6] It is fallacious to assume that the pathway from glucose *via* glycogen is more efficient energetically than the direct breakdown. The formation of glycogen from glucose demands two phosphorylation steps, because the synthesis proceeds *via* UDP-glucose (see below). In other words, only *part* of the energy expended is actually preserved.

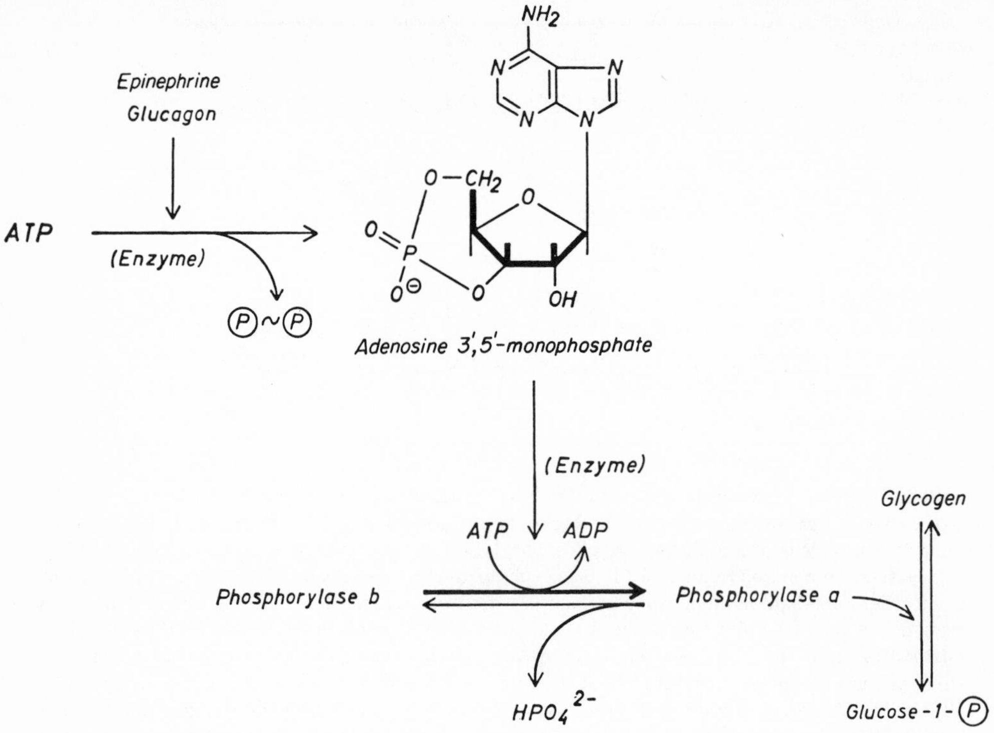

Adenosine 3',5'-monophosphate

and the cofactor molecule, now converted to glucose-6-P, is the product of the reaction. The entire process is analogous to the conversion of glycerate-3-P to glycerate-2-P. Phosphoglucomutase provides the link to the glycolytic pathway (Chapt. XV–7).

The phosphorylase reaction is freely reversible. The condensation reaction, however, requires a primer molecule. If an enzyme preparation is incubated with glucose-1-P, there is no reaction at first. The addition of a little dextrin as acceptor for the glucose residues initiates the formation of glycogen by adding glucose residues.

**Synthesis of Glycogen.** Glycogen synthesis can be demonstrated *in vitro* with glucose-1-P, but this reversal of phosphorolysis is not observed in intact cells. Phosphorylase seems to function primarily degradatively. *In vivo* glucose-1-P probably cannot be concentrated sufficiently to effect a synthesis of glycogen. According to recent work, the synthesis proceeds *via uridine diphosphate glucose*, i.e. with a more highly activated molecule. The principle of this type of glycoside synthesis has already been discussed (cf. Section 4). Here too, a primer molecule (glycogen or dextrin) is necessary to allow the attachment of glucose residues in 1 → 4 linkage.

Some energy is wasted in this reaction, since 2 ATP are consumed in the formation of UDP-glucose from glucose. But, on the other hand, the equilibrium favors glycogen synthesis (being highly exergonic) and the separation of the synthetic and degradative pathways offers the advantage that the two can be regulated independently. The principle of separate reaction pathways holds also with various other types of material (e.g. with fatty acid synthesis, Chapt. XII-6).

Glycogen (or starch) synthesis represents a special case of synthesizing transglycosidation discussed above (section 3). For the formation of natural branched polysaccharides, a second special transglycosidase, the "branching enzyme" (Q-enzyme), is required. The enzyme removes one chain link from the $1 \rightarrow 4$ linkage and reattaches it at the 6-hydroxyl group. A new branch point is thus created upon which phosphorylase can then act further.

# 7. Mucopolysaccharides

Several polysaccharides are composed not only of simple sugars but also of derivatives of sugars, such as *amino sugars* and *uronic acids*. Most of these are structural support material for connective tissue or mucous substances of the body. A few have very special functions, and it is expected that further discoveries will be made in this field.

The mucopolysaccharides have a common structural feature. They consist of disaccharide units in which a uronic acid is bound glycosidically to the 3-position of an acetylated or sulfurated (in heparin) amino sugar. These disaccharide residues are polymerized by $1 \rightarrow 4$ bonds to a linear macromolecule; the uronic acid and sulfuric acid residues impart to these substances a strongly acidic character. Besides D-*glucuronic acid*, one can also find L-*iduronic acid*, distinguished from glucuronic acid only by the steric configuration at C-5.

**Hyaluronic Acid** is the least complicated member of the series. It consists of glucuronic acid and N-acetylglucosamine linked according to the principle just discussed. The formula is:

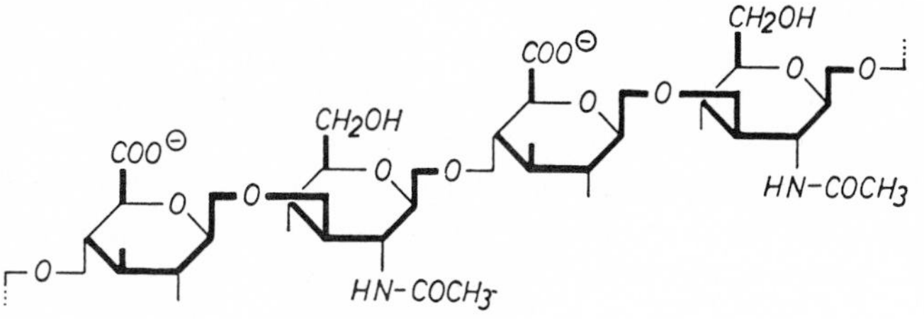

*Hyaluronic acid*

The molecule is probably not branched, or only slightly so. The molecular weight is very great (several million). Hyaluronic acid is a principal component of the ground substance of connective tissue. It is found, among other places, in the synovial fluid, in the vitreous humor of the eye, and in skin, usually in combination with protein. Frequently it is prepared from umbilical cord.

It is physiologically significant that hyaluronic acid is split swiftly by the hyaluronidases. Two enzymic effects have been distinguished: First, the depolymerizing effect, which causes a rapid drop in viscosity of a hyaluronic acid solution without setting free any reducing groups; second, cleavage to smaller fragments (even-numbered oligosaccharides).

Hyaluronidase is the "spreading factor" of skin and connective tissue. The depolymerizing effect permits any foreign bodies, such as ink, colloidal pigments, but also pathogenic bacteria, to penetrate the tissue, since the cementing substance is being dissolved. Hyaluronidase also has a physiological role in fertilization. The sperm is rich in the enzyme and it can thus advance better in the cervical canal and finally reach the ovum.

**Chondroitin Sulfate,** along with hyaluronic acid, forms part of the structure of connective tissue. Cartilage has the highest content of chondroitin. Several polysaccharides of this type have been isolated and designated as chondroitin sulfate A, B, and C. The formula shown represents chondroitin sulfate C, which is composed of glucuronic acid and N-acetylgalactosamine 6-sulfate. In type A, the sulfate is bound in the 4-position, while chondroitin sulfate B contains the L-iduronic acid mentioned above.

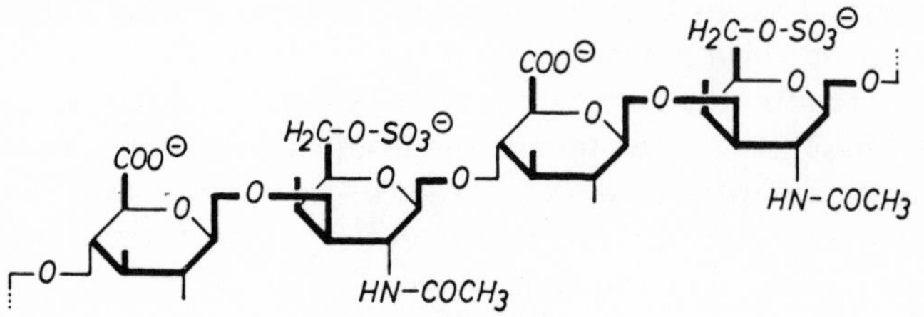

*Chondroitin sulfate C*

Chondroitin sulfate is very often associated with collagen, and possibly with other proteins, too. It seems to augment the formation of the fibrillar structure of collagen.

**Heparin** is a polysaccharide composed of sulfonylaminoglucose (= glucosamine N-sulfate) and the sulfate esters of glucuronic acid. The type of linkage is again $1 \rightarrow 3$—$1 \rightarrow 4$; the molecular weight is 17,000–20,000. The sulfate content is very high and corresponds to 4–5 molecules per tetrasaccharide residue. The relative positions of the residues have not yet been substantiated.

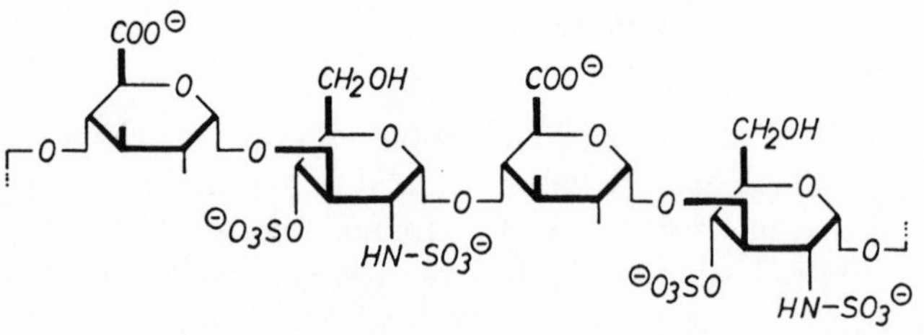

*Heparin*

Heparin acts as an anticoagulant. It prevents blood clotting by inhibiting the prothrombin-thrombin conversion and thus eliminating the thrombin effect on fibrinogen. Heparin is used therapeutically.

**Submaxillary Mucin** and related substances have a different structure. The "backbone" is a polypeptide chain, a protein molecule of random coil configuration (at least as extracted from sheep). The free carboxyl groups of the side chains (i.e. of aspartic and glutamic acid residues) are esterified with disaccharide units by glycosidic bonds. The disaccharide N-acetylneuraminyl-(2 → 6)-N-acetylgalactosamine is bound as the prosthetic group, and the terminal N-acetylneuraminic acid (= sialic acid) can easily be split off enzymically without fragmentation of the entire molecule. The enzyme, neuraminidase, is a glycosidase specific for glycosidically bound neuraminic acid (cf. Chapt. XII-4).

**Glycoproteins.** In contrast to the mucoids, the glycoproteins contain less carbohydrate, especially less amino sugar. $\alpha_1$-*Glycoprotein* of blood plasma has as prosthetic group a complicated polysaccharide of 10–15 sugar residues (including mannose, galactose, fucose, N-acetylglucosamine, and N-acetylneuraminate). The polysaccharide is linked by an ester—glycoside bond to an asparagine residue of the peptide chain.

**Capsular Material of Bacteria.** The cell walls of many bacteria contain polysaccharides which are responsible, among other things, for their serologic specificity (cf. Chapt. IV-7). The capsular material of pneumococci has been studied especially well. The material from type III consists of glucuronic acid-(1) → (4)-glucose-(1) → (3)-glucuronic acid (note the switch of 1 → 4 to 1 → 3 bonds). Type XIV contains galactose-(1) → (4)-N-acetylglucosamine; other types have even more complicated polysaccharides.

The synthesis of the capsular material is genetically determined. It has been possible to "smuggle" hereditary factors into cells so that the bacteria become transformed from one type to another (transformation of pneumococci, Chapt. VII-4).

**Blood Group Substances.** These polysaccharide substances occur in erythrocytes. Their specific serologic reaction with isoagglutinins results in the disruption of blood cells (hemolysis) when incompatible blood groups are transfused. Surprisingly, substances with the serologic specificity of the human blood group A have been detected in saliva, in ovarian cysts, and even in mucin of the hog stomach. Blood-group-specific mucins seem to be widely distributed.

The substances of the groups A, B, O and Le$^a$ have been obtained in highly purified form. The structure of these substances, all with high molecular weights (around 260,000), has not yet been elucidated. Among the hydrolytic products are 12 different amino acids, of which 29% is threonine and 18% proline; the carbohydrates L-fucose (6-deoxy-L-galactose), D-galactose, glucosamine, and galactosamine have been identified.

Mild hydrolysis breaks down blood group substances only partially; their specificity is lost, but the cross reaction with antiserum to the pneumococcal strain XIV increases. The degradation product consists of galactose, glucosamine, galactosamine in the ratio of 2:1:1. The cross reaction may be due to the sequence . . . galactose-(1) → (4)-N-acetylglucosamine . . . which is common to both substances.

Kabat has proposed that the side chains that are removed first during acid treatment hang from the linear polymer. The side chains consist of L-fucose-containing oligosaccharides and impart blood group specificity. If this is true, the chemical constitution of blood group substances would be reduced to a modification of the ground substance.

The familiar blood groups A, B, and O are characterized by the occurrence of their antibodies in blood (see Chapt. IV–9). Many more blood groups can be distinguished, however. The antibodies to substances of the blood groups arise only after blood transfusions and after repeated transfusions can cause disturbances (shock, incompatibility, hemolysis). Blood group characteristics are hereditary and represent a very important group of properties in human genetics.

The "rhesus factor" should also be mentioned. This blood group property was discovered first in monkeys (*Macaca rhesus*) and later in man. The Rh-factor turned out to be a group of different substances (called C, D, E). The genes C, D, E are responsible for the formation of the corresponding substances whose appearance in erythrocytes causes the latter to be *Rh-positive* (common is the . . . D . . .-substance). Erythroblastosis of the newborn may set in when the mother possesses the genetic characteristics c, d, e, but the embryo inherited the characteristic D from the father. If any of the D-substance appears in the organism of the mother, then antibodies against D are formed in the maternal serum which may diffuse back into the fetal blood through the placenta and destroy the blood corpuscles there.

BIBLIOGRAPHY

M. Florkin and E. Stotz (editors), "Comprehensive Biochemistry," Vol. 5: Carbohydrates, Elsevier, Amsterdam, 1963.

H. Gibian, "Mucopolysaccharide und Mucopolysaccharidasen," F. Deuticke, Vienna, 1959.

W. Z. Hassid, Biosynthesis of complex saccharides, *in* "Metabolic Pathways" (D. M. Greenberg, editor), Vol. I, Academic Press, New York, 1960.

E. A. Kabat, "Blood Group Substances," Academic Press, New York, 1956.

L. F. Leloir, C. E. Cardini, and E. Cabib, Utilisation of free energy for the biosynthesis of saccharides, *in* "Comparative Biochemistry" (M. Florkin and H. S. Mason, eds.), Vol. II, pp. 97–138, Academic Press, New York, 1960.

W. Pigman, "The Carbohydrates. Chemistry, Biochemistry, Physiology," Academic Press, New York, 1957.

D. W. Russell and R. J. Sturgeon, Heteromeric saccharides, *Ann. Rept. Chem. Soc. London* **60**, 486–500 (1963).

H. H. Schlubach, The metabolism of carbohydrates in grasses, *Fortschr. Chem. org. Naturstoffe*, **15**, 1–30 (1958); Carbohydrate metabolism in rye and wheat, *ibid.*, **19**, 291–315 (1961).

# CHAPTER XVIII

# Correlations in

# Intermediary Metabolism

We have pointed out in various places the manifold interrelationships which exist among the intermediary products of the metabolism of fats, carbohydrates, and proteins. Now we wish to discuss these relationships with special reference to the synthetic abilities of the organism and the interchangeability of foodstuffs.

The end products of catabolism are mainly $CO_2$ and $H_2O$. Carbon dioxide arises largely from decarboxylation in the citric acid cycle; water originates from biologic oxidation in the respiratory chain. Since the breakdown products of the three main foodstuffs, carbohydrates, fats, and proteins, all enter these common terminal pathways, it is not surprising that these foodstuffs can replace each other as nutrients.

The phenomenon of interchangeability was discovered by physiologists more than 50 years ago and has been the basis of calculations of the caloric value of food intake. Problems of nutrition connected with these interrelationships will be discussed in Chapt. XXI.

The citrate[1] cycle is indeed the pivot on which the metabolic processes revolve, with respect both to the terminal oxidation of foodstuffs and to the synthetic activities. The citrate cycle requires acetyl-CoA, which is also the universal starting material for the synthesis of endogenous substances. Acetyl-CoA (active acetate) is formed mainly in two reaction sequences: from the breakdown of fatty acids and from the breakdown of carbohydrates. The various interrelationships have been represented graphically on the fold-out chart in the back of this book.

## 1. Metabolism of Carbohydrates

The Catabolism of Carbohydrates starts either with glycogen or with free glucose. In the first case, phosphorolysis yields the phosphate of glucose (glucose-1-P)

---

[1] Again, we will speak of the anions of acids, rather than the free acids, because at the prevailing pH of the living cell only the anions can exist.

directly; in the second case, ATP is needed. The various monosaccharide phosphates are interconvertible by several pathways, as is illustrated near the upper edge of the chart. Most of the sugars enter the glycolytic pathway in this manner. But these same interconversion routes also permit the synthesis of various disaccharides (e.g., lactose), polysaccharides, and glycolipids, all of which contain sugars in glycosidic linkage. The coenzyme for glycoside formation is uridine diphosphate.

The direct oxidation of glucose *via* pentoses is of significance for the formation of pentoses (and indirectly for nucleic acid synthesis). Nicotinamide-adenine dinucleotide phosphate (NADP) is the hydrogen acceptor here. The reduced form[2], $NADPH_2$, is necessary for many synthetic processes, e.g., for the synthesis of fatty acids, for the biosynthesis of cholesterol, and for hydroxylation reactions. The direct oxidation of glucose to pentoses, therefore, has this second function: It provides the necessary "reduction equivalents" for other anabolic processes. It is not a source of energy.

From 75 to 90% of the glucose is oxidized through the Embden-Meyerhof pathway and then through the citrate cycle. The principal steps of glycolysis are shown on the chart (a few intermediates have been omitted). The true starting point of the breakdown is hexose diphosphate (fructose diphosphate) which is split into two molecules of triose phosphate. 3-Phosphoglyceraldehyde undergoes another reaction (a dehydrogenation) to give phosphoglycerate. In the process, 1 mole of ATP is obtained from the intermediate diphosphoglycerate. Another mole of ATP arises from the conversion of phosphoenolpyruvate to pyruvate. These processes are called substrate-linked ATP syntheses. As detailed in Chapt. XV-7, 2 moles of ATP are obtained from the breakdown of each mole of glucose to pyruvate and $NADH_2$. Anaerobically, pyruvate is metabolized to lactate; aerobically, to acetyl-CoA.

**Minor Pathways.** Dihydroxyacetone phosphate can be transformed to glycerol phosphate, which is used for the synthesis of fats and glycerophosphatides. Phosphoglycerate can be converted to 3-phosphohydroxypyruvate and further to hydroxypyruvate. This last compound is possibly related to glycolate (by oxidative decarboxylation) and to glyoxylate, and hence to glycine. Pyruvate is related to alanine by transamination, and hydroxypyruvate, to serine.

**Gluconeogenesis** (reversal of glycolysis). Starting material for the synthesis of glucose is primarily lactate, which arises during anaerobic glycolysis, and, second-

---

[2] By recent, official recommendation (see Chapt. VI-4) the two hydrogen-transferring coenzymes, formerly known as di- and triphosphopyridine nucleotide (abbreviated as DPN and TPN) are, to be called nicotinamide-adenine dinucleotide (NAD) and nicotinamide-adenine dinucleotide phosphate (NADP). The new nomenclature offers greater correctness and consistency, among other advantages.

To indicate the oxidized and reduced forms, two equally correct forms are recommended:

    *a.* Oxidized: $NAD^+$, $NADP^+$; reduced: $NADH + H^+$, $NADPH + H^+$.

    *b.* Oxidized: NAD, NADP; reduced: $NADH_2$, $NADPH_2$.

The two forms must, however, never be "mixed." We have chosen form *b* throughout this book, except in a few cases where there was some value in showing the loss of electrons.

arily, a group of amino acids derived from proteins. The key substance for both pathways is phosphoenolpyruvate. It can be formed from pyruvate and ATP in theory, but the equilibrium is so unfavorable that high concentrations of ATP would be required. A detour over *oxaloacetate* is adopted instead. Oxaloacetate arises either directly from pyruvate by the action of a $^-$OOC—biotin enzyme (i.e. with the consumption of ATP), or by reductive carboxylation of pyruvate to malate and subsequent dehydrogenation (with NAD). Oxaloacetate in turn in phosphorylated and at the same time decarboxylated to yield phosphoenolpyruvate. The reaction then proceeds along the reverse of the glycolytic pathway, requiring only one additional ATP.

Amino acids can also turn into carbohydrates by several other pathways: The decarboxylation of hydroxypyruvate (arising from serine by transamination) yields "active glycolaldehyde," which is then available for the transketolase reaction. Thus two $\alpha$-carbons of serine can enter carbohydrate.

## 2. Metabolism of Fatty Acids

**The Breakdown of Fats** (in the chart, upper right) begins with hydrolysis to fatty acids and glycerol. The latter is closely related to the trioses. The further breakdown of the fatty acids demands activation first (consumption of ATP and combination with coenzyme A to give the thioester) and then proceeds through dehydrogenation (by a flavoprotein), addition of water, and a second dehydrogenation to the $\beta$-keto acid. The whole process is commonly known as $\beta$-oxidation. Thioclastic cleavage of the activated $\beta$-keto acid releases acetyl-CoA and a shorter fatty acid in its activated form, which then can undergo the same sequence of reactions several times, until the entire carbon chain is broken down to $C_2$ fragments.

Modifications of the breakdown are necessitated by methyl branching. Branched-chain fatty acids arise also from the amino acids leucine, isoleucine, and valine (cf. Chapt. XII-5). Propionyl-CoA (instead of acetyl-CoA), is formed from isoleucine and valine, and this is converted to succinate by carboxylation and isomerization.

**Acetyl-CoA, the Main Crossing Point of the Metabolism of Carbon.** Acetyl-CoA, active acetate, arises partly from oxidative decarboxylation of pyruvate and partly from $\beta$-oxidation of long-chain fatty acids and several amino acids. It is no exaggeration to call active acetate a metabolite of cardinal importance.

The energy content of acetyl-CoA, i.e. its free energy of hydrolysis, is a little higher than that of ATP. And yet, this reactive thioester cannot be considered to be the universal reservoir of energy. Rather, acetyl-CoA is the reactive intermediate which provides the $C_2$ fragment for so many conversions and syntheses. By being converted to acetyl-CoA the various intermediary metabolites enter the terminal pathway of breakdown, known as the citrate cycle (see below). Active acetate, therefore, is essential for the proper functioning of the citrate cycle. It can be supplied from many sources. The availability of its reaction partner, oxaloacetate, sometimes is limiting. Oxaloacetate is derived either from carbohydrate (by a carboxylation) or from aspartate.

**Syntheses with Active Acetate.** Acetyl-CoA is an important starting material for biosynthetic reactions. First of all, *fatty acids* can be formed from it. This is the major pathway followed during the conversion of carbohydrate to fat.

Although synthesis and degradation are basically similar, synthesis does deviate from breakdown in one important step: Malonate (as malonyl-CoA), and not active acetate, reacts with activated fatty acids. The products are again the $\beta$-keto acids which then give rise (in principle by reversal of the breakdown) to the saturated fatty acids in their CoA-form. NADPH$_2$ donates hydrogen for the reduction of the unsaturated fatty acids. The formation of fats and phospholipids, furthermore, requires glycerol, the alcohol component of fats. This is derived from the metabolism of carbohydrates. The phosphatidic acids are intermediates in the synthesis of neutral fat (cf. also Chapt. XII-6). But the biosynthesis of *phosphatides* requires free diglycerides that react with cytidine diphosphate ethanolamine (cf. Chapt. XIII-3). Adenosylmethionine can methylate phosphatidyl ethanolamine ( = cephalin) to produce phosphatidyl choline ( = lecithin).

A second important anabolic pathway of acetyl-CoA produces the *isoprenoid lipids*, especially the steroids. Three molecules of acetyl-CoA condense at first to form a branched-chain compound, hydroxymethylglutaryl-CoA. With a superabundance of acetyl-CoA, such as occurs in some pathologic metabolic conditions (like diabetes, cf. Chapt. XX–10), acetoacetate can be formed from hydroxymethylglutaryl-CoA (ketogenesis). But normally, the reduction of the thioester group of that compound yields mevalonate which is then converted to isopentenyl pyrophosphate with an expenditure of 3 moles of ATP. The subsequent synthesis of squalene and cholesterol does not require any further energy supply.

In addition to steroids, the carotenoids and the various terpenoids are formed by analogous routes in plants and microorganisms. The side chains of the lipoid quinones (vitamins E and K, and ubiquinone) also arise in this fashion in some mammalian organisms. Furthermore, many microorganisms can synthesize from mevalonate or similar precursors the C skeleton of the branched-chain amino acids (leucine, valine, isoleucine), which are essential for man.

Finally, it must be mentioned that acetyl-CoA is available for a variety of ester and amide syntheses (reactions which helped in the discovery of active acetate). These reactions are merely indicated in the metabolic chart, although very important substances such as acetylcholine, acetylglucosamine, etc., are formed in this manner.

## 3. Citrate Cycle and Respiratory Chain

Both processes have already been discussed in detail (cf. Chapt. X and XI).

**Citrate Cycle.** The biologic purpose of the cycle is to decompose acetate (which enters the cycle as acetyl-CoA), with the help of 2 H$_2$O, into CO$_2$ and [H].

$$CH_3COOH + 2\ H_2O = 2\ CO_2 + 8[H]$$

The decomposition commences with an enlargement of the molecule, by the condensation of acetyl-CoA and oxaloacetate to give citrate, from which the cycle is named. Isomerization yields isocitrate; dehydrogenation and decarboxylation produce ketoglutarate. Next, an oxidative decarboxylation with *thiamine pyrophosphate* and *lipoate* is interposed. The product, active succinate ( = succinyl-CoA), is converted to succinate with a gain of 1 ATP. Succinate is then dehydrogenated (with a flavoprotein) to form fumarate. The uptake of water and subsequent dehydrogenation complete the cycle, yielding oxaloacetate again.

Only 1 ATP is gained from the citrate cycle, namely by the oxidative decarboxylation of ketoglutarate. But almost all the carbon dioxide is produced in the cycle. Most of the energy expected from the decomposition of foodstuffs is produced in the *respiratory chain*. The reduced coenzyme ($NADH_2$) is oxidized by the enzymes of the respiratory chain and at the end of the chain by atmospheric oxygen. The formation of water thus occurs in a stepwise fashion which at three places is coupled with the phosphorylation of ADP. Respiratory-chain-linked phosphorylation (or oxidative phosphorylation) is the most important source of chemical free energy.

The respiratory chain could in theory be coupled with any $NADH_2$-dependent dehydrogenation. This coupling is particularly close with the citrate cycle, first because of the spatial proximity of the enzymes within mitochondria and second because the citrate cycle produces so much of the reduced coenzyme.

Another significant function of the citrate cycle is its central location between various degradative and synthetic pathways. The first connection with the *metabolism of amino acids* is found in ketoglutarate, which is a very general reaction partner in transamination. A second branch point is provided by succinyl-CoA, which can unite with glycine to form β-aminolevulinate; the latter condenses to form porphobilinogen, a key intermediate in the biosynthesis of the hemin ring system (cf. Chapt. IX).

Shemin has pointed out that the oxidative deamination of aminolevulinate and the subsequent oxidation of ketoglutarate semialdehyde to give ketoglutarate constitute a second cycle which would effect complete oxidation of glycine. The significance of this is still obscure.

The steps of the citrate cycle involving dicarboxylic acids—from succinate to oxaloacetate—are even richer in correlations with other metabolic pathways. Fumarate is a fragment of the breakdown of tyrosine; it is also formed from aspartate in the course of the formation of urea (see below). Oxaloacetate can be converted by reversible transamination into aspartate, one of the nonessential amino acids. Another pathway leads from oxaloacetate to phosphoenolpyruvate and hence to the synthesis of carbohydrates.

The latter pathway is important for a group of glucogenic amino acids and is the route of gluconeogenesis. Carbon atoms of the fats also end up in carbohydrates by this route. A net synthesis is not possible, however, since two C atoms are lost along the way. Mammals cannot synthesize sugar from acetyl-CoA.

The glyoxylate cycle (cf. Chapt. XI-4) has recently been discovered in certain bacteria. In it, two molecules of acetate are united to form succinate and thus a net synthesis of carbohydrate can be achieved by way of the familiar reactions. This cycle is not shown on the metabolic chart because it seems to be without significance for the mammalian organism.

## 4. Metabolism of Proteins

Proteins are broken down to amino acids by proteolytic enzymes. The metabolism of the different amino acids is as individual as their structures. Only a few steps can be integrated into one general scheme.

**Metabolism of Nitrogen.** This proceeds by transamination to glutamate and aspartate and on to urea (other N-containing substances have only subordinate significance for the excretion of nitrogen in man and most other mammals). Urea synthesis itself proceeds by a cyclic process. In this case energy is consumed (3 moles of ATP per mole of urea) rather than produced. The pathway from ornithine *via* citrulline or arginine and back to ornithine is shown in the diagram on the chart. The key compound for the first step is carbamyl phosphate. For more information on the individual steps refer to Chapt. VIII–8. The ammonia donors glutamate and aspartate enter the citrate cycle after their deamination, unless they are charged again with amino groups by transamination; this is highly probable for $\alpha$-ketoglutarate, at least.

The direct oxidation of amino acids (oxidative deamination) is insignificant compared to transamination. Decarboxylation is important only for some special metabolic processes. Serine, e.g., is transformed to ethanolamine, one of the major components of the phosphatides. Similarly, cysteine can become $\beta$-mercaptoethylamine, a constituent of coenzyme A. Decarboxylation also plays a role in the formation of certain hormones (cf. Chapt. VIII–5).

**Carbon Metabolism of Amino Acids.** Nine of the 18 common amino acids are related directly or indirectly to the dicarboxylic acids of the citrate cycle. Proline, histidine, and arginine (or ornithine) produce glutamate and thence $\alpha$-ketoglutarate (on the chart, below the citrate cycle). The aromatic amino acids are broken down to fumarate, which is also formed from aspartate in the urea cycle. Lastly, alanine should be included, since it can enter the citrate cycle *via* pyruvate and acetyl-CoA. The fact that the carbon chains of amino acids enter the citrate cycle is important both for their complete degradation and for their conversion to carbohydrates (as mentioned already, cf. Chapt. XV–10). The synthesis of amino acids cannot always proceed by a reversal of the breakdown; many of them are essential components of the diet (cf. Chapt. XXII–2).

Some amino acids enter the pathway of fatty acid catabolism after transamination or oxidative deamination. Since they give rise to branched-chain fatty acids, they undergo several changes (cf. Chapt. XII–5, and the right side of the fold-out chart). Leucine is broken down *via* hydroxymethylglutarate. If the shortening of the carbon chain yields propionyl-CoA, as in the case of isoleucine, then succinate can be obtained by carboxylation.

$C_1$ **Metabolism.** The metabolism of glycine and serine should be mentioned briefly because of their numerous relationships with other classes of compounds. An outline has been provided (large diagram of formulas, Chapt. VIII–12). By transamination of serine, hydroxypyruvate arises; it can enter the metabolism of carbohydrates. Decarboxylation of serine produces ethanolamine, which can be converted (by methylation with methionine) to choline, another important component of phosphatides. Serine is especially important as a donor of the $C_1$ fragment. Formaldehyde and formate (in its activated form) originate here; they are utilized primarily in the synthesis of the purine derivatives (to form nucleotides).

**Synthesis of Proteins.** From the available pool of free amino acids, proteins are synthesized. The synthesis requires ATP and specific nucleic acids as cofactors and as templates. This is the place where hereditary factors (deoxyribonucleic acids) take effect, since they bear the information for the structure of the proteins (including enzyme proteins). This information is transcribed to messenger RNA which then adheres to ribosomes and serves as the template for the lining-up of activated amino acids. Protein synthesis is one of the most important energy-consuming processes.

Frequently, an organism is unable to synthesize certain amino acids (for indispensable amino acids cf. also Chapt. VIII–6). Protein synthesis cannot proceed if even one of the required amino acids is lacking.

**Metabolism of Nucleic Acids.** Our knowledge is quite incomplete here. In degradation, the high molecular substances are first broken down to mononucleotides and then to the components of the latter. The sugar moiety enters carbohydrate metabolism, and the purine bases are oxidized to uric acid and excreted as such.

The biosynthesis of purine and pyrimidine bases has been described in Chapt. VII–2. It proceeds largely from small fragments that are closely related to the metabolism of protein. Note that $C_1$ fragments (active formate) are used extensively.

Vitamins are often required in the biosynthesis of nucleotide coenzymes (Chapt. XXII–3).

## 5. The Common Pool of Intermediary Metabolism

The folding chart and the preceding discussions reveal that the main metabolic pathways are interconnected in many ways. In order to be understood properly, the entire diagram must be considered to be a dynamic equilibrium (see Chapt. V–4). On the one hand, substances are continuously added, and on the other, waste products are excreted. Quantitatively, carbon dioxide is the principal waste product, with around 1 kg being discarded each day (we have emphasized repeatedly that $CO_2$ can re-enter metabolism).

Many tissues depend on a supply of glucose as the substrate for their metabolism. The concentration of glucose circulating in blood ("blood sugar") is remarkably constant. The cells, therefore, are provided with a constant supply and are capable of maintaining stable concentrations of intermediates in their dynamic equilibria. Thus, there is a constant flux of material through the chains of reactions. For the smooth functioning of many enzyme systems, this is a condition of prime importance. Unusual concentrations of a reactant upset the state of equilibrium, with the result that metabolism is directed into completely different pathways.

The metabolic chart also reveals that various foodstuffs and endogenous substances are broken down constantly to produce common intermediates. This is often referred to as forming a "common pool of metabolites."[3] Acetyl-CoA is a very typical example; it is derived from many different sources. The metabolic pool, therefore, has numerous inlets as well as outlets; one of the outlets flows to the citrate cycle, another to fat synthesis, another to isoprenoid synthesis, etc. Molecules are mixed uniformly in such a pool; once submerged in the pool, the origin of a molecule (whether from fat or from carbohydrate) can no longer be stated with certainty. This explains how radioactively labeled fragments can be spread over an entire organism.

In theory, there exists a metabolic pool of this kind for every substance. Such pools are particularly significant if they consist of metabolites situated at the junctions of metabolic pathways, e.g. acetate, pyruvate, $\alpha$-keto-glutarate, succinate, and oxaloacetate, or of hydrogen (the reduced coenzymes, $NADH_2$ and $NADPH_2$), or of ATP, which in a sense is the common pool for chemical energy.

A clear distinction must be made between size of the metabolic pool and rates of flow into it and out of it. The *steady concentration* of a metabolite, i.e. the size of the pool, can be rather low, although a large amount of material is actually metabolized. Concentrations of metabolites range within the order of magnitude of $10^{-3}$ mole/liter. Greater concentrations are attained by storage substances. The turnover, in contrast, can be gigantic indeed. It can be calculated for example (cf. Chapt. XXII–1) that the human body produces during 24 hours as much as 70 kg of ATP; its own weight! Of course, ATP is used up as fast as it is produced; it is usually split to ADP and phosphate and can be resynthesized from these components.

BIBLIOGRAPHY

✓E. Baldwin, "Dynamic Aspects of Biochemistry," 4th ed., Cambridge Univ. Press, London and New York, 1964.

D. M. Greenberg, editor, "Metabolic Pathways," 2 Vols., Academic Press, New York, 1960, 1961.

H. A. Krebs, and H. L. Kornberg, A survey of the energy transformations in living matter, *Ergeb. Physiol. biol. Chem. u. exptl. Parmakol.*, **49**, 212–298 (1957).

---

[3] The term *metabolic pool* is used in different senses. At one time, it may refer to the total amount of a substance present in the whole organism (or in certain organs, such as blood); at another time, it may have the more restricted and original meaning, namely the amount of a substance that is in a state of active turnover. The second is the proper meaning for the expression "the common pool of metabolism." Pool size is usually determined by administering a radioactive substance and measuring the dilution that it undergoes.

# CHAPTER XIX

# Topochemistry

# of the Cell

The preceding chapter deals with the multiplicity of reactions that proceed simultaneously and with considerable interdependence. Now we come to the question of how metabolism is regulated and adapted to the requirements of an organism.

One essential aspect of regulation is the subdivision of the cell into definite submicroscopic structures that fulfill different tasks. The enzymes catalyzing the various reactions are not all (or even mostly) dissolved in the cell sap. Some are bound to definite structures, others are encapsulated in subcellular particles. Between these structures and the cell sap there exist certain permeability barriers. The modern concept that the cell consists of many different compartments is diametrically opposed to the old idea of the "protoplasm as a colloidal system." Only in very recent times has it become possible to gain insight into structure and biochemical function. The main tools have been the electron microscope and the technique of differential centrifugation of cell homogenates, which allows the centrifugal sedimentation, one at a time, of cell debris, nuclei, mitochondria, and microsomes.[1]

In this chapter we intend to describe briefly the structure and the main biochemical functions of the individual cellular components and to point out some principles of regulation. Knowledge of the individual reaction sequences and cycles (respiratory chain, glycolysis, citrate cycle, etc.) is a prerequisite. When in doubt, refer to the fold-out chart at the back of the book. A schematic diagram of cellular organization is presented in Fig. 47.

## 1. The Nucleus of the Cell

The biochemical functions of the nucleus are related primarily to its content of genetic material, i.e. the *chromosomes*, containing deoxyribonucleic acids. The fine structure of the chromosomes can best be studied in the giant chromosomes of cer-

---

[1] Fractions obtained in this manner are, however, not always uniform, and the results must therefore be evaluated with caution.

FIG. 46. Part of the first chromosome of the salivary gland of the mosquito *Chironomus tentans*. The dark crossbands are the gene loci, where deoxyribonucleic acids are concentrated. (Light microscopic photograph by Dr. Clever)

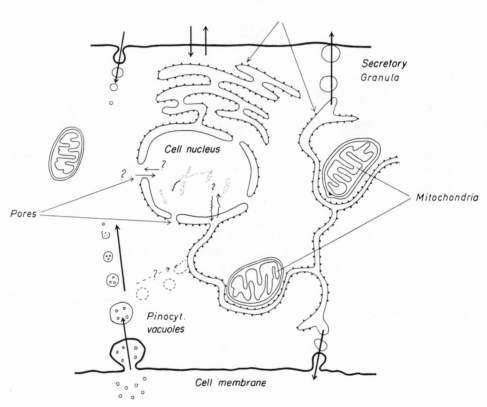

FIG. 47. Diagram of the submicroscopic structure of the cell. The cell nucleus is connected with the cytoplasm through pores; the perinuclear area, furthermore, enlarges (between the two lamellae of the nuclear membrane) to become the cisternae of the endoplasmic reticulum (cf. also the electron microscopic photograph of Fig. 48). Several mitochondria are almost engulfed by the endoplasmic reticulum. The bold arrows indicate transport activity. (After Siekewitz)

Figs. 47 and 48 from Siekewitz, "Cell Structure and Metabolic Regulation" (Ciba Foundation Symposium), Churchill, London, 1959.

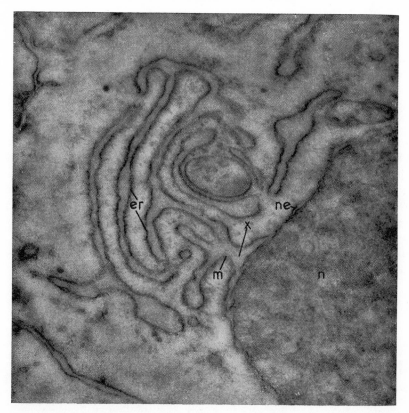

FIG. 48. Electron microscopic photograph of a cell nucleus with a connection to the endoplasmic reticulum at "X". n = nucleus; ne = nuclear membrane with perinuclear space; m = membrane of the endoplasmic reticulum (= er). Enlargement: 27,000-fold. (Photograph by K. R. Porster)

tain insects (flies, mosquitoes). There, highly stained crossbands can be distinguished from weakly stained interbands. The crossbands consist of deoxyribonucleic acids (shown by Feulgen staining), basic and nonbasic proteins, whereas the interbands contain only nonbasic protein (Fig. 46). The crossbands correspond to the gene loci. Ribonucleic acid is present only in small amounts, being concentrated in the nucleolus.

The nuclear content of a normal cell (without giant chromosomes) does not reveal any details with the electron microscope; it consists merely of granular or fibrillar structures. Deoxyribonucleic acid usually cannot be distinguished. The nuclear membrane consists of two lamellae which enclose the so-called perinuclear space. The latter is in contact with the cisternae of the ergastoplasm (see below). In the nuclear membranes pores can be seen that are usually closed by a very fragile diaphragm.

Evidence from investigation on giant chromosomes shows that ribonucleic acid is synthesized at various times at the gene loci (Beermann). Protein is accumulated

simultaneously at the same sites. It is probable (but not proved yet) that this ribonucleic acid migrates through the pores of the nuclear membrane and into the cytoplasm and becomes attached to the endoplasmic reticulum (see below). This process
agrees well with the concept of transfer of genetic information. According to that
concept, deoxyribonucleic acid imparts a certain pattern to the newly synthesized
messenger RNA; this pattern then becomes the template (or matrix) for the synthesis of definite and specific proteins, e.g. an enzyme (cf. Chapt. VII).

The transition of an inactive gene to the functional state may be accompanied,
in the giant chromosomes, by a puffing of the corresponding crossbands (the so-
called puffing phenomenon). Ribonucleic acid is being synthesized at the sites of
puffing. Usually only a relatively small number of genes is activated; it is largely a
matter of conjecture as to what mechanism might regulate the activity of genes.
In insects, however, it was possible to provoke puffing of a certain gene locus by
administration of a hormone (Clever and Karlson). This observation points to one
mechanism by which the activity of genes could be controlled by factors from the
cytoplasm.

## 2. The Endoplasmic Reticulum

This cellular structure, closely related to the nucleus, consists of two components;
a membrane and small granula. With the electron microscope a three-dimensional
network of tubules and globules with a diameter of 100–150 m$\mu$ can be distinguished.
The interior (cisternae of the ergastoplasm) of these structures is encased in a membrane, on the outside of which are attached small granula with a diameter of 15
m$\mu$. The granula are the ribosomes, a subdivision of the microsomes (cf. Fig. 47
and 48). The interior appears to be connected with the perinuclear space, and
sometimes also with the extracellular space (through pores in the cell surface). The
endoplasmic reticulum is very well developed in tissues with active protein synthesis, e.g. in exocrine cells of the pancreas.

*The cisternae* (enclosed spaces) of the endoplasmic reticulum possibly play a role
in the exchange of material between the cell and the extracellular fluid. It seems
entirely possible that this exchange of material occurs not only by diffusion and
active transport, but also according to the principles of phagocytosis: A small area
of the cellular membrane engulfs the material, forming a vacuole, which is then
transported to the interior of the cell. The cellular membrane re-forms, the entering
vacuole disintegrates within the cell, and its content mixes with the cytoplasm. The
process is properly called pinocytosis. In the opposite direction, small portions of
the membrane of the endoplasmic reticulum can leave the cell and spill their content to the exterior.

In the process of homogenization the fine membranes of the ergastoplasm are
torn apart, and with differential centrifugation a fraction called the *microsomal
fraction* can be obtained which contains the fragments of this cytoplasmic structure

FIG. 49. Ribosomes of a bacterial cell (*E. coli*), isolated by centrifugation. Enlargement: 100,000-fold. (Photograph by Dr. Hofschneider)

(originally defined as that fraction which can be sedimented in the ultracentrifuge at forces of 100,000 G). In these "microsomes" one can find chiefly hydroxylating enzymes. They also contain a special cytochrome, *cytochrome $b_5$*, and a $NADH_2$-cytochrome $b_5$ reductase (a flavoprotein). The biologic function of this "microsomal redox chain" is still unknown.

**Ribosomes,** often called ribonucleoprotein particles, have become popular as the site of protein biosynthesis. Figure 49 is an electron micrograph of such particles. Their particle weight is about 3 million; in $Mg^{++}$-free solutions they dissociate to two subunits of 1 and 2 million particle weight which reaggregate on addition of $Mg^{++}$. (Bacterial ribosomes are a little smaller; 2.8 million, with corresponding subunits.) Each subunit contains one molecule of RNA with molecular weights of 600,000 and 1,200,000, respectively. Other constituents are basic proteins and low molecular weight bases whose function might well be to neutralize the nucleic acids. Ribosomes are not able to synthesize protein until they are charged with messenger RNA (cf. "Protein Biosynthesis," Chapt. VII-6).

**Lysosomes** are particles of a size between that of microsomes and mitochondria and are shaped like grana or vacuoles (de Duve). They contain many hydrolases: phosphatases, cathepsin (i.e. a protease), ribonuclease, $\beta$-glucuronidase, and perhaps others. It is assumed that these hydrolases are in a manner "wrapped up" there and separated from their substrates. Only after the membrane of the lysosomes is disrupted can the hydrolases enter the cytoplasm and exercise their specific functions. This may conceivably occur only under conditions of cytolysis.

## 3. Mitochondria

**Structure.** The mitochondria are the most thoroughly studied of the cell components. They can be seen in the light microscope as elongated oval bodies of varying sizes. A thin section in the electron microscope reveals a three-layered membrane and individual protrusions of the membrane jutting into the interior, the so-called *cristae mitochondriales*. These internal protuberances are commonly in the shape of stemmed leaves, but tubular structures are also found. The interior structure varies considerably: On one hand, it depends on the physiological state; on the other, it differs from organ to organ. As a general rule, mitochondria are full of lamellae, if their main job is respiration and energy production (as, for example, in aerobically working muscles). But they have fewer internal membranes (as in liver cells) if they contain many enzymes with synthetic tasks (Vogell and Klingenberg).

Mitochondria are rich in lipids, especially in phospholipids and isoprenoid lipids. These substances are structural components of the membrane and probably represent the middle layer, whereas the outside and inside lamellae consist of protein.

Mitochondria are highly sensitive toward osmotic changes; they are best isolated in hypertonic media (usually 0.25 $M$ sucrose).

**Biochemical Function.** Mitochondria contain numerous enzyme systems. First, we may mention the respiratory chain. Though cytochrome is also found outside of mitochondria, the cytochrome oxidase is located exclusively within them. The enzyme is also found in mitochondrial fragments. Damage to the particles, however, first impairs oxidative phosphorylation rather than oxidation itself, and eventually abolishes it completely. The decrease of phosphorylation parallels the degree of destruction of the *cristae mitochondriales*, whose structural integrity seems to be a requirement for this process. From partially destroyed mitochondria, particles have been centrifuged off which still contain parts of the respiratory chain and which have been named by D. E. Green "electron-transport particles." These particles are composed of the following enzymes: The flavoproteins succinate dehydrogenase and $NADH_2$-oxidase, the cytochromes b, c (and $c_1$), and a, and several lipoproteins and ubiquinone. Current concepts emphasize the importance of the spatial arrangement of the water-soluble lipoprotein enzymes in the membrane layers for the proper functioning of the respiratory chain and for oxidative phosphorylation.

**Regulation of Respiration within Mitochondria.** With normal metabolic activity the respiratory chain is not utilized to the limits of its capacity. This has been observed when certain additions to mitochondrial preparations were employed to stimulate respiration. Particularly effective in this regard have been the so-called uncoupling agents, which separate the process of phosphorylation from that of electron transport (and in effect eliminate phosphorylation). Some popular uncoupling agents are dinitrophenol, dicumarol and thyroxine. From these and other observations, it has been concluded that the limiting factor is not electron transport, but rather phosphorylation, or more specifically, the restricted supply of adenosine diphosphate (ADP) (cf. also Chapt. X-4, last paragraph).

The mechanism just described is self-regulatory. If much ATP is consumed in the cell, e.g. for muscle contraction or synthetic activity, then ADP is released in large

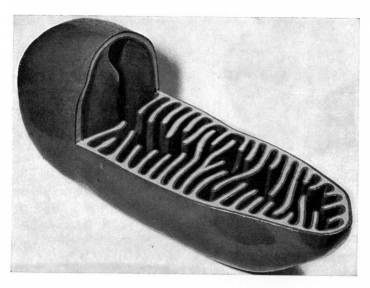

FIG. 50. Model of a mitochondrion, reconstructed according to electron optical photographs. The individual leaves inside are the "cristae mitochondriales" (cf. Fig. 51).

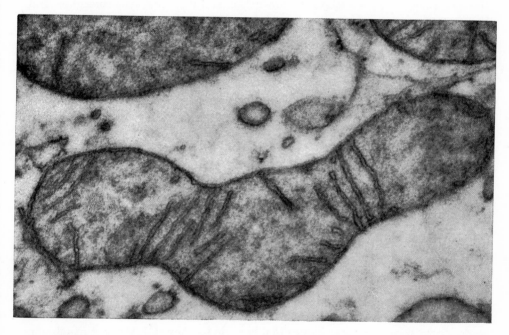

FIG. 51. Electron optical representation of a mitochondrion from human kidney tissue. Several cristae have been sectioned and are easily recognizable. Enlargement: 40,000–fold.

Figs. 50 and 51 taken from A. Thiel, *Deut. med. Wochschr.*, **84,** 2038 (1959).

quantities; the respiratory chain uses this ADP to stimulate phosphorylation, and hence respiration.

Phosphate is not the only possible limiting factor of respiration. A deficiency of substrate or of oxygen also poses limits. Limitation by oxygen, however, approaches pathologic conditions. Finally, many metabolic processes (including respiration) are regulated by hormones. But hormonal regulation implies a change in course, a transition to another position of the dynamic equilibrium (to another steady state), rather than the maintenance of the existing dynamic equilibrium (cf. Chapt. XX–10, carbohydrate metabolism; Chapt. XX–4, thyroxine).

**The "Cyclophorase" System.** Besides the electron transport chain and the system for ATP production, the mitochondria also contain the citrate cycle. A few of its enzymes may be found in the "cytoplasm," but the intact cycle operates only within the mitochondria. Green has called this multi-enzyme system "cyclophorase." It is no accident that the citrate cycle and the respiratory chain are in such close proximity, because the citrate cycle can operate continuously only when $NADH_2$ is reoxidized through the respiratory chain.

The enzymes connected with fatty acid breakdown also are found in the mitochondria. One structural principle can be derived from the observation that both the formation of active acetate by $\beta$-oxidation and its subsequent consumption in the citrate cycle take place in the same subcellular particle, the mitochondrion.

# 4. The Cytoplasm

The cytoplasm or "hyaloplasm" (an expression used in electron microscopy) contains no discernible structures. Possibly it is pervaded by extremely fine fibrils that still defy resolution in the electron microscope. The cytoplasm is generally defined as the unstructured, "soluble" portion of the cell. The "supernatant" that remains after centrifugation of the particulate fraction of a homogenate contains all the enzymes and substrates of the cytoplasm.

The content of the endoplasmic reticulum becomes intermixed, however, with the original cytoplasm during the preparation of the soluble fraction in the centrifuge. With present biochemical methodology it is impossible to investigate these two cellular compartments separately. Often, however, especially the interaction between mitochondria and cytoplasm is important, in which case the "soluble fraction" is taken as the "hyaloplasm," undifferentiated electron microscopically.

**Enzymes.** The soluble fraction of the cell homogenate contains all the enzymes of glycolysis. Every observation supports the fact that the Embden-Meyerhof pathway operates here. The possibility cannot be excluded, however, that the membranes of the endoplasmic reticulum have many enzymes of glycolysis adsorbed to themselves and that some enzymic activity may be anchored even within the membranes. If this is the case, then glycolysis is also structure-bound.

Glycolytic products can penetrate to the interior of the mitochondria; frequently pyruvate will be captured and subjected to oxidative decarboxylation. In special tissues (such as the flight muscle of locusts), it is reported (Bücher and Zebe), the system dihydroxyacetone phosphate $\rightleftharpoons$ glycerol phosphate appears to function as a hydrogen transfer system between cytoplasm and mitochondria. The system acetoacetate $\rightleftharpoons$ $\beta$-hydroxybutyrate has also been proposed for hydrogen exchange. The usual coenzymes $NADH_2$ and $NADPH_2$ apparently cannot shuttle unhindered between the two compartments; but they are probably able to donate their hydrogen to the mitochondrial enzymes in a manner still unknown.

**The Pasteur Effect.** It is an old observation that cells, e.g. of muscle or yeast, transform much glucose (to lactate or ethanol) under anaerobic conditions. If oxygen is supplied, however, then not only is anaerobic glycolysis inhibited, but much less glucose actually enters the Embden-Meyerhof pathway. Evidently, the oxidative processes of mitochondria exert some influence back on the cytoplasm. This seems rather "sensible" physiologically, since in aerobiosis a great quantity of ATP is produced in the respiratory chain and the demands for energy can well be met with less substrate. However, this does not explain the mechanism responsible for the effect, which is known as the "Pasteur effect."

Some have attempted to explain the Pasteur effect on the basis of concentration changes of inorganic phosphate and ATP; others have postulated a direct influence on the enzymes. So far, the question remains unsolved.

## 5. Significance of the Compartments

The results and problems discussed in the preceding section indicate that permeability and transport phenomena are very significant for the activity within the cell. The electron microscopic picture actually can be interpreted to mean that membranes with the largest possible surfaces are formed in the cell. The purpose is to facilitate transport processes and at the same time to erect permeability barriers that permit a regulated operation of the many interacting enzymic reactions. This principle of spatial arrangement and order among interacting enzymes is realized very strikingly by the mitochondrion, the "chemical factory of the cell," and applied very efficiently by the respiratory chain.

Our knowledge in this field is still very fragmentary. Modern methods of cell fractionation have permitted the initial inventory-taking of the distribution of enzymes. We have, at best, some notions about the interrelationship of enzymes. Hopkins defined life as "a dynamic equilibrium in a polyphasic system." Enzymology has provided much understanding of the first part—the reactions and dynamic equilibria—the electron microscope has shown us just *how* polyphasic the system is. Now the two areas of knowledge must be bridged; the beginning has been made, but much remains to be done.

BIBLIOGRAPHY

H. R. V. Arnstein, The structure and function of ribosomes in protein biosynthesis, *Ann. Rept. Chem. Soc., London* **60,** 512–528 (1963).

G. H. Bourne, "Division of Labor in Cells," 248 pp., Academic Press, New York, 1962.

J. Brachet and A. E. Mirsky, editors, "The Cell," 6 vols., Academic Press, New York, 1959–1964.

"Regulation of Cell Metabolism," Ciba Foundation Symposium, Churchill, London, 1959.

"Functional and Morphological Organisation of the Cell," Wissenschaftliche Konferenz der Gesellschaft deutscher Naturforscher und Ärzte, Springer Verlag, Berlin, 1963.

*Scientific American,* **205** No. 3, (1961), "The Living Cell"; the entire issue is devoted to this general topic.

K. E. Wohlfarth–Bottermann, Basic elements of cell structure, *Naturwissenschaften,* **50,** 237–249 (1963).

# CHAPTER XX

# Hormones

## 1. Principle of Hormonal Regulation

The regulation of biochemical processes *within* the cell usually follows two principles: feedback by limiting the reactants (e.g. ADP) and compartmentalization of the cell. A *multicellular* organism with organs has in addition neural and humoral control mechanisms.

It is difficult to decide which of these principles is the older phylogenetically. Even some unicellular organisms are known to be equipped with acetylcholine and epinephrine. Perhaps both mechanisms developed from one common precursor mechanism.

Humoral or hormonal control means that peripheral tissue is influenced by substances with specific effects. These active substances are formed in specialized glands or tissues (endocrine glands) and secreted into the blood stream. This can also be called *"internal secretion"*; the substances produced by endocrine (or endosecretory) glands are the *hormones*.

The concept *hormone* has been applied more or less broadly in the past. A hundred years ago, C. Bernard coined the term "internal secretion" to describe the production of glucose by the liver. The example has been dropped, but the term has been kept. The situation is similar with Starling's "secretin," which occasioned the formulation of the term *hormone*. Secretin is not a hormone of the endocrine glands, but rather one of the tissue hormones, which today constitute a separate group. A critical discussion of the hormonal concept is given by Verzar.[1]

Isolation of Hormones is difficult because they always occur in minute amounts. Often a 100,000- to 1,000,000-fold enrichment of the biologic material is required before the active substance can be crystallized. A workable biologic assay is needed for the isolation, because initially the hormone can be recognized only by its activity, and the enrichment procedure is pursued by following the rise in activity.

---

[1] F. Verzar, "Lehrbuch der inneren Sekretion," Liestal, Ars medici Lüdin, 609 pp., Basel, 1948.

The isolation and elucidation of structure of the steroid hormones was performed mainly by Butenandt, Doisy, Kendall, and Reichstein. Thyroxine was isolated by Kendall and its constitution determined by Harington. Banting and Best first prepared pure insulin. The hypophyseal hormones have been enriched and finally isolated in pure form chiefly by Evans and Li.

**The Principle of the Master Gland.** Several hypophyseal ( = pituitary) hormones act on "peripheral" endocrine glands. The activity of the hypophysis is itself regulated by yet another hormone,[2] so that there evidently exists a hierarchy of hormone glands, which comprises three levels in the case of the hypophyseal-adrenocortical system (cf. the accompanying diagram). Certain centers of the midbrain elaborate a neurosecretion which travels through the pituitary stalk to the anterior lobe of the hypophysis, where it stimulates the release of the adrenocorticotropic hormone (ACTH). ACTH is itself a glandotropic hormone; its target is the adrenal cortex, which is stimulated to produce increased amounts of the so-called corticosteroids and to release them to the blood circulation. A feedback system controls the master gland, the hypophysis, in that its activity is adjusted by the amount of circulating peripheral hormone; an increase of the level of corticosteroids inhibits the activity of the hypophysis.

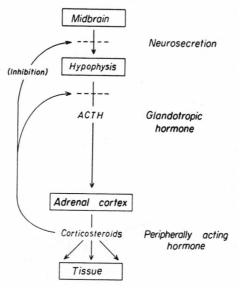

**Metabolism of Hormones.** Hormones are regulatory substances; they act in trace amounts. Being endogenous substances, they are produced by the organism itself. This is in contrast to the vitamins, which also are effective in very small amounts, but which must be supplied from the environment. A few glands (e.g. thyroid) store some of the hormones that they produce; others, however, release their hormones into the circulation at the same rate at which they form them (e.g. the adrenal cortex).

---

[2] The principle of the "master gland" can be detected at rather early stages of phylogenesis; several endocrine glands of insects are guided by the endocrine activity of certain nerve cells (neurosecretion; cf. Sections 9 and 12).

Regulation is of course practicable only if the hormones can be removed again from the blood, for otherwise the organism would soon be flooded with hormones. The study of the biochemical pathways of synthesis and degradation of hormones is an intriguing aspect of intermediary metabolism.

**Mode of Action of Hormones.**[3] Another interesting chapter in biochemistry is the manner in which hormones exert their activity. As a chemical substance, a hormone can have only chemical effects; it must influence some chemical processes. The observed "physiologic effects" usually appear much later, as a consequence of the primary chemical effect.

The former theory that the primary effect consists in a direct interaction with certain enzymes (perhaps in the manner that vitamins act as components of co-enzymes) has not been upheld for most hormones. Examples of quick responding metabolic regulation, such as the control of blood glucose, depend in all likelihood on permeability changes of cell membranes. Another mechanism of action is seen in the stimulation of specific gene loci (Clever and Karlson). This promotes the production of *messenger RNA* and ultimately the synthesis of specific enzymes. The mechanism resembles that of enzyme induction in bacteria (cf. Fig. 52, and also Chapt. VII-7).

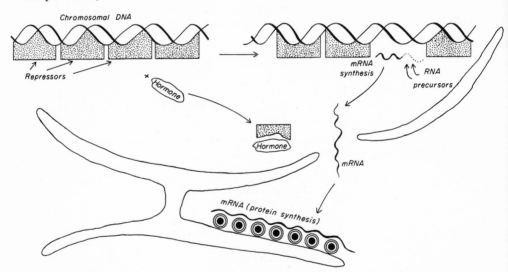

FIG. 52. Diagram of the action of hormones by enzyme induction. At left is shown chromosomal DNA covered with repressors. The hormone traps a repressor, and the corresponding gene starts to produce messenger RNA (m-RNA). m-RNA, in turn, migrates into the cytoplasm and directs the synthesis of the corresponding protein. (According to Karlson, modified.)

---

[3] For a broader treatment, see P. Karlson, New concepts on the mode of action of hormones, *Perspectives Biol. Med.*, **6,** 203 (1963).

**Classification of Hormones.** Depending upon their chemical constitutions and their patterns of biosynthesis, three groups of hormones can be distinguished: (1) Steroid hormones, (2) Amino acid-derived hormones, and (3) Peptide and protein hormones. Table XVIII gives a survey of known hormones and their effects.

In subsequent sections the individual hormones will be discussed with reference to their biogenesis and metabolism and their physiological effects will be briefly characterized. Finally, a few examples will be given of hormonal regulation in which several hormones cooperate.

A number of hormones including the adrenocortical hormones, are steroids (see Table XVIII). The chemistry of steroids has already been discussed briefly. With the exception of the follicular hormone estrone, all steroid hormones have an $\alpha,\beta$-unsaturated keto group in ring A.

## 2. Adrenocortical Hormones

All adrenocortical hormones have 21 C atoms. Besides the unsaturated keto group in position 3, which is never absent, they also have a keto and an alcohol group in the side chain (the so-called ketol group).

The *biogenesis* proceeds from progesterone (cf. Chapt. XIV-6). Hydroxylases mediate the introduction of hydroxyl groups into the steroid skeleton in the following order: the 17-position, the 21-position, and the 11$\beta$-position. In addition to the 11$\beta$-hydroxy compounds corticosterone and cortisol, the 11-keto analogs 11-dehydrocorticosterone and cortisone are also found. The gland, however, elaborates predominantly 11-hydroxy compounds. Out of the multiplicity of adrenocortical steroids found in the gland, only the three compounds cortisol, corticosterone, and aldosterone can be considered true hormones of the adrenal cortex. The formulas of the three hormones are shown again here; the *per diem* production in man is indicated along with the formulas:

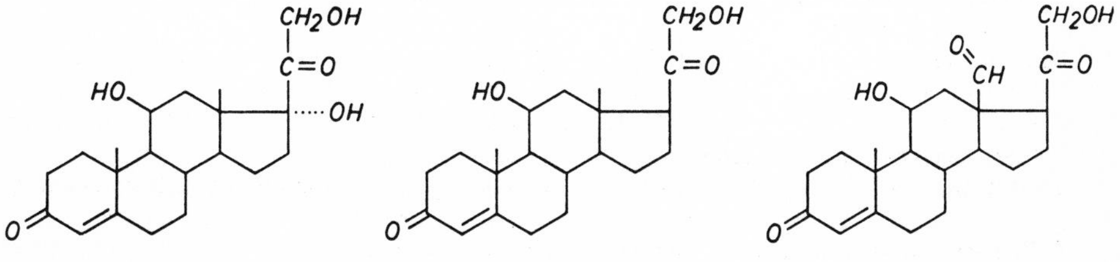

| Cortisol | Corticosterone | Aldosterone |
| --- | --- | --- |
| Daily release: 10 - 20mg | 3mg | 0.3mg |

Although the adrenal cortex contains very little hormone, its synthetic capabilities are extensive. It secretes several times its total content into the blood every minute; the entire amount of corticosteroid hormones circulating in the human

TABLE XVIII
HORMONES OF THE ENDOCRINE GLANDS OF VERTEBRATES

| Hormone | Abbreviation | Gland Producing the Hormone | Effect |
|---|---|---|---|
| **Steroid hormones** | | | |
| Corticosteroids | — | Adrenal cortex | Mineral balance: $Na^+$ retention Metabolism: Gluconeogenesis |
| Progesterone | — | Ovary (corpus luteum) | Proliferation of the uterine mucosa (secretory phase) |
| Estradiol | — | Ovary (follicles) | Proliferation of the uterine mucosa (estrus). |
| Testosterone | — | Testes (interstitial cells) | Maintenance of the accessory glands of the genital tract and secondary sex characteristics |
| **Amino acid–derived hormones** | | | |
| Thyroxine | Thx, T-4 | Thyroid gland | Increase of basal metabolic rate; development |
| Epinephrine (adrenalin) | — | Adrenal medulla | Glycogen breakdown |
| Melatonin | — | Pineal gland | Contraction of melanophores |
| **Peptide and protein hormones** | | | |
| Relaxin | — | Ovary | Relaxation of pelvic ligaments during pregnancy |
| Parathyroid hormone (parathormone) | — | Parathyroid gland | $Ca^{++}$ mobilization |
| Insulin | — | Pancreas | Lowering of blood sugar level |
| Glucagon | — | Pancreas | Raising of blood sugar level |
| Ocytocin | — | Pituitary gland, posterior lobe | Contraction of uterus |
| Vasopressin | — | Pituitary gland, posterior lobe | Antidiuretic action |
| Melanotropin (melanocyte-stimulating hormone; intermedin) | MSH | Pituitary gland, middle lobe | Dilation of melanophores |
| Somatotropin (growth hormone) | STH | Pituitary gland, anterior lobe | Growth and metabolism |
| Corticotropin (adrenocorticotropic hormone) | ACTH | Pituitary gland, anterior lobe | Stimulation of the adrenal cortex |
| Thyrotropin | TSH | Pituitary gland, anterior lobe | Stimulation of thyroid gland |
| Follicle-stimulating hormone | FSH | Pituitary gland, anterior lobe | Stimulation of production of estradiol in ovary |
| Luteinizing hormone (interstitial cell–stimulating hormone) | LH (or ICSH) | Pituitary gland, anterior lobe | Stimulation of production of sex hormones |
| Luteo-mammotropic hormone (Luteotropin, prolactin) | LTH (LMTH) | Pituitary gland, anterior lobe | Stimulation of mammary gland and of corpora lutea |
| Gonadotropin (Chorionic gonadotropin) | (HCG) | Placenta | Similar to LH |

organism is renewed completely every two to three hours. This synthetic activity is matched by an equally active breakdown in the liver, which proceeds partly to the tetrahydro compounds (saturated ring A, $3\alpha$-ol) and partly to the 17-keto steroids (cf. Chapt. XIV–6). It should be recalled that hormonal regulation entails both production of the active substance and its inactivation and removal from circulation.

**Biologic Significance of the Adrenal Cortex.** The adrenocortical hormones constitute some of the most vital substances. Extirpation of the adrenal gland in experimental animals is followed by most serious disturbances and, in a few days, by death. Among other things, the metabolism of electrolytes is unbalanced (increased $Na^+$ excretion). This effect can be reversed by administration of adrenocortical hormones, some of which (especially aldosterone) effect the retention of sodium and excretion of potassium (cf. Chapt. XXI–5).

Besides the *mineralcorticoid* effect on the electrolyte metabolism, the adrenocortical hormones also influence the metabolism of glucose by promoting glycogen formation in the liver, especially from protein. This effect is termed the *glucocorticoid* effect and is manifested especially by the $11\beta$-hydroxy compounds. Emphasizing the breakdown of protein, this effect is also called the *catabolic effect*. The mechanism of this hormone action seems to involve the *de novo* formation of more enzymes of amino acid metabolism, e.g., tyrosine $\alpha$-ketoglutarate transaminase, tryptophan pyrrolase, etc. (cf. "Enzyme Induction," Chapt. VII–7).

It is not possible, however, to separate the effects very clearly; one cannot ascribe the glucocorticoid effect alone to one hormone and the mineralcorticoid effect alone to another. But within the range of physiological concentrations, aldosterone appears to regulate electrolyte balance, and cortisol, gluconeogenesis.

The adrenocortical hormones have been highly effective drugs in many diseases (arthritis, skin disorders, inflammations). Modification of the chemical structure, particularly by introduction of fluoro or methyl groups, has provided substances with different action spectra and with much greater effectiveness than the natural hormones. From the multitude of such compounds we present the following two formulas. Both substances have strong anti-inflammatory properties, but relatively low mineral-corticoid effects.

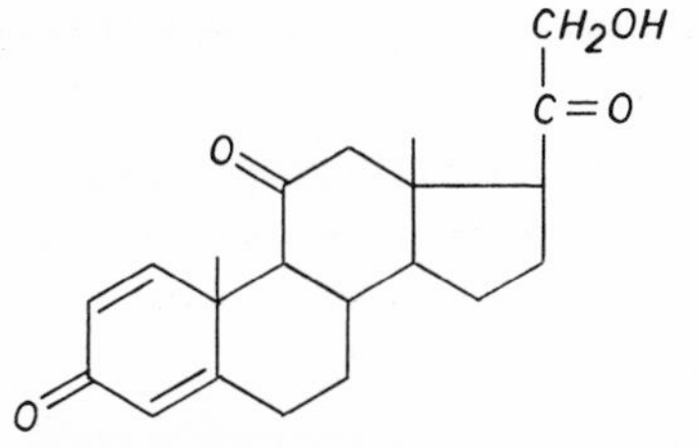

*Prednisone* 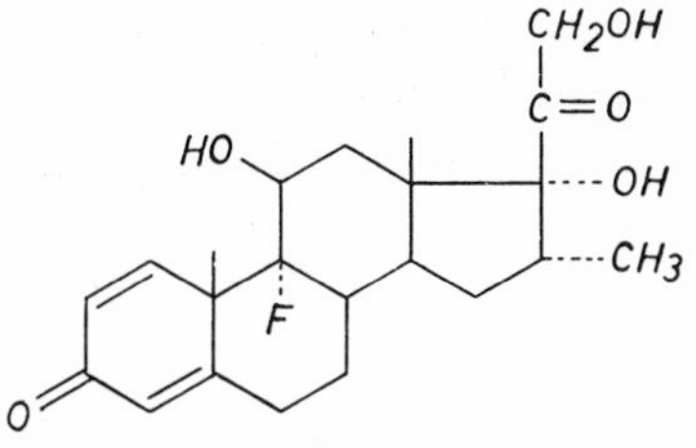          *Dexamethasone*

# 3. Gonadal Hormones

**Male Sex Hormones** (androgenic hormones). The true testicular hormone is *testosterone* ($\Delta^4$-androstene-17$\beta$-ol-3-one), formed by the interstitial cells of the testicular tissue from 17-hydroxyprogesterone (cf. Chapt. XIV–6).

Hormones with androgenic activity are produced not only by the testes, but by the adrenal cortex as well, e.g. *androstenedione* and *11-hydroxyandrostenedione*. Under certain conditions, such as tumor of the adrenal cortex, the androgen production may rise greatly; in women this causes the pathologic condition known as virilism.

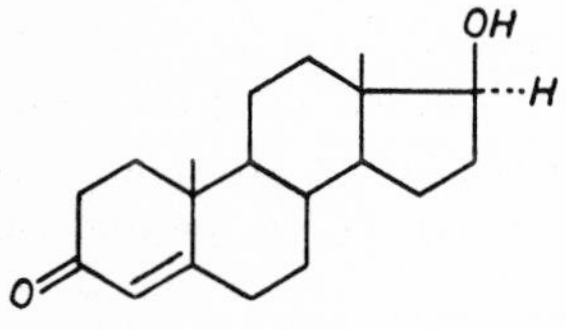

Testosterone 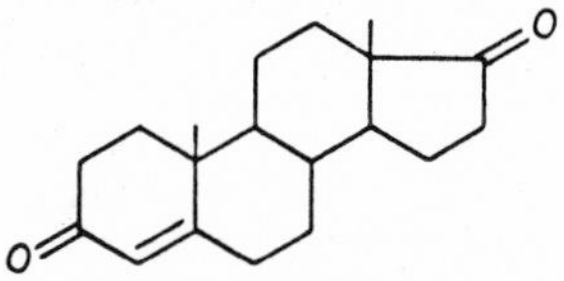      Androstenedione 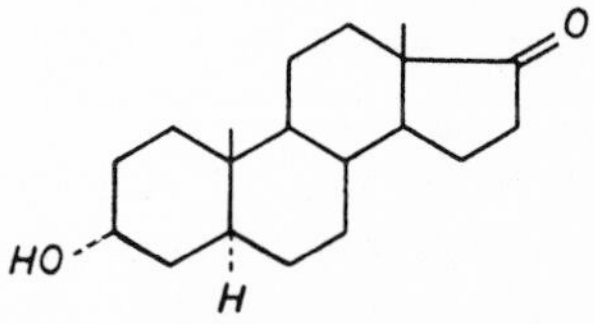      Androsterone

In order to be *excreted*, testosterone is converted into androsterone and 5$\beta$-androstanolone, both of which can be detected in urine. Androsterone, which retains considerable androgenic activity, was the first androgen to be isolated in pure form (Butenandt).

*Biologic Function.* The effects of castration have long been known and need not be listed here. The reversal of these effects by transplantation is a classical experiment from the beginning of hormone research (Berthold 1849). Androgens effect the development of secondary sex characteristics; thus the changes during puberty depend on testosterone. In the adult male organism the continuous production of the hormone is necessary for the maturation of sperm and the activity of the accessory glands of the genital tract.

Beyond this specific effect on the genital tract, the androgens also have a general effect on metabolism. They promote protein synthesis and elevate nitrogen retention. This *anabolic effect* is also found with several steroids that have been derived by modification of the natural hormone. These derivatives lack androgenic properties, for example, *1-methyl-$\Delta^1$-androstenolone*. "Anabolic steroids" are very useful therapeutically.

**Female Sex Hormones.** The female organism produces two physiologically distinct sex hormones, the estrogens (follicular hormones) and the gestagens (progestins; corpus luteum hormones).

*Estrogens* are characterized chemically by their aromatic ring. Only one substituent can be attached to each C atom of an aromatic ring; the angular methyl group at C-10, present in all other steroids, is therefore absent here. The oxygen function at C-3 is a *phenolic OH group*, since ring A is aromatic.

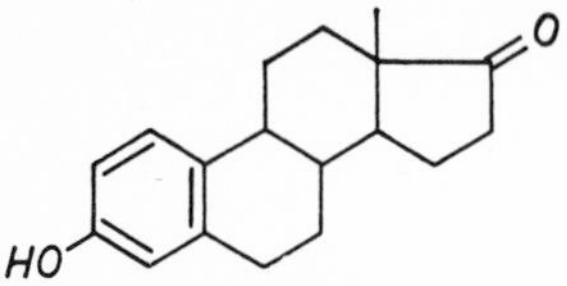

Estrone 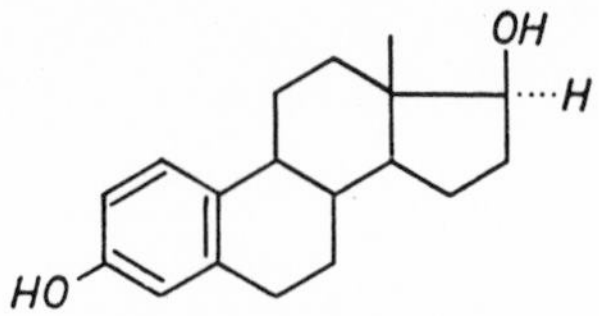      Estradiol 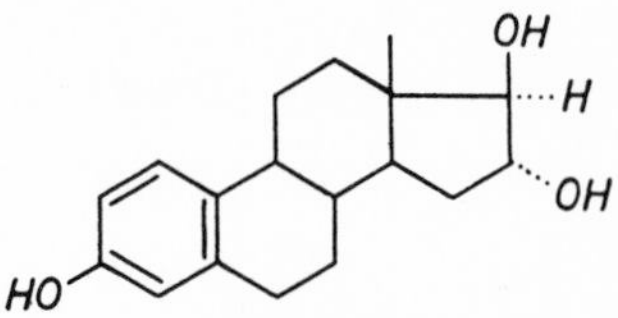      Estriol

The naturally occurring estrogens are *estradiol-3,17β*; *estrone* (with a keto group at C-17); and *estriol-3,16α,17β*. The follicles contain chiefly estradiol, the true estrogen. In the placenta an enzyme has been found which reduces estrone to estradiol with NADPH$_2$ but which dehydrogenates estradiol to estrone with NAD. The net result of the two reactions is a "transhydrogenase effect": NADPH$_2$ + NAD $\rightleftharpoons$ NADP + NADH$_2$, and this effect was once assumed to be the biochemical mode of action of estradiol. The assumption could not be substantiated however. The principal effect of estradiol is on the biosynthesis of nucleic acids and proteins; perhaps certain genes are activated first.

The biogenesis of estrogens has been discussed in Chapt. XIV-6. The precursor is testosterone, which is hydroxylated at C-19; this angular group is then lost in the course of aromatization of ring A.

Little is known about the inactivation of estrogens. A certain fraction is oxidized in the liver and bound to protein; while another portion is excreted in urine as sulfates or glucuronides.

*Physiological Effects.* The follicular hormone (estrogen) is responsible primarily for the regular course of the genital cycles, which are the estrus cycles (assay procedures on laboratory animals) or the menstrual cycles (in man and monkeys). Estrone causes uterine mucosa to proliferate. During the cycle it acts in conjunction with progesterone and the hypophyseal hormones (cf. also Section 11.)

*Gestagens* (corpus luteum hormones, pregnancy hormones). The principal hormone of the corpus luteum is *progesterone*, a steroid that has already been mentioned as a starting material for the biosynthesis of adrenocortical hormones. It is formed in the corpus luteum and in the placenta from cholesterol by a shortening of the side chain and dehydrogenation of the 3β-OH group. The double bond of cholesterol then migrates so as to be in conjugation with the keto group. In addition to progesterone, the two *pregnenolones* (20α-OH and 20β-OH) have been found; both are biologically active.

Progesterone is produced only during certain phases of menstruation and during pregnancy. Excretion products in urine are the glucuronides of pregnanediol and some stereoisomers thereof; as in the case of the adrenal corticoids, inactivation is accomplished by reduction of ring A.

Progesterone          Pregnanediol

*The Biologic Function* of progesterone consists in the regulation of the reproductive organs. In the human it is formed after the rupture of the follicle and among

other things it prepares the uterine mucosa for the deposition of the fertilized ovum
(secretory phase). Its prime function is to maintain pregnancy. The hormonal
regulation of the menstrual cycle will be discussed as a separate topic in Section 11.

## 4. Thyroid Hormones

**Thyroxine and Triiodothyronine.** Thyroxine is one of the earliest recognized hormones (isolation in 1915 by Kendall; determination of structure and synthesis in
1925 by Harington). It is an iodine-containing aromatic amino acid. The non-
iodinated parent compound of thyroxine is called *thyronine*. The unusual structural
feature is the diphenyl ether group. Iodine atoms may be substituted at the positions 3, 5, 3', 5'. A few diiodo- and triiodothyronines have physiological significance,
especially *3,5,3'-triiodothyronine*, which is about five times as active as *thyroxine*
itself.

Thyronine                                              Thyroxine

*Biosynthesis.* Thyroxine is formed in the thyroid gland (Greek, *thyreoides* =
shield-shaped) from protein-bound tyrosine (Greek, *tyros* = cheese), which is
iodinated first. Iodine ions are removed from blood (against a concentration gradient), oxidized to elemental iodine, and inserted into the tyrosine radical. Thyronine seems to be formed with particular ease; in fact, it arises nonenzymically from
iodinated protein or iodinated tyrosine peptides. The reaction probably proceeds
*via* semiquinone radicals as shown on page 341.

The iodine-containing protein is called *"thyroglobulin."*

Depending on the requirements of the organism or the stimulation of the gland
by the thyrotropic hormone (see below), thyroglobulin is broken down to a lesser
or greater extent and thyroxine (or triiodothyronine) is secreted into the blood
stream. The entire activity of the thyroid gland can be represented schematically,
as shown in Fig. 53.

Thyroxine and triiodothyronine can be synthesized by the organism only when sufficient iodine
is supplied in the diet. Iodine therefore is one of the vital trace elements (for a list of these see
Chapt. XXII-2) whose function is understood. If too little iodine is present in the diet, especially
in drinking water and table salt (as, for example, in remote areas of the Alps), the result is goiter.
The tissue of the thyroid gland hypertrophies in order to compensate as well as possible for the
underproduction of thyroxine.

**Antithyroid Substances.** Various substances are able to interfere with the normal
process of thyroxine synthesis. First of all, several univalent anions (e.g. thio-

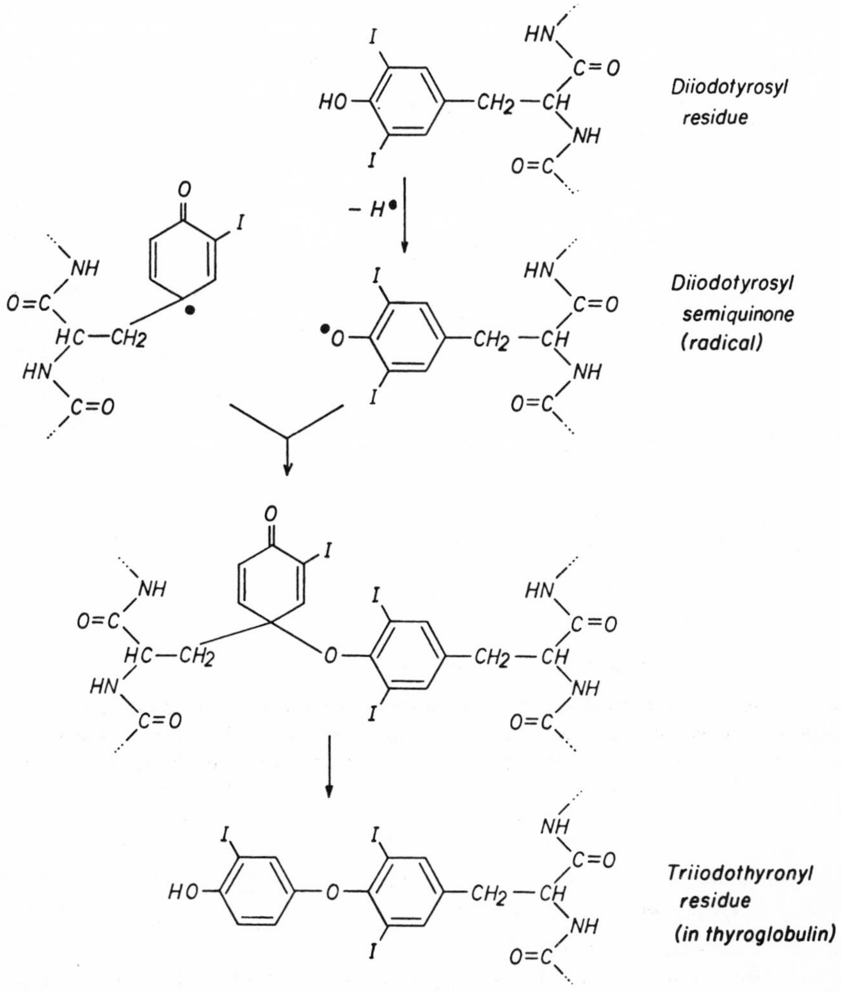

*Diiodotyrosyl residue*

*Diiodotyrosyl semiquinone (radical)*

*Triiodothyronyl residue (in thyroglobulin)*

cyanate, nitrate, chlorate, iodate) block the active transport of iodine and thus prevent its accumulation. A second important group of antithyroid substances includes the goiterogenic, sulfur-containing compounds found in certain plants (e.g. cabbage). These compounds damage the thyroid gland of rabbits that are fed exclusively on cabbage. Numerous substances of this type have been synthesized for pharmaceutical application in hyperthyroidism. Their primary effect is to inhibit the incorporation of iodine into organic compounds; but they also interfere with iodine uptake. Perhaps a specific enzyme, an iodine oxidase, is poisoned. Finally, some substances appear to compete with tyrosine for the available iodine, e.g. *p*-aminosalicylic acid, many sulfonamides, and simple phenols, such as resorcinol, etc.

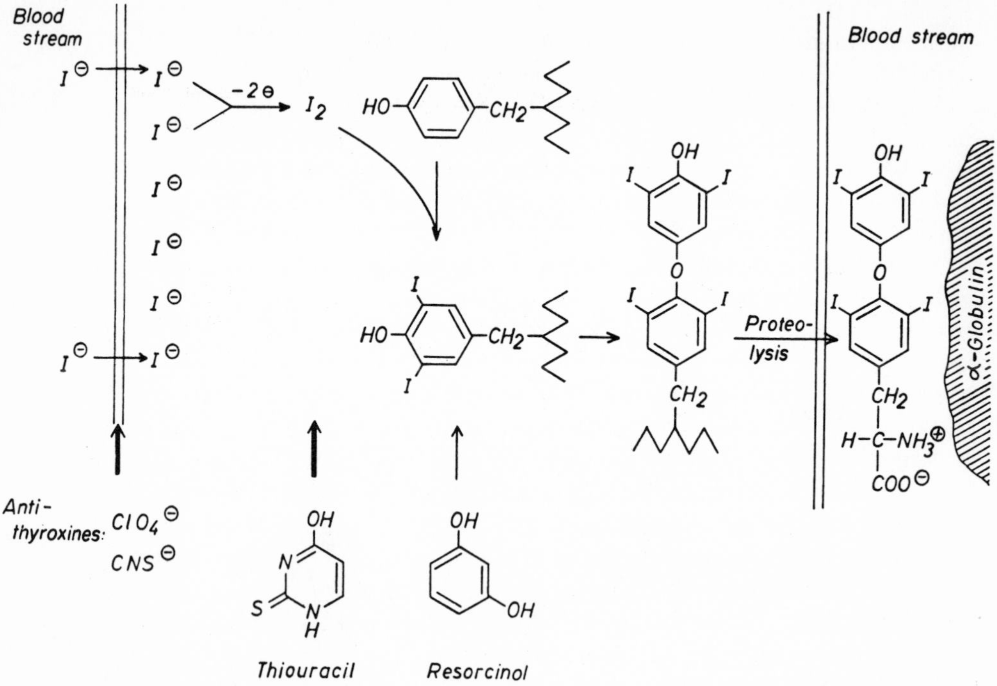

Fig. 53. Diagram of thyroid activity. Iodine ions are taken up from blood (left), oxidized in the gland by removal of electrons and bound organically. From the iodinated tyrosine residues in the thyroglobulin molecule arise tri- and tetraiodothyronine, which are freed by proteolysis and released to the blood stream. At right is the addition compound with α-globulins. At the bottom, the sites of action of the inhibitors (antithyroid substances) are indicated.

**Thyroxine Metabolism.** Thyroxine or triiodothyronine, elaborated by the gland into the blood, is bound to a specific protein,[4] a glycoprotein, which is one of the α-globulins (thyroxine-binding globulin, TBG).

Both thyroxine and triiodothyronine are deaminated when they are metabolized, just as all other amino acids are (either oxidatively or by transamination). The resulting thyropyruvic acid is decarboxylated to give thyroacetic acid which still retains hormonal activity. Thyroxine and its catabolic products may also be bound to glucuronic acid and enter the bile. For the proper iodine balance of the organism it is important that iodine be liberated from iodine-containing catabolites by a specific deiodinase and returned to the thyroid gland as iodide.

**Biologic Effect of the Thyroid Hormone.** The thyroid gland regulates the entire metabolism of the adult organism. Disturbances of the thyroid function are reflected in the basal metabolic rate (metabolism while resting, cf. Chapt. XXII-1). In hyperthyroidism (thyrotoxicosis) the rate is elevated; during hypofunction (clinical manifestation: myxedema), it is lowered. This phenomenon is used frequently in judging thyroid function. Administration of thyroxine raises the basal

---

[4] The binding may be demonstrated easily by the use of radioactive iodine ($^{131}$I), which is detectable by its intense γ-radiation. The investigation of thyroid function has profited greatly by the use of this isotope.

metabolic rate; the effect is delayed several days, but then lingers on for some time. Triiodothyronine acts more quickly (and more strongly), but for a shorter time.

Martius discovered that the hormone affects the respiratory chain *in vitro* by uncoupling oxidative phosphorylation. In accordance with this observation, the stimulating effect of thyroxine on general metabolism could be explained as a counter-effect (increased metabolic rate during decreased usefulness). For several reasons (unspecificity of the effect, magnitude of the required dosage) it is however extremely improbable that the regulation of normal metabolism rests on this effect, although it might be responsible for thyrotoxicosis (pathologically elevated thyroxine production accompanied by a greatly elevated metabolic rate). With physiological hormone doses, Lehninger and co-workers have observed a swelling of the mitochondria which probably derives from changes of permeability and which might well be the true site of metabolic control. On the other hand, the administration of inhibitors of protein synthesis can block the effect of thyroxine completely. This would be an argument for a mechanism involving enzyme induction.

Besides influencing metabolism, thyroxine very characteristically also affects growth and development. The experimental extirpation of the thyroid gland from animals at an early developmental stage results in delayed growth and delayed sexual maturity. In amphibia, the metamorphosis of larvae (tadpoles) can be initiated precociously by the administration of thyroxine. In this case, the first noticeable effect is an elevation of ribonucleic acid turnover and protein biosynthesis. In biochemistry we must distinguish the developmental-physiological effects of thyroxine from its effects on the regulation of metabolism.

## 5. Hormones of the Adrenal Medulla

One of the hormones of the adrenal medulla, *epinephrine* (adrenalin), was the first hormone to be isolated in pure form. Much later, a second hormone, the closely related *norepinephrine* (noradrenalin), was found in the same gland.

Both hormones are pyrocatechol (*o*-dihydroxybenzene) derivatives, which are easily oxidized. This fact explains the histochemical reaction of the "chromaffin tissue." The hormonal content of the adrenal medulla is relatively high (several mg per gm of gland). The two active substances of the adrenal medulla, epinephrine and norepinephrine, are both derivatives of phenyl ethylamine, which possesses strong pharmacologic effects.

**The Biosynthesis** begins with tyrosine. The pathway of reactions shown here also provides information about the chemical nature of the hormones.

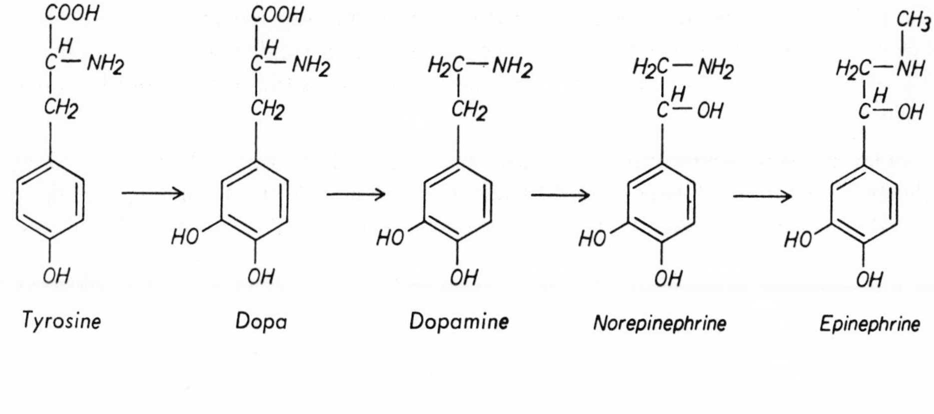

Tyrosine     Dopa     Dopamine     Norepinephrine     Epinephrine

Tyrosine is first oxidized to give dihydroxyphenylalanine (= dopa), an intermediate in the formation of melanin (cf. Chapt. VIII-11), which is subsequently decarboxylated to dopamine. Dopamine already possesses some biologic activity; it is one of the "tissue hormones" (cf. Section 12). The next step is hydroxylation of the side chain. The resulting norepinephrine is finally methylated by active methionine. The first step in the inactivation of the hormone is the methylation of the 3-OH group; this is followed by conversions on the side chains.

**Biologic Effect.** The main pharmacologic effect of norepinephrine is on the vascular system. Norepinephrine causes vasoconstriction and raises the blood pressure, but epinephrine causes vasodilation and vasoconstriction in different regions. The principal biochemical effect of epinephrine is to elevate blood glucose by mobilizing glycogen reserves (cf. Chapt. XVII-6). Together with norepinephrine, it also aids in the transmission of neural excitation in the adrenergic nerves (cf. also Chapt. XXIII-7). (This close relationship is understandable, since the adrenal medulla developed from nerve tissue.) Epinephrine thus provides a link between the conventional hormones and the so-called tissue hormones and substances with hormone-like activity. Once again we observe that conceptualization draws arbitrary boundaries, although in reality there may be a continuous, boundary-free transition.

## 6. The Hormone of the Pineal Gland

Melatonin is found in the pineal gland (= epiphysis) in high concentrations. As is evident from the formula, it is an indole derivative which probably arises from tryptophan and is closely related to serotonin (cf. Section 12). Melatonin blanches amphibial skin; it is the melanophore-contracting principle (the antagonist of melanotropin, Section 9). No other physiological effects of this substance, which was isolated only recently, are known.

$$H_3CO \qquad\qquad\qquad CH_2-CH_2-NH-CO-CH_3$$

*Melatonin*

## 7. The Parathyroid Hormone

The parathyroid glands elaborate a vital hormone often called *parathormone*. It is a polypeptide that has been obtained in pure form very recently. Its molecular weight is 8600. The hormone dissociates under certain conditions to yield smaller peptides that retain some activity. Oxidation inactivates the parathyroid hormone rapidly.

**Biologic Effect.** Parathormone regulates the ionic milieu, especially the $Ca^{++}$ and phosphate content of tissues and blood. A deficiency of the hormone, e.g. after parathyroidectomy, quickly results in a decrease of the $Ca^{++}$ level in blood and eventually in tetanic convulsions due to changes in the electrolyte balance in muscular and nervous tissue. Injection of the hormone results in an increase of blood phosphate, citrate, and $Ca^{++}$ concentration and increased phosphate excretion by the kidney. The hormone exerts an influence on the metabolism of bone and mobilizes the mineral content. This explains the elevation of $Ca^{++}$ in blood (hypercalcemia). But parathormone also affects the kidney directly and regulates phosphate excretion; it reduces the reabsorption, so that more phosphate is flushed out.

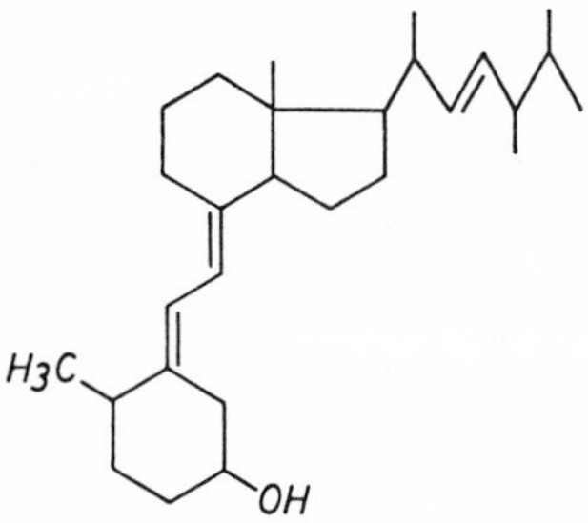

Dihydrotachysterol          Vitamin $D_2$
"AT 10"

Another substance, chemically related to vitamin $D_2$ (calciferol), has an effect similar to that of parathormone. This is *dihydrotachysterol* (*AT 10*). The effect is, however, in some aspects more comparable to D-hypervitaminosis. Dihydrotachysterol is used frequently in tetany caused by a deficiency of the parathyroid hormone, because the peptide hormone is not readily available.

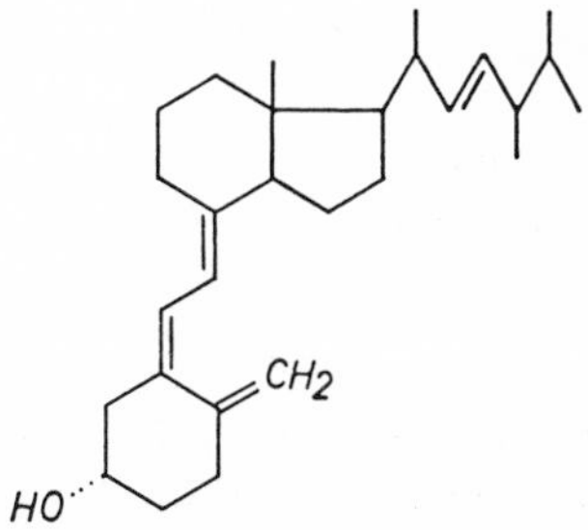

## 8. The Pancreatic Hormones

The pancreas produces the digestive enzymes and two hormones, insulin and glucagon. The hormones are synthesized in the islets of Langerhans. This tissue consists of two types of cells, the $\alpha$-cells which produce glucagon and the $\beta$-cells which produce insulin. Both hormones are polypeptides.

**Insulin.** The chemical structure of insulin has been elucidated completely by the brilliant work of F. Sanger. The amino acid sequence is shown in Chapt. III-3. The polypeptide consists of two chains that are cross-linked by sulfur bridges. The molecular weight is around 6,000. Insulin easily binds zinc; in the process, double molecules with a molecular weight of 12,000, or higher aggregates, are formed (cf. Fig. 13, Chapt. IV-5).

*The Biosynthesis* of insulin follows the general principles of protein synthesis (cf. Chapt. VII-8). Inactivation is accomplished by proteolytic breakdown, possibly by the specific enzyme *insulinase*.

*Biologic Effects.* Insulin lowers the level of blood glucose very drastically. It increases the permeability of cell membranes for glucose and a few other sugars; at the same time it enhances the breakdown of carbohydrates in the cell and, to a certain extent, the biosynthesis of fats. Concerning the regulation of blood glucose cf. also Section 10.

A long-known metabolic disease is *diabetes mellitus,* characterized by elevated blood sugar and urinary excretion of sugar, and often of ketone bodies. Classical diabetes is an insulin deficiency disease. The symptoms can be relieved by insulin injections (being a polypeptide, insulin is destroyed in the gastro-intestinal tract and is thus ineffective when administered orally). The treatment is called substitution therapy. In some cases, special orally effective preparations are used successfully.

*Alloxan Diabetes.* Diabetes in animals can be initiated artificially by the administration of alloxan. The results resemble those following pancreatectomy. The β-cells of the insular apparatus are damaged by alloxan, and insulin is no longer produced.

**Glucagon.** The molecular weight of glucagon in 3500. It consists of one polypeptide chain with 29 amino acid residues, whose sequence is known. The sequence differs greatly from that of insulin.

Glucagon is produced by the α-cells. Its synthesis can be inhibited specifically by administration of $Co^{++}$, which creates a condition analogous to alloxan diabetes, but with the opposite symptoms.

*Biologic Effect.* In contrast to insulin, glucagon raises the blood sugar level. It mobilizes the carbohydrate reserves, mostly liver glycogen, by increasing phosphorylase activity (cf. Chapt. XVII–6).

## 9. Hypophyseal Hormones

The hypophysis (pituitary gland) is an accessory gland of the brain. It consists of two anatomically distinct organs, the anterior lobe and the posterior lobe, and each lobe elaborates several different hormones. A middle lobe (pars intermedia; developed to different extents in different animals), produces another hormone. The second part of Table XVIII (Section 1) lists all the different hypophyseal hormones. Many hormones of the anterior lobe are master hormones (Section 1).

Since the hypophyseal hormones are all peptides, their chemical nature is very similar. Their molecular weights, however, differ considerably; they range from about 1000 to 50,000. Some contain a carbohydrate component and are therefore glycoproteins. Unlike other hormones, these peptides and protein hormones possess a certain degree of species specificity; their amino acid sequences may differ from one animal species to the next (cf. Chapts. III-3 and IV-2).

**Neurosecretion.** The posterior lobe of the hypophysis contains two hormones, ocytocin and vasopressin, but both are formed actually in the hypothalamus and not in the posterior lobe. It has been demonstrated that the two hormones are synthesized in neurosecretory cells and transported through the axon of the connecting neuron. The whole process is termed *neurosecretion.* The transported product of neurosecretion is granular and visible in the light microscope; it can be stained specifically by certain methods. Its chemical composition is not known; it probably consists of lipoprotein particles that contain the hormones.

**Hormones of the Posterior Lobe of the Hypophysis** ( = neurohypophysis). Although the hormones of the posterior lobe differ greatly physiologically, they are very similar chemically: They are oligopeptides consisting of nine amino acid residues with one disulfide bridge. The ring structure arises secondarily by oxidation of the cysteine residues in the molecule. As shown in the formula only two positions (3 and 8) differ: *Ocytocin* contains isoleucine in position 3 and leucine in 8; *vasopressin* has phenylalanine and lysine (or arginine) in the corresponding places.[5] *Vasotocin* has been extracted from reptiles, amphibia, and fish; it has isoleucine in position 3 and arginine in 8.

Van Dyke has isolated a protein from the neurohypophysis that possesses the activity of both ocytocin and vasopressin (the "Van Dyke protein"). By suitable physical methods, ocytocin and vasopressin can be liberated from the protein. The protein may be considered a storage and transport form of the low molecular peptides.

**Physiologic Effect. Ocytocin**[6] acts on the smooth muscle of the uterus and enhances contraction; it undoubtedly plays a major role during parturition (by initiating labor). In addition, ocytocin acts on the lactating mammary gland by stimulating the ejection of milk (also through muscle contraction).

**Vasopressin,** as the name indicates, influences blood pressure; an injection of the substance causes a long-lasting elevation of blood pressure. Furthermore, it excites the smooth musculature of the intestines. In normal physiology, however, the effect on the kidney is most significant. Vasopressin inhibits diuresis, i.e. it helps in the reabsorption of water and consequently in the concentration of urine. Impaired production of vasopressin results in the syndrome called *diabetes insipidus* in which huge quantities of very dilute urine are excreted; in one documented case, as much as 56 liters per day! A corresponding thirst accompanies such a loss of liquid. Injection of the hormone relieves the symptoms.

**Middle Lobe of the Hypophysis.** The middle lobe (or pars intermedia) produces *melanotropin*. Its chemical constitution is known, but it has been prepared in pure form only recently (A. B. Lerner; C. H. Li). It closely resembles corticotropin (cf. the reverse side of the fold-out chart at the end of the volume).

---

[5] Compared to the greatly differing physiological effects, the chemical differences at first appear minor. But too often one overlooks the fact that the side chains of amino acids are after all quite different. And if one were to compare the complete structural formulas of the peptides, then the differences would indeed appear much greater than they are, for example, among progesterone, corticosterone, and testosterone.

[6] The name of the hormone is derived from the Greek, meaning "fast birth." An alternate spelling is "oxytocin." The form *ocytocin* is preferred in order to avoid confusion with the prefix oxy = oxygen-containing.

Melanotropin promotes the dilation of melanophores in the skin of amphibia and fishes, which darken as a consequence. The hormone can also be extracted from mammals, which do not possess melanophores. It can nevertheless cause a darkening of the skin in man (A. B. Lerner). Its biologic significance in mammals is not known. Some evidence indicates that it assists in dark adaptation and facilitates the resynthesis of visual purple.

**Hormones of the Anterior Lobe of the Hypophysis.** Table XVIII in Section 2 shows that the anterior lobe produces six different hormones: somatotropin, thyrotropin, corticotropin, luteotropic hormone, follicle-stimulating, and interstitial cell-stimulating hormones. The last three hormones are grouped together under the generic term gonadotropic hormones.

**The Growth Hormone,** or *somatotropin,* possesses the greatest species specificity. The hormone isolated from bovine pituitaries is ineffective in man. Most recently, growth hormone has been isolated from human pituitaries (autopsy material) and tested clinically with some success.

All somatotropins studied are proteins. Their molecular weights differ as follows:

| Somatotropin from | Molecular Weight | Number of Amino Acids |
|---|---|---|
| Beef | 46,000 | 396 |
| Ape | 25,400 | 241 |
| Man | 27,100 | 245 |

Growth is a complicated process, and the growth hormone must influence a multiplicity of physiological processes. Bone and cartilage growth is stimulated; fat is burned at a higher rate; nitrogen is retained and more protein synthesized; blood sugar is elevated and weight is increased. The weight gain has been used as an assay method for the hormone (along with bone growth). Some effects on metabolism will be discussed later in connection with blood sugar regulation (Section 10).

**The Thyrotropic Hormone,** or *thyrotropin,* is one of the glandotropic hormones; it stimulates the thyroid gland. It appears to be a relatively low molecular weight glycoprotein with a molecular weight of around 10,000. Complete purification has not yet been achieved.

Its biologic effect consists in the control of the thyroid gland. Thyrotropin stimulates the elaboration of thyroxine, while the iodine content of the gland drops drastically. Circulating thyroxine has a feedback effect on the hypophysis, inhibiting the further elaboration of the stimulating hormone (compare with corticotropin, below).

**Adrenocorticotropic Hormone** (corticotropin) is usually abbreviated ACTH. Corticotropins from different animal sources have been prepared in pure form. They are peptides consisting of 39 amino acid residues whose sequences are known (cf. Chapt. III-3 and the reverse side of the fold-out chart).

The physiological effect of corticotropin consists in the stimulation of the adrenal cortex. The production of corticoid hormones is enhanced, and stored cholesterol is drawn on as starting material. The peripheral effects observed after administration of corticotropin are caused by the corticoid hormones.

*Control of Corticotropin Production.* The elaboration of corticotropin depends closely on the concentration of circulating adrenocortical hormones (cf. the diagram in Section 1) and also on many other factors. Selye's group of especially stressful factors (trauma, infections, cold, etc., and even psychic factors) result in increased corticoid production (chiefly cortisol). This response constitutes a defensive reaction.

**Corticotropin-Releasing Factor.** A hormone-like factor found recently in the mid-brain affects the adenohypophysis. This factor, like the hormones of the hypophyseal posterior lobe, is a neurosecretion. Progress has been made in its enrichment; it may be related to the hormones of the neurohypophysis. It is not yet clear whether this factor is a link in the chain of the self-regulation of the hypophysis–adrenal cortex system, or whether it merely releases the stress reaction.

**Gonadotropic Hormones.** Numerous hormones exert an influence on the activity of the gonads. It has not been easy to observe the individual effects separately in animal experiments and, as a result, the nomenclature has become thoroughly confused. Today three effects are distinguished:

1. The *follicle-stimulating effect* (FSH = follicle-stimulating hormone), which promotes the development of the follicles in the ovary and the germinal cells of the testes.

2. The *interstitial cell-stimulating effect* (ICSH = interstitial cell-stimulating hormone), enhances the production of hormones in the interstitial cells (esterone or testosterone), and is identical with the luteinizing effect (LH) (conversion of the follicles to the corpus luteum).

3. The *luteotropic effect* (LTH = luteotropic hormone) stimulates the production of progesterone in the corpora lutea.

For each of these effects there is one hormone in the hypophysis. In addition, several other gonadotropins are found in urine, some of them originating in the hypophysis, and some in the placenta. The latter differ chemically from the hypophyseal hormones, but have the same effect.

Gonadotropic hormones exhibit a certain species specificity in their chemical constitution, but as far as is known, hormones from other species are effective physiologically.

The *luteotropic hormone* (LTH) is identical with the *lactotropic* (or mammotropic) *hormone,* also called *prolactin* or *lactotropin* (for effects, see below). The hormone has been purified from sheep hypophyses and found to be a protein with a molecular weight of 24,000; the amino acid sequence is partially known.

Lactotropin stimulates the secretion of milk in the mammary gland. The tissue grows and the production of milk rises. One of the best assays, however, uses the pigeon; the secretion in the pigeon's crop is stimulated (connected with the care of the young). Lactotropin releases the breeding instinct in many animals, and thus has a strong psychic effect.

Another characteristic property of the hormone is its luteotropic effect: In animal experiments, lactotropin stimulates progesterone production in the corpus luteum. It is not yet known whether lactotropin and LTH are identical in all species. For the regulation of the cycle see Section II.

*Follicle-Stimulating Hormone* (FSH). This hormone also varies with its origin. Molecular weights between 25,000 and 30,000 are reported. Besides amino acids, the molecule also contains carbohydrates (galactose, mannose, fucose, hexosamine; the total carbohydrate content is 7.5%).

The follicle-stimulating hormone augments growth and development of the gonads; in the ovary, the follicles enlarge, but the estrogen production in the follicles is stimulated only by very high doses. In the testes, spermatogenesis is stimulated. The hormone is particularly active during the menstrual cycle (see Section 11).

*Interstitial Cell-Stimulating Hormone* (ICSH) or *luteinizing hormone* (LH). This, too, is a glycoprotein with a molecular weight of 30,000 (from hog hypophyses). Its structure is still unknown.

The interstitial cell-stimulating hormone of the hypophysis controls the production of gonadal hormones. In the testes, Leydig's cells are stimulated to produce testosterone and estrone; in the female organism the follicles are stimulated to produce progesterone (see also Section 11).

**Chorionic Gonadotropins.** During pregnancy, much gonadotropic hormone is excreted in urine. This fact is the basis of several pregnancy tests. The hormone is produced in the placenta and not in the hypophysis. Human chorionic gonadotropin (HCG) resembles the interstitial cell-stimulating hormone in its effects; it enhances estrone and progesterone production and thus, secondarily, the development of the uterus. Chemically, it resembles the hypophyseal hormones, since it is also a glycoprotein.

Gonadotropins have also been found in the postmenopausal urine of women; the preparation is called human menopausal gonadotropin (HMG). Its effect is that of a follicle-stimulating hormone; but it is possibly a derivative of the hypophyseal hormone, because its activity is less.

**Relaxin.** Relaxin may be considered to be an additional female sex hormone. It is formed probably in the ovaries. Its purification has not yet been achieved, though it appears to be a protein with a molecular weight of 12,000.

Its physiological effect consists in relaxing and softening the symphysis pubis. Many mammals (e.g. guinea pigs) cannot have a normal birth without relaxin. Relaxin has been detected even in man and should be important in the initial phases of birth.

## 10. Hormonal Regulation of Blood Glucose

Blood normally contains 0.06 to 0.10% glucose.[7] The content of glucose in blood is held extraordinarily constant; this is significant for the nourishment of the indi-

---

[7] Reducing methods yield higher values (0.1 to 0.12%), because other substances with reducing properties are also present.

vidual tissues. The brain, for example, has practically no reserves of oxidizable carbohydrate and depends for its proper function on the blood sugar. Moreover, one must consider that sugar is not taken up continuously and steadily, but rather intermittently in batches, with food during meal times. Sugar is at first stored in the liver as glycogen. The control of the sugar level therefore involves both glucose-producing and glucose-consuming processes; these processes are:

| Glucose Producing | Glucose Consuming |
|---|---|
| Glycogen breakdown | Glycogen formation |
| Conversion of galactose | Oxidation |
| and fructose | Fat formation |
| Gluconeogenesis | |

The entire system of regulation is represented schematically in Fig. 54. As with most diagrams, it oversimplifies somewhat.

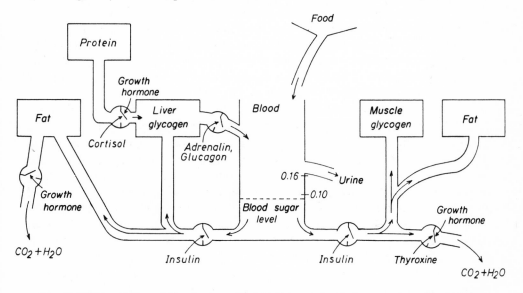

FIG. 54. The regulation of blood sugar. At right the peripheral phenomena are illustrated; at left the metabolism in the liver. Flip-flop valves, which can be open or shut, have been inserted in the various pathways. The action of the hormones has been symbolized as the opening or shutting of the valves. Further explanations are found in the text.

The *lowering of blood glucose* is effected by *insulin*. It acts predominantly in the peripheral tissues by promoting the influx of glucose into the tissues and its subsequent utilization. In muscle, insulin enhances both glycogen formation and glucose oxidation. In the liver, it stimulates glycogen formation and glucose oxidation, and—as discovered recently—fat formation (from carbohydrate) in the adipose tissue. At the same time insulin inhibits the release of free fatty acids into blood plasma. The effect on the adipose tissue is significant for the understanding of diabetes (see below).

*Elevation* of blood glucose content is achieved most easily by a mobilization of the depot, i.e. by phosphorolysis of glycogen. Two hormones are active here; *epinephrine* and *glucagon*. Epinephrine stimulates the breakdown of glycogen in liver and in muscle by catalyzing the conversion of the inactive form of phosphorylase into the active form, according to recent investigations (Chapt. XVII–6).

At first, the glycogen of the liver is degraded, but glycolysis in muscle is also accelerated and lactate is produced. The lactate is then in part reconverted to liver glycogen, so that paradoxically more glycogen is present in the liver in the end than in the beginning (shift from muscle to liver).

The mechanism of action of glucagon is still unclear. Glucagon also promotes the breakdown of liver glycogen by mobilizing active phosphorylase. As to its peripheral effects, various opinions are held.

Besides the interconversion glycogen $\rightleftharpoons$ glucose, the rate of oxidation to $CO_2$ and $H_2O$ and the *de novo* formation of glucose from intermediates of protein and carbohydrate metabolism play a central role in the maintenance of glucose levels. Thyroxine, the hormone stimulating catabolism, is of subordinate significance in this case, but the adrenocortical hormones, primarily the glucocorticoids *cortisol* and *cortisone*, are much more important. The latter stimulate gluconeogenesis from protein (Chapt. VIII–9 and XV–10). (One of the bioassays for adrenocorticoid hormones tests for glycogen formation in the rat.) Gluconeogenesis raises blood sugar levels. Cortisol, therefore, possesses "diabetogenic" effects and thus antagonizes insulin. Cortisol also inhibits the oxidation of carbohydrates.

*Growth Hormone* (somatotropin) acts more or less in the opposite direction. It generally promotes synthetic processes, especially protein synthesis, and decreases the breakdown of amino acids, which are, of course, indispensable for the synthesis of proteins. In other words, growth hormone inhibits gluconeogenesis in favor of accelerated protein production. Nevertheless it is "diabetogenic"; it is antagonistic to insulin in that it raises the level of blood sugar (mainly by inhibiting the oxidation of glucose). In summary, both carbohydrate and protein oxidation are suppressed, while fat catabolism is enhanced.

Very generally, it can be stated that the various regulatory mechanisms not only maintain the concentration of blood glucose very constant, but at the same time direct metabolism into different pathways. The guidance of metabolism is the principal function of the adrenal cortex and the hypophysis; the maintenance of a constant level of glucose is primarily the task of insulin. This is reflected in the observation that an elevated content of blood glucose (e.g. by increased food intake) increases the secretion of insulin. A complete feedback loop is in operation here. The action of epinephrine is an emergency reaction which comes into play during drastic lowering of the blood sugar or when unusual circumstances require excessive amounts of sugar. The epinephrine effect is controlled directly by the nervous system.

**Diabetes Mellitus.** Diabetes is one metabolic disease that has supplied biochemistry with a host of problems. The disease is based on a relative deficiency of insulin (insufficient production of insulin or increased elaboration of the antagonistic hormones glucagon, somatotropin, and cortisol). The chief metabolic signs of diabetes mellitus are increased blood glucose levels (possibly accompanied by glucosuria), appearance of "ketone bodies" (= acetone, acetoacetate, and its reduction product, $\beta$-hydroxybutyrate) in blood and urine with concomitant lowering of alkali reserves in the blood, and an elevation of plasma nonesterified fatty acids.

Because of the conspicuous *hyperglycemia* and *glucosuria*, diabetes has always been considered a disturbance of the metabolism of carbohydrates. However, the elevation of blood sugar constitutes in reality a regulatory mechanism: the decreased ability of the periphery to take up glucose from blood is compensated partially by the higher concentration. Disturbances of fat metabolism are probably of at least equal significance. During insulin deficiency, ever increasing quantities of free fatty acids pass from the *adipose tissue* into the blood, and thence into the liver where they are broken down to acetyl-CoA by $\beta$-oxidation. The large supply of acetyl-CoA then exceeds the capacity of the citrate cycle so that acetyl-CoA is rerouted to the formation of acetoacetyl-CoA and further to free acetoacetate (see Chapt. XII-4). This explanation of ketogenesis, still hypothetical in some aspects, can answer only some of the problems of the metabolic disturbances in diabetes.

## 11. Hormonal Control of the Menstrual Cycle

Cyclic phenomena of physiological activity frequently are regulated hormonally. One example is provided by the genital cycle, which differs greatly in different animal species. The estrus cycle of rodents has been of paramount importance in the investigation of the gonadal and gonadotropic hormones and the main bioassays are performed on rodents (mouse, rat, rabbit). We will limit ourselves to man, however.

The genital cycle of women is characterized by the periodic maturation of follicles in the ovaries and by the periodic changes of the uterine mucosa. During menstrual bleeding the uterine mucosa is extensively sloughed off. The new cycle is initiated by the hypophysis which at first elaborates the follicle-stimulating hormone (FSH) and later the interstitial cell-stimulating hormone (ICSH). The follicle-stimulating hormone acts on the gonadal cells directly and promotes the maturation of a new follicle. Under the influence of the interstitial cell-stimulating hormone the follicle produces the follicular hormone (estrone or estradiol). With the rising concentration of ICSH, its "luteinizing" effect becomes more prominent. At a certain ratio of ICSH/FSH, ovulation (rupture of the follicle) occurs and the corpus luteum is developed (cf. Fig. 55).

The hypophysis influences mainly the ovaries, whereas the processes of the *uterus* are regulated by the gonadal hormones. The estrogen effects production of new mucosa (*proliferation phase*) which ceases shortly before ovulation. Estrone simultaneously exerts an influence back on the hypophysis by inhibiting the elaboration of FSH and enhancing production of prolactin and the interstitial cell—

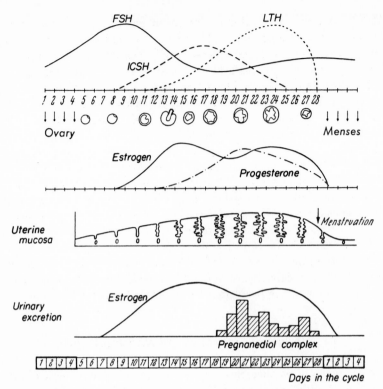

FIG. 55. The menstrual cycle. Top: Relative concentrations of the hypophysis hormones, and below it the activity of the ovaries. Second group of curves: Relative concentrations of the gonadal hormones, and below it the functional state of the uterine mucosa dependent on these concentrations. Excretion of the hormone catabolites follows the concentration of the hormones (last curve). After W. Dirscherl *in* "Fermente, Hormone, Vitamine," (R. Ammon and W. Dirscherl, eds.), 3rd ed., Vol. II: "Hormone," p. 169, Georg Thieme, Stuttgart, 1960.

stimulating (= luteinizing) hormone, which in turn initiates production of progesterone shortly before ovulation. Progesterone promotes transformation of the uterine mucosa to the pregravid state and prepares for the lodging of the fertilized ovum (*secretory phase* of the uterine mucosa). This state persists as long as progesterone is produced.

If the ovum is not fertilized, the corpus luteum atrophies, because production of the luteotropic hormone by the hypophysis slows down. In this phase, the stimulating influence of the estrogen on the elaboration of LTH by the hypophysis is presumably missing; perhaps progesterone inhibits production of ICSH. Regression of the corpus luteum results in decreased hormone production. The secretory mucosa cannot be maintained in the absence of progesterone; it is discarded during menstruation.

With menstrual bleeding the uterine mucosa is returned to the starting point of the cycle. The new maturing follicle produces estrone, necessary for proliferation, and the process is repeated anew. *The cyclic process depends principally on the alternating stimulation of the ovary by the hypophysis and the back reaction of ovarian hormones on the hypophysis.*

## 12. Tissue Hormones

The term *tissue hormone* has been applied to a group of substances which have much in common with the "classical" hormones produced in special glands, but which cannot be included among the hormones in the strict sense.

The catalytic agents of the gastro-intestinal tract can be considered to be one group of tissue hormones. They are not secreted by discrete glands, but rather are produced by mucosal tissue. They do reach the target organ *via* the blood stream, however, (and for this reason are often classified as true hormones). Another group of agents, histamine, acetylcholine, etc., are produced in many tissues and their target organ is the site of origin. These substances can be numbered among the hormones only in a very abstract sense. It would indeed be better to introduce a new and neutral name for these primarily pharmacologically active substances.

**The Hormones of the Gastro-Intestinal Tract** excite the digestive glands. The following can be distinguished:

a. *Secretin*, the study of which induced Bayliss and Starling to coin the word *"hormone"*. The entrance of acidic food pulp initiates the elaboration of secretin by the duodenal mucosa. The active principle stimulates the pancreas to produce digestive juice and bicarbonate. Secretin consists of a group of polypeptides.

b. *Pancreozymin*, which also arises in the duodenum and also furthers pancreatic enzyme production.

c. *Cholecystokinin*, which induces the gall bladder to contract and to emit bile. It has been extracted from intestinal mucosa.

d. *Gastrin*, which incites the gastric mucosa to activity; it reportedly differs from histamine, which has similar activity.

e. *Enterogastrone* (from the small intestine) and *urogastrone* (from urine), which are antagonists to gastrin; they inhibit motility and acid production in the stomach.

The existence of various other substances has been postulated, but they are neither chemically nor physiologically sufficiently characterized to be included here.

**Locally Acting Tissue Hormones** generally regulate blood pressure and the contraction of smooth muscles. *Angiotensin* (formerly *angio*tonin or hyper*tensin*) is a decapeptide that arises from a precursor by the action of the protease *renin* (from kidneys). The structure of angiotensin is known and its synthesis has been accomplished. The physiological significance of the substance is still debated; pathologically, it is responsible for renal high blood pressure.

Concerning *histamine*, ponderous volumes have been written. It invariably can be demonstrated in the tissues (skin, leucocytes) of mammals, but exists there in a bound and inactive form. Its chief effects are: dilation of the blood capillaries, elevation of the secretion of gastric juice, and phenomena resembling anaphylactic shock. It is suspected that histamine controls local blood circulation in the normal organism. Histamine also plays a role in the production of allergic reactions. Consequently, substances that inhibit the physiological effects of histamine (antihistamines) are used therapeutically.

Histamine is formed by the enzymic decarboxylation of histidine. It is degraded by diamine oxidase (a flavoprotein) to give the aldehyde and $NH_3$ and thus is inactivated. The reaction is analogous to oxidative deamination of amino acids.

*Serotonin* (5-hydroxytryptamine, enteramine) occurs widely in both animals, and plants. It arises from tryptophan by hydroxylation in the 5-position and subsequent decarboxylation (the reverse sequence, proceeding *via* tryptamine, has been excluded). It affects the blood pressure and, among other effects, migrates from the platelets into the serum during blood clotting. Furthermore, it occurs in the intestinal mucosa, where it promotes peristalsis. Finally, it has been found in the central nervous system and appears to function in several psychic phenomena in a manner not yet understood.

5-Hydroxytryptophan

Serotonin
(5-Hydroxytryptamine)

*Tyramine* raises the blood pressure and stimulates smooth musculature (e.g. uterus). More important is *hydroxytyramine* (dopamine) which is formed by hydroxylation of tyrosine and subsequent decarboxylation. On the one hand, hydroxytyramine is the parent substance for the hormones norepinephrine and epinephrine (cf. Section 5), and on the other hand it may be another transfer compound, like norepinephrine, liberated at the ends of sympathetic (= adrenergic) nerves (cf. also Chapt. XXIII-7).

*Acetylcholine* is the transfer substance at most nerve ends (cholinergic nerves; cf. Chapt. XXIII-7). Acetylcholine also, lowers peripheral blood pressure.

*γ-Aminobutyric Acid*, our last entry in this group, is the decarboxylation product of glutamic acid. The substance arises mainly in the brain. The function of γ-aminobutyrate is not yet known in detail, but evidently it blocks the synapses. Nervous tissue contains both the decarboxylase that produces γ-aminobutyrate and the transaminase that breaks it down.

## 13. Hormones of Invertebrates

Hormones are found even among invertebrates. We will single out the hormones of insects from this rather comprehensive area, because they have been investigated most thoroughly.

The juvenile development of insects proceeds through a series of moltings (molting of larvae; among the holometabola also molting of pupae) to result eventually in the adult insect. The most familiar example is the development caterpillar-pupa-butterfly. The process of molting involves three hormones, as shown in Fig. 56.

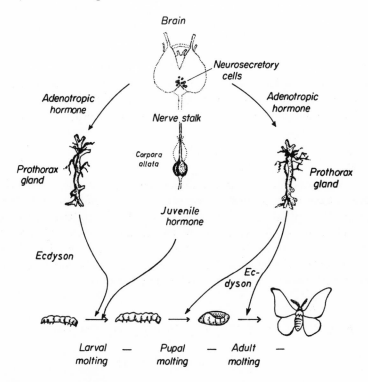

Fig. 56. Action of insect hormones. In the upper part, the hormone-producing glands are represented. Below that, the molting stages initiated by the hormones are shown.

Each shedding is initiated by the activity of neurosecretory cells in the brain; these cells produce a hormone which induces another gland located in the prothorax to elaborate the true molting hormone, *ecdysone*. If ecdysone alone is active, then molting transforms the caterpillar to the pupa and the pupa to the butterfly. Larval shedding (caterpillar to caterpillar) is effected by the elaboration of a second hormone by the *corpora allata* in addition to ecdysone. The second hormone is the so-called juvenile hormone, responsible for the development of larval characteristics. For maintaining the caterpillar stage, two hormones are necessary; for development to the pupal stage, or to the butterfly, only one.

Of the hormones mentioned, only *ecdysone* has been obtained pure and crystalline (Butenandt and Karlson). Surprisingly, the structural formula turned out to be that of a steroid hormone; the preliminary formula is presented below. In the larvae of flies ecdysone brings about formation of the puparium by acting on the metabolism of tyrosine (Karlson). The first recognizable effect is the activation of certain genes.

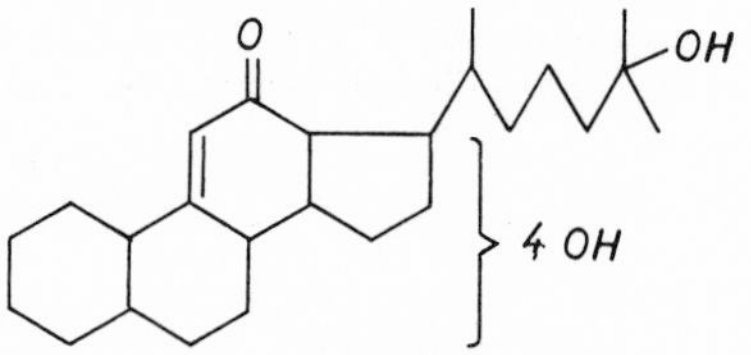

*Ecdysone*

The *juvenile hormone* has been obtained as highly active extracts; it is found not only among invertebrates, but also among vertebrates (Schneiderman). High doses of *farnesol* have the same effect as the natural juvenile hormone.

## 14. Pheromones

Active substances that mediate humoral correlations among individuals of a given species have been designated *pheromones* by Karlson and Lüscher. Classical examples are the sex attractants of insects, which are emitted by the female and which attract males, often across remarkable distances. In the silk moth this active principle is produced in special scent glands; it has been extracted from the glands and has been purified. The sex attractant of the silk moth is a long-chain alcohol with two double bonds (Butenandt, Hecker, and Stamm).

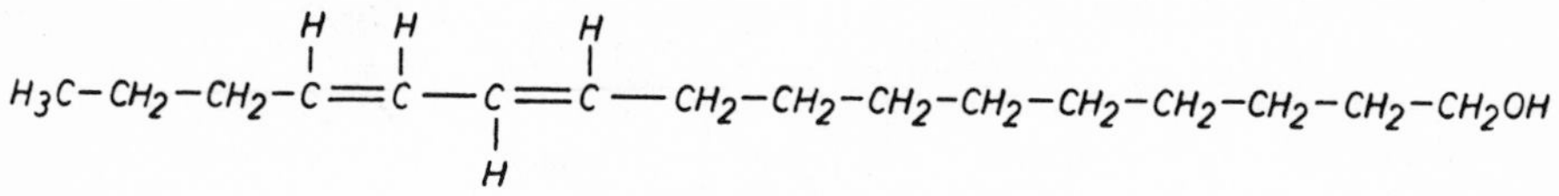

*Sex attractant of the silk moth*

The steric configuration at the double bonds is very critical for biologic activity. The pheromone is received by the male with its olfactory sense. Probably only a few molecules per sensory cell suffice to release the biologic reaction (Schneider).

## 15. Growth Substances of Plants

The growth substances of plants are also known as *phytohormones*.

*Auxin* (β-indolylacetic acid) is a phytohormone that effects elongation of cells. It is formed in the apex of the plant, especially the germinal shoot, and promotes stretching of the basally located cells. Auxin is also involved in the various tropisms of the plant.

CH₂—COOH

$-CH_2-COOH$

Auxin
(= Indolylacetic acid)

Gibberellic acid

O=C—O
HO
CH₃ HOOC
OH
CH₂

Kinetin

HN—CH₂

*Gibberellic acid* was isolated initially as a product of a phytopathogenic fungus; other gibberellins have also been found in higher plants. They, too, effect cell elongation (particularly of the chief axis) and cause gigantism, but may also stimulate cell division. Gibberellic acid possesses some effects that are also ascribed to the as yet hypothetical "flowering hormone."

A pronounced mitotic effect is exhibited by *kinetin* (6-furfurylaminopurine), which has been isolated as a conversion product of deoxyribonucleic acids (derived from animal sources). It can be assumed that similar substances are present in plants.

A number of "growth substances" of microorganisms are not hormones, but rather vitamins. For nearly every water-soluble vitamin some definite bacterial strain is known that requires just this substance as "growth substance" (growth vitamin).

## BIBLIOGRAPHY

R. Ammon and W. Dirscherl, editors, "Fermente, Hormone, Vitamine," 3rd ed., Vol. II: "Hormone," Georg Thieme, Stuttgart, 1960.

L. L. Engel and L. J. Langer, Biochemistry of steroid hormones, *Ann. Rev. Biochem.*, **30**, 499–525 (1961).

E. B. Flink, Adenohypophysis and adrenal cortex, *Ann. Rev. Physiol.*, **23**, 229–262 (1961).

W. F. Ganong, The central nervous system and the synthesis and release of adrenocorticotropic hormone, *in* "Advances in Neuroendocrinology" (A. V. Nalbandov, ed.), p. 92, Univ. of Illinois Press, Urbana, Illinois, 1964.

J. Ginsburg and A. F. Cobbold, Effects of adrenaline, noradrenaline, and isopropylnoradrenaline in man, *in* "Adrenergic Mechanisms," Ciba Foundation Symposium, p. 173 ff., Churchill, London, 1960; and other chapters.

R. Guillemin and A. Schally, Recent advances in the chemistry of neuroendocrine mediators originating in the central nervous system, *in* "Advances in Neuroendocrinology" (A. V. Nalbandov, ed.), p. 314, Univ. of Illinois Press, Urbana, Illinois, 1964.

P. Karlson, Chemistry and mechanism of action of insect hormones, *4th Intern. Congr. Biochem.* XII, 37–47 (1959).

P. Karlson, Pheromones, *Ergeb. Biol.*, **22**, 212–225 (1960).

P. Karlson, Eighth Symposium of Endocrinology, Munich 1961.

C. H. Li, Hormones of the anterior pituitary gland, Part. I. *Advances in Protein Chem.*, **11**, 102–190; Part II, **12**, 270–317 (1957).

G. Pincus (editor), "Recent Progress in Hormone Research" (Proceedings of the Laurentian Hormone Conferences), annual volumes, Academic Press, New York.

G. Pincus and K. V. Thimann, "The Hormones," 5 Vols., Academic Press, New York, 1948–1964.

R. Pitt-Rivers and J. R. Tata, "The Thyroid Hormones," Pergamon Press, New York, 1959.

J. R. Tata, Action of thyroid hormones, *Ann. Rept. Chem. Soc., London* **60**, 501–511 (1963).

C. A. Villee and L. L. Engel (editors), "Mechanism of Action of Steroid Hormones," Pergamon Press, London, 1961.

# CHAPTER XXI

# Mineral Metabolism

Inorganic ions and metal complexes have frequently been mentioned in the preceding chapters. These substances are also metabolized. They are taken up in food and eliminated again in urine, feces and sweat.

The metabolism of inorganic ions, or simply "mineral metabolism," differs in one essential point from the metabolism of substances discussed so far. In contrast to proteins, carbohydrates or fats, minerals are neither produced nor consumed in the organism. Their intake from food can be regulated only very roughly, if at all. Most animal species, nevertheless, in the course of evolution have developed the ability to keep the concentration of ions constant in the body fluids, thus providing a constant *"milieu interne."* This is achieved principally by regulating excretion. Several ions have special depots which can be mobilized in periods of insufficient intake.

Salt regulation is of special significance in aquatic animals. Fresh water fish have a much higher concentration of salt in their blood than in their environment. The opposite is true for salt water fish. Very considerable demands of the salt regulatory mechanism are made by species—such as salmon—which migrate from the sea into rivers and must inhabit regions of widely differing salt content, and yet the salt concentration of the body fluids does not change appreciably with the location of the species.

Mineral metabolism and osmo-regulation should interest not only the biologist but also the medical man, because disturbances in the electrolyte balance in man are rather common. Although our discussion will center around the situation in man, we will point out unusual cases of biologic interest.

## 1. Water Balance

Water is by far the most important inorganic component of the organism. In man, 71 to 73% of the fat-free body mass is made up of water. In some animals (for example the jellyfish) the water content may be as high as 98%. It is the common solvent and imbibition medium of organic material; it is indispensable for the function of proteins and the metabolic processes in cells—the old maxim still applies, *"corpora non agunt nisi soluta,"*—and, finally, it can participate as a reactant in metabolic conversions. Outside of the cells it becomes the vehicle for transport, as exemplified so well by the blood circulation. Lastly, it assists in the regulation of temperature. Evaporation is the principal method of conducting heat to the outside and of dissipating it (consult textbooks of physiology).

**Distribution of Water.** In a discussion of the distribution of water and minerals in the organism, we must distinguish three major compartments: The *intracellular space*, that is, the total space occupied by the fluids within all the cells; the *extracellular space*, which is further subdivided into the water of blood plasma and the interstitial fluids; and the *transcellular space*, which is the content of the intestinal tract. These compartments are not rigidly separated. A considerable amount of fluid is constantly shifted around: For instance, the digestive tract is flooded daily by over 8 liters of a fluid consisting of saliva, gastric juice and pancreatic secretion. The bulk of the water is reabsorbed by the lower small intestine and the colon. Furthermore, the blood vessels and the cell membranes are very permeable to most substances, especially to "nutrient substances," such as glucose or amino acids.

*Inulin,* a polysaccharide of fructose, easily enters the interstitial space but cannot enter the cells and, for this reason, is used to estimate the size of the interstitial space. A certain amount of inulin is injected, and after equilibrium has been reached, the concentration in the blood is determined. From this the total amount of the fluid in which inulin was distributed can be calculated. This amount is equivalent to the "extracellular space"; by subtracting the blood volume from this, one calculates the interstitial space. Substances other than inulin have been used for the determination of these physiological values.

**Water Balance.** The organism possesses a relatively limited supply of water. Excessive fluctuations in water content must be avoided. Normally the water content is well balanced. The intake of water from beverages, from the water content of solid food, and from the water of oxidation is compensated by the excretion of urine and feces and by perspiration.

There is one item on the intake side which is usually overlooked and that is the *water of oxidation.* As we have seen, the respiratory chain is the most important energy-yielding process. It constantly produces water; in the normally nourished man, about 300 gm per day. In some organisms the water of oxidation can fill the total requirement for water (desert animals, clothes moths). In these cases, the excretion of water is reduced to a minimum.

In hot climates we must further consider the output of water through perspiration which is aggravated by strenuous exercise. It can amount to several liters per day and must be balanced by an increased intake of fluids.

**Regulation of the Water Balance.** The water balance is regulated chiefly by two mechanisms: Thirst, which demands an increased intake of fluids, and the activity of the kidneys, which either conserves water or flushes it out. It is well known that the kidneys produce about 180 liters of primary urine each day. Of this, 178–179 liters are reabsorbed. This function of the kidneys is controlled by *vasopressin*, a hormone of the hypophyseal posterior lobe (cf. Chapt. XX–9). In severe cases of *diabetes insipidus* (vasopressin deficiency) reabsorption is greatly diminished and large volumes of urine (20–30 liters per day) are excreted.

Thirst provides the counterbalance in this regulation. Even with excessive perspiration, the fluid balance can be restored by the sensation of thirst, which demands an increased intake of water. But from a quantitative standpoint this regulation is imperfect and only very approximate. A complete diurnal balance generally is not achieved. Input and output are balanced only over longer periods of time.

## 2. Water as Solvent

Water is an excellent solvent for organic and inorganic substances. Most salts dissociate completely to their individual ions upon dissolving in water; acids only to a small extent (cf. Chapt. I–2, dissociation of carboxylic acids). Organic substances are usually classified as either hydrophilic or hydrophobic. The first group includes amino acids and proteins, nucleic acids, and carbohydrates; the second group covers fats and lipids (cf. Chapt. XII to XIV).

The behavior of solutions is governed by a series of physical and chemical laws which, of course, apply within the organisms as well. We will briefly discuss these laws, which also hold for nonaqueous solutions.

**Units of Amount and Concentration.** In chemistry, the customary unit of amount is the *mole* (1 mole equals the molecular weight expressed in grams) and the unit of concentration is *moles per liter*. Since in biochemistry we almost always deal with small amounts and low concentrations, we use units which are smaller by the factor of 1000; they are the *millimole* (mmol), for amounts, and the *millimole per liter* ($mM$), for concentrations. The unit for coenzymes often is the micromole, $\mu$mol, being equal to $10^{-6}$ moles. Care should be taken not to use the abbreviation of concentration $mM$ (= millimolar) incorrectly for millimoles, which are amounts.

In dealing with electrolytes, it is frequently advantageous to take into account the valence of the ions and to express amounts in *equivalents* or *milliequivalents*. The equivalent weight is the atomic or molecular weight divided by the valence of the ion. In the case of calcium, for example, 1 milliequivalent equals 40.1 mg divided by 2, (the atomic weight of calcium is 40.1), which is electrochemically equivalent to 1 milliequivalent of $Na^+$ or 23 mg. Concentrations are measured by the unit *milliequivalent per liter*, which is abbreviated as meq/liter. We shall make much use of this unit.

In the older medical literature, concentrations are often expressed as mg/100 ml; this has been called completely incorrectly "milligram percent," and has been abbreviated as mg%. Reputable scientific journals[1] do not permit this designation; it should be avoided under all circumstances. If for some reason concentrations are expressed in terms of weight per volume instead of moles per volume, the internationally acceptable designation of parts per million should be used; 1 mg to 100 ml corresponds approximately to 10 ppm.

*Osmolarity* is a measure of the osmotically active concentration. For nonelectrolytes it is identical with molarity, but for dissociable substances, the molarity must be multiplied by the number of particles (ions) which arise during dissociation (cf. this Section, below).

---

[1] For instance, the *Journal of Biological Chemistry*; see "Suggestions to Authors."

For calculations in which the interaction among the individual ions is significant, the concept of *ionic concentration* has been introduced. The ionic concentration is arrived at by adding the products of the molar concentration of each ionic species and the *square of its charge*:

$$\Gamma = c_1 \times z_1^2 + c_2 \times z_2^2 + c_3 \times z_3^2 + \cdots + \cdots$$

For a 0.5 $M$ CaCl$_2$ solution, the following ionic concentration can be calculated, corresponding to the dissociation of

$$CaCl_2 \rightleftharpoons Ca^{2+} + 2\ Cl^-$$

$$\Gamma = (0.5 \times 2^2) + (2 \times 0.5 \times 1^2) = 3.0$$

One-half of the ionic concentration is called "ionic strength of the solution," and symbolized with $\mu$; it also plays a very important role.

**Diffusion.** Free diffusion can be observed in all states of matter, but here we are mostly concerned with diffusion in liquids. If a pure solvent is carefully layered on top of a solution, one may observe a gradual mixing. This process is called diffusion (Fig. 57). The dilution of the solution is explained by the spontaneous and exergonic nature of the process, accompanied by a rise of molecular disorder; that is, a considerable increase of entropy.

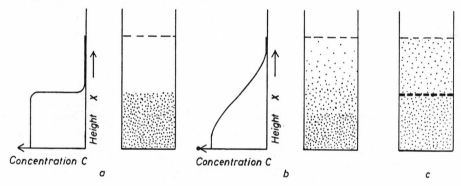

FIG. 57. Diagram illustrating diffusion. In *a* the solution has been covered with a layer of pure solvent; the concentration changes abruptly, as indicated by the concentration curve (at left). In *b* partial mixing has occurred; the concentration curve has flattened out. In *c* a membrane represents inhibited diffusion. Since free diffusion takes much less time, complete homogeneity is reached within each compartment long before the two compartments are equalized; the change in concentration is localized at the membrane.

The velocity at which diffusion proceeds depends on the difference of concentrations and on the diffusion constant $D$:

$$dn/dt = -D \times q \times dc/dx$$

where $dn/dt$ = transport of substance per unit time, $q$ = cross section, and $dc/dx$ = change of concentration along the $x$ axis (cf. Fig. 57, a and b).

For spherical molecules Einstein has evolved a relation between $D$ and the molecular radius $r$ as follows:

$$D = \frac{RT}{N_L \times f} = \frac{RT}{N_L \times 6\pi \times \eta \times r}$$

The formula is derived from Stokes' law for the friction of a sphere moving through a liquid of a viscosity $\eta$. The friction coefficient $f$ is then equal to $6\pi\eta r$. Friction increases as the shape of the molecule deviates from that of the sphere; this is taken into account by the ratio of frictions $f/f_0$, which is greater than unity. This value is of particular importance in protein chemistry; it permits predictions concerning the asymmetry, or the ratio of axes, of macromolecules.

**Restricted Diffusion and Facilitated Diffusion.** If we insert into the tube (Fig. 57, c) a membrane through which both solvent and dissolved substance can pass, that is, a completely permeable membrane, then diffusion of dissolved substance (and in exchange for it, solvent) will take place, but at a reduced rate. The rate now depends on the pore size and the thickness of the membrane, which determines the pathway. We may introduce a membrane constant $M_K$ which depends on $D$, the thickness $d$, and the effective pore area $q$. The law of diffusion can then be expressed as $dn/dt = -M_K \times c$ ($c$ = difference of concentrations).

In some circumstances, diffusion is very slow because of the very small pore size. But several substances or ionic species may be observed to penetrate more rapidly than expected. This phenomenon is called *facilitated diffusion*. The mechanism resembles that of active transport, although its main criterion, namely the migration of material against a concentration gradient, does not apply here (cf. Section 3).

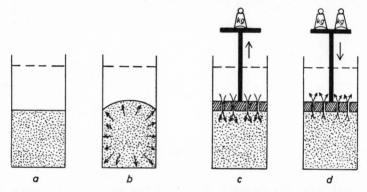

FIG. 58. A diagram of osmosis. In $a$ the start of the experiment is shown; the barrier is supposed to be semipermeable. Equilibrium is reached in $b$: solvent has migrated to the inside; the pressure has risen and is balanced by mechanical pressure of the membrane. The drawings $c$ and $d$ illustrate osmotic work. The piston is lifted in $c$, letting the solution become more dilute (water flows in). In $d$ the solution becomes more concentrated when water is pressed out through an expenditure of mechanical work.

**Osmosis.** If we replace the fully permeable membrane of Fig. 57 with a semipermeable one, then we obtain the situation represented in Fig. 58. The solute cannot become diluted by diffusion; dilution is achieved by the infiltration of water (solvent) into the lower compartment, whereby the pressure in this area is increased (in the drawing this is indicated by a bulging of the membrane). This pressure can be measured, for example, with a mercury manometer and the following relationship is observed:

$$\Pi = c \times RT$$

or, expressed in words, the osmotic pressure is directly proportional to the concentration $c$ ($R$ = the general gas constant, $T$ = the absolute temperature).

The osmotic pressure is an additive effect of the individually dissolved particles. In the case of NaCl, due to electrolytic dissociation, we have in solution the ion $Na^+$ along with the $Cl^-$ ion; $Na_2SO_4$ dissociates into the ions $Na^+$, $Na^+$, and $SO_4^{--}$. With electrolytes, therefore, one must multiply the molar concentration by the number of ions which are expected during solution in order to arrive at the osmotically effective concentration, the *osmolarity*. In addition, with not very dilute solutions, the activity coefficients must be taken into account.

The phenomena of vapor pressure depression, melting point depression, and boiling point elevation are closely related to osmotic pressure. All these effects can be explained by the fact that the solvent loses some of its "chemical potential" upon dissolving a substance. An aqueous solution of the concentration of 1 osmole shows a melting point depression of 1.68° and an osmotic pressure of 22.4 atm. (at 0°).

*Osmotic Work.* Figure 58,c represents a cylinder with a freely mobile, but well-insulated, piston which we imagine to be semipermeable. As solvent diffuses into the area closed off by the piston, the volume of the enclosed compartment increases, the piston is lifted, and work is performed (the lifting of a load). The amount of mechanical work can be calculated from the law of the dependency of concentration on free energy as follows:

$$\Delta F = \Pi \times V = RT \times \ln\frac{c_2}{c_1}$$

($\Pi$ = osmotic pressure; $V$ = volume increase; $c_1$ and $c_2$ = the concentrations before and after dilution.)

In principle, osmosis can result either in an increase of concentration (by external expenditure of mechanical work) or in a decrease of concentration. The former—the increase of concentration by pressure—is found in the colloid-osmotic phenomena (see below). The second is far more common, since it corresponds to spontaneously occurring processes. In the organism, osmosis is primarily responsible for shifting fluids among the various fluid compartments; for example, if much salt has penetrated into the interstitial space, then water is removed from the cells by osmosis, whereby the concentration inside the cells goes up.

*The Colloid-Osmotic Pressure.* Besides semipermeable membranes which allow passage only for water and not for dissolved substances, there are also those which allow substances of low molecular weight, but not of high molecular weight, to penetrate. It can easily be seen that there may be pores whose diameter is smaller than that of protein molecules. In this case, salts can diffuse freely and give no cause for differences in pressure, while the law of osmosis still applies to macromolecules. Since the number of macromolecules[2] is relatively small, the pressures that result from them commonly are small, too. The organism, however, can develop mechanical

---

[2] A 6% protein solution (mol. weight of 60,000) is only 0.001 molar; the osmotic pressure of this solution therefore is only 0.0255 atm. (at 37°).

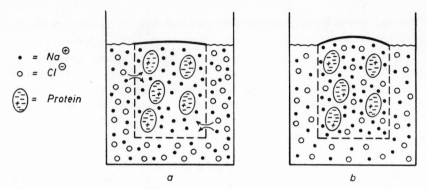

FIG. 59. Donnan distribution. The inner compartment contains a protein solution; protein anions are neutralized by $Na^+$ ions. In $a$, NaCl has been added to the outer compartment; in $b$, Donnan equilibrium has been reached. It can be seen that the inner compartment contains more $Na^+$; the outer one, more $Cl^-$. Inside, the osmotic pressure is higher.

pressures greater than that and can press out fluids. In the capillary beds, the arterial pressure is high enough to enable fluids to pass over into the interstitial space; in the venous section, the hydrostatic pressure drops low enough so that the proteins of the blood plasma absorb fluids from the interstitial area.

Ultrafiltration in the glomeruli, too, depends on the reversal of osmotic dilution. The hydrostatic pressure of the capillary system actually pushes fluids into Bowman's capsule. With respect to proteins, a concentration increase is achieved since proteins are not able to pass through.

**Donnan Distribution.** As discussed extensively in Chap. IV, proteins are polyelectrolytes. Most of them exist as anions at physiological pH values. And with this, a complicating factor must be introduced in our discussion of colloid osmosis, namely that of electroneutrality: Within the same osmotic cell, the negative charges of proteins hold an equal number of cations (Fig. 59). If the inner compartment has a $Na^+$ ion and a protein$^-$ ion, and if we add NaCl to the outside, then $Cl^-$ is able to migrate to the interior but has to be accompanied by a $Na^+$ ion (against a concentration gradient). For this reason, the concentrations assume a relationship which has been expressed by Donnan in the following way:

$$\frac{[Na^+]_0}{[Na^+]_i} = \frac{[Cl^-]_i}{[Cl^-]_0}; \qquad [Na^+]_0 \cdot [Cl^-]_0 = [Na^+]_i \cdot [Cl^-]_i.$$

From this quantitative relationship the following qualitative effects can be deduced:

(1) Protein anions displace equivalent ions to the outside; more $Cl^-$ ions will be found outside (and more $Na^+$ ions inside). All other diffusible anions present distribute themselves in accordance with $Cl^-$; cations, on the other hand, follow the distribution of $Na^+$. This holds true also for $H^+$; as a consequence, pH changes occur between the inside and the outside. These effects are larger, the higher the protein concentrations (and charges), and the smaller the electrolyte concentrations.

(2) The Donnan distribution does not result in osmotic equilibrium. The sum of diffusible ions is higher inside than outside and, consequently, the pressure inside must be higher. This is aggravated by the colloid-osmotic pressure of the macromolecules. The cell walls have to adjust to the rise of pressure; if this is not possible, the cells burst. This is the case, for example, with erythrocytes if they become permeable to cations and become subject to the Donnan laws (osmotic hemolysis).

(3) The measured colloid-osmotic pressure of proteins in salt or buffered solutions will be too high because of the unequal distribution of the small ions. This effect can be calculated in advance and taken into account as a so-called "Donnan correction." These effects are larger the higher the net charge on the proteins; at the isoelectric point, however, the Donnan effects disappear completely.

(4) The rearrangement of ions results in an electric potential difference; with negatively charged protein ions, the colloidal compartment becomes positive. The size of the potential difference may be calculated from the laws governing concentration cells, using the following formula:

$$E = \frac{RT}{nF} \ln \frac{[Na^+]_i}{[Na^+]_0}.$$

## 3. Active Transport

According to the principles of diffusion, we can expect only dilution to occur. By osmosis, and the expenditure of mechanical work, a concentration may be achieved; we have seen that the organism makes use of this principle in ultrafiltration and colloid osmosis. For low molecular weight substances, very considerable pressures would be required and, for this reason, another principle is used, namely *active transport*.

Active transport is a generic term for the transport of substances not subject to osmosis or diffusion. It usually overcomes a concentration gradient and, by its very essence, is an endergonic process requiring chemical energy; it is known today that ATP is used also for this performance of the organism.

Numerous models have been devised to explain active transport. Almost all of them postulate the existence of a carrier substance which is supposed to combine with the ion or the molecule that is to be transported—probably in connection with the expenditure of ATP, as diagrammatically represented in Fig. 60. Substance A (for example, an amino acid), in order to be transported, reacts with the energy-rich carrier $\sim X$ to form the compound AX, which is split again at the inside of the membrane into A and the energy-poor carrier $-X$. By some endergonic reaction, which requires ATP or an analogous energy-rich phosphate, $\sim X$ is regenerated.

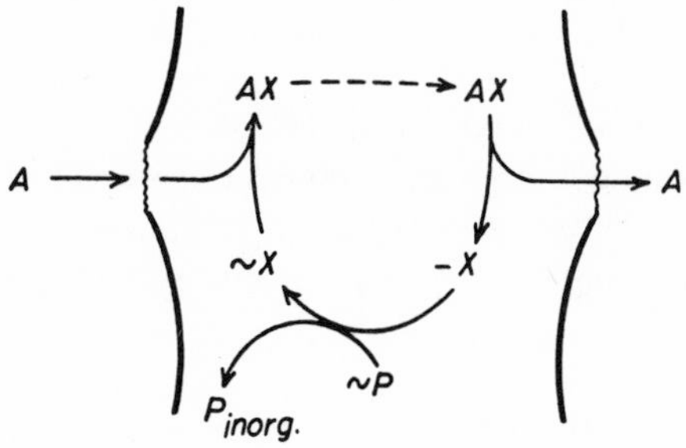

FIG. 60. Diagram of active transport (after Heinz, modified). Substance A diffuses from the outside (at left) into the membrane; there combines with carrier X; and then is released to the interior of the cell (at right). The transport across the membrane is ATP dependent.

In the diagram, the protrusion in the cell wall indicates that transport can take place only at certain places of the membrane. It has been calculated that there are only about 1000 such transport loci on the surface of the erythrocyte membrane.

Active transport mechanisms have been observed for a large number of substances. A variety of ions are transported actively, for example, $Na^+$, $K^+$, $Ca^{++}$, and even $H^+$ ions (for the production of gastric juice). Among organic substances, the transport of sugars is particularly important (the flow of glucose into cells), as well as that of amino acids and other low molecular weight substances which are reabsorbed by the kidney tubules. In several specialized tissues, active transport is a prerequisite for their function, especially in nerves (cf. Chapt. XXIII-7). Also in the muscle, excitability cannot be maintained if active transport has come to a standstill (Chapt. XXIII-6).

## 4. Acid-Base Equilibrium

**pH of Blood Plasma.** Among the ions whose metabolism we are to consider in this section, the $H^+$ ion assumes a special position. The $H^+$-ion concentration is rather low, amounting to $4 \times 10^{-8}$ eq/liter or, in the usual units of the pH scale, the pH value in the extracellular space is 7.4. This value is held remarkably constant; normal deviations lie between 7.35 and 7.45.

"Transcellular fluids" may differ greatly in their pH values: Gastric juice is very acidic (pH 1.5); the content of the small intestine is alkaline with a pH around 8; urine is usually slightly acidic with a pH of 5. Very few data are available about the pH of cells; it is generally somewhat lower than that of extracellular fluids.

**Ionic Composition and Buffer Composition of Blood.** The cations and anions of blood plasma can be compared best in a diagram as shown in Fig. 61.[3] Such a solution can be thought to consist of the bases $NaOH$, $KOH$, $Ca(OH)_2$, and $Mg(OH)_2$ (in the amounts indicated) and of the acids $H_3PO_4$, $H_2SO_4$, $HCl$, and proteins. For the $HCO_3^-$ ion, which makes up 25 meq, the acid $H_2CO_3$ would have to be used, which is in equilibrium with $CO_2$. The $H_2CO_3$ concentration in plasma corresponds to a partial pressure of $CO_2$ of 40 mm Hg. For attaining equilibrium between $CO_2$ and $H_2CO_3$, there exists a special enzyme called *carbonic anhydrase*. It is a Zn-containing protein with a molecular weight of 30,000, having a very high turnover number.

The system $HCO_3^-$: $H_2CO_3$ is the most important buffer system of the entire organism. At the pH of blood (7.4), $HCO_3^-$ and $H_2CO_3$ are at a ratio of 20:1.

---

[3] The diagram illustrates clearly that meq/liter as the unit of concentration is much to be preferred to the outmoded unit of "mg%." First, if expressed in mg per cent, the columns for the cations and anions would not be of the same height. Second, the proteins with 7.2%, i.e. with 7200 mg/100 ml, would stretch the axis intolerably. Last, a completely distorted picture of the relative significance of the various ions would result.

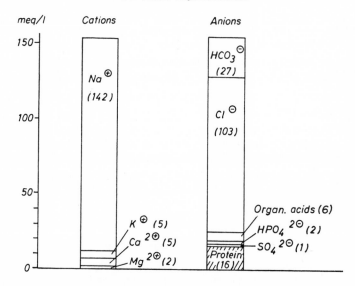

FIG. 61. "Ionograph" of blood plasma. The concentrations of the ions are given in meq/liter.

According to the Henderson-Hasselbalch equation (cf. Chapt. 1-2), the pH of a buffer solution does not depend on absolute amounts, but rather on the *ratio* of concentrations of *undissociated acid to anion*. The $pK_1$ value of carbonic acid is 6.1. For a nonvolatile acid the ideal buffer region lies around the pK value. But since $CO_2$ is volatile and carbonic anhydrase rapidly brings $CO_2$ and $H_2CO_3$ into equilibrium, the actual concentration of $H_2CO_3$ depends closely on the partial pressure of $CO_2$. The great excess of $HCO_3^-$ in the buffer system of blood now reveals its advantage; $H^+$ ions can be trapped and bound as $H_2O$ while gaseous $CO_2$ escapes into the atmosphere. The buffer furthermore is practically inexhaustible; any $H_2CO_3$ lost can be resupplied immediately, since $CO_2$ is always available.

Two other factors participate in maintaining the pH of blood constant. First, the phosphate system $H_2PO_4^-$: $HPO_4^{2-}$ is an excellent buffer at the pH of blood, since the $pK_2$ of phosphoric acid is 7. Second, hemoglobin of the erythrocytes also acts as a buffer. When hemoglobin is charged with oxygen, its acid strength goes up, and $H^+$ ions are dissociated; as a result, more $CO_2$ is eliminated in the lungs. In the peripheral tissue, the reverse takes place (Bohr effect, cf. also Chapt. IX-4).

**Alkali Reserve and Acidosis.** Since $HCO_3^-$ can neutralize the $H^+$ ions of a strong acid (entering the blood stream, for example) according to the equation $H^+ + HCO_3^- = H_2CO_3$, the quantity of $HCO_3^-$ is often, but somewhat incorrectly, called *"alkali reserve."* The normal value of the alkali reserve in blood is 25 meq/liter. A situation in which the alkali reserve is diminished greatly is called *"compensated acidosis,"* as long as the pH remains normal; if the pH drops, it is called *"uncompensated acidosis."* Alkalosis refers to the reverse situation and is characterized by a strongly elevated $HCO_3^-$ concentration.

**Regulation of the Acid-Base Balance.** In compensated acidosis the pH can be held constant only if the drop of $HCO_3^-$ concentration is accompanied by a proportionate drop of the undissociated acid $H_2CO_3$, according to the Henderson-Hasselbalch equation. Indeed, the regulatory function of the lungs operates on this principle and consists in lowering the $CO_2$ tension: Accelerated ventilation removes $CO_2$ faster and keeps its partial pressure low.

The kidneys also participate in the regulation of the acid-base balance. By stepping up the acid output into the urine, they can counteract a rise of acid content in the blood. The kidneys accomplish this by exchanging $H^+$ for $Na^+$ in the tubules, or by eliminating $NH_4^+$ in the urine, in principle according to the equation $NH_3 + H^+ \rightleftharpoons NH_4^+$.

A partial failure of kidney function consequently is reflected by the ionic composition, by the alkali reserve, and possibly by the pH of blood. The regulation by the lungs also may lose its effectiveness and permit corresponding shifts of the alkali reserve (= *respiratory acidosis* or *alkalosis*). Finally, a metabolic defect may cause overproduction of organic acids, as has been known longest in the case of diabetes mellitus. The last situation is termed *"metabolic acidosis."* There are other pathological shifts of acid-base equilibria and of the electrolyte balance that are not discussed here.

## 5. Metabolism of Alkali and of Chloride

*Sodium* and *potassium* are distributed characteristically unevenly in the organism: $Na^+$ in extracellular fluids, especially in the interstitial spaces; $K^+$ in the cells. The intracellular $K^+$ concentration is less than the extracellular $Na^+$ concentration; since the cells contain relatively much osmotically active material, osmotic equilibrium would not be ensured otherwise. In some organs (nerve, muscle) this uneven distribution is the basis of their function, i.e. of excitability.

The dietary *sodium intake* fluctuates widely (75–300 meq/day). A large sodium reserve is found in bony tissue; about one-third of the total $Na^+$ content is bound in bones and can be mobilized in deficiency states. The *excretion* of $Na^+$ in urine is adjusted very closely to the intake by the kidneys. With a low $Na^+$ intake more $Na^+$ is reabsorbed and *vice versa*. The concentration in the extracellular space thus is maintained very constant at 135–140 meq/liter. This regulation is aided by another effect, the shift of water from the cells to the interstitium, which functions primarily by absorbing the initial shock of a sudden $Na^+$ intake.

The reabsorption of NaCl is under hormonal control by the adrenal cortex; insufficient activity of the gland results in drastic losses of $Na^+$ and $Cl^-$. The chief "mineral corticoid" is *aldosterone*; it also controls $K^+$ excretion, but in the opposite sense. The $Na^+$:$K^+$ ratio of the urine, therefore, is an indicator of adrenal cortex function.

With a normal diet, about 100 meq *potassium* are taken in daily. Not all of this is absorbed; 5–10% is excreted in the feces, and the remainder is eliminated by the kidneys. The reabsorption in the kidney is never complete, not even during periods of extensive $K^+$ depletion. $K^+$ deficiency shows up, among others, as muscular weakness and lethargy.

*Chloride* is taken up mainly through table salt. It is found mainly, but not exclusively, in the extracellular space and makes up the bulk of the anions in blood plasma.

Chloride ions are required for the production of HCl in the stomach, where they accompany the $H^+$ ions, which are secreted actively; the $Cl^-$ ions follow the $H^+$ ions passively to maintain electroneutrality. Because of the high concentration of $Cl^-$ ions in the stomach, persistent vomiting can lead to a state of chloride deficiency.

## 6. Calcium and Phosphate Metabolism

*Calcium* is not always available in sufficient amounts from the diet because it is usually absorbed incompletely. Absorbability of dietary $Ca^{++}$ depends greatly on the other food components. *Oxalate* and *phytin* (inositol hexaphosphate), in particular, impede the absorption in the small intestines by forming slightly soluble salts. *Citrate*, on the other hand, enhances the availability of $Ca^{++}$, probably by forming soluble complex salts. Lastly, *vitamin D* greatly improves the absorbability of $Ca^{++}$; the value of the vitamin in treating rickets is based, at least in part, on this effect.

Only part of the calcium present in blood is in the free, diffusible ionic form. The other part is bound to proteins. Hence, it is possible to have an overall calcium concentration as high as 5 meq/liter without any precipitation of insoluble $Ca^{++}$ salts.

**Metabolism of Bone.** The huge reservoir of calcium contained in the bones plays a unique role in the metabolism of calcium. More than 1 kg is bound there, whereas the daily intake is only around 1 gm. Bound calcium nevertheless performs a vital task; $Ca^{++}$ salts essential for the supportive tissue are mainly the minerals *hydroxyapatite* and *carbonate apatite*, and secondarily apatites with anions of organic acids. Their structure is illustrated in the diagram below.

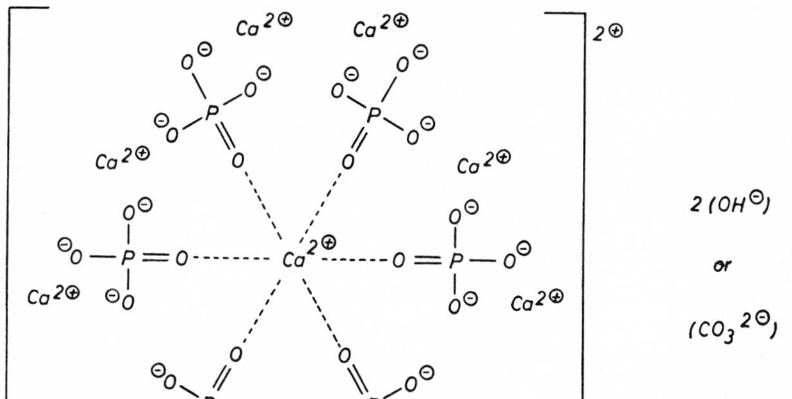

Apatites evidently consist of a complex cation with $Ca^{++}$ as the central atom surrounded by $Ca_3(PO_4)_2$ as ligands. Hydroxyapatite is the most common one. The mechanism of how these minerals are formed is still not clear; it probably involves a crystallization process on the surface of microcrystallites.

In spite of its relative insolubility, apatite is remarkably active metabolically. There is a continuous exchange between it and the $Ca^{++}$ and $HPO_4^{2-}$ ions circulating in blood. This rapid exchange between circulating $Ca^{++}$ ions and bony substance could be demonstrated only through the use of radioactive isotopes. This exchange is significant insofar as ions related to $Ca^{++}$, especially *strontium*, can be incorporated as well. During the past decade, large amounts of radioactive strontius ($Sr^{90}$) have been produced by repeated atmospheric atomic explosions and have been spread in the stratosphere. Rainfall brings it back to the surface of the earth, where it can be taken up by plants and eventually enter food (milk, for instance). Since radioactive strontium is an isotope with a very intense emission, considerable radiation damage (including genetic damage) results from a contamination with it. The danger is increased by the fact that strontium is locally concentrated and held in place in bone tissue.

The formation and breakdown of bone are vital processes carried out by special cells. *Mineralization* occurs in the *osteoblasts*, apparently involving alkaline phosphatase. The enzyme is especially abundant in areas of active ossification, while cartilage is free of it. The breakdown of bone in the *osteoclasts* serves to mobilize mineral material. The solubilization of apatite probably is a surface phenomenon, analogous to its formation.

**Regulation of Calcium Level.** *Parathormone* controls the metabolism of $Ca^{++}$. It activates the osteoclasts and thereby causes a demineralization of bone and a rise of the $Ca^{++}$ level in blood. It is not yet clear how these minerals are dissolved. *Citrate* probably plays a key role; at least, it occurs in relatively high concentrations in bony tissue. Bone tissue contains the enzyme system for forming citrate, but little aconitase and isocitrate dehydrogenase.

The production of parathormone normally is adjusted by the $Ca^{++}$ level in blood, a true feedback control mechanism. How this control mechanism operates is not known in detail. Generally, no "monitor organs" for such concentrations are known and not even a conceptual model has been developed.

*Phosphoric acid* is important not only as a component of bone. We have already seen that the various esters of phosphoric acid are indispensable for many metabolic reactions, for example in glycolysis or nucleic acid metabolism. The system $ATP \rightleftharpoons ADP + P_i$ is particularly important for innumerable cell functions. The formation of ATP occurs primarily in the respiratory chain.

In man the uptake and elimination of phosphate is generally balanced, with a tendency perhaps to take up too much rather than too little. Renal excretion is governed by parathormone (cf. Chapt. XX–7).

# 7. Iron and Zinc

Iron has already been discussed as a component of hemoglobin and cell hemins, both very important biocatalysts. Thus it is a vital element. The human organism contains 4–5 gm, of which $\frac{3}{4}$ is in hemoglobin. The cytochromes and iron-containing flavoproteins sequester only a small fraction of the total iron.

There is a special storage form for iron; a protein called *apoferritin* can absorb as much as 23% $Fe^{3+}$, to become known as *ferritin*. Ferritin occurs in the spleen and in the intestinal mucosa, where it regulates the absorption of iron. In blood, iron is transported bound to the closely related protein siderophilin (and not ferritin). Compared to hemoglobin, however, the amount of siderophilin is rather small.

The average life span of erythrocytes is about 2 months. One can calculate that every day 8–9 gm of hemoglobin are broken down and must be replaced. The iron freed during the breakdown of hemoglobin is conserved, however, instead of being excreted. In spite of this unusual recycling, iron must be supplied continually to make up for some inevitable losses. But absorption is generally poor and depends on the amount already present in the organism, since ferritin is involved in the absorption of iron. If the ferritin protein is saturated with iron, no further iron can be taken up; the uptake is inhibited with an oversupply. A deficiency state can be compensated only as long as the reserves last. *Iron deficiencies* caused by insufficient intake are quite common in some parts of the world. Women are affected particularly because they can lose appreciable amounts of iron through menstrual bleeding (subject to large individual differences).

**Zinc.** The organism contains between 2 and 4 gm of zinc, almost as much as iron. While iron occurs predominantly in blood bound in hemoglobin, zinc is in the cells. Some organs have a conspicuously high content of zinc; the eyes, up to 0.5%.

Zinc combines easily with proteins. That insulin binds zinc has already been mentioned (Chapt. IV–5). It is of functional significance in several enzymes, *carbonic anhydrase* and *peptidases*, for instance (Chapt. VIII–3). But otherwise too little is known about the role of zinc.

BIBLIOGRAPHY

C. L. Comar and F. Bronner (editors), "Mineral Metabolism," 2 Vols., Academic Press, New York, 1960–1963.

C. M. Coons, Iron metabolism, *Ann. Rev. Biochem.* **33**, 459–480 (1964).

H. W. Davenport, "The ABC of Acid-Base Chemistry," 14th ed., University of Chicago Press, Chicago, Illinois, 1958.

I. S. Edelman and J. Leibman, *Am. J. Med.*, **27**, 256 (1959).

J. R. Elkington and T. S. Danowski, "The Body Fluids," Williams & Wilkins, Baltimore, Maryland, 1955.

H. F. Weisberg, "Water, Electrolyte and Acid-Base Balance," 2nd ed., Williams & Wilkins, Baltimore, Maryland, 1961.

# CHAPTER XXII

# Nutrition and

# Vitamins

## 1. Caloric Value and ATP Yield

**Heat of Combustion.** Carbohydrates, fats, and proteins can replace each other as nutrients to a large extent. This is not very surprising in view of our discussion of metabolism (Chapt. XVIII), in which the concept of a "common terminal metabolic pathway" (Netter) through the citrate cycle and the respiratory chain was developed.

Physiologists have chosen the heat of combustion as the proper unit in which to express mutually equivalent amounts of nutrients. According to the "isodynamic law," the various foodstuffs may be substituted for each other as long as their heat of combustion remains the same. For purposes of calculation the following approximate values of physiological heats of combustion are generally used:

|              |              |
|--------------|--------------|
| carbohydrate | 4.1 kcal/gm  |
| protein      | 4.1 kcal/gm  |
| fat·         | 9.3 kcal/gm  |

In biochemistry, it is the custom to base all theoretical considerations on free energy, $\Delta F$, and not on the heat of reaction. This applies also to the above calculations, but the error incurred by using heat of combustion instead of free energy is rather minor (e.g. 4% with glucose).

**Production and Consumption of ATP.** A far better measure of the utilization of energy would be ATP production, since we have repeatedly described ATP as the driving power of numerous processes. In a sense, ATP is the organism's energy currency, a highly negotiable means of payment. One might easily think that it would be extraordinarily rare, because it is often obtained only by extensive detours, but the amount turned over is not at all small. It is easy to calculate[1] that during 24 hours

---

[1] The calculation is based on a turnover of energy of 2500 kcal and a storage of energy (as ATP) of 40%. This means that 1000 kcal of chemical energy are used for ATP synthesis, $1000 \div 7 = 140$ moles $= 140 \times 510$ gm $= 72$ kg ATP can be synthesized. (This is only an approximate value, of course, because $\Delta F$ is concentration dependent.)

man produces (and obviously breaks down again) some 70 kg of ATP, an amount equal to his body weight! Most of this (95%) is generated by oxidative phosphorylation in the respiratory chain.

The useful energy made available, expressed in percent yield of ATP, is practically the same for the oxidation of all principal foodstuffs. It actually represents the energy yield of the respiratory chain. About 40% of the free energy of oxidation is initially converted to ATP.

**Basal Metabolism.** For maintenance of body functions, temperature, and thermodynamic nonequilibria (e.g. concentration gradients), the organism requires a definite minimum amount of energy. This constitutes the so-called *basal metabolism.* Depending on size (body surface), age, and sex, the minimum energy may range between 1400 and 2000 kcal per day and thus is a rather flexible value. Hyperfunction of the thyroid gland elevates basal metabolism, whereas a period of malnutrition may depress it. Added to basal metabolism is the metabolism during activity; this may raise the total energy turnover to 2500 kcal per day for light or sedentary activity, and to 3500 kcal per day or more for heavy labor. Food intake is usually adapted to the requirements so well that body weight does not fluctuate appreciably. Imprudent habits, however, can easily result in undesirable accumulation of fat.

It has been noted that protein ingestion can effect a rise of basal metabolism. In addition to the normal turnover, 15–20% of the overall caloric intake is converted to heat. Rubner called this a "specific-dynamic effect," a rather unfortunate term, for its specificity is obscure and it is debatable whether there is a "dynamic" effect. Today one would say that the regulation of metabolism has been influenced, but the site of the effect cannot be defined.

Basal metabolism provides both the material and the energy for *de novo* synthesis and replacement of endogenous substances. In earlier days a distinction was made between the metabolism of structural substances and of fuel substances. Isotope tracer methods then showed that practically *all* structural substances of the organism are continuously renewed as well, with the possible exception of DNA, the genetic material. The biologic half-life may of course differ greatly in various tissues. Liver characteristically has a very rapid turnover.

**The Respiratory Quotient.** The end products of metabolism are chiefly $CO_2$, $H_2O$, and urea. The ratio

$$R.Q. = \frac{\text{volume of } CO_2 \text{ formed}}{\text{volume of } O_2 \text{ formed}},$$

called respiratory quotient, allows some conclusions as to the nature of foodstuffs combusted. Pure carbohydrate, oxidized according to the general formula

$$C_6H_{12}O_6 + 6\ O_2 = 6\ CO_2 + 6\ H_2O,$$

must have a ratio of $CO_2/O_2 = 1.00$. Similarly it can be shown that the biologic oxidation of fats has a respiratory quotient of 0.7, and of proteins, about 0.8. These quotients are the basis of many calculations in nutritional physiology.

## 2. Essential Food Components

**Nitrogen and Trace Elements.** For energy production the principal foodstuffs can replace one another extensively; even carbohydrates, usually the main source of calories, are not indispensable, as is shown by the dietary habits of Eskimos. The intake and elimination of the chemical elements must, of course, be balanced. Carbon and hydrogen are contained in all foodstuffs; oxygen is in the air. Nitrogen is derived predominantly from proteins. A certain minimum of protein must be taken in to maintain nitrogen balance. Since a certain amount of urea is excreted continuously—even during basal metabolism (at rest)—a corresponding amount of protein must be contained in food. The minimum of protein in the diet of man is around 20–30 gm per day (0.3 to 0.4 gm/kg body weight).

The mineral elements necessary for maintenance of the animal organism are: the *anions*, phosphate, chloride, iodide, and fluoride; and the *cations*, sodium, potassium, calcium, magnesium, iron, zinc, copper, manganese, cobalt, and possibly others.

Among the heavy metals, *iron* and *zinc* occupy the first place; they have been discussed in detail in Chapt. XXI–7. Many mineral substances are required only in minute amounts (trace elements). They are widely distributed and usually present in sufficient amounts in the diet. After all, our food is derived exclusively from living material, from plants or animals, and for that reason should contain all the essential elements. In some circumstances, however, deficiency symptoms may develop (the most widely known examples are the endemic goiter due to iodine deficiency, and anemia due to iron deficiency).

**Essential Amino Acids.** As mentioned before (Chapt. VIII–6), several amino acids found in proteins are not synthesized in the animal organism and are therefore indispensable components of the food. The following amino acids are essential for man:

| | | | |
|---|---|---|---|
| Valine | Isoleucine | Methionine | Phenylalanine |
| Leucine | Lysine | Threonine | Tryptophan |

The rat, whose nutritional requirements are even better known, needs histidine in addition to the above. Growing organisms have higher requirements than mature organisms; furthermore, even some nonessential amino acids (e.g., arginine and histidine) are growth promoting, because these apparently are not synthesized in sufficient quantities during conditions of growth.

**Essential Fatty Acids.** The higher unsaturated fatty acids are indispensable for the rat. Deprivation of these fatty acids results in loss of hair, disturbances of fluid balance, loss of reproductive faculty, and ultimately in death. Similar deficiency symptoms have not been observed in man, because the amounts required are so small (in the rat only 20 mg linoleic acid per day) and an absolutely fat-free diet is practically unknown. It is established, however, that man cannot synthesize the higher unsaturated fatty acids either. They should be particulary important in the nutrition of infants; the adult organism has large reserves to draw on.

## 3. Vitamins

Vitamins are essential food components, just as the essential amino acids are. The significance of vitamins, however, is much better appreciated by the general public.

The concept *vitamin* has undergone extensive revisions during the history of biochemistry. Hofmeister's definition—vitamins are substances which are indispensable for the growth and maintenance of the animal organism, which occur both in animals and plants and are present only in small amounts in food—is still valid today, but has been interpreted in various ways. Originally it was believed that there was only *one* vitamin, but soon a list had to be started. The substances prepared in pure form turned out to belong to completely different chemical classes of compounds. The categorical phrase "not synthesized in the animal body" became shaky and had to be replaced by more specific statements (such as what vitamin and what animal species). Indeed, for some time it was believed that the distinction between vitamins and hormones was no longer justifiable, although the two classes of active substances differ fundamentally: Hormones are regulatory substances, vitamins are accessory nutrients.

A thorough understanding of the vitamins has been provided by biochemical genetics. Plants and many primitive organisms are capable of synthesizing all necessary substances from the simplest starting materials, i.e. from simple sources of carbon and nitrogen, from minerals, and from energy. The more advanced organisms have lost some of these capabilities. Probably as a result of some mutational changes, the chains of synthesis of some important compounds were interrupted or abolished entirely. The compounds are no longer synthesized by the organism and have to be supplied in the diet. It is of secondary significance in this connection whether or not an essential food component possesses a catalytic function.

Vitamins are ordinarily defined as substances that act in *trace amounts*. Hence, the definition includes only substances with *catalytic functions*. Table XIX reveals that man's daily requirement for any vitamin (except ascorbate[2]) is less than 10 mg. The nature of the catalytic function is known for most vitamins: They are incorporated into coenzymes (cf. Chapt. VI).

**Deficiency Diseases.** A deficiency of certain vitamins is reflected in characteristic disturbances (deficiency diseases); occasionally only arrested growth is observed. Despite all the progress registered by "vitaminology" during past decades, culminating in the recognition of the role of vitamins as coenzymes, it still cannot be explained why the deficiency is expressed in terms of specific diseases instead of the expected general disturbances. The unusual sensitivity of the skin towards the lack of various vitamins is very conspicuous.

**Filling the Requirement of Vitamins.** Deficiency diseases appear very rarely under adequate nutritional situations. Such diseases are the consequence of unbalanced nutrition. *Hypovitaminoses* are actually clinically more significant than the avitami-

---

[2] The requirement for ascorbate is 75 mg per day. This requirement approaches that of the essential amino acids (for tryptophan, e.g., 250 mg; for threonine, 500 mg). If ascorbate were to be discovered as an essential factor today, perhaps it would not even be classified as a vitamin.

noses. A hypovitaminosis is a state of relative deficiency, without the classical symptoms of disease. This is the appropriate area for vitamin therapy.

The animal organism is able to perform the last synthetic step in the production of some vitamins; i.e. it can transform *provitamins* to the true vitamins. In such cases (e.g. vitamin A), the requirement is filled largely by consumption of provitamins.

Intestinal bacteria contribute considerably toward fulfilling the vitamin requirements listed in Table XIX. This can be considered an example of symbiosis. Man's requirement of vitamin K, for example, is filled almost entirely by the bacteria. Cows which received no thiamine or riboflavin still produced milk with a normal content of vitamins. And on the other hand, high doses of sulfonamides or antibiotics can liquidate the intestinal flora to such an extent that the source of vitamins stops suddenly and serious avitaminoses may develop unless the diet is corrected.

**Classification of Vitamins.** Vitamins are classified as either fat soluble or water soluble. This rather superficial classification is still useful because it indicates the best food source of a vitamin. Table XIX presents the principal vitamins; several factors whose significance is still debated (inositol, choline) have not been included.

## 4. Fat-Soluble Vitamins

**Vitamin A** is one of the isoprenoid lipids. It is closely related to *carotene*, its provitamin. The organism can produce vitamin A from carotene (cf. formula in Chapt. XIV–8). Two closely related substances, vitamin $A_1$ and vitamin $A_2$, are distinguished. Vitamin A alcohol is easily dehydrogenated by the organism to give the aldehyde (by an alcohol dehydrogenase and NAD). Vitamin A aldehydes are components of visual purple (see Chapt. XIV–8). The role in the visual process is the only well-established biochemical function of vitamin A.

In animal experiments, *vitamin A deficiency* is manifested first by cessation of growth; hence vitamin A was formerly thought to be a "growth vitamin." Evidently there must be roles for the vitamin other than in the visual process, and it is significant that these other roles can be filled by vitamin A acid. The acid (oxidation product of vitamin A aldehyde) is not reduced by the organism and cannot function in the visual process, but does support growth.

Several deficiency symptoms are known in man. At first, night blindness sets in; later, cornification of the epithelia around the eye (xerophthalmia) may develop.

**Vitamin D,** also called *calciferol*, is related to the steroids. It arises from $\Delta^{5,7}$-unsaturated sterols, the provitamins, by ultraviolet irradiation (cf. the diagram of formulas in Chapt. XIV–4). Thus, vitamin $D_2$ (ergocalciferol) arises from ergosterol; vitamin $D_3$ (cholecalciferol) from $\Delta^7$-dehydrocholesterol. In this connection it is important that $\Delta^7$-dehydrocholesterol is concentrated in the skin and therefore exposed to irradiation.

TABLE XIX

VITAMINS

| Letter | Name | Formula in Chapter | Role as Coenzyme | Deficiency Disease of Man | Daily Requirement[a] of Man |
|---|---|---|---|---|---|
| **I. Fat-Soluble Vitamins** | | | | | |
| A | (Axerophthol) | XIV-7 | Unknown (opsin) | Night blindness, xerophthalmia | 1.5–2.0 mg |
| D | Calciferol | XIV-4 | Unknown | Rachitis | 0.025 mg |
| E | Tocopherol | } XIV-9 | } In electron transport | Unknown (muscular dystrophy ?) | [5 mg] |
| K | Phylloquinone | | | Delayed blood clotting | [0.001 mg] own synthesis of the side chain |
| Q | Ubiquinone | } XII-1 | | Unknown | Probably own synthesis |
| F | Essential fatty acids | | — | Debated (dermatitis ?) | Unknown |
| | Thioctic acid (α-lipoic acid) | VI-4 | In oxidative decarboxylation | Unknown | Unknown (own synthesis?) |
| **II. Water-Soluble Vitamins** | | | | | |
| B$_1$ | Thiamine | VI-5 | Thiamine pyrophosphate | Beriberi (polyneuritis) | 0.5–1.0 mg |
| B$_2$ com-plex | } Riboflavin | VI-4 | Flavin-adenine dinucleotide | "Pellagra sine pellagra" | 1 mg |
| | Nicotinamide | VI-4 | Nicotinamide-adenine dinucleotide (phosphate) | Pellagra | Own synthesis[b] |
| plex | } Folic acid | VI-5 | Coenzyme F | Megaloblastic anemia | [1–2 mg] |
| | Pantothenic acid | VI-5 | Coenzyme A | Burning foot syndrome | [3–5 mg] |
| B$_6$ | Pyridoxine | VI-5 | Pyridoxal phosphate | Unknown | [1.5 mg] |
| B$_{12}$ | Cobalamin | VI-6 | In carboxyl shifts (in bound form) | Pernicious anemia | 0.001 mg |
| C | Ascorbic acid | XV-4 | In redox systems | Scurvy | 75 mg |
| H | Biotin | VI-5 | In carboxylations (enzyme bound) | Very rare ("egg white injury," dermatitis) | [0.25 mg] |

[a] Values in brackets indicate estimated amounts.

[b] Pellagra occurs only under the special condition when the body's own synthesis from tryptophan is restricted.

Little is known about the biochemical mechanism of vitamin D action. It promotes the absorption of $Ca^{++}$-ions in the gastro-intestinal tract and influences the metabolism of bone tissue. Deficiency of vitamin D results in the clinical syndrome *rachitis* (also in animal experiments), characterized by a softening (inadequate calcification) of the bones. Excessive administration of vitamin D produces a hypervitaminosis, during which calcium is again mobilized out of the bone structure; this hypervitaminosis resembles the action of the parathyroid hormone.

**Vitamin E** (*tocopherol*) is related to the quinones with the isoprenoid side chain and can easily be oxidized to a quinone (tocoquinone). The formula and synthesis have been discussed in Chapt. XIV–9. Various homologs of tocopherol occur naturally; they differ only in the number of methyl groups. Not enough is known about the biochemical mechanism of action of this vitamin. Several authors believe that it is involved in the respiratory chain (cf. Chapt. X–4).

Vitamin E was discovered as the antisterility factor of the female rat. Deficiency in experimental animals results mainly in atrophy of the testes and dystrophy of muscles. In man, a deficiency disease is not known; some authors, however, suspect that muscular dystrophy may be connected with vitamin E deficiency.

**Vitamin K** (antihemorrhagic vitamin, *phylloquinone*) is a naphthoquinone with an isoprenoid side chain. The side chain can be synthesized by the mammalian organism (Chapt. XIV–1, 9). For this reason, *menadione* ( = 2-methyl-1,4-naphthoquinone) has phylloquinone activity. Biochemically, vitamin K seems to be involved as a redox catalyst in the respiratory chain (Chapt. X–4), but the question is not yet solved.

The symptoms of vitamin K deficiency are a tendency to bleed and *disturbances in blood clotting*. Of the many clotting factors (end of Chapt. IV–9), prothrombin is affected primarily; it is produced in insufficient amounts in vitamin K deficiency. In man the deficiency symptoms are rather rare, because the intestinal flora produces enough of the vitamin to contribute materially in the supply.

**Ubiquinone** (*coenzyme Q*). The vitamin nature of this factor which has been discovered only recently is still uncertain. As with vitamin K, the side chain is synthesized by the mammalian organism (following the principle of isoprenoid synthesis, Chapt. XIV–1). Whether the aromatic ring is derived from an essential dietary component is still unknown.

Ubiquinone, as the name indicates, is distributed ubiquitously. This may well explain why deficiency symptoms have not yet been observed. It is assumed to be a redox component in the respiratory chain. Mitochondria contain relatively high proportions of ubiquinone.

**Vitamin F** is the designation for *essential fatty acids* (cf. Chapt. XII–1, and this Chapter, Section 2).

**Lipoic Acid** (*thioctic acid*) seems to be required only by microorganisms.

## 5. Water-Soluble Vitamins

**Thiamine** (*Vitamin $B_1$*) is one of the longest-known vitamins. Its chemical structure is somewhat complicated; it contains two heterocyclic rings (a pyrimidine and a thiazol ring, formula in Chapt. VI–5) connected at a quaternary N atom. It can easily be converted to the dihydro form, but its catalytic function does not seem to be that of a redox system. *Thiamine pyrophosphate* is the coenzyme of decarboxylases and aldehyde transferases. It plays a key role in *oxidative decarboxylation* of pyruvate (in the breakdown of carbohydrate) and of $\alpha$-keto glutarate (in the citrate cycle). Man's requirements of thiamine are calculated in conjunction with his caloric intake, since the demand for the coenzyme is apparently higher with a high overall metabolic rate.

*Beriberi* is the deficiency disease. It appears in individuals on an exclusive diet of polished rice, and results in neuritic symptoms and disturbances of heart functions. Some of the deficiency symptoms can be explained on the basis of the role of the vitamin in metabolism. Similar symptoms can be evoked artificially in birds (polyneuritis). Some evidence points to a role of thiamine in neural physiology; in any case, nerves contain unusually large amounts of thiamine.

**Vitamin $B_2$.** The deficiency symptoms—in man, chiefly lesions of the mucosa— were formerly explained by the lack of "vitamin $B_2$," but now are recognized to be more complex and to result from the absence of a number of factors. One speaks, therefore, of the "vitamin $B_2$ complex." The individual vitamins of the complex follow:

**Riboflavin** is an isoalloxazine derivative. Its chemical properties have already been discussed in Chapt. VI–4. It occurs in bound form in most foods as *flavin mononucleotide* (FMN) or *flavin-adenine dinucleotide* (FAD), or in *flavoproteins*. Milk alone contains free riboflavin.

The biochemical role has already been presented in detail (Chapt. VI–4, X–4). Riboflavin is a component of the "yellow enzymes," which are dehydrogenases. The isoalloxazine ring acts as a reversible redox system.

In *experimental animals* a deficiency of riboflavin impairs normal growth and causes symptoms of the skin. In man the principal symptoms of ariboflavinosis are dermatitis ("pellagra sine pellagra"), cheilosis (changes around the lips), and disorders of the eyes. The nutritional supply of the vitamin is adequate in general. Excessive amounts of riboflavin in the body are excreted in urine.

**Nicotinamide,** *niacinamide,* "pellagra-preventive factor," is a relatively simple compound (pyridine 3-carboxylic amide, formula in Chapt. VI–4). In the mammalian organism, including man, it can arise from tryptophan (cf. Chapt. VIII–11). Deficiencies, therefore, develop only under very special circumstances.

*Biochemical role.* Nicotinamide functions as a constituent of the *pyridine nucleotides*, which occupy a central role as hydrogen-transferring coenzymes (transport metabolites for hydrogen).

Deficiency of nicotinic acid may cause pellagra (a special form of dermatitis), diarrhea, and delirium. Interestingly enough, pellagra can be cured by the administration of tryptophan. This proves that the "vitamin" can be synthesized by the human organism. Pellagra appears endemically only where corn is the main constituent of food. Corn apparently contains a factor that restricts the biosynthesis of the vitamin; furthermore, corn protein contains little tryptophan.

**Folic Acid,** *pteroylglutamate*, is a derivative of pteridine; for chemical properties see Chapt. VI-5.

The biochemically active form, *tetrahydrofolate*, is the cofactor for the metabolism of single carbon fragments; it transfers activated formate or activated formaldehyde.

Folate was discovered as a growth substance for microorganisms. The situation is complicated by the fact that some organisms require only one component of the molecule, e.g. *p*-aminobenzoate, and other organisms need the entire folate molecule or even N-formyltetrahydrofolate ( = folinate or "citrovorum factor," named after *Leuconostoc citrovorum*).

In man, folate affects primarily the composition of blood (anemia, thrombocytopenia). A common cause of deficiency symptoms is a disturbance in the utilization of folate rather than inadequate dietary intake. Vitamin $B_{12}$ acts synergistically with folate.

**Pantothenic Acid** is a dipeptide and consists of *α,γ-dihydroxy-β,β-dimethylbutyric acid* and *β-alanine*. It can combine with *β-mercaptoethylamine* to give *pantetheine* (formula in Chapt. VI–5), which in turn is a component of *coenzyme A*. The SH group of the mercaptoethylamine is the active group of the coenzyme, which activates acetate and higher fatty acids and thus plays an extremely important role in metabolism.

In various animals, experimental deficiency of pantothenic acid causes various pathological conditions (pellagra in chickens; graying of hair in rats). True deficiency diseases are not known in man. A conjugate of pantothenic acid, pantetheine, is a growth factor for many microorganisms (the "*Lactobacillus bulgaricus* factor").

**Vitamin $B_6$** (*Pyridoxine*), is a substituted pyridine. Closely related are pyridoxamine phosphate and *pyridoxal phosphate*, which are important coenzymes for the metabolism of amino acids (Chapt. VIII–4). The generic term covering all these different compounds is vitamin $B_6$.

*Vitamin $B_6$ deficiency* may produce seborrhea-like symptoms. In addition, tryptophan catabolism is disturbed; kynurenine, 3-hydroxy-kynurenine, and xanthurenic acid appear in urine. Excess pyridoxine is oxidized to pyridoxinic acid (like pyridoxal, but with a carboxyl in place of the aldehyde group) and excreted.

**Cobalamin** (*vitamin $B_{12}$*) has by far the most complicated structure of all the vitamins (cf. Chapt. VI–6). The cyanide ion of cyanocobalamin may be replaced by other ions ($OH^-$, $NO_2^-$); the corresponding substances are then called hydroxycobalamin, nitritocobalamin, etc. Some analogs have a purine (adenine or hypoxanthine) in the nucleoside moiety in place of the benzimidazole residue. The ring structure resembles that of the porphyrins, but differs by the absence of one methine group.

Cobalamin is the *anti-pernicious anemia factor*. Minutest amounts (a few micrograms) cure pernicious anemia in man. The disease is characterized by a drastic decrease of the erythrocyte count (due to a disturbance in the maturation of red blood cells). Pernicious anemia does not arise from a dietary deficiency, but rather is caused by a defect in the absorption of the vitamin. Cobalamin (designated the *extrinsic factor*, in this connection) can be taken up by the human organism only in the presence of the *intrinsic factor*, a mucoprotein. The latter is formed in the gastric mucosa; its absence causes pernicious anemia.

Several other effects of cobalamin are known. Cobalamin is an essential growth factor for several bacteria. Furthermore, it is identical with the "animal protein factor," which has been noted to accompany animal proteins, but not plant proteins. Exclusive feeding of plant proteins to chickens, rats, and mice retards their growth and increases the mortality of their offspring.

**Vitamin C,** ascorbic acid, is a derivative of carbohydrates (formula in Chapt. XV–4). Ascorbate is part of one of the biochemical redox systems; it can be oxidized (reversibly) to give dehydroascorbate (formulas in Chapt. XV–4). Ascorbate oxidases are also known. Ascorbate is not a vitamin for most mammals, because it is biosynthesized by them to fill their own requirements.

The name *ascorbic acid* derives from scurvy, a deficiency disease much feared by mariners through the ages and curable by ascorbic acid. The principal manifestations are capillary lesions, hemorrhages, gingivitis, and loosening of the teeth. Man's requirement for the vitamin exceeds that of other vitamins by one or two orders of magnitude. The reason for this is obscure.

**Biotin** contains a condensed ring system consisting of two five-membered heterocycles (formula in Chapt. VI–5). In the conjugate *biocytin*, the carboxyl group of biotin is linked peptidically with the ε-amino group of lysine. A similar bond probably holds the vitamin to the protein molecule in the biotin-containing enzymes, which catalyze carboxylations (see Chapt. XII–6).

Biotin was discovered as a growth factor of yeast. Experiments with animals also produced deficiency symptoms (dermatitis, loss of hair) when avidin was administered. *Avidin* is a protein isolated from raw egg white that firmly binds biotin, and thus inactivates the vitamin. Excessive consumption of raw egg white apparently may cause biotin deficiency even in man.

BIBLIOGRAPHY

A. A. Albanese, "Protein and Amino Acid Nutrition," Academic Press, New York, 1959.
R. Ammon and W. Dirscherl, editors, "Fermente, Hormone, Vitamine," 3rd ed., Vol. 3: "Vitamine," Georg Thieme, Stuttgart, 1960.
R. S. Harris and K. V. Thimann, editors, *Vitamins and Hormones* (annual), Academic Press, New York.
M. Kleiber, "The Fire of Life," Wiley, New York, 1961.
W. H. Sebrell and R. S. Harris, "The Vitamins," 3 Vols., Academic Press, New York, 1954.

# CHAPTER XXIII

# Special Biochemical Functions
# of Certain Organs

Just as certain special structures perform particular biochemical functions within the cell (cf. Chapt. XIX), so do certain definite organs perform particular functions within the organism. Since this division of labor is very easily observed and need not be determined laboriously from quantitative measurements and from electron optical pictures, it has been known for a much longer time.

The primary tasks of the individual organs can be characterized as follows:

| | |
|---|---|
| Stomach, gut, kidney, lung | Digestion, absorption, excretion |
| Blood | Transport |
| Liver | Metabolism |
| Muscle | Conversion of chemical into mechanical energy (locomotion) |
| Bone and connective tissue | Support |
| Nervous system | Reception and conduction of stimuli. Neural correlation |
| Endocrine glands | Regulation of metabolism and development. Humoral correlation |

These functions are investigated both in physiology and in biochemistry. We can leave the discussion of the function of the organs to the physiologists and will limit ourselves to the biochemical basis of the functions, especially those of the digestive tract and of the nerves and muscles.

## 1. The Digestive Tract

Food is digested by hydrolases which catalyze the cleavage of high molecular foodstuffs (proteins, starch, neutral fat) to low molecular, largely water-soluble components (amino acids, simple sugars, glycerol, fatty acids). These hydrolytic products are more easily absorbed than the polymeric compounds. Hydrolysis commences in the oral cavity with the action of saliva, which contains *amylase* and attacks starches in particular. Hydrolysis continues in the stomach and gut, where the proteases and lipases predominate. The various enzymes have been discussed in connection with their substrates (cf. Chapt. VIII–1, XVII–6); the mechanical events during digestion are treated in textbooks of physiology. In addition

384

to the enzymes the secretions of the digestive glands contain *mucin* (a mixture of mucoproteins and mucopolysaccharides); the slippery mucus insures a smooth passage of the foodpulp.

The secretion of *hydrochloric acid* into the stomach is a remarkable accomplishment of the *gastric mucosa*. The acid is surprisingly concentrated (pH around 1.5). Such a low pH is bactericidal and thus provides an effective protection against infections. The chief cells of the stomach produce *pepsinogen*, which is activated to *pepsin* by the acidity (cf. Chapt. VIII–2), and also a mixture of mucoproteins, which includes the *intrinsic factor* (cf. Chapt. XXII–5).

The generation of acidity entails the active transport of $H^+$ ions against a concentration gradient. Osmotic work is performed and the presence of ATP is required (i.e. a lack of oxygen brings the the process to a halt). The $H^+$ ions are derived from $H_2O$ (which of course dissociates spontaneously to $H^+$ and $OH^-$). They are transported against a concentration gradient of 1:1,000,000 (from pH 7 to pH 1). The $OH^-$ ions, which would shift the pH toward the alkaline side and would aggravate the osmotic work, are buffered by carbon dioxide: $HO^- + CO_2 = HCO_3^-$. The enzyme carbonic anhydrase is involved in this last reaction and ensures the rapid attainment of equilibrium between $CO_2$ and $H_2O$, or rather $CO_2$ and $OH^-$.

The *pancreas* is the most important site of production of digestive enzymes: proteinases, peptidases, lipases, nucleases, etc. (cf. Chapt. VII–9, VIII–1, and XII–2). The amount of enzymes produced has been estimated to be 15–30 gm per day, which is considerable. The pancreatic juice, itself alkaline, enters the intestine and first neutralizes the acidity coming from the stomach. When acidic food pulp passes the pylorus, the latter stimulates the pancreas to elaborate more of its digestive enzymes. The secretion of pancreatic juice is regulated by tissue hormones ("secretin," Chapt. XX–12).

*Bile*, formed in the liver, contains as its principal component the bile acids (Chapt. XIV–5), which aid the digestion and resorption of fat; bile also contains cholesterol and bile pigments, which are the end products of hemoglobin catabolism. Some of the components are reabsorbed by the intestine and are passed through the blood and liver back to the gall bladder (entero-hepatic circulation). Part of the bile pigments invariably enter the colon and impart the normal brown color to feces.

*Absorption.* The cleavage products formed by the action of digestive enzymes are initially dissolved in the digestive juices—of which more than 8 liters per day may be produced. From this solution, the small intestine absorbs the low molecular substances and water; the colon absorbs chiefly water. Part of the absorption follows the laws of osmosis and diffusion (passive transport) and part of it proceeds by active transport, by mechanisms which are still largely unknown. The absorbed substances reach the liver through the portal vein.

## 2. The Liver

Only a small portion of the absorbed hydrolysis products is burned in the liver for the immediate production of free chemical energy. The larger portion is utilized for the synthesis of endogenous substances (such as glycogen, proteins; some fats. but many phosphatides, and cholesterol). Modern concepts no longer permit a distinction between structural metabolites and fuel metabolites; the same substances serve both purposes. The structural components of the organism are being broken down continuously, used for the production of energy, and replaced by newly formed substances.[1] Indeed, "life is characterized by continuous chemical motion" (Knoop).

The liver is the organ where very many of these interconversions and synthetic processes occur; if we were to enumerate all the biochemical functions that are localized in the liver, the greater part of this book would have to be reprinted here. Liver cells are particularly rich in mitochondria (up to 2000 per cell) and for that reason are especially well equipped to carry out metabolic processes.

The liver occupies a central role in *protein metabolism*. Almost all the amino acids freed by intestinal digestion reach the liver through the portal vein. Some are used for the synthesis of proteins (e.g. the blood proteins *albumin* and *fibrinogen*); some are broken down further. Nitrogen appears as urea; a large portion of the carbon skeletons is used for the synthesis of glycogen. Glycogen formation from protein (*gluconeogenesis*) is the true source of *liver glycogen*. The process is stimulated by the adrenocortical hormones (= corticoids) and may be carried out even at the expense of liver protein. The significance of liver glycogen and of hepatic gluconeogenesis for the overall balance of carbohydrate and the constancy of blood sugar has already been discussed in connection with the regulation of blood sugar (cf. Chapt. XX–10).

## 3. Blood

Blood consists of cellular elements and of plasma. Its function is to transport material.

*Blood plasma* can be studied only if clotting is prevented by the addition of certain anticoagulants (see Chapt. IV–9, at the end). If blood (or plasma) is allowed to clot and the clot is centrifuged off, serum is obtained, which still contains nearly all of the proteins of blood. The properties of these proteins are discussed in Chapt. IV–9. Under pathologic conditions, proteins from cells of diseased organs—even enzyme proteins—are found in blood. This is the basis of diagnosis by serum enzymes.

Blood also contains many low molecular weight substances. The content of N-containing, low molecular weight substances varies. The nonprotein nitrogen content (or "residual nitrogen," mainly urea, some amino acids, uric acid, creatine, creatinine) is an indicator of kidney function; the concentration is usually low be-

---

[1] No biochemical necessity for this can be easily recognized, but, this principle, which requires considerable expenditure of free energy, is observed in all phyla of the animal kingdom and appears to be advantageous to the species in the evolutionary process of natural selection.

cause these substances are excreted. The glucose content is regulated by hormones and generally is very constant (cf. Chapt. XX-10). Lactate appears in blood as a product of anaerobic glycolysis. The concentration is low at rest (below 20 mg/100 ml), but may climb to 140 mg/100 ml with strenuous muscular exertion. For the mineral content and the buffer capacity of blood see Chapt. XXI-4.

The most numerous cellular components of blood are the erythrocytes; there are about 5 million per cubic millimeter. In addition, there are leucocytes and platelets. The morphology of blood obviously has diagnostic value, but cannot be discussed here. Erythrocytes contain hemoglobin, the red blood pigment, whose function (oxygen transport) was explained in Chapt. IX-4.

*The Lung.* Erythrocytes are charged with oxygen in the lungs. Of all the gases of the air, only oxygen is absorbed and bound reversibly to hemoglobin. In areas of low oxygen tension, i.e. in peripheral tissues and organs with very active oxidative metabolism, oxygen is released again[2] and is reduced to $H_2O$ by the respiratory chain. Carbon dioxide arises from decarboxylation reactions usually proceeding at the same place, i.e. in the identical cell. Carbon dioxide is transported in the blood stream to the lungs and exhaled, if it does not reenter metabolism (cf. $CO_2$ fixation, Chapt. VI-5, "Biotin," and XV-9).

## 4. Kidney and Urine

The kidney is an organ for both excretion and metabolism. It contains relatively high concentrations of amine oxidases and amino acid oxidases, i.e. enzymes involved in the production of free ammonia. This helps to explain the very high concentration of $NH_4^+$ ions in urine. The enzymes of oxidative metabolism (citrate cycle, respiratory chain) are also present—as in all cells. The kidney consumes relatively large proportions of oxygen and produces much ATP, which it needs for its excretionary activity.

Kidney function comprises three processes which are localized in histologically separate sections:

1. Ultrafiltration of plasma; the result is primary urine, free of proteins and cells, but with the same concentration of low molecular substances as the plasma.

2. Reabsorption of water and dissolved substances back into the blood stream. This process entails active transport and consequently consumes energy.

3. Secretion of certain substances into urine, also by an active transport mechanism.

**Ultrafiltration.** This term refers to the filtration of low molecular substances with the retention of high molecular ones, particularly the proteins. Blood proteins are retained in the glomeruli and normally do not enter primary urine at all. Protein in urine is invariably a sign of kidney damage or other diseases.

---

[2] A very intriguing aspect of comparative biochemistry is the comparison of dissociation curves of hemoglobin (as a function of decreasing oxygen tension) with the general behavior of the corresponding animal species.

**Reabsorption.** Water is the substance reabsorbed in the greatest amount. It is an open question whether water molecules are themselves transported actively or transported in conjunction with the active transport of dissolved substances (see Chapt. XXI–3).

The concentration of primary urine to about 1/100 of its original volume demands osmotic work. Calculations show, however, that this osmotic work is almost negligible compared with the total energy production by the kidney. The highly selective process of secretion apparently requires much additional expenditure of energy.

Most of the low molecular substances that are flushed into the primary urine during ultrafiltration are reabsorbed to a large extent. This is true even for such typical excretion products as urea and uric acid, but especially for free amino acids and glucose, which are reabsorbed completely so long as the blood sugar level stays normal. If the level exceeds 0.16%, some of the sugar is excreted in the urine. Reabsorption is active transport (Chapt. XXI–3) and the enzymic apparatus of active transport can no longer cope with the amounts delivered by the blood. Similar conditions prevail for other substances; the capacity for reabsorption (formerly called "kidney threshold") differs widely for various substances.

**The Secretory Activity of the Renal Tubules** also constitutes an active transport of substances from the blood stream into the urine. Ammonium ions originating from metabolic processes in kidney tissue enter urine in this fashion; the $NH_4^+$ concentration is very low in blood. $H^+$ ions are also secreted actively; urine, consequently, is appreciably more acidic (pH 5–6.5) than blood (pH 7.4). Foreign substances, such as penicillin and other drugs, are also removed from blood by active transport.

**Hormonal Regulation of Kidney Function.** Three different hormones act on the kidney: the *adrenocortical hormone* (mineralcorticoid effect, cf. Chapt. XX–2), the *parathyroid hormone* (parathormone, cf. Chapt. XX–7), and the *antidiuretic hormone* (ADH, vasopressin, cf. Chapt. XX–9) of the hypophyseal posterior lobe.

Aldosterone restricts the excretion of $Na^+$ while stimulating the excretion of $K^+$. Parathormone also acts on the mineral balance by promoting phosphate excretion through the kidney. The most important hormone undoubtedly is vasopressin, which is responsible primarily for the reabsorption of water. In its absence, enormous volumes of very dilute urine are excreted (Chapt. XX–9).

**Urine.** The composition and the daily amount of urine depend on the intake of liquids. Data on the daily excretion of various substances, therefore, are always given on a 24-hour basis. Urea is the chief waste product. The excretion of N-containing compounds generally is of prime importance (carbon in food is largely exhaled as $CO_2$). The amount of urea excreted can be correlated directly with the amount of protein catabolized: 1 gm urea nitrogen = 6.25 gm protein.

Other nitrogen-containing excretion products are uric acid, creatinine (arising from creatine by ring closure), the $NH_4^+$ already mentioned, and various other components occurring in small amounts.

The significance of excreting inorganic salts (especially the alkali salts of chloride, sulfate, phosphate) has been mentioned. Certain combinations of ions result in precipitation of slightly soluble salts in the urine or in the passage ways (kidney or bladder stones).

*Pathologic Components of Urine.* In various diseases one can often find anomalous components in the urine; for this reason urine analysis has always had great diagnostic value. It is even more valuable today, since refined quantitative techniques can measure changes in concentrations of normal components and detect traces of hormone metabolites (cf. Chapt. XIV–6). Discussion of these anomalous conditions is the subject of pathologic physiology and of diagnostics; only a very few substances will be pointed out.

*Proteins* in the urine usually indicate kidney damage. Albumin (with the lowest molecular weight) is excreted predominantly. The Bence-Jones protein, which appears in certain bone marrow tumors, was noticed because of its peculiar solubility properties; the protein precipitates when a solution of it is warmed to 45–60°, and dissolves again at 80°; evidently it is not denatured by heat.

*Sugar.* Glucose excretion either is due to a high intake of carbohydrates (alimentary glucosuria) or is symptomatic of diabetes mellitus. In many severe cases "ketone bodies" (acetone, acetoacetate, β-hydroxybutyrate) are excreted along with sugar.

Galactosuria and pentosuria, if not of alimentary origin, are caused by hereditary defects.

*Pigments.* Bile pigments appear with hepatitis; they are derived from the metabolism of hemoglobin (Chapt. IX–5). Uro- and coproporphyrins may enter the skin in cases of poisoning or of genetic defects of the biosynthesis of the hemin pigment.

## 5. Other Excretion Products

Quantitatively carbon dioxide is the most important waste product. It is eliminated by the lungs. The establishment of the equilibrium between dissolved and gaseous carbon dioxide is catalyzed by carbonic anhydrase, a Zn-containing enzyme. Furthermore, hemoglobin becomes a stronger acid by addition of oxygen, i.e. it releases $H^+$ ions, and thus enhances the evolution of $CO_2$ from $HCO_3^-$:

$$HCO_3^- + H^+ \rightleftharpoons H_2O + CO_2$$

Compare Chapt. XXI–4 for the significance of this reaction for the acid-base relationship.

*Feces* consist largely of mucous substances from the gastro-intestinal tract and remnants of intestinal bacteria. Their odor is due to indole and scatol; their color is due to the bile pigments (Chapt. IX–5).

Both water and salts are excreted with *sweat*. It contains about 0.4% NaCl, but only traces of organic substances.

## 6. Biochemistry of Muscles

Muscles convert chemical energy to mechanical energy. Some muscles perform work continuously (e.g. heart muscle), others only intermittently (skeletal muscle). Chemical energy (ATP) is generated by the conversion and especially by the oxidation of the foodstuffs, for the most part in the muscle itself.

**Enzymes in Muscle.** The enzymes of skeletal muscles are primarily those of anaerobic glycolysis. They are present in high concentrations; according to Bucher, more than 40% of the total dissolved protein is enzyme protein. Anaerobic glycolysis produces ATP, which provides the energy required for muscle contraction.

In other muscles, especially the heart muscle, sufficient energy for contraction is supplied by oxidative metabolism. These muscles contain unusually large mitochondria (called sarcosomes) in which the enzymes of the citrate cycle and the respiratory chain are localized. This is true, too, of the flight muscles of insects, which must perform continuously, or at least for prolonged periods of time. Skeletal muscles, of course, also have oxidative metabolism; there is even a special oxygen carrier, *myoglobin*, which binds oxygen molecules reversibly, as hemoglobin does, but with greater affinity.

**Energy-Rich Phosphates.** The immediate fuel to power the muscle is adenosine triphosphate, the hydrolysis of which provides the energy for contraction. Creatine phosphate, another energy-rich phosphate in equilibrium with ATP, is the energy reserve:

$$\text{Creatine-P} + \text{ADP} \rightleftharpoons \text{ATP} + \text{creatine}$$

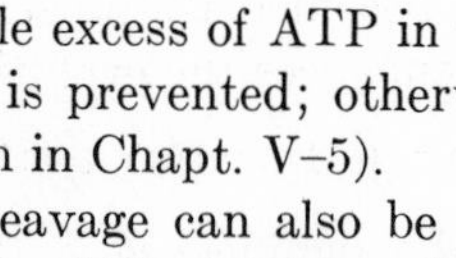

*Creatine phosphate*

Creatine phosphate[3] is always readily available to regenerate ATP. This system has an advantage over a simple excess of ATP in that an unfavorable ATP/ADP ratio due to ATP hydrolysis is prevented; otherwise this would limit the work capacity of ATP (cf. the graph in Chapt. V–5).

The free energy of ADP cleavage can also be used. Muscle and other tissues contain the enzyme *myokinase*, which catalyzes the following reaction:

$$2 \text{ ADP} \rightleftharpoons \text{ATP} + \text{AMP}$$

At equilibrium, the three phosphates are present at roughly equal concentrations. By this reaction ATP is formed at the expense of ADP, or AMP is phosphorylated

---

[3] In crustaceans, creatine phosphate is replaced by arginine phosphate; here, too, the phosphate group is bound to the guanidino nitrogen.

to give ADP, which can in turn be phosphorylated further, in the respiratory chain, for example.

**Contractile Proteins of the Muscle Fibrils.** The fibrils of muscle contain, besides the insoluble and little-studied structural proteins, also a few soluble, fibrillar proteins, which participate actively in muscle contraction: they are myosin, actin, and tropomyosin.

The protein *myosin* has the solubility properties of a globulin. Its X-ray diagram reveals it to be a fibrous protein of the $\alpha$-keratin type (structure: $\alpha$-helix). Its molecular weight is 600,000. Myosin can be broken down under relatively mild conditions to two components: *L-meromyosin*, with a molecular weight of 120,000, and *H-meromyosin*, of molecular weight 320,000. L-meromyosin can be subdivided with urea to subunits with molecular weights of 4,600. Myosin possesses enzymic properties and cleaves ATP; the reaction is stimulated greatly by $Ca^{++}$ and inhibited by $Mg^{++}$.

*Actin* is less soluble than myosin. It occurs in two forms. Globular *G-actin* has a molecular weight of 70,000 (as the monomer) or 140,000 (as the dimer). The addition of salts converts it to the polymeric *F-actin*, a fibrillar protein that has a high molecular weight and sediments quickly in the ultracentrifuge. In solution, actin and myosin combine easily to give *actomyosin*. Under certain conditions, one can isolate native actomyosin from muscle.

*Tropomyosin* forms very viscous solutions of polymeric particles. The protein can be obtained crystalline and has a molecular weight of 50,000 to 150,000 (depending on the animal species). The molecule is very asymmetric. It is a component of the myofibrils, particularly of smooth musculature.

**Electron Microscopic Structure of the Muscle Cell.** The usual cell components are of little significance in striated muscles. The cells are filled with myofibrils which produce the familiar striped pattern. Electron optical studies reveal that the A-bands consist of thick, thread-like molecules, presumably myosin. The space between these molecules is occupied by thin filaments which continue into the isotropic area (I-band) and end at the Z-line. The latter consists of actin and tropomyosin (cf. Fig. 62 and 63). According to recent investigations by A. F. Huxley and H. E. Huxley, the thin fibrils slide past the myosin fibrils during contraction so that the I-bands eventually disappear and the Z-line approaches the end of the myosin fibrils.

**Contraction by Model Systems.** It is possible to prepare threads from the isolated proteins myosin and actin. Alternatively, by extracting muscle with glycerol, all soluble material is removed and only the contractile proteins are left. Either system contracts upon addition of ATP; this phenomenon strongly supports the assumption that ATP reacts directly with the contractile proteins. Mechanical work can be performed by these systems, and in the case of the glycerol extract this work is of the same order of magnitude as the mechanical tensions observed *in vivo* (4 kg/sq cm cross section; H. H. Weber and co-workers). Contraction is not accompanied by changes in secondary structure of the proteins; the $\alpha$-helix is retained as the predominating structural feature. Again, the same applies to the living muscle.

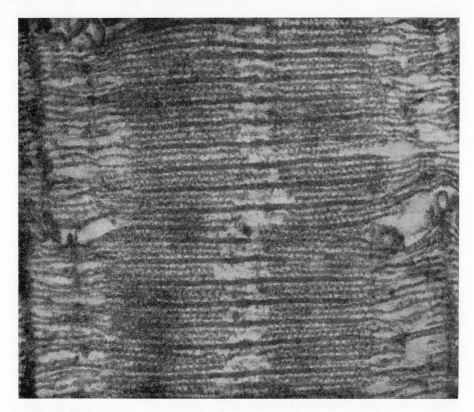

FIG. 62. Electron microscopic photograph of muscle (thin section; cf. schematic drawing in Fig. 63). A large number of small cross links can be distinguished between the thin filaments, which are linked together (near the edges of the photograph) in the Z-line, and the thick lines. Enlargement: 120,000-fold.

From H. E. Huxley, in D. Nachmansohn (Ed.), "Molecular Biology," Academic Press, New York, 1960.

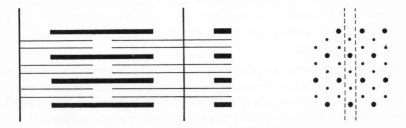

FIG. 63. Schematic representation of myofibrils. The heavy lines represent myosin filaments; the light horizontal lines, the actin filaments. The vertical lines are the Z-lines. At right, a cross section is shown. It reveals the hexagonal symmetry of the arrangement of the filaments. The direction of the cut of the thin section is indicated by the broken lines. Compare with the electron optical picture in Fig. 62.

ATP is important not only for contraction, but also for relaxation. It affects the elastic properties of the muscle and renders it stretchable (H. H. Weber). The softening effect (plasticity effect) is clearly differentiated from the contracting effect. Pyrophosphate and various nucleotide triphosphates also possess this softening effect, but to a less pronounced degree. Probably the interaction between actin and myosin is weakened and actomyosin dissociates to its components.

The softening effect of ATP must be distinguished from the physiological relaxing factor of the muscle. The relaxing factor can be isolated in the form of small grana with a diameter of 700–1000 Å. They contain an enzyme system catalyzing the active transport of calcium ions; 1 ATP is required for each $Ca^{++}$ ion transported inside.

**Contraction of the Living Muscle.** It is not yet possible to provide a final picture of the biochemical and biophysical processes occurring during contraction. Szent-Györgyi has stated: "Theories on muscle contraction are available by the dozens. The author himself [i.e. Szent-Györgyi] is responsible for a few of them."

Today every theory of muscle contraction must be based on the observation by electron optical methods that during contraction actin and myosin filaments slide into each other in telescopic fashion. This process is accompanied by ATP cleavage. It is believed now that the resting muscle contains a system in which the ATP-ase effect of myosin is largely inhibited by the lack of $Ca^{++}$. The inflow of $Ca^{++}$ ions induces "excitation" and ATP cleavage, accompanied by a strong interaction between the myosin and actin filament. As a result, the muscle can no longer be stretched. The side chains of the protein molecules presumably react with one another under the influence of ATP; it is not known what groups in particular react. In any case, the system of filaments now develops mechanical forces, and the muscle shortens because bundles of filaments slide into each other.

The end of the twitch and subsequent relaxation of the muscle is brought about by the relaxing factor, which is closely associated with the grana fraction just mentioned. These grana contain, first, a $Ca^{++}$-accumulating system. This "ion pump" removes the $Ca^{++}$ ions from the cytoplasmic space and the ATP-ase activity appears inhibited as a consequence. Secondly, the grana probably also produce a labile relaxing factor which splits the bonds between actin and myosin and thus enables the muscle to be stretched passively back to its resting position. *Rigor mortis* essentially is caused by the absence of this relaxing factor, leaving the strong bonds between myosin and actin intact.

# 7. Biochemistry of Nerve Conduction

The nervous system serves essentially for the transmission of excitation. This includes the transmission of stimuli across synapses and nerve ends to the muscles. Stimuli are transmitted by chemical means: Active agents are released which can be identified at the synapses and the nerve ends. According to the nature of these active agents, we distinguish between *adrenergic* and *cholinergic* nerves. Adrenergic (postganglionic sympathetic) fibers elaborate *norepinephrine* (formula and biosynthesis in Chapt. XX–5); this compound also possesses the activity of the "accelerating substance" (Loewi). At the motor end plates and at many synapses ("cholinergic nerves"), *acetylcholine* is released, which is identical with Loewi's "vagus substance." Acetylcholine is cleaved by a special enzyme acetylcholine esterase, thus ensuring the rapid disappearance of the effect.

**Fine Structure of Nerves.** The conducting elements of the nervous system are the long nerve fibers, most of which are clad in relatively thick myelin sheaths (myelin-containing nerves). The sheath is discontinuous at the "rings of Ranvier" and only a thin membrane separates the neuroplasm from its surroundings at these points. Neural excitation leaps from one such ring to the next (saltatory conduction).

The *myelin sheath* consists of numerous lamellae which develop from a triple-layered membrane (protein-lipid-protein). This membrane is produced by the Schwann cells and envelopes the nerve axon; in the process, two protein layers are always brought in close contact. The lipid layer consists mostly of various phosphatides and cholesterol in an ordered arrangement, and imparts insulating properties to the myelin sheath.

**Bioelectric Potentials of the Nerve.** In the resting state, the interior of the nerve, i.e. the axoplasm, has a potential of $-60$ mV with respect to the surrounding liquid. This membrane potential is established by an appropriate distribution of ions: the $Na^+$-ion concentration is very low inside, but relatively high on the outside, and the permeability of the membrane for $Na^+$ ions is very small. The interior contains more $K^+$ and $Cl^-$. This typical nonequilibrium is maintained by a continuous supply of energy: $Na^+$ ions diffusing into the interior are transported back out. Very graphically, one speaks of a "sodium pump powered by ATP." This apt expression, however, does not provide a scientific explanation of the phenomenon. The mechanism of active transport has yet to be explained.

ATP is derived primarily from oxidative metabolism (oxidative phosphorylation in the respiratory chain).

**Excitation of the Nerve** momentarily changes the permeability. $Na^+$ ions flow in (passively, following the concentration gradient) and the polarization is reversed. As a result, the interior becomes positively charged. $K^+$ ions then flow out. The state of increased permeability lasts only a few milliseconds; it is followed by the original state of low permeability, during which the $Na^+$ ions distribute themselves (and later are pumped out again). Finally, the resting potential is re-established.

The shock of the action potential induces a drop of the resting potential at an adjacent location (in myelated nerves, at the next ring), resulting in excitation accompanied by a repetition of ion migrations ($Na^+$ inflow, $K^+$ outflow). The excitation travels in this manner along the nerve to the synapse or to the end plate.

**Cause of the Permeability Change.** The ionic theory of nerve conduction, which is well supported by measurements of the concentration of ions, assumes changes of permeability to be the *cause* of the excitation. Nachmansohn hypothesizes that acetylcholine is essentially involved in the sudden development of permeability. Electrical stimulation liberates acetylcholine from its storage form (probably bound to a protein) and it then forms complexes with an active protein. One can conceive that the protein layers become permeable by changes in their tertiary structure and let $Na^+$ ions stream into the interior of the nerve cell. This condition, however, does not last. Acetylcholine is split by choline esterase to choline and

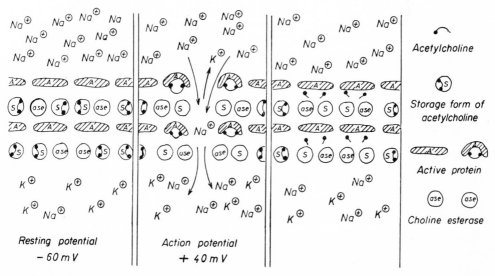

FIG. 64. According to Nachmansohn's hypothesis of permeability changes in nerves. The diagram shows three phases: left, the resting state; middle, the influx of Na⁺ with concomitant reversal of potential; right, the state after hydrolysis of actylcholine. *S*, *A*, and *ase* represent the proteins. Further explanations in the text.

acetate; the protein reassumes its original configurations, so that the "holes" are plugged again, and the very brief changes in permeability are ended (see the diagram, Fig. 64). The great rapidity of the processes—complete permeability lasts less than 1 millisecond—can be explained satisfactorily by the very high turnover number of the enzyme choline esterase, which amounts to 18 million. This means that each enzyme molecule can split 300 molecules of acetylcholine per millisecond.

For complete restitution of the original state, the resynthesis of acetylcholine (from choline and acetyl-CoA, which can come from metabolism or intermediary activation of acetate by ATP) and the removal of Na⁺ by the "sodium pump" are required.

Nachmansohn's hypothesis is not yet proved, although it is supported by considerable experimental evidence. Electrophysiologists generally reject the hypothesis without offering another explanation of the changes of permeability. Further work must be performed in order to elucidate these phenomena of molecular biology.

## 8. Summary

Our understanding of the activity of cells and organs has been advanced greatly by biochemical methods and the ancillary instrument, the electron microscope. Much remains to be accomplished, and the successes thus far achieved promise more. The methods have demonstrated their usefulness and will certainly solve many more problems.

A scientific explanation of biologic phenomena can be expected to come only from the study of molecules. In this region morphology, physiology, and biochemistry meet; a clear distinction among these disciplines has ceased to exist.

BIBLIOGRAPHY

B. Andersen and H. H. Ussing, Active transport, *in* "Comparative Biochemistry," M. Florkin and H. S. Mason, eds., Vol. II, p. 371. Academic Press, New York, 1960.

W. Hasselbach, The coupling of chemical and mechanical reactions during contraction and relaxation of the muscle, *Fortschr. Zoo.*, **15** (1962).

W. W. Kielley, The biochemistry of muscle, *Ann. Rev. Biochem.* **33**, 403–430 (1964).

D. Nachmansohn, editor, "Molecular Biology," Academic Press, New York, 1960.

S. V. Perry, Muscular contraction, *in* "Comparative Biochemistry," (M. Florkin and H. S. Mason, eds.), Vol. II, p. 245. Academic Press, New York, 1960.

H. Reichel, "Physiologie des Muskels," Springer, Berlin, 1960.

# Appendix

## List of Abbreviations Frequently Used in Biochemical Literature

**Introduction.** Abbreviations are used in the current biochemical literature to an alarming extent. Some publications are rendered almost unintelligible by the numerous abbreviations, and often this is the vehicle for introducing "lab" jargon into the literature. We have been intentionally conservative about the use of abbreviations and should like to suggest that abbreviations be used cautiously, especially since no general agreement has yet been reached for many of them.

Abbreviations are justified in formulas of proteins and other high molecular weight substances whose individual components are indicated by such symbols. In a sense, this is nothing but an extension of the use of chemical symbols. Monomers are abbreviated by lower case letters; they are listed in the Systematic List, below.

Though we discourage the use of abbreviations in general, we provide a list here because they do appear frequently in the literature, especially in original contributions.

### 1. Alphabetic List

| | |
|---|---|
| Acetyl-CoA | Acetyl coenzyme A, "active acetate" |
| ACTH | Adrenocorticotropic hormone |
| Ad (or A) | Adenine |
| ADH | Alcohol dehydrogenase |
| ADP | Adenosine diphosphate |
| AMP | Adenosine monophosphate |
| AT-10 | Dehydrotachysterol (antitetany compound 10) |
| ATP | Adenosine triphosphate |
| BAL | 2,3-Dimercaptopropanol (British antilewisite) |
| CDP | Cytidine diphosphate |
| CF | Citrovorum factor (a folate derivative) |
| ChE | Choline esterase |
| CMP | Cytidine monophosphate |
| Co I, Co II | Codehydrogenase I and II, Diphospho- and triphosphopyridine nucleotide, now officially nicotinamide-adenine dinucleotide (phosphate) |
| CoA | Coenzyme A ("A" stands for acyl activation) |
| CoF | Coenzyme F ("F" stands for formyl and formaldehyde activation) |
| CTP | Cytidine triphosphate |

| | |
|---|---|
| DFP | Diisopropylfluorophosphate |
| DNA | Deoxyribonucleic acid |
| DNP | Dinitrophenyl- (substituted amino acid, e.g.) |
| DNS | Desoxyribonucleinsäure (German) |
| DOC | Deoxycorticosterone |
| DOCA | Deoxycorticosterone acetate |
| DPN, DPN$^+$ | Diphosphopyridine nucleotide |
| DPNH, DPNH$_2$ | Reduced diphosphopyridine nucleotide |
| e, or e$^-$ | Electron |
| EDTA | Ethylene diamine tetraacetic acid |
| FAD | Flavin-adenine dinucleotide |
| FADH$_2$ | Flavin-adenine dinucleotide, reduced form |
| FMN | Flavin mononucleotide |
| FSH | Follicle-stimulating hormone |
| GDH | Glucose dehydrogenase |
| $\alpha$-GP | $\alpha$-Glycerophosphate (glycerol 1-phosphate) |
| GSH | Glutathione (reduced form) |
| GSSG | Glutathione (oxidized form) |
| Hb | Hemoglobin |
| HbO$_2$ | Oxyhemoglobin |
| HCG | Human chorionic gonadotropin |
| HDP | Hexose diphosphate |
| HMG | Human menopausal gonadotropin |
| HMP | Hexose monophosphate |
| ICSH | Interstitial cell-stimulating hormone |
| IDP | Inosine diphosphate |
| IMP | Inosine monophosphate |
| INH | Isonicotinic hydrazide |
| IP | Isoelectric point |
| ITP | Inosine triphosphate |
| $\alpha$-KG | $\alpha$-Ketoglutaric acid (oxoglutarate) |
| LDH | Lactate dehydrogenase |
| LH | Luteinizing hormone |
| LTH | Luteotropic hormone |
| MSH | Melanocyte-stimulating hormone |
| MW | Molecular weight |
| NAD, NAD$^+$ | Nicotinamide-adenine dinucleotide, formerly DPN |
| NADH, NADH$_2$ | Reduced nicotinamide-adenine dinucleotide |
| NADP, NADP$^+$ | Nicotinamide-adenine dinucleotide phosphate, formerly TPN |
| NADPH, NADPH$_2$ | Reduced nicotinamide-adenine dinucleotide phosphate |
| NMN | Nicotinamide mononucleotide |
| PABA | $p$-Aminobenzoic acid |
| PAL | Pyridoxal phosphate |
| PAMP | Pyridoxamine phosphate |
| PAS | $p$-Aminosalicylic acid |
| PCMB | $p$-Chloromercuribenzoate |
| PEP | Phosphoenolpyruvate |
| P | Inorganic phosphate |
| PMSG | Pregnant mare serum gonadotropin |
| PNA | Pentose nucleic acid |
| PP | Pyrophosphate (inorganic) |

| | |
|---|---|
| RNA | Ribonucleic acid |
| RNS | Ribonucleinsäure (German) |
| STH | Somatotropic hormone |
| TCA | Trichloroacetic acid |
| Thx | Thyroxine |
| TPN, TPN$^+$ | Triphosphopyridine nucleotide |
| TPNH, TPNH$_2$ | Reduced triphosphopyridine nucleotide |
| TPP | Thiamine pyrophosphate |
| TSH | Thyrotropic hormone |
| TTC | Triphenyl tetrazolium chloride |
| UDP | Uridine diphosphate |
| UDP-Gal | Uridine diphosphate galactose |
| UDP-Glc (UDP-G) | Uridine diphosphate glucose |
| UMP | Uridine monophosphate |
| UTP | Uridine triphosphate |

# 2. Systematic List

## (a) Amino Acids

| | | | | |
|---|---|---|---|---|
| Ala | Alanine | | Ileu, i-Leu | Isoleucine |
| Arg | Arginine | | Leu | Leucine |
| Asp | Aspartic acid | | Lys | Lysine |
| Asp-NH$_2$ | Asparagine | | Met | Methionine |
| Cys-SH | Cysteine | | Pro | Proline |
| Cys-S- | $\frac{1}{2}$ Cystine | | Phe | Phenylalanine |
| Cys-SO$_3$H | Cysteic acid | | Ser | Serine |
| Dopa | Dihydroxyphenylalanine | | Thr | Threonine |
| Glu | Glutamic acid | | Thx | Thyroxine |
| Glu-NH$_2$ | Glutamine | | Try | Tryptophan |
| Gly | Glycine | | Tyr | Tyrosine |
| His | Histidine | | Val | Valine |

## (b) Nucleoside Phosphates

| Abbreviation for the | | | | Name of the |
|---|---|---|---|---|
| Monophosphate | Diphosphate | Triphosphate[1] | Nucleoside | Nucleoside |
| AMP | ADP | ATP | A (Ade) | Adenosine |
| CMP | CDP | CTP | C (Cyt) | Cytidine |
| GMP | GDP | GTP | G (Gua) | Guanosine |
| IMP | IDP | ITP | I (Ino) | Inosine |
| TMP | TDP | TTP | T (Thy) | Thymidine |
| UMP | UDP | UTP | U (Uri) | Uridine |

[1] These abbreviations refer to the 5'-phosphates or 5'-polyphosphates. 3'-Phosphate is designated by numerals, e.g. A-3-P = adenosine 3-phosphate; if ambiguous, the 5'-phosphates can also be expressed in the same manner: A-5-P$_2$ stands for adenosine 5-pyrophosphate (ADP).

## (c) Sugars

| Rib | Ribose | Glc | Glucose[2] |
|-----|--------|-----|-----------|
| deRib | Deoxyribose | Gal | Galactose |
| Rul | Ribulose | Man | Mannose |
| Xyl | Xylose | Fru | Fructose |
| Xul | Xylulose | | |

[2] Glucose may not be abbreviated as Glu, since this symbol has already been reserved for glutamic acid. The often used abbreviation G should also be avoided because of the possible confusion with guanine (=G). Sugar phosphates may be abbreviated in the same way: Glc-6-P = glucose 6-phosphate, and Fru-1-P,6-P = fructose 1,6-diphosphate.

## (d) Coenzymes: Cf. Table X (Chapt. VI-3).

## (e) Hormones: Cf. Table XVIII (Chapt. XX-1).

## Chronological Table of Important Biochemical Discoveries

| | |
|---|---|
| 1773 | Discovery of urea (Rouelle) |
| 1779 | Preparation of glycerol from olive oil (Scheele) |
| 1783 | Discovery of extracellular digestion of proteins (Spallanzani) |
| 1789 | Respiration as oxidation (Lavoisier) |
| 1815 | Elucidation of the over-all reaction of alcoholic fermentation (Gay-Lussac) |
| 1815 | Discovery of optical activity (Biot) |
| 1828 | Synthesis of urea from ammonium cyanate: The first synthesis of an organic compound occurring in a living organism (Wöhler) |
| 1837 | Investigation of the enzymic cleavage of amygdalin with almond emulsin (Liebig and Wöhler) |
| 1836–39 | Establishment of fermentation as a catalytic process (Berzelius and Liebig) |
| 1847 | Diastatic degradation of starch to maltose (Dubrunfaut) |
| 1857 | The vitalists' theory of fermentation (essentially dependent on living cells) by Pasteur |
| 1869 | Discovery of nucleic acids (Miescher) |
| 1890 | First crystallized protein: Egg albumin (Hofmeister) |
| 1893 | Classification of enzymes as catalysts in the sense of physical chemistry (Ostwald) |
| 1897 | Discovery of cell-free fermentation (E. and H. Buchner) |
| 1902 | Formulation of proteins as polypeptides (Hofmeister, E. Fischer) |
| 1903 | Isolation of the first hormone: Epinephrine (Takamine, Aldrich) |
| 1905 | Role of phosphoric acid in fermentation (Harden and Young) |
| 1905 | Discovery of β-oxidation (Knoop) |
| 1912 | Theory of dehydrogenation in biologic oxidations (Wieland) |
| 1922 | Isoprene rule as a building principle of numerous natural products (Ruzicka) |
| 1925 | Rediscovery of cell hemins (cytochromes) (Keilin) |
| 1925 | Formulation of sugars as pyranoses (Haworth) |
| 1926 | Isolation of the first vitamin: Thiamine (Jansen and Donath) |
| 1926 | First crystallized enzyme: Urease (Sumner) |
| 1925–30 | Determination of molecular weights of many proteins with the ultracentrifuge (Svedberg) |
| 1929 | Discovery of "labile" phosphate: Adenosine triphosphate (Lohmann; Fiske; and Subarrow) |

1929      Characterization of the "Atmungsferment" as a hemin compound (Warburg)
1929–34 Isolation of many steroid hormones (Butenandt, Doisy, Laqueur, Reichstein)
1932      Discovery of the yellow enzyme (Warburg; Theorell)
1932      Discovery of the ornithine or urea cycle (Krebs and Henseleit)
1933      New scheme of glycolysis and alcoholic fermentation (Embden-Meyerhof)
1935–36 Discovery of the connection between vitamins and coenzymes. Isolation of the pyridine
          and flavin coenzymes (v. Euler, Theorell, Warburg)
1935      Threonine as a new, and the first essential, amino acid (Rose)
1935      Isolation of the first crystallized virus: Tobacco mosaic virus (Stanley)
1937      Formulation of the citric acid cycle (Krebs; Knoop and Martius)
1938      Discovery of transamination (Braunstein and Kritzmann)
1939–44 Isolation and structural determination of the first antibiotic: Penicillin (Fleming, Florey,
          Chain, Johnson)
1944      Mechanism of action of gene factors through enzymes (Butenandt, Kühn)
1944      Isolation of the pneumococcal transformation factor and its characterization as deoxy-
          ribonucleic acid (Avery)
1948      Introduction of the centrifugation method for the isolation of cell fragments (Schneider
          and Hoogeboom, Potter)
1951      Elucidation of "active" acetate (Lipmann; Lynen)
1952      Helical structure of proteins (Pauling) ∟
1953      Structural determination of insulin (Sanger)
1953      Discovery of the pentose phosphate cycle in glucose breakdown (Horecker; Dickens)
1954      ↙Helical model of nucleic acids (Watson and Crick)
1958      Proof of the infectivity of pure virus nucleic acids (Gierer and Schramm)
1958      Isopentenyl pyrophosphate as active isoprene (Lynen)
1961      Decoding of the base code of nucleic acids (Nirenberg; Ochoa)

# Index

Acid references are included among entries for the ions (salt forms) of the acids, with a few exceptions. Thus, for example, "citrate" includes all entries for citric acid.

## A

A-bands, 391
Abbreviations, alphabetic list of, 397–399
  of amino acids, 399
  of nucleoside phosphates, 399
  of sugars, 400
Absorption, in digestive tract, 384
Absorption spectra of nicotinamide-adenine dinucleotides, 96
Accelerators and blood clotting, 65, 66
Accelerin, 66
Acetal(s), 7, 259, 294
Acetal phosphatide (artifact), 226
  formula of, 229
Acetaldehyde, from pyruvate, 279
  from threonine, 167, 168
  redox potential of, 192
Acetate, 10
  activation of 107
  oxidation of, 318–319
Acetoacetate, 220
  and amino acids, 159, 160, 161–163
  formation of, 219–220
  from leucine, 221, 222
Acetoacetate cycle, 219
Acetoacetyl coenzyme A, 219, 235–236
Acetoin formation, 279
Acetone, 219, 220
Acetylcholine, 356
  and nerves, 393, 394
  formation of, 107
Acetylcholine esterase, mechanism of action, 82
Acetyl coenzyme A, 77, 107, 220, 221
  and biosynthesis of cholesterol, 235, 236
  and fatty acid synthesis, 222, 223
  and ketogenesis, 219
  $\Delta F°$ of hydrolysis, 77
  formation of, 280
  from fatty acid oxidation, 217
  from leucine, 221, 222
  key intermediate, 317–318
  reactions of, 107–108
    of carboxyl group, 107
    of methyl group, 108
  syntheses with, 318
Acetyl-coenzyme A carboxylase, 88, 222

N-Acetylgalactosamine, 234, 266, 312
N-Acetylglucosamine, 311, 313
N-Acetylglutamate, 158
N-Acetylneuraminic acid (sialic acid), 234, 313
N-Acetylneuraminyl-(2→6)-N-acetylgalactosamine, 313
3-Acetylpyridine, 98
Acid anhydride, 12
Acid-base balance, 368–370
  regulation of, 369
Acid chloride, 12
Acidosis, 369
  metabolic, 370
  respiratory, 370
Aconitase, 207
  inhibited by fluorocitrate, 79
cis-Aconitate, and citrate cycle, 207, 211
ACTH, see Adrenocorticotropic hormone
Actin, 391, 393
F-Actin, 391
G-Actin, 391
Action potential, in nerves, 394–395
Activated acid derivatives, 12
Activated aldehyde, 160
Activated fatty acid and oxidative decarboxylation, 160
Activated glucuronate, 302
Activated succinate, from $\alpha$-keto glutarate, 170, 172
Activation of amino acids, 132
  of monosaccharides, 300
  of phosphorylase, 309, 310
Active acetaldehyde, 160
  formula of, 111
Active acetate, 160, see also Acetyl CoA
  and anabolism, 318
  and citrate cycle, 205, 206, 207, 210–211
  and coenzyme A, 107
  key intermediate, 317–318
Active bicarbonate, 220, 221, 222, 223
Active carbonate (biotin), 110
Active carbon dioxide (biotin), 110, 111, 158, 221, 222
Active carboxyl, 222, 223
Active $C_1$ fragment, 108–109
Active formaldehyde, 109, 120, 167, 168, 292–293

Active formate, 109, 167, 168
  from histidine, 171
Active glucose, 105, 302
  reactions of, 301–303
Active glycolaldehyde, 111, 269, 270
Active isoprene, 236, 237
Active methyl, 104, 166
Active site of enzymes, 82
Active state of respiratory chain, 198
Active sulfate, formation of, 103
  formula of, 104
Active transport, 367–388
  definition of, 367
  diagram of, 367
  HCl production, 385
  in kidney, 387, 388
Activity coefficient, 10
Actomysin, 391, 393
Acyl adenylate, 217
Acyl coenzyme A, and fatty acid synthesis, 222, 223
  and phosphatide synthesis, 229
Acyl coenzyme A dehydrogenase, 86
Acyl dehydrogenase, 217, 220
S-Acyldihydrolipoate, 208
Acyl residue, 12
Acyloin formation, 269–270
N-Acylsphingosine, 226
Adenine, 116, 117, 118, 123, 124, 125, 133, 134
Adenohypophysis, 349
Adenosine, 117, 118, 121
  in coenzymes, 95, 99
Adenosine diphosphate (ADP), 101
  and muscle, 390
  and oxidative phosphorylation, 200–201
  and regulation of respiration, 328–330
  and respiratory chain, 198
  formula of, 101
  phosphorylation of, 276, 319
Adenosine 3′,5′-diphosphate and coenzyme A, 106
Adenosine monophosphate (AMP), 100
  formula of, 101
  transfer of, 103
Adenosine 3′,5′-monophosphate, cyclic, 309, 310
  formation of, 103
  formula of, 310
Adenosine 5′-phosphate, 121, 122
Adenosine phosphorylsulfate, 103
Adenosine pyrophosphate (ADP), 101
Adenosine triphosphatase activity, in muscle, 393

Adenosine triphosphate (ATP), 77, 93, 100, 101–103, 310
  and active transport, 367
  and amino acid activation, 132
  and bicarbonate activation, 222, 223
  and bile acids, 244, 245
  and cholesterol biosynthesis, 237
  and coupled reactions, 75
  and fatty acids, 216–217
  and glycolysis, 274–275
  and group transfer, 102–103
  and HCl production, 385
  and muscle contraction, 390, 391, 393
  and phosphatide synthesis, 230
  and phosphorylase activation, 309, 310
  and photosynthesis, 287
  and respiratory chain, 193–194, 198, 199–201
  and urea formation, 157–159
  consumption of, 374–375
  energy turnover, 374–375
  $\Delta F°$ of hydrolysis, 77
  $\Delta F$ of hydrolysis depending on concentrations, 77
  formation of, 316, 319
    from citrate cycle, 210
    in photosynthesis, 285–286
    with kinases, 103
  formula of, 75, 101
  hydrolysis of, 102
  in methionine activation, 166
  production, 374–375
  reactions of, 102–103
  yield, 374–375
Adenosyl group, transfer of, 102–103
Adenosylhomocysteine, 105
Adenosylmethionine, 93, 230, 318
  formation of, 104
  formula of, 104
  as methyl donor, 104
Adenotropic hormones, 348
Adenylic acid, 121, see also Adenosine 5′-monophosphate
Adenylic acid system, and coupled reactions, 76
  and photosynthesis, 285–286
Adermin, 112
Adipose tissue, and insulin, 351
ADP, see Adenosine diphosphate
Adrenal cortex, 335, 338
  biologic significance of, 337
  synthetic capability of, 337
Adrenal medulla, 343
Adrenaline, see Epinephrine

Adrenergic nerves, 393
Adrenocortical hormones, 335–337, 386
    biosynthesis of, 335–336
    therapeutical effects, 337
Adrenocorticotropic hormone (ACTH), 348–
    349, see also Corticotropin
    structure, 38
Aerobic dehydrogenases, 202
Aerobic glycolysis, 280–281
Agar agar, 265, 306
Aggregates of proteins, 55–56
Aglycon, 295
Agmatine, 154
Alanine, 25
    and transamination, 155
    catabolism of, 159–160
    formula of, 21
    from tryptophan, 164–165
β-Alanine, 29, 37, 119, 154, 292–293, 382
    and coenzyme A, 106
Albinism, 137
Albumin(s), 61, 64
    and bilirubin, 182
    and electrophoresis, 62–63
    egg, 55
    in urine, 389
    as plasma fraction V, 63
    serum (human), 55
Alcaptonuria, 137, 162
Alcohol(s), 4
    dehydrogenation of, 5
    oxidation of, 189
Alcohol dehydrogenase, 86
    and ethanol, 279
    and visual process, 252
    mechanism of action, 97
Alcoholate ion, 189
Alcoholic fermentation, 273–279
Aldehyde(s), 6
    formation of, 189
Aldehyde dehydrogenase, 279
Aldehyde hydrate, 7, 259
Aldolase, 87, 269, 275
Aldolase reaction, 269
Aldol condensation, 8, 207, 269
    and photosynthesis, 290
Aldopentoses, 264
Aldoses, 256–258
Aldosterone, 337
    and kidneys, 388
    formula of, 247
Alkali, metabolism of, 370
Alkali reserve, 369

Alkaloids
    plant, amino acids in synthesis of, 154
    steroid, 241–242
Alkalosis, 370
Allantoin, 122
Allopregnane derivatives, 247
Allothreonine, 27
    and isomerism, 17
    in phalloidin, 41
Alloxan diabetes, 346
Alloxazine, 3
Amaurotic idiocy, Tay-Sachs type, 232
Amide(s), 12
    formation, 6
        and acetyl coenzyme A, 107
Amine(s), 5
    dehydrogenation of, 6
Amine oxidases, in kidney, 387
Amino acid(s), 20ff.
    activation of, 132–133
    and alkaloid synthesis, 154
    aromatic, metabolism, 161–165
    catabolism of, 320
    chemical properties of, 20–24
    classification of, 24–25
    decarboxylation of, 154
    dissociation constants of, 22
    essential, 156, 376
    fate of carbon skeleton, 159ff., 320
    glucogenic, 159
    and gluconeogenesis, 281–283
    indispensable, see Amino acids, essential
    ketogenic, 159
    outline of metabolism of, 152–154
    oxidative decarboxylation of, 159–161
    requirements in mutants, 156
    separation of, 30–33
    supplying $C_1$ fragments, 165–167
    transamination of, 155–156
    utilization in the liver, 386
Amino acid-activating enzymes, 88, 114
Amino acid decarboxylases, 155
    and reaction specificity, 78
Amino acid-derived hormones, 336
Amino acid oxidase(s), 86, 157
    in kidney, 387
    and reaction specificity, 78
Amino acid transaminases and reaction speci-
    ficity, 78
Amino acid sequence, and base code, 134–135
    information for, 133
    and messenger RNA, 133
    in peptides, 35

Aminoacyl-AMP, 77
    $\Delta F°$ of hydrolysis, 77
$\alpha$-Aminoadipate, 29, 169, 170
$p$-Aminobenzoate, 108–109, 382
$\gamma$-Aminobutyrate, 29, 154, 356
Aminoethanol, 155
Aminohexoses, in gangliosides, 233–234
$\alpha$-Amino-$\beta$-keto adipate, 173, 174
$\delta$-Aminolevulinate, 170, 172–174, 178
Aminopeptidase, 147, 148, 152
Aminopropanol, 155
$p$-Aminosalicylate, 341
Amino sugars, 266, 311
Ammonia, and urea cycle, 157, 158
    formation in kidney, 387
AMP, see Adenosine monophosphate
Amygdalin, 295
Amylase, 87
    action of, 307
    dextrinogenic, 307
    saccharogenic, 307
    salivary, 384
$\alpha$-Amylase, 307
$\beta$-Amylase, 308
Amylopectin, 305–306
Amylose, 305
Amytal, and NADH$_2$ dehydrogenase, 199
Anaerobic glycolysis, diagram of, 278
    in muscle, 390
Androgens, 338
    biologic function, 338
    biosynthesis of, 247–248
$5\alpha$-Androstane, 239
$5\beta$-Androstane (etiocholane), 239
$5\beta$-Androstanolone, 247, 338
Androstenedione, 248, 338
Androsterone, 247, 248, 338
Anemia, megaloblastic, 379, 383
    pernicious, 379, 383
Angiotensin, 355
Angiotonin, 355
Animal starch, 306
Anions, essential in diet, 376
Anserine, 37, 38
Anterior lobe, hormones of, 348
    of hypophysis, 346
Anthranilic acid, and tryptophan, 292
Anthrone, 263
Antibiotics, 30, 40–41
Antibodies, 60
Anticoagulant, heparin, 312
Antigens, 60
Antihemophilic globulin, 66

Anti-pernicious anemia factor, 383
Antithyroid substances, 340–342
Apatites, 371
Apoenzyme, 68–69, 90
Apoferritin, 372
Appendix, 397–401
Arabinose, 264
    formula of, 257
Arachidonic acid, formula of, 214
Arginase, 170
    and urea cycle, 158
Arginine, 29, 154
    and metabolism of glycine, 168
    and urea cycle, 158
    catabolism of, 170–171
    formula of, 21
Arginine phosphate, 390
Argininosuccinate, 158
Ariboflavinosis, 381
Aromatic amino acids, metabolism of, 161–165
Aromatic compounds, biosynthesis by plants,
    291–292
Aromatic plant products, 291–292
Aromatic ring, 2
    enzymic cleavage of, 202
    in estrogens, 338, 339
    hydroxylations of, 203–204
Aromatic ring A, and estrogens, 248
Ascorbate, 267–268, 379, 383
    formula of, 268
    redox potential of, 192
Ascorbate oxidase, 202, 268, 383
Asparagine, 21, 25, 28
Aspartate, 28, 154
    formula of, 21
    metabolism of, 169
    and purine synthesis, 120, 121, 122
    and pyrimidine synthesis, 119
    and transamination, 156
    and urea cycle, 158, 159
Assay, optical, with NAD, 96
Assimilation, 284ff.
Association, of insulin, 55–56
    of protein molecules, 55
Astaxanthine, 249
Asymmetric carbon atom, 15
Atmungsferment, 185, 194, 196
ATP, see Adenosine triphosphate
Auxin, 358, 359
Auxotrophic, 156
Avidin, 110, 383
Axerophthol, 379
Axial, 228

Axial orientation, and steroids, 240
8-Azaguanine, 122
Azaserine, 30

**B**

Bacterial viruses, 140–141
Basal matabolism, 373
    definition, 373
    dependent factors, 373
    and thyroxine, 340–341
Base code, 134
    and amino acid sequence, 134
    and messenger RNA, 134–135
Base pairing, 125, 126, 127, 128, 130, 131
Base ratios in DNA, 123
    in RNA, 137
Base sequence as code for amino acid sequence,
    128, 134
Base sequence of DNA, and amino acid se-
    quence, 133
Bases, organic and cyclic, 6
$B_{12}$ coenzyme, 93
Beeswax, 215
Beet sugar, *see* Sucrose
Bee venom, 231
Bence-Jones protein, in urine, 389
Benedict's test, 263
Benzaldehyde, 295
Benzene ring, 3
    biosynthesis of, by plants, 291–292
Benzoylglycine, 25
Benzyl penicillin, 40
Betaine, 25
    degradation of, 167, 168
Beriberi, 379, 381
Bial's test, 263
Bicarbonate, and purine biosynthesis, 121
    and urea cycle, 157
Bicarbonate buffer system in blood, 369
Bifidus factor, 267
Bile, 385
Bile acids, 244, 385
Bile pigments, 182, 385
Bilirubin, 182, 183, 303
Bilirubin glucuronide, 182
Biliverdin, 182, 183
Biocytin, 383
Biogenic amines, 154, 155
Biologic oxidation, 187ff.
Biopterin, 108
Biotin, 93, 110–111, 220, 221, 222, 281, 379, 383
    and avidin, 110
    formula of, 110

Biotin enzyme, 220
Bisphosphatidylglycerol, 231
Blood, 386–387
    function of, 386
    ionic composition of, 368–369
    normal components, 386–387
    pathological components, 386
Blood clotting, 62, 65–66, 379, 380
    diagram of, 66
Blood glucose, 387
    elevation of, 352
    hormonal regulation, 350–353
    and insulin, 345–346
    lowering of, 351
    regulation of, diagrammed, 351
Blood group substances, 313–314
Blood pigment, 180–182, 387
Blood plasma, 61, 386
    enzymes in, 65
    ionograph of, 369
    pH of, 368
Blood pressure, and vasopressin, 347
Blood serum, 62, 386
Blood sugar, *see also* Blood glucose
    of insects, 297
Boat form of cyclohexane ring, 239–240
Body fluids, 361
    and pH values, 368
Bohr effect, 181
Bone, metabolism of, 371–372
Brain, main ganglioside of, 233
Branched-chain fatty acids, metabolism of,
    220–222
Branched-chain starch, 305
$\alpha$-Branching, 220–221
$\beta$-Branching, 221–221
Branching in amylose and glycogen, 305, 306
Branching enzyme, 311
Breeding instinct, and lactotropin, 349
5-Bromouracil, 128
Buffer composition of blood, 368–369
Buffers, 11–12
Burning oot syndrome, 379
Butyrate, 10
Butyryl coenzyme A, 219

**C**

$C^{14}$, 174
C-acylation with active acetate, 107
Cadaverine, 154
Caffeine, 122
Calciferol, 243, 378, 379

Calcium, absorption of, 371
    and blood clotting, 65, 66
    and myosin, 391, 393
    and parathormone, 344–345
    in bone, 371
    metabolism of, 371–372
    protein-bound, 371
Calcium levels, regulation of, 372
Caloric value, 374–375
Cane sugar, *see* Sucrose
Capsular material of bacteria, 129, 313
Carbamylaspartate, 119
Carbamyl phosphate, formation of, 157–158
    in pyrimidine synthesis, 119
Carbobenzoxy amino acid, 36
Carbobenzoxy derivatives of amino acids, 23
Carbocyclic rings, 3
Carbohydrates, 256ff., *see also* Mono- and Di-
    saccharides
    catabolism of, 315–316
    color reactions of, 263
    definition of, 256
    heat of combustion, 374
    metabolism of, 315–317
    respiratory quotient, 375
Carbon, fixed forms, 284
    radioactive, 173, 174
Carbon cycle, 284
Carbon dioxide, 121
    and HCl secretion, 385
    and urea cycle, 157
    assimilation of, 284ff.
    chief waste product, 389
    fixation of, 288–290
    formation of, 205ff.
    reduction to carbohydrate, 288–290
    transport in blood, 387
Carbonate apatite, 371
Carbonic acid in blood, 368–369
Carbonic anhydrase, 389
    and carbamyl phosphate, 158
    and HCl secretion, 385
    and zinc, 373
    in blood, 368
Carbon monoxide, 181
Carbonium cation, 207
Carbonyl compounds, 6
Carbonyl group, 6
Carboxybiotin, 111, 158
Carboxybiotin-enzyme complex, 110
Carboxylation, of actyl CoA, 222, 223
    of pyruvate, 280–281
    reductive, 281

Carboxylic acid(s), 9
    dissociation of, 9
    formation of, 7
Carboxyl shift and vitamin $B_{12}$, 113
Carboxypeptidases, 87, 147, 148, 151
    and amino acid sequence, 43
Cardiac stimulants, 242
Cardiolipin, 228, 231
Carnosine, 37, 38
Carotenes, 249, 250, 378
    cleavage of, 251
$\alpha$-Carotene, 249, 250
$\beta$-Carotene, 249, 250
$\gamma$-Carotene, 249, 250
Carotenoids, 249–251
Cartilage, 312
Casein, 151
Catabolic effect, 337
Catalase, 181, 185
Catalysis, 72–73
Catalysts, function diagrammed, 72
Catechol, 189
    oxidation of, 204
Catecholase effect, 204
Cathepsin, 147, 149
Cations, essential in diet, 376
Cell hemins, 93
Cellobiose, 297, 303
    formula of, 298
Cellular organization, diagram of, 324
Cellulase, 308
Cellulose, 303–304, 308
Cephalins, 199, 226, 227
    hydrolysis of, 227–228
    methylation of, 230
Cerebron, 233
Cerebrosides, 225ff., 226, 233
Ceruloplasmin, 65
Cetyl palmitate, 215
$C_1$ fragments from amino acids, 165–167
$C_2$ fragment and carbohydrates, 269–270
$C_3$ fragments and carbohydrates, 268–269, 270
Chair form of cyclohexane rings, 239–240
Checks of purity of proteins, 58–60
Chenodeoxycholate, 244, 245
Cheilosis, 381
Chitin, 304, 305
Chitinases, 304
Chitobiose, 304–305
Chitosamine, 266
Chloramphenicol, 30
Chlorate, 341, 342

Chloride, metabolism of, 370
Chlorohemin, 180
Chloromycetin, 30
Chlorophyll, 180, 185–186
    and photolysis of water, 287
    and photosynthesis, 285–286
Chlorophyll a, formula of, 186
Chlorophyll b, formula of, 186
Chloroplasts, 251, 286
    and plastoquinone, 254
Cholecalciferol (vitamin $D_3$), 244, 378
Cholecystokinin, 355
Choleglobin, 182, 183
Cholestane, 1, 248
    formula and numbering, 238
Cholestanol, 240
    formula, 240
Cholesterol, 1, 240, 241
    and bile acids, 244
    and hormones, 245, 246
    in bile, 385
    biosynthesis of, 235–238, 316
    formula of, 237
    in lipoproteins, 65
Cholic acid, 240, 244, 245
Choline, 107, 224, 225
    and serine metabolism, 168
    phosphorylation of, 229, 230
Choline acetyltransferase, 86
Choline esterase, 394–395
Cholinergic nerves, 393
Chondroitin sulfate, 312
Chondrosamine, 266
Chorionic gonadotropins, 350
Christmas factor, 66
Chromaffin tissue, 343
Chroman, 3
Chromatography, 30–33
Chromoprotein, 249, 251
Chromosomes, 127, 323, 326
    giant, 323, 325, 326
    light micrograph, 324
    and synthesis of RNA, 131
Chymotrypsin, 87, 147, 150–151
    activation of, 150, 151
    active site of, 150
    mechanism, of action of, 151
        of proteolysis, 82, 83
α-Chymotrypsin, 151
δ-Chymotrypsin, 151
Chymotrypsinogen, 150
Cisternae of ergastoplasm, 326, 327

Citrate, 14
    and blood clotting, 65
    and calcium absorption, 371
    and citrate cycle, 206, 207, 211
    and demineralization, 372
    formation of, 108
Citrate cycle, 205ff., 318–320
    detailed formulation of, 206, 207
    and efficiency of energy conversion, 210
    and energy yield, 209–210
    in mitochrondria, 330
    and synthetic tasks, 210–211
Citrovorum factor, 382
Citrulline and urea cycle, 158
Closed system and equilibrium, 73
Clotting of blood, 62, 65–66
Clupein, 38
$C_1$ metabolism, 321
CoA, see Coenzyme A
Cobalamin, 93, 379, 382–383
    mechanism of formation, 175
Cobalt, 113
    and glucagon, 346
Cocarboxylase, see Codecarboxylase
Codecarboxylase (thiamine pyrophosphate), 111
Codehydrogenase I, see Nicotinamide-adenine dinucleotide
Codehydrogenase II, see Nicotinamide-adenine dinucleotide phosphate
Code of amino acid sequence, 134
Codons, 134
Coenzymes, 68, 69, 90ff.
    catalytic nature of, 91
    classification of, 92–94
    definition of, 90–92
    group-transferring, 93, 100–112
    hydrogen-transferring, 93
        as redox systems, 192
    mechanism of enzyme catalysis, 81
    of isomerases and lyases, 93
    of the oxidoreductases, 94–100
    redox potentials, table, 192
    structure of, 92
    table of, 93
    and vitamins, 92, 93
Coenzyme I, see Nicotinamide-adenine dinucleotide
Coenzyme II, see Nicotinamide-adenine dinucleotide phosphate
Coenzyme A, 93, 106–108, 113, 154, 379, 382
    and bile acids, 244, 245
    and fatty acids, 216–218

and group transfer, 106–108
components of, 106
formula of, 107
in oxidative decarboxylation, 160, 208
Coenzyme F, 109, 379, *see also* Tetrahydrofolic acid
Coenzyme Q, 254, 380, *see also* Uniquinone and Ubihydroquinone
Collagen, 26, 312
secondary structure of, 50, 51
Colloidal solutions, 56
Colloid-osmotic pressure, 57, 365–366
Colloids, 56–57
Colon, 385
Color reactions of carbohydrates, 263
Combustion, 187
Commission on Enzymes of the International Union of Biochemistry, 95
Common pool of metabolites, 321–322
Comparative biochemistry, hemoglobin, 387
Compartments in cells, 323–332
Competitive inhibition, 85
Complex proteins, 61
Concentration units, 362
Condensing enzyme of the urea cycle, 158
Conformation and steroids, 239
Coniferin, 292
Coniferyl alcohol, 292
Contraction by muscle, 391, 393
Copper, 199, 268
and ascorbate oxidase, 268
and cytochrome oxidase, 197, 202
and hydroxylases, 203
and oxidases, 202
Coproporphyrin I, 178
Coproporphyrin III, 178, 179
Coprostan-$3\alpha,7\alpha$-diol, 245
Coprostan-$3\alpha,7\alpha,12\alpha$-triol, 245
Coprostanol, 240, 241
Cori ester *see* Glucose 1-phosphate
Corpora allata in insects, 357
Corpus luteum hormones, 338, 339
Corticoids, 246, 386
Corticosteroids, 335, 336
Corticosterone, 337
formula of, 246
Corticotropin(s), 336, 348–349, *see also* Adrenocorticotropic hormone
control of production of, 349
physiological effect of, 348–349
structure, 38, 39
species, differences in, 38
Corticotropin-releasing factor, 349

Cortisol, 240, 337
and blood glucose, 352
formula of, 246
Cortisone, and blood glucose, 352
formula of, 246
Cosubstrates, 90, 91, 92
Cotton, 303
Coupled reactions, and energy-rich compounds, 74
free energy change in, 73
Creatine, formation of, 105
and glycine metabolism, 168
Creatine kinase, mechanism of action, 82, 84
Creatine phosphate, 77
$\Delta F°$ of hydrolysis, 77
and muscle contraction, 390
Cristae mitochondriales, 328, 329
Crocetin, 250
Crotonase, 217
C,U,U, bases coding for leucine, 135
Cyanocobalamin, 382
Cyclic adenosine 3′,5′-monophosphate, formation of, 103
Cyclic peroxide of benzene ring, 202
Cyclic 2′,3′-phosphodiester in alkaline hydrolysis of RNA, 117
Cyclitols, 266
Cyclobutane dicarboxylic acid, 15
Cyclohexane, 3
Cyclopentadiene, 3
Cyclopentane, 3
Cyclopentanoperhydrophenanthrene, 238
Cyclophorase system, 330
Cycloserine, 30
Cymarose, and sterol glycoside, 242
Cystathionine, 166
Cysteamine, 155, *see also* Mercaptoethylamine
Cysteic acid, 29, 30, 166
Cysteine, 27, 154
formula of, 21
metabolism of, 166
and metabolism of serine, 168
Cytidine, 117, 118
Cytidine diphosphate, 93, 229
as coenzyme, 106
Cytidine diphosphate choline, 106, 230
Cytidine diphosphate diglyceride, 231
Cytidine monophosphate, 230
Cytidine triphosphate, 119, 229
formula of, 106
and phosphatide synthesis, 106
Cytochrome(s), 184–185, 208
and hemin, 100

redox systems, 191
in respiratory chain, 193–194, 197, 198, 199
Cytochrome(s) a (a₃), 180, 185, 197
redox potential, 192
Cytochrome b, 180, 184–185, 195, 197
redox potential of, 192
Cytochrome b₅, 185, 327
Cytochrome c, 55, 180, 184, 197, 199
and oxidative phosphorylation, 200
redox potential of, 192
Cytochrome f, 285–286
Cytochrome oxidase, 180, 201, 328
in respiratory chain, 193–194, 197
see also Cytochrome a
Cytochrome reductases, 196
Cytochrome c reductase, 195
Cytohemin, 180
in cytochrome oxidase, 180, 197
formula of, 185
Cytoplasm, 328–329
enzymes of, 329
structure of, 328–329
Cytosine, 117, 118, 123, 125, 133, 134

D

Dark reaction, 285, 288, 290
Deaminase, and porphyrin synthesis, 175
Deamination, oxidative, 156–157, 320
Decalin, 3, 238, 239
Decarboxylases, coenzymes of, 113
Decarboxylation(s), of amino acids, 154–155
and carbon dioxide, 205
of α-keto glutarate, detailed mechanism,
208
Dehydroascorbate, 267, 268, 383
Δ⁷-Dehydrocholesterol, 240, 242, 244, 378
optical assay of, 96
Dehydrogenases, 202
optical assay of, 96
Dehydroquinic acid, 291–292
Dehydroshikimic acid, 291–292
Denaturation, and entropy, 54
of proteins, 53–54
Denaturing agents, 54, 54
Deoxyadenosine triphosphate, 129
Deoxycholic acid, 244, 245
Deoxycorticosterone, 240
formula of, 246
Deoxycytosine triphosphate, 129
6-Deoxy-L-galactose, 266, 313
Deoxyguanosine triphosphate, 129
Deoxyhexoses, 266

6-Deoxy-L-mannose, 266
Deoxyribonucleases, 142
Deoxyribonucleic acid(s) (DNA), 123ff., 264
base constituents of, 123
biosynthesis of, 129–131
in cell nucleus, 325, 326
as genetic material, 127–128
molecular weights of, 123
in phages, 127, 140–141
replication of, 128–129
structure of, 123–124, 125, 126
transforming principle, 129
Deoxyribonucleic acid polymerase, 129
Deoxyribose, 264
β-D-2-Deoxyribose, formula of, 115
Deoxythymidine triphosphate, 129
Deoxyuridine 5'-phosphate, 120
Depot fat, 215
Dermatitis, 379, 382, 383
Desmolase, 89
Determining the sequence of amino acids, 43–45
Detoxication, 295, 303
with active sulfate, 104
Deuterium and mechanism of action of hydro-
gen transfer, 97
Dexamethasone, 337
Dextrin, 308
as primer for synthesis, 310
Dextrorotatory, 16
Dextrose, see Glucose
Diabetes, and acetyl CoA, 219
alloxan, 346
Diabetes insipidus, and vasopressin, 347
and water balance, 362
Diabetes mellitus, 352–353
and insulin, 346
Diagnosis by serum enzymes, 386
Diagnostics, and urine, 389
Dialysis, 57
Diaminophosphatides, 232
α,ε-Diaminopimelate, 29
Diaminopropane, 326
Diaphorase, 195, 208
Dicumarol, 200
and blood clotting, 66
Diesterase, 144
Difarnesyl side chains, 253
Diffusion, 363–364
facilitated, 364
of proteins through membranes, 57
restricted, 364
velocity of (equations), 363
Diffusion constant and the ultracentrifuge, 55

Digestion of starches, 306–308
Digestive enzymes, 147
Digestive tract, 384–385
    absorption in, 385
    hydrolases of, 384–385
Digitalin, 295
Digitaloids, 241–242
Digitogenin, 241, 242
Digitonin, 241–242, 295
Diglyceride, 226
    formula of, 212
    and phosphatide synthesis, 230
Diglyceride phosphate (phosphatidic acid), 223,
    224
Diguanidino-scyllo-inositol, 295
Dihydrolipoate, 100–101, 160, 208
    and diaphorase, 195
Dihydrolipoate dehydrogenase, 100
Dihydro-orotic acid, 119
Dihydropyridine system, 96
Dihydrosphingosine, 231
Dihydrotachysterol (AT 10), 345
Dihydrothioctate, 100
Dihydrouracil dehydrogenase, 86
Dihydroxyacetone, 14, 257, 269
Dihydroxyacetone phosphate, 226, 264
    and aldose transfer, 268–269
    and fat synthesis, 223
    from fructose 1-phosphate, 279, 280
    and glycolysis, 275
$3\alpha,7\alpha$-Dihydroxycholanic acid, 244
$3\alpha,12\alpha$-Dihydroxycholanic acid, 244
1,3-Dihydroxycyclopentane, and isomerism, 18
$\alpha,\gamma$-Dihydroxy-$\beta,\beta$-dimethylbutyrate, 106, 382
3,4-Dihydroxyphenylalanine (Dopa), 154, 163,
    203, 344
Diiodothyronines, 340
Diisopropylfluorophosphate, 150
Dimethylallyl pyrophosphate, 236, 237
Dimethylglycine, 167, 168
6,7-Dimethyl-9-ribityl-isoalloxazine, 98
Dinitrophenol, 200
Dinitrophenylamino acids, 35, 36
Dinucleotides, as coenzymes, 94–99
Dipeptidase, 147, 148, 152
Dipeptide, 34
$o$-Diphenol, 189
$o$-Diphenolate ion, 189
1,3-Diphosphoglycerate, 276, 289
2,3-Diphosphoglycerate, 277
Diphosphopyridine nucleotide, see Nicotin-
    amide–adenine dinucleotide

Diphtheria toxin, 55
Disaccharides, 295–298
    biosynthesis of, 302
Discoveries, table of, 400–401
Dissociation constant of an acid, 11
    of enzyme-substrate complex, 79, 80
Diuresis, and vasopressin, 347
Dodecylsulfate, 53
Donnan correction, 367
Donnan distribution, 366
Donnan equilibrium, 366–367
Dopa, 163, 203, 343, 344
Dopachrome, 163
Dopamine, 343, 356
    from tyrosine, 344
Dopaquinone, 163
Double bond, 2
Double stranded DNA, 125
DPN, see Nicotinamide-adenine dinucleotide
Dynamic equilibrium, 73–74, 321–322, 330, 332
    and respiratory chain, 197–198

E

Ecdysone, 357–358
Edman degradation, 35
Egg white injury, 379, 383
Elaidic acid, 214
Electric potentials, and nerve conduction, 394–
    395
Electrochemical cell, 190
Electrolyte(s), metabolism of, and adrenal cor-
    tex, 337
Electrolyte balance, and aldosterone, 335
Electrons and oxidation-reduction, 188–190
Electron microscopy, of cells, 325, 328, 329
    of muscle cell, 391–392
Electron transport, 191, 198–199
    and plastoquinone, 254
Electron-transport particles, 198–199, 328
    respiratory chain and, 328
Electropherogram of normal serum, 62
Electrophoresis, 58
Electrophoretic separation of serum proteins,
    58, 62
Embden-Meyerhof pathway, 272–273, 274, 279,
    316
Emulsin, 299
Enantiomers, 15, 17
Enclosure compounds, 305
End group analysis, 151
End-oxidase, 201

Endopeptidases, 147, 148–151
  specificity of, 148
Endoplasmic reticulum, 326–327
Enediols (en-diols), and oxidases, 202
Energetic coupling of reactions, 74
Energetics, 69–71
Energy of activation, 72
Energy consumption in kidney, 387
Energy conversion, efficiency of, 210
Energy of light quanta, 287
Energy-rich bond, 76
Energy-rich compounds, 74–76
  table of standard free energies of hydrolysis, 77
Energy-rich phosphates, in muscle, 390–391
  and quinones, 254
Energy yield, of aerobic glycolysis, 281
  of anaerobic glycolysis, 278–279
  from fatty acid oxidation, 218
Enol(s), 8, 263
Enol ether, 226
Enol formation, 8
Enolase, and glycolysis, 277
Enolate ion, 8
Enteramine, 356
Enterogastrone, 355
Enterohepatic circulation, 182, 183, 244, 385
Enterokinase, 149
Enthalpy, 71
Entropy, definition, 54
  and denaturation of proteins, 54, 71
Entropy content, change of ($\Delta S$), 71
Enzyme(s), as catalysts, 68ff., 72–73
  chemical nature of, 68–69
  classification of, 85–89
  definition of, 68
  in muscle, 390
  nomenclature of, 85–89
  table of, 86–88
Enzyme activators, 85
Enzyme catalysis, mechanism of, 81–84
Enzyme complex, and fatty acid synthesis, 222
Enzyme complexes and NAD catalysis, 98
Enzyme induction, 137
Enzyme inhibitors, 85
Enzyme-substrate complex, 79
  and mechanism of action, 81–82
Enzyme units, definition of, 81
Enzymes in blood plasma, 65
4-Epimerase (galactowaldenase), 301
Epimeric sugars, 263
Epimerization, 268
  at C–4, 299

Epinephrine (adrenaline), 154, 336, 341, 344
  biologic effects, 344
  biosynthesis of, 343–344
  and blood glucose, 352
  and cyclic AMP formation, 309, 310
  and tyrosine, 161, 162, 163
Epiphysis, 344
Equation of state, 71
Equatorial, 228
Equatorial orientation in steroids, 240
Equilibria, and catalysis, 72–73
  and chemical energetics, 69–71
  dynamic, 73–74
  and energy of activation, 72–73
  and respiratory chain, 197–198
  shift of, 73
Equilibrium constant ($K$), 70
Equilibrium reaction, diagrammed, 71
Equivalent, 362
Erepsin, 151
Ergocalciferol (Vitamin $D_2$), 243, 244, 378
Ergosterol, 240, 244
  and vitamin D, 242–243
Erythrocytes, 313, 314, 387
  and iron metabolism, 373
  life span, 182, 373
  relative size of, 64
D-Erythrose, formula of, 257
Erythrose 4-phosphate, 272, 290, 291
Erythrulose, 264
Essential amino acids, 156
Ester(s), 12
Ester condensation with acetyl CoA, 107
Ester formation, 4, 5
  and acetyl CoA, 107
  and equilibrium, 71
  of monosaccharides, 262
Esterases, 87, 215
Esterification of glycerol, 223–224
Estradiol, 240, 336, 338, 339
17β-Estradiol, formula of, 248
Estriol, 248, 338, 339
Estrogen(s), 338–339
  biosynthesis of, 248, 339
  and menstrual cycle, 354–355
  physiological effects, 339
Estrone, 338, 339
  formula of, 248
  and ICSH, 350
Estrone sulfuric acid, 104
Ethanol, redox potential of, 192

Ethanolamine, 154, 167, 226, 227
    activation of, 230
    and serine metabolism, 168
Ethanolamine cephalins, 227
    formation of, 230
Ether formation, 5
Ethers of monosaccharides, 262
D(+)-Ethyl lactate, 17
Etiocholanolone, see 5β-Androstanolone
Etioporphyrin, 175
Events, biochemical, table of, 400–401
Exchange reactions, high energy, 201
Excitation of nerve, 394–395
Exergonic, 70
Exoglycosidases, 308
Exopeptidases, 147, 148, 151–152
Extracellular space (body fluids), 361
Extrinsic factor, 383
Eyes, zinc content of, 373

**F**

$\Delta F$, 70
FAD, see Flavin-adenine dinucleotide
Farnesol, 358
Farnesyl phosphate, 254
Farnesyl pyrophosphate, 236, 237
    and rubber, 254
Farnesyl side chains, 253
Fasting and acetyl CoA, 219
Fat(s), 212ff.
    biosynthesis, insulin and, 346
    breakdown of, 317
    chemical composition, 212–215
    as depot material, 215
    formation from carbohydrate, 222
    hardening of, 214–215
    heat of combustion, 374
    hydrolysis, 215
    metabolism of, 212ff.
    neutral, 212–213
    respiratory quotient, 375
    synthesis from fatty acids, 223–224
Fat formation, and insulin, 346, 353
Fat metabolism and diabetes, 353
Fatty aldehyde, 231
Fatty acids, activation of, 216–217
    biosynthesis of, 222–223
    branched chain, metabolism of, 220–222
    deficiencies, 376
    description, 213–214
    essential, 214, 376, 379, 380
    formation of, 222–223
    formulas of, 213–214

    free, and lipase action, 215
        in waxes, 215
    heat of combustion, 187
    hydroxy, 215
    metabolism of, 317–318
    β-oxidation of, 216–218
    unsaturated, 214
Fatty acid oxidation spiral (cycle), diagram of, 218
Fatty acyl-CoA, and β-oxidation, 217–218
    and synthesis of neutral fat, 223–224
Feces, 389
Feedback, and calcium levels, 372
    and regulation of blood glucose, 352
    and thyroxine, 348
Fehling's test, 263
Female sex hormones, 338–340
Ferment, 68, 273
Fermentation, 68
    alcoholic, 273–279
Ferredoxin, 285, 286
    and photolysis of water, 287
Ferritin, 372, 373
Ferroporphyrin, 180
    and tryptophan oxidase, 203
Ferroprotoporphyrin, 178
Fertilization, and hyaluronidase, 312
Fetal hemoglobin, 44, 181
Feulgen's nuclear staining, 264
Fibrils of muscle, 391–393
Fibrin, 65, 66
Fibrinogen, 64, 65, 66
    in plasma fraction I, 63
Fibrinolysin, 66
Fischer's projection formulas, 258, 260
Flavanone glycoside, 295
Flavin, 196
    in $H_2O_2$-forming enzymes, 202
    and phosphorylation, 201
Flavin-adenine dinucleotide (FAD), 93, 99, 113, 196, 223, 379, 381
    in acyl dehydrogenase, 217, 218
    formula of, 99
    and respiratory chain, 195–196
Flavin catalysis, 195–196
Flavin enzymes, 195, 202
Flavin mononucleotide (FMN), 93, 99, 195, 223, 381
    and amino acid oxidase, 157
Flavin nucleotide, 98–99
Flavoprotein(s), 99, 100, 160, 195, 202, 208, 209, 381
    and β-oxidation of fatty acids, 217

and oxidative phosphorylation, 200
    redox potential of, 192
    reduction product, 99
    in respiratory chain, 193–200
Fluoride and blood clotting, 66
Fluoroacetate, 79
Fluorocitrate, 79
Fluorodinitrobenzene, 35, 36
FMN, see Flavin mononucleotide
Folding isomerism, 52–53
Folic acid, 93, 108, 109, 379, 382
Folinate, 382
Follicles, and ICSH, 350
Follicle-stimulating hormone (FSH), 336, 350
    and menstruation, 353
Follicular hormones, 338
    and menstrual cycle, 353
Fölling's imbecility, 137
Food components, essential, 376
Formaldehyde and folate, 109
Formate, 10
    and tryptophan catabolism, 165
Formiminoglutamate, 171
Formyl coenzyme F, 121
Formylkynurenine, 164–165
Formyltetrahydrofolate, 108–109, 382
$N^5$-Formyltetrahydrofolate, 109
$N^{10}$-Formyltetrahydrofolate (active formate), 109, 110
Four-electron transfer, 202
Four-electron-transferring oxidase, 268
Free energy and redox potential, 191
Free energy change ($\Delta F$), 70
    dependence on concentrations, 76, 77
    thermodynamic definition, 71
$\beta$-D-Fructofuranose, 265
$\beta$-Fructofuranosidase (invertase), 299
Fructokinase, 279
Fructose, 306
$\beta$-D-Fructose, Haworth formulas, 265
    projection formula, 265
D-($-$)-Fructose, description of, 266
Fructose diphosphate, and photosynthesis, 290
Fructose 1,6-diphosphate, 266, 275
    and aldose transfer, 268–269
Fructose, free, metabolism of, 279–280
Fructose 1-phosphate, 279, 280
Fructose 6-phosphate, 266, 272
    and glycolysis, 275
    and photosynthesis, 290
    and transaldolase, 269
Fuchsin sulfurous acid, 264
L-Fucose, 258, 266, 313

Fumarase, 209
Fumarate, 10, 15
    from aspartate, 169
    and citrate cycle, 206, 209, 211
    and purine synthesis, 120, 121, 122
    from tyrosine, 161–163
    and urea cycle, 158
Fumarate hydratase, 87
Fumarylacetoacetate, 162–163
Functional groups, 4
Furan, 3
Furanose, 259
Furfural, 262
    derivatives, 263
6-Furfurylaminopurine, 358

G

Galactosamine, 266, 313
Galactose, 266, 306, 313
    in glycolipids, 232, 233
    and sterol glycoside, 242
D-($+$)-Galactose, 265
L-Galactose, 265
Galactosemia, 301
Galactose 1-phosphate, conversion to glucose 1-phosphate, 301
Galactosidase, 299
$\beta$-Galactosidase, and enzyme induction, 137
    and substrate specificity, 78
Galactosides, 294
6-Galactosidolactose, formation and formula of, 300
Galactowaldenase, 265, 301
Galacturonic acid, 267
Gallbladder, 385
Galvanic elements, 190
Ganglionic cells, 233
Gangliosides, 225ff., 232, 233–234
Gas constant (R), 70
Gas-gangrene bacilli, 231
Gastrin, 355
Gastro-intestinal tract, hormones of, 355
Gaucher's disease, 232
Gene(s), 127, 128, 135–138
    and synthesis of enzymes, 137
    content of cells, 128
    mode of action of, 135–138
Gene loci, 324, 325, 326
Genetic information, transfer of, 127, 128, 326
Genetic material, 128, 323–326
Genetics as a biochemical tool, 291
Genital cycle of women, and hormones, 353–355
Gentiobiose, 295, 297

Geranyl pyrophosphate, 236, 237
Geranylgeranyl pyrophosphate, 249
Gestagens, 338, 339, 340
    biologic function of, 339
Gibberellic acid, 358–359
Gibberellins, 358
Glandotropic hormone, 335
Gliadins, 55, 60
Globin, 180
Globular proteins, 42
    classification of, 60–61
Globulins, 61, 65
    and electrophoresis, 62–63
    in plasma fractions II and III, 63
α-Globulins, and thyroxine transport, 342
$α_1$-Globulins, 64
$α_2$-Globulins, 64
β-Globulins, 64
γ-Globulins, 64, 65
Glomeruli, 387
Glucagon, 40, 336, 346
    blood glucose, 352
    and cyclic AMP formation, 309, 310
Glucanes, 303
Glucocerebrosides, 232
Glucocorticoid effect, 337
Glucogenic amino acids, 159
Gluconate, formation and formula of, 263, 271
Gluconate, 6-phosphate, dehydrogenation of,
    271, 272
Gluconeogenesis, 281–283, 316–317, 386
    from amino acids, 282–283
    and cortisol, 337
    and glucocorticoids, 352
    from lactate, 281–282
Gluconolactone, formula of, 263
Gluconolactone 6-phosphate, 270, 271
α-Glucopyranosido-β-fructofuranoside (sucrose),
    297
Glucosamine, 266, 313
Glucosamine N-sulfate, 312
Glucose, 226
    activated, reactions of, 301–303
    in blood, 350–351
    decarboxylation of, 270–271
    direct oxidation of, 316
    α- and β-forms, 260–261
    and glycogen synthesis, 310
    in glycolipids, 232
    heat of combustion, 187
    optical rotation of, 261
    phosphorylation of, 274, 275
    resynthesis of, 281–283

    from starch, 308
    and sterol glycosides, 242
    in urine, 389
    various representations of, 260
α-D-Glucose, 260, 264
    physical constants, 261
β-D-Glucose, 260–261, 264, 265
    physical constants, 261
Glucose-consuming processes, 351
Glucose 1,6-diphosphate, 264, 309
    as coenzyme, 113
Glucose oxidase, 86
Glucose oxidation, 270–273
Glucose 6-phosphatase, mechanism of action, 82
Glucose 1-phosphate, 264, 274, 309, 310
    and UDP-glucose formation, 301
    from polysaccharides, 308–309
α-D-Glucose 1-phosphate, formula of, 262
Glucose 6-phosphate, 264, 272, 309
    formation of, energetics, 75
    formula of, 262
    and glycolysis, 274–275
    oxidation of, 270–271
Glucose-6-phosphate dehydrogenase, 271
Glucose-phosphate isomerase, 87
Glucose phosphate-uridyl transferase, 301
Glucose-producing processes, 351
α-Glucosidase, 299, 308
    and substrate specificity, 78
δ-Glucosidase, 298, 299
Glucosides, 294
4α-Glucosido-glucose (maltose), 296
Glucosuria, 353
Glucuronate, 182, 267, 311–313
    and steroids, 247
    and thyroxine catabolism, 342
β-Glucuronidases, 299
Glucuronide formation, 302–303
Glucuronides, 267, 295
    and steroids, 247
Glutamate, 28, 154
    in folic acid, 109
    formation of, 170–171
    formula of, 21
    key position of, in metabolism, 171–172
    and oxidative deamination, 157
    and transamination, 155, 156
    and urea formation, 158, 159
L-Glutamate dehydrogenase, 155
Glutamate semialdehyde, 170, 171
Glutamine, 25, 28
    formula of, 21
    and purine biosynthesis, 120, 121, 122

Glutamine synthetase, 88
Glutarate, 10, 169, 170
Glutathione, 37, 163
Glutathione synthetase, 88
Glutelins, 60
Glycane, 303
Glyceraldehyde 14, 256, 257
    free, from fructose 1-phosphate, 279, 280
    optical rotation of, 16
    oxidation of and coupled reactions, 75
    reduction of, 280
D-Glyceraldehyde, 264, 280
    formula of, 257
Glyceraldehyde 3-phosphate and aldose transfer, 269
    dehydrogenation of, 276
    and glycolysis, 275
    and transketolase, 270
Glyceraldehyde-3-phosphate dehydrogenase, 86
Glycerate, 10
    free, from fructose catabolism, 279, 280
    and metabolism of serine, 168
D-(−)-Glycerate, 17
Glycerol, 256
    and fats, 212
    and lipase action, 215, 216
    from glyceraldehyde, 280
Glycerol diester, 226
Glycerol ester, 226
Glycerophosphate, 229
    and fat synthesis, 223–224
    and hydrogen transport, 195
α-L-Glycerophosphate, 226
Glycerophosphatides, 226–229
    biosynthesis of, 229–231
    degradation of, 231
Glycerophosphorylcholine diesterase, 231
Glycine, 25, 172
    and bile acids, 244, 245
    formula of, 21
    isotopically labeled, 174
    key metabolite, 321
    metabolism of, 167, 168
    and porphyrin synthesis, 173, 174
    and purine biosynthesis, 120–121
Glycine conjugates, 25
Glycolaldehyde, 270
Glycocholic acid, 244, 245
Glycodeoxycholic acid, 244, 245
Glycogen, 264, 274, 303, 306, 351
    phosphorolysis of, 308–310
    synthesis of, 310–311, 386
        and adrenocortical hormones, 337, 386

    and glucagon, 346, 352
    and insulin, 351
Glycolipids, 232
    classification of, 225–226
    occurrence, 225–226
    table, 226
Glycolysis, 273–279, 316
    history of, 273–274
    principles and summary, 274
Glycolytic pathway, 273–279
α₁-Glycoprotein, of blood plasma, 312
Glycoproteins, 313
Glycosidases, 299
β-Glycosidase, 87
Glycoside bond, 294–295
N-Glycoside bond, 116
Glycosides, 294ff.
    biosynthesis of, 299–303
    cardiac, 242
    hydrolysis of, 298–303
    and sterols, 241–242
N-Glycosides, 295
O-Glycosides, 295
N-Glycosidic linkage in coenzymes, 94–99
4-Glycosido-protocatechuic acid, 295
Glycylglycine, detailed molecular structure of, 45–46
Glycylglycine dipeptidase, 152
Glyoxylate, 167, 168
    active formate donor, 109
    formation of, 210–211
Glyoxylate cycle, 210–211, 319–320
Goiter, 340
Goiterogenic compounds, 340–341
Gonadal hormones, 338–340
    and menstrual cycle, 353, 354
    production of, and ICSH, 350
Gonadotropic hormones, 348, 349–350
Gonadotropin (Chorionic gonadotropin), 336, 350
Gonads, and follicle-stimulating hormone, 350
Gout, 122
Gramicidin S, 41
Grape sugar, see Glucose
Green hematin, 180
Ground substance, 311
Growth factors and mutation, 136
Growth hormone, 348
    and blood glucose, 352
Growth substances of plants, 358–359
Guanidine, 9, 116
    as denaturing agent, 53

Guanidinoacetate, 105, 168
Guanidinoacetate methyltransferase, 86
Guanine, 116, 117, 118, 121, 122, 123, 124
Guanosine, 117, 118, 121, 122
Guanosine diphosphate, 209
Guanosine diphosphate mannose, 303
Guanosine 5′-phosphate, 121, 122
Guanosine triphosphate, formation of, 209
Guanylic acid, 121
Guanylic acid system, 209
Gum arabic, 264

# H

Half-cell potential depending on concentrations, 191
Half-cells, 190
Half-life of depot fat, 215
Half-maximal velocity, 80
Half-time of liver protein, 146
Hardening of fats, 214
Harden-Young ester, see Fructose 1,6-diphosphate
Haworth formulas, 260
Hb, see Hemoglobin
Head oil of sperm whale, 215
Heat content, change of ($\Delta H$), 71
Heat of combustion, 187, 374
Helical structure of amylose, 305
$\alpha$-Helix, 48–50, 59
    and keratins, 50
    and optical rotation of proteins, 51
Helix model of DNA, 125, 126
Hematin, green, 180
Heme ($Fe^{++}$-protoporphyrin), 180
    chemical description, 178
    in cytochrome b, 197
    formation of, 178
Heme enzymes, 179–180
Hemiacetal, 7, 259
Hemin ($Fe^{+++}$-protoporphyrin), 180
    as prosthetic group, 100
Hemin a, 185
Hemin catalysis, 197
Hemins, 173ff.
Hemochromogens, 181
Hemocyanin (lobster), 55
Hemoglobin (Hb), 180–182, 387
    catabolism, 385
    complete structure, 44, see also reverse side
    of large fold-out chart
    degradation of, 182–183
    dissociation of, 55
    dissociation curves and oxygen tension, 387

fetal, 44
    relative size of, 64
    sickle-cell, 44
    structure of, 44
    tertiary structure of, 51–53
Hemoglobin A, 181
Hemoglobin C, 44
Hemoglobin F (fetal), 181
Hemophilia, 66
Henderson-Hasselbalch equation, 11, 369
Heparin, 312
    and blood clotting, 66
Hepatic gluconeogeneses, 386
Heptoses, 266
Hereditary factors, 127
Hesperidin, 295, 296
Heterocycles, 3
Heterocyclic compounds, 2
Heterglycanes, 303
Hexokinase, 274–275
Hexosamine, 226
Hexoses, 226, 258, 264–266
High-energy exchange reactions, 201
Hippuric acid, 25
Hirudin, 66
Histamine, 154, 356
Histidase, 87
Histidine, 29, 154
    active formate donor, 109
    catabolism of, 170–171
    formula of, 21
    and hemoglobin, 178, 181
Histidine-ammonia lyase, 87
Histones, 61
Holoenzyme, 68, 90
Homocysteine, 27, 28, 30, 166
Homogentisate, 162
    and genetic defects, 137
    oxidation of, 202
Homoglycanes, 303
Homolog, 14
Homoserine, 166
Hormonal control, 333–335
Hormones, 333ff.
    of adrenal medulla, 343–344
    adrenocortical, 335–337
    adrenocorticotropic, 348
    classifications of, 335
    definition of, 333
    gonadal, 338–340
    gonadotropic, 348, 349–350
    hierarchy of, 334–335
    hypophyseal, 334, 346–350

of invertebrates, 357–358
isolation of, 332–333
and kidneys, 388
mechanism of action, 334
metabolism of, 333
pancreatic, 345–346
of pineal gland, 344
pituitary, *see* Hormones, hypophyseal
in plants, 358–359
steroid, 244–248
table of, 336
thyroid, 340–343
tissue, 355–356
Host cells and viruses, 138
Human chorionic gonadotropin (HCG), 350
Hyaloplasm, 330, 331
Hyaluronic acid, 311–312
Hyaluronidases, 311–312
Hybridization, 126
Hybrids between DNA and RNA, 126
Hydantoin derivative of an amino acid, 35
Hydride ion (H⁻), 97, 189
Hydrindane, 3
Hydrocarbons, 1
in waxes, 215
Hydrochloric acid, in stomach, 385
Hydrogen
exchange between cell compartments, 331
between cytoplasm and mitochondria, 195
oxidation of, 188, 190
Hydrogenation of fats, 215
Hydrogen bond, and base pairing in DNA, 125
definition of, 46
Hydrogen cyanide, 295
Hydrogen peroxide, formation, 202
Hydrogenolysis of carbobenzoxy group, 36
Hydrolases in lysosomes, 327
partial list, 87
Hydrolysis of polysaccharides, 307–308
Hydroquinone, 195, 196
and oxidases, 202
oxidation of, 189
p-Hydroquinone oxidase, 202
Hydroquinone-quinone system, 201
β-Hydroxyacyl dehydrogenase, 217, 220
11-Hydroxyandrostenedione, 338
3-Hydroxyanthranilate, 164, 165
and genetic block, 136
oxidation of, 202
Hydroxyapatite, 371
p-Hydroxybenzoate, 291

β-Hydroxybutyrate, 219, 220
and hydrogen transport, 195
7α-Hydroxycholesterol, 245
17α-Hydroxydeoxycorticosterone, 246, 248
Hydroxy fatty acids, 215
β-Hydroxyglutarate, 170
3-Hydroxykynurenine, 164, 165, 382
and genetic block, 136
Hydroxylating enzymes, 202, 203–204
Hydroxylation of aromatic rings, 203–204
enzymic, 203–204
of steroids, 203
Hydroxyleucine, 41
Hydroxyl groups, 4
Hydroxyl ions, oxidation of, 287
Hydroxylsine, 28
β-Hydroxy-α-methylbutyryl coenzyme A, 221
5-Hydroxymethylcytosine, 117, 118
Hydroxymethylfurfural, 263
β-Hydroxy-β-methylglutaryl coenzyme A, 221–222, 236
and acetoacetate formation, 219
Hydroxymethyltetrahydrofolate, 292, 293
5-Hydroxymethyluracil, 117
p-Hydroxyphenylpyruvate, 161–162
17α-Hydroxyprogesterone, 248
formula of, 246, 248
Hydroxyproline, 26, 170, 171
Hydroxypyruvate, 167, 168
5-Hydroxytryptamine, 356
5-Hydroxytryptophan, 154, 165, 356
Hydroxytyramine (dopamine), 356
Hypercalcemia, 345
Hyperglycemia, 353
Hypertensin, 355
Hyperthyroidism, 342
Hypophyseal hormones, 346–350
Hypophysis, 335, 346
and menstrual cycle, 353, 354
Hypothyroidism, 342
Hypovitaminoses, definition, 377–378
Hypoxanthine, 116, 117, 118, 121, 122

**I**

I-bands, 391
Icterus, 182
Identical replication, 127, 128
Identity periods in X-ray diffraction, 45
L-Iduronic acid, 311, 312
Imidazole ring, 3, 178
Imidazolonepropionate, 171
Imines, 9
Imino acid, 156

Imino group, 6, 26
Immunoelectropherogram, 63
Immunoelectrophoresis, 62–63
Immunology, 60
Immunoproteins, 65
Inborn errors of metabolism, 137
Indene, 3
Indican, 104, 295
Indigo, 99
Indole, 3
    from tryptophan, 165
Indoleacetate, 165
Indolepyruvate, 165
Indolquinone, 163
β-Indolylacetate, 358–359
Indoxyl, 295
Indoxyl sulfuric acid, 104
Influenza virus, 140, 142
Inhibitor constant ($K_i$), 80
Inhibitors, 79
Inorganic ions, metabolism of, 360ff.
Inosine, 117, 118, 122
Inosine triphosphate, 281
Inosinic acid, 120, 121, 122
Inositides, 226, 231
Inositol, 226, 228, 231
meso-Inositol, 228
myo-Inositol, formula, 228
Inositol hexaphosphate, 371
Inositol phosphatides (inositides), 228
    formation of, 231
Insects, hormones of, 357–358
    action of, 357
    juvenile, development of, 357
    molting of, 359
    pheromones of, 358
    sex attractants of, 358
Insulin, 40, 43, 345
    and adipose tissue, 353
    aggregation of, 55–56
    biologic effects, 345–346
    biosynthesis of, 345
    and blood glucose, 351
    structure (formula), 39
Insulinase, 345
Interconversion of metabolites, 313–322
Interrelations in metabolism, 315–322
Intermedin, see Melanocyte-stimulating hormone
Interstitial cell-stimulating hormone (ICSH), 350
    and menstruation, 353
Intestinal mucosa, and iron absorption, 372

Intestinal wall, and lipases, 215
Intestine, 385
Intracellular space (body fluids), 361
Intrinsic factor (of mucoproteins), 383, 385
Inulin, 306
    and extracellular fluid, 361
Inversion of sucrose, 297
Invert sugar, 297
Invertase, 299
Iodate, 341
Iodine, and amylose, 305
    radioactive, 342
    and thyrotropin, 348
    and thyroxine, 340–342
Iodine oxidase, 341
Ion-exchange chromatography, 31–33
Ion-exchange resins, 31
Ionic concentration, 363
Ionic strength, 363
Ionograph of blood plasma, 369
α-Ionone structure, 249
β-Ionone structure, 249
Ion transport, and nerve conduction, 394–395
Iron, in cytochromes, 100
    content of organisms, 372
    deficiency, 373
    in hemoglobin, 181
    and hydroxylases, 203
    metabolism of, 372–373
    non-heme bound, 195, 199
    storage form, 372
    and succinate dehydrogenase, 196
    transport of, 373
Iron porphyrin, 179
    and cytochrome oxidase, 197
Islets of Langerhans, 345
Isoagglutinins, 65, 313
Isoalloxazine, 98–99
Isobutyryl coenzyme A, 161, 220
Isocaproate, 245
Isocitrate, 14
    and citrate cycle, 206, 207, 210, 211
Isocitrate dehydrogenase, 207
Isodynamic law, 374
Isoelectric point, 58
    of amino acids, 22
Isoenzymes, 85
Isoleucine, 25
    catabolism of, 160–161
    formula of, 21
    and β-oxidation, 220–221
Isomaltose, 298, 305

Isomerases, coenzymes of, 113
  partial list, 87
  and porphyrin synthesis, 175, 178
Isomerism, 13
  *cis-trans*, 14
  geometrical, 14
  mirror-image, 15
  positional, 14
Isomerization of monosaccharides, 268
Isopentenyl pyrophosphate, 236, 237
Isoprene, 235
Isoprene rule, 235
Isoprene units, 254
Isoprenoid lipids, 235ff.
Isotope method, 173–174
Isotopic labeling, 173–174
Isotrehalose, 297
Iso-urea, 158, 159
Isovalerate, 10
Isovaleryl CoA, 161, 221

### J

Jaundice, 182
Juvenile development of insects, 359
Juvenile hormone, 357–358
  formula, 358

### K

$\alpha$-Keto acids, and catabolism of amino acids, 159
  and oxidative deamination, 156
  oxidative decarboxylation of, 160
  and transamination, 155–156
$\alpha$-Keto adipate, 169, 170
$\alpha$-Ketobutyrate, 166
Ketogenesis, 219–220
  in diabetes, 353
Ketogenic amino acids, 159
3-Keto gluconate 6-phosphate, 271
$\alpha$-Keto glutarate, 170, 171
  and citrate cycle, 206, 207
  key metabolite, 319
  and oxidative deamination, 157
  and transamination, 155, 156
$\beta$-Ketoglutarate, 170
$\alpha$-Keto glutarate oxidase, 195
2-Keto-L-gulonic acid, 267
$\alpha$-Keto isovalerate, 292, 293
Ketone bodies, 353
Ketones, 6
Ketopentoses, cleavage of, 270
Ketoses, 256–258

$\beta$-Keto thiolase, 217
Kidney(s), enzymes, 387
  excretion products, 387
  function, 387
  hormonal control of, 388
  and regulation of acid-base balance, 370
  secretory activity, 387, 388
  and urine, 387–388
  and water balance, 361–362
Kidney damage, 387
Kidney threshold, 387
Kinases, 102–103
  general definition, 274
  mechanism of action, 82–84
Kinetin, 358–359
Krebs' cycle *see* Citrate cycle
Kynurenic acid, 164, 165
Kynurenine, 164, 165, 382
  and genetic block, 133, 134
Kynurenine hydroxylase, 134

### L

Laccase, 202
Lactalbumin (cow), 55
Lactate, 10,14
  in blood, 387
  and gluconeogenesis, 281–282
  redox potential of, 192
D-(−)-Lactate, 17
Lactate dehydrogenase, 278
  forms of, 85
  mechanism of action and stereospecificity, 98
$\beta$-Lactoglobulin (cow), 55
Lactonase, 271
Lactose, 265, 298
  formation of, 302
  and gangliosides, 234
Lactose 1-phosphate, 302
Lactotropic hormone (lactotropin), *see* Luteotropic hormone
Lactotropin, *see* Luteotropic hormone
Lanosterol, 237, 241
Lanthionine, 29, 30
Law of mass action, 9, 69, 70
  equation of, 11
  and Michaelis' theory, 79
Lecithins, 199, 226, 227
  formation of, 230, 318
  hydrolysis of, 227–228
  specific cleavages of, 231

Leucine, 25, 139
    bases coding for, 135
    catabolism of, 160–161
    formula of, 21
    and β-oxidation, 221–222
Leucine aminopeptidase, 87
Leucocytes, 387
Leucodystrophy, Scholz type, 232
Leucovorin, 109
Leucyl aminopeptidase, 152
Levorotatory, 16
Levulose, see Fructose
Leydig's cells, 350
Ligases, 89
    coenzymes of, 114
    partial list, 88
Light quantum, 285, 287
Light reaction, 285, 286, 287
Light scattering and molecular weight, 55
Lignin, 291, 292, 303, 304
Lignoceric acid, 232
Limit dextrin, 308
Linoleic acid, formula of, 214
Linolenic acid, formula of, 214
Lipases, 87, 215–216
Lipid, see Fat, Glycolipids, Phosphatides, Sterols
Lipoamide, 160, see also Lipoate
Lipoate, 93, 100, 113, 208
    formula of, 100
    mechanism of action, 101
    and oxidation of active acetaldehyde, 100
    in oxidative decarboxylation, 100
    and thiamine pyrophosphate, 112
Lipochromes, 249
Lipoic acid, see Lipoate, Lipoamide
Lipoproteins, 65, 196, 197
    and electron-transport particle, 199
    as plasma fraction IV–1, 63
$\alpha_1$-Lipoprotein, 64
$\beta_1$-Lipoprotein, 64, 65
Liver, 385–386
    biochemical functions, 386
    in protein metabolism, 386
Liver glycogen, 386
Lumisterol, 243
Lungs and regulation of alkali reserve, 369
Lutein, 249, 258
Luteinizing hormone (LH), 336, 350
Luteo-mammotropic hormone, see Luteotropic hormone

Luteotropic hormone (LTH, luteotropin, lactotropin, prolactin), 336, 349–350
    luteotropic effect, 349, 350
Lyases, 89
    partial list, 87
Lycopene, 249, 250
Lysine, 28, 154
    catabolism of, 169
    formula of, 21
Lysocephalins, 228
Lysolecithins, 228, 231
Lysosomes, 149, 327
D-Lyxose, formula of, 257

## M

Macromolecules, 13
Macropeptides, 34
Magnesium, 279
    and myosin, 391
Magnesium porphyrin, 180
Malate, 10
    from aspartate, 169
    and citrate cycle, 206, 209, 210, 211
    formation of, 281
Malate dehydrogenase, 209
Maleate, 15
Male sex hormones, 338
Maleylacetoacetate, 162
Maleylacetoacetate isomerase, 87
Malic enzyme, 281
Malonate, 10
    as inhibitor, 79, 209
Malonyl CoA, 222, 223
Maltases, 299, 308
Maltose, 297, 305
    formula of, 296
Maltose type, 296
Maltotriose, 308
Mammotropic hormone, see Luteotropic hormone
Manganese, and hydroxylations, 203
Mannitol, 263
Mannosamine, 233, 267
D-(+)-Mannose, 265
    metabolism of, 303
Many-center reaction, 82, 84
Master gland and hormones, 333–334, 346
Maximum velocity ($V_{max}$), 80
Mechanism of enzyme catalysis, 81–84
Melanin, formation of, 203–204
    and genetic block, 137
    and tyrosine, 161–163

Melanocyte-stimulating hormone (MSH) (Melanotropin), 336, 347–348
    structure, 38
Melanophore-contracting principle, 344
Melanophores, 348
Melanotropin (melanocyte-stimulating hormone; intermedin), *see* Melanocyte-stimulating hormone (MSH)
Melatonin, 154, 336, 344
Menadione, 254, 380
Menstrual cycle, diagram of, 354
    hormonal control of, 339, 353–355
Menstruation, 339, 350
$\beta$-Mercaptoethylamine, 154, 216, 382
    and coenzyme A, 106–107
6-Mercaptopurine, 122
$\beta$-Mercaptopyruvate, 166
H-Meromyosin, 391
L-Meromyosin, 391
Mesobilifuscin, 182
Mesobilirubin, 182
Mesobilirubinogen, 182, 183
Messenger RNA, 124, 131, 132, 133, 134, 135
    and amino acid sequence, 134
    and base code, 134–135
    synthesis, 138
    template for protein synthesis, 133, 134, 135
Metabolic pathways, 315–322
Metabolic pool, 322
Metabolism, intermediary, 315–322
Metalloproteins, 65
Metals, in diet, 376
Metastable, 72
Methemoglobin, 181–182
Methene groups, *see* Methine group
$N^5, N^{10}$-Methenyltetrahydrofolate, 109, 110
Methine group (bridge), 173–175, 182
Methionine, 27
    activation of, 166
    and cephalin formation, 227
    and epinephrine formation, 344
    formula of, 21
    metabolism of, 166
Methyl donor, 166
Methylamine, 167
1-Methyl-$\Delta^1$-androstenolone, 336
Methylation of ethanolamine cephalins, 227, 230
$\alpha$-Methylbutyryl coenzyme A, 220, 221
$\beta$-Methylcrotonyl coenzyme A, 221
5-Methylcytosine, 118

Methylene blue, 99, 196, 202
    redox potential, 192
Methylene groups (bridge), 182
N-Methyl-L-glucosamine, 295
Methylglucosides, 294
N-Methylglycine (sarcosine), 167, 168
Methylindole, 163
Methylmalonate, 14, 113, 160
Methylmalonate semialdehyde, 220
Methylmalonyl coenzyme A, 220, 221
Methylmalonyl-coenzyme A mutase, 87
2-Methylnaphthoquinone, 254, 380
Methylpentose, 258
Methyl transfer, 104–105
Mevalonate, and carotenoids, 236, 249
    formation of, 235–236
    and ubiquinone, 254
Mevalonic pyrophosphate, 236, 237
Micelles, in cellulose, 304
    of keratins, 50
Michaelis constant ($K_m$), definition of, 80
    description, 81
Michaelis' theory, 79ff.
Microsomal fraction, 327
Microsomes, 327
    and hydroxylating enzymes, 203
Midbrain, 335, 349
Milk secretion, and lactotropin, 349
Milk sugar, 265
Mineral elements, essential in diet, 376
Mineral metabolism, 360ff.
Mineralocorticoid effect, 337
Mitochondria, 184, 286, 324, 328–330
    biochemical function, 328
    electron micrograph of, 329
    and electron-transport particles, 198–199
    in liver, 386
    model of, 329
    and respiratory chain, 193, 196
    structure, 328, 329
    and ubiquinone, 254
Mole, 362
Molecular activity of enzymes, 81
Molecular solution, 56
Molecular weights of proteins, 54–55
    table, 55
Mole quantum, 287
Molisch test, 263
Molting of insects, 357
Monodisperse solutions, 57
Monoesterase, 144
Monoglyceride, formula of, 212
Monophosphodiesterase, 229

Monosaccharides, 256ff.
    definition of, 256–258
    general reactions of, 261–263
    interconversion of, 268–271
    nomenclature of, 256–258
MSH, *see* Melanotropin
Mucic acid, 263, 265
Mucin, blood group specific, 313–314
    definition of, 385
    submaxillary, 313
Mucopolysaccharides, 301–314
Muscle, biochemistry of, 390–393
    contraction, 391–393
    model systems, 391–393
Muscle fibers, 391–393
Muscular dystrophy, 379
Mutants, 136, 137, 138, 139
    and amino acid requirement, 156
Mutarotation, 261
Mutases, coenzymes of, 113
Mutation, 128, 129, 138
Myelin sheath, 232, 394
Myoglobin, 55, 390
    primary structure compared to hemo-
        globin, 44 (and reverse of large fold-out
        chart)
    tertiary structure of, 51–52
Myokinase, 390
Myosin, 391–393
Myricin, 215
Myricyl alcohol, 215
Myxedema, 342

N

N¹⁵, 173
NAD, *see* Nicotinamide-adenine dinucleotide
NADH₂-cytochrome b₅ reductase, 327
NADH₂-cytochrome c reductases, 195, 199
NADH₂ dehydrogenase, 195
    inhibitors of, 199
NADH₂-ubiquinone reductase, 195
NADP, *see* Nicotinamide-adenine dinucleotide
    phosphate
Naphthalene, 3
α-Naphthol, 263
Naphthoquinone, 253–255
Natural rubber, 237, 254
Neoretinene b, formula of, 251
    and visual process, 251–252
Neotrehalose, 297
Nerve conduction, 393–395
Nerves, electric potential of, 394
    structure of, 394

Nervonic acid, 232
Neuraminic acid, 226, 233–234, 266–267
Neuraminidase, 313
Neurohypophysis, 347
Neurosecretion, 335, 346–347, 349
    in insects, 357
Neurosporene, 249
Neutral fat, formation of, 223–224
Niacin, as coenzyme, 94
Niaciniamide, 93, 94, 379, 381–382
Nicotinamide, 93, 94, 379, 381–382
    from tryptophan, 163–165
Nicotinamide-adenine dinucleotide (NAD), 93,
    113, 207–209, 379
    absorption spectra of, 96
    analogs of, 98
    and 4-epimerase, 301
    formula of, 95
    and L-glutamate dehydrogenase, 157
    and glycolysis, 276
    nomenclature of, 316
    optical enzyme assay with, 96
    and β-oxidation, 217, 218
    redox potential of, 192
    reduced, and acetaldehyde reduction, 299
        formation of, 316
        oxidation of, 280, 319
        and oxidative phosphorylation, 200
        and visual process, 252
    in respiratory chain, 193–195, 198
Nicotinamide-adenine dinucleotide phosphate,
    (NADP), 93, 207, 379
    formula of, 95
    and glucose oxidation, 271–272
    nomenclature of, 316
    and photosynthesis, 287, 289
    reduced, 271–272
        and cholesterol biosynthesis, 236
        and fatty acid synthesis, 222, 223
        and hydroxylations, 203–204
        and steroids, 246
    and respiratory chain, 195
Nicotinamide mononucleotide, 93
Nicotinamide pyridinium salt, 94
Nicotinic acid, 94, 98, 136, 382
    from tryptophan, 163–165
Niemann-Pick's disease, 232
Night blindness, 378, 379
Ninhydrin reaction with amino acids, 24
Nitrate, 341
Nitrile, 4

Nitrogen, in food, 376
  metabolism of, 320
  non-protein in blood, 386–387
Nitrous acid, and amino acids, 23
  and mutation of viruses, 139
Nomenclature of enzymes, 85–89, 207
Noradrenaline, see Norepinephrine
Norbixin, 250
Norepinephrine, 343–344
  biologic effects, 344
  and nerves, 393
Nucleases see Phosphatases
Nucleic acids, 115ff.
  biosynthesis, 130
  cleavage, 142–145
  helical nature, 125
  metabolism of, 321
Nucleolus, 325
Nucleoproteins and viruses, 139
Nucleosidases, 87, 145
Nucleosides, 116–117, 295
5'-Nucleotidases, 144, 145
Nucleotides, 117
  biosynthesis of, 119ff.
  as coenzymes, 92, 94
  degradation of, 119ff.
Nucleus, 323–326
Nutrition, 374ff.

O

Ocytocin, 335, 346, 347
  formula of, 38
  physiological effect, 347
Oil, 214
Oleic acid, formula of, 214
Oligopeptide, 34
Oligosaccharides, 294ff., 296, 307
  biosynthesis of, 299–303
Ommochromes from tryptophan, 164–165
One-electron transfer, 189, 195
Open systems, and biocatalysis, 74
  and dynamic equilibrium, 73, 74
Opsin, 251–252
Optical antipodes, 16
Optical assay with NAD, 96
Optical rotation, 16
  of glucose, 261
  and steric configuration, 258
Optimum pH, 84
Orcinol, 263
Organs and their functions, 384ff.
Orientation of groups in steroids, 238–239

Ornithine, 29, 154, 170
  and urea cycle, 158, 159
Ornithine carbamoyltransferase, 86
Orotic acid, 119
Orotidine 5'-phosphate, 119
Orthophosphate, transfer of, 102–103
Osazone, formation, 262
  formula of, 262
Osmolarity, 362, 365
Osmosis, 364–367
Osmotic pressure, 364–365
Osmotic work, 365
  HCl production, 385
  in kidney, 386
Osteoblasts, 372
Osteoclasts, 372
Ovaries, 350, 353
Ovulation, 354
Oxalacetate, see Oxaloacetate
Oxalate, 10
  and blood clotting, 66
  and calcium absorption, 371
  from glycine, 167
Oxaloacetate, and aspartate metabolism, 169
  and citrate cycle, 206, 207, 209–211
  key position in metabolism of, 169, 319
  phosphorylation of, 279–281
  from pyruvate, 281, 317
Oxalosuccinate, and citrate cycle, 206, 207
Oxidases, electron-transferring, 201, 202
  facultative, 202
Oxidation, and loss of electrons, 188–190
$\beta$-Oxidation, and energy yield, 218
  of fatty acids, 216–218
  reversal of, 222, 223
$\beta$-Oxidation spiral (cycle), diagram of, 218
Oxidative cleavage of aromatic ring, 202
Oxidative deamination, 156–157
Oxidative decarboxylation, 381
  and aerobiosis, 280
  of amino acids, 159–161
  and lipoic acid, 100–101
  and thiamine pyrophosphate, 111
Oxidative metabolism, in muscle, 390
Oxidative phosphorylation, 199–201, 319, 328
  and quinones, 254
  uncoupling of, 200
Oxidoreductases, partial list, 86
Oxime formation, 262
Oxygen, and cytochrome oxidase, 197
  evolution of, 286, 287
  isotopically labeled, 204
  as oxidizing agent, 188, 201, 202

redox potential of, 192
and respiratory chain, 319
transport in blood, 387
Oxygen-activating enzymes, 201–204
Oxygen transferases, 201, 202–203
Oxygenases, 180, 191
Oxygenases with mixed functions, 202, 203–204
Oxytocin, *see* Ocytocin

**P**

Palmitic acid, formula of, 213
Palmitic aldehyde, 231
Pancreas, 385
and lipases, 215
Pancreatic juice, 385
Pancreozymin, 355
Pantetheine, 106, 107, 382
Pantetheine phosphate, 106, 107
Pantoic acid, 106, 292–293
Pantothenic acid, 93, 154, 379, 382
biosynthesis by plants, 292–293
in coenzyme A, 106–107
Pantoyl-adenosine monophosphate, 292–293
Papain, 147, 149
Paper chromatography, 30–31
Paracasein, 151
Parathormone, 40, 336, 344–345
biologic effects, 344–345
and calcium levels, 372
and kidneys, 388
Parathyroid hormone (parathormone), 40, 336, 344–345
Pars intermedia, 346, 347
Particle size and solutions, table, 57
Pasteur effect, 331
Paucidisperse solutions, 57
Pectin(s), 267, 306
Pellagra, 376, 382
Pellagra-preventive factor, 94, 381
Pellagra sine pellagra, 379, 381
Penicillanic acid, 40
Penicillin, 40–41
Pentose phosphate cycle, 271–273
Pentoses, 258, 264
formation of, 316
Pepsin, 55, 87, 147–149, 151
specificity of, 148
in stomach, 385
Pepsin-inhibitor complex, 148
Pepsinogen, 148
in stomach, 385
Peptidases, and zinc, 373

Peptide bond, 34
cleavage of, 146
interatomic distances in, 46
planarity of, 45
resonance in, 46
Peptide grid, 46, 47
Peptide hormones, 38–40
Peptide and protein hormones, list of, 336
Peptide synthesis, 36
Peptide synthetase, 88
Peptides, 23, 34ff.
amino acid sequence in, 35
definition of, 34
naturally occurring, 37
Peptones, 149
Perinuclear space, 324, 325
Permeability change, and nerve conduction, 394, 395
Peroxidase(s), 185
animal, 180
plant, 180
pH, definition of, 10
and enzyme activity, 84
pH optima of digestive enzymes, 84
pH scale, 11
pH values of body fluids, 368
Phages, 140–141
Phagocytosis, 327
Phalloidin, 41
Phenanthrene, 3, 238
Phenolase, 203, 204
Phenolase complex, 203
Phenolate ion, 8
Phenol oxidase, 190, 203, 204
mechanism of action, 204
Phenols, 8
Phenol sulfuric acid, 104
Phenol treatment of virus particle, 139
Phenylacetate, 161
Phenylalanine, 27
biosynthesis of, by plants, 291–292
catabolism of, 161–162
code word for, 135
formula of, 21
and genetic block, 137
mechanism of hydroxylation, 203
D-Phenylalanine, 41
Phenylhydrazine and monosaccharides, 262
Phenylhydrazone formation, 7
Phenylketonuria, 137
Phenylpyruvate, 161, 291–292

Phenylserine, 30
Pheromones, 358
Phosphatases, 87, 142–145
    acid, 144
    alkaline, 144
    and fat synthesis, 224
Phosphate, metabolism of, 371–372
    and oxidative phosphorylation, 200–201
    and parathormone, 344–345
Phosphate buffer system in blood, 369
Phosphate ester formation, 4
Phosphate esters of monosaccharides, 262
Phosphatidase(s), 231
Phosphatidase A, B, C, and D, 231
Phosphatide biosynthesis and cytidine triphosphate, 106
Phosphatide group transfer, 231
Phosphatides, 154, 199, 225ff.
    classification of, 225–226
    occurrence, 225–226
    table, 226
Phosphatidic acid, 223, 224, 226, 227, 229
Phosphoadenyl sulfate, 93
Phosphocholine, 230
Phosphodiesterases, 231
Phosphoenolpyruvate, 77
    and benzene ring biosynthesis, 291–292
    cleavage of, 75
    $\Delta F°$ of hydrolysis, 77
    and glycolysis, 277
    key intermediate, 317
    from oxaloacetate, 281–282
Phosphoesterases, nonspecific, 144
1-Phosphofructoaldolase, 279, 280
Phosphoglucomutase, 309
    mechanism of action and cofactor of, 309
3-Phosphoglyceraldehyde, 264
Phosphoglycerate, 289
    and gluconeogenesis, 282
2-Phosphoglycerate, 277, 279, 280
3-Phosphoglycerate, and glycolysis, 276, 277
    precursor for phosphoserine, 167
Phosphoglycerate kinase, 276
Phosphoglyceromutase, 277
Phosphoglyceryl phosphate, 77
    $\Delta F°$ of hydrolysis, 77
Phosphohexokinase, 275
Phosphohexose isomerase, 275
Phospholipids, in lipoproteins, 65
    see also Phosphatides
Phosphomonoesterases, 144–145
Phosphopyruvate kinase, 277
5-Phosphoribose 1-pyrophosphate, 103

5-Phosphoribosylamine, 120
Phosphoribosyl pyrophosphate, 119, 120
Phosphorolysis, of nucleoside bond, 145
    of starch and glycogen, 308–310
Phosphorylase, activation of, 309, 310
Phosphorylase a, 309
Phosphorylase b, 309
Phosphorylation, oxidative, 199–201
    and photosynthesis, 285–286
    in respiratory chain, 199–201
Phosphorylcholine, formula of, 106
Phosphoserine, 167, 168
Phosphotriose dehydrogenase, 276
Phosphotriose isomerase, 275, 276
Photolysis of water, 286–288
Photophosphorylation, 285–286
    cyclic, 286
Photosynthesis, 284ff., 290
    definition of, 284–285
Phyllohydroquinone, redox potential of, 192
Phylloquinone reductase, 195
Phylloquinones, 252–255, 379, 380
    formula of, 255
    redox potential of, 192
Phytin, and calcium absorption, 371
Phytoene, 249, 250
Phytofluene, 249
Phytohormones, 358
Phytol, 253
Phytosphingosine, 231
Phytosterols (plant sterols), 241–242
Phytyl side chain, 185, 253
pI, 58
Pineal gland, 344
Pinocytosis, 327
Pipecolate, 169, 170
Piperidine, 3
$\Delta^1$-Piperidine-2-carboxylic acid, 169, 170
Pituitary, see Hypophyseal
Pituitary gland, see Hypophysis
pK, 11
Placenta, 339
Plane of symmetry, 228
Plane-polarized light, 16
Plant hormones, 358–359
Plants, growth substances of, 358–359
Plasma, 61
Plasma fractionation, 62–63
Plasma proteins, 61–66
    molecular dimensions of, 64
    properties of, table, 64
    separation of, 62–63

Plasmal reaction, 228–229
Plasmalogens, 226, 228–229
Plasmin, 66
Plasminogen, 66
Plastoquinone, 196, 252–254, 285, 286
Plastoquinone/Plastohydroquinone system, 285
Platelets, 387
Platinum as catalyst, 72
Pleated-sheet structure, 46, 48
*Pneumococci*, capsular material, 129, 313
    and transformation, 129
Polyacetals, 13
Polyadenylic acid, 132
Polyalcohols, 263
Polyamides, 13
Polydisperse solutions, 57
Polyesters, 13
Polyfructosan, 306
Polyfructoside, formation from sucrose, 301
Polygalacturonic acid, 306
Polymeric compounds, 13
Polyneuritis, 379, 381
Polynucleotide(s), 123, 295
    synthetic, 131, 132, 135
Polypeptide, 34
Polyphasic system, 332
Polyphenylalanine, 135
Polysaccharides, 294ff., 303–306
    breakdown of, 306–309
    classification of, 303
    hydrolysis of, 307–308
    phosphorolysis of, 308–310
Polyuridine, 135
Polyuridylic acid, 132
Pool size, 322
P/O ratio, 200
Porphine, 178
Porphine ring, opened, 182, 183
Porphobilinogen, 175
    formation of, 173, 174
Porphyria, 178
Porphyrin(s), 173ff.
    catalysis by, 179
Porphyrin proteins, function of, table, 180
Porphyrin ring system, 173
    biosynthesis of, 173–178
    as coenzyme, 100
    formation of, 175–178
    isomerism in, 175
Porphyrinogen, 175
Portal vein, 385, 386
Posterior lobe, 346

Potassium, metabolism of, 370
Precalciferol, 243
Precipitation of proteins, 58–59
Prednisone, 337
Pregnancy, 340
Pregnane, 245, 246
Pregnanediol, 339
    and menstruation, 353
Pregnanediol glucuronide, 295
Pregnene-3$\beta$-ol-20-one, 245, 246
Pregnenolones, 339
Prephenic acid, 291, 292
Primary phosphate, 201
Primary structure of proteins, 43–45
Primary urine, 361, 368
Primer DNA, 131
Primer for glycogen synthesis, 310
Primer for RNA polymerase, 131
Proaccelerin, 65
Procarboxypeptidase, 151
Proenzyme, 149
Profibrinolysin, 66
Proflavin, 128
Progesterone, 240, 336, 339
    biosynthesis, 245, 246
    formula of, 246
    and ICSH, 350
    and menstrual cycle, 354–355
Progestins, 338
Projection formulas, 16, 258, 260
Prolactin, 349–350
Prolidase, 152
Proliferation phase in menstrual cycle, 353
Prolinase, 152
Proline, 25
    and blood group substances, 313
    catabolism of, 170–171
    formation of, 170, 171
    formula of, 21
Propanolamine, 154
Propionaldehyde, 220
Propionate, 10
    and valine catabolism, 220
Propionyl coenzyme A, 220, 221
Prosthetic group, definition of, 90–92
    of enzymes, 68
Protamines, 38, 60
Proteases, 146, 147
    classification of, 147
    intracellular (cathepsins), 149
    specificity of, 148
Protein(s), 42ff.
    aggregation of, 55–56

chromatography of, 59
classification of, 42
colloidal nature of, 56–57
complex, and classification of, 61
contractile, in muscle, 391–393
denaturation of, 53–54
determination of amino acid sequence, 43–45
globular, 42
  classification of, 60–61
heat of combustion, 374
immunologic differentiation of, 60
metabolism of, 146ff., 320–321
minimum in diet, 376
molecular weights of, 54–55
  table, 55
plasma, 61–66
precipitation of, 58–59
primary structure of, 43
purification of, 58–59
respiratory quotient, 375
salting-out of, 59
secondary structure of, 45–50
synthesis of, 321
tertiary structure of, 50–53
in urine, 389
Protein biosynthesis, 132–135
Protein metabolism, in liver, 386
Protein synthesis, and ribosomes, 133, 134, 135, 326
Proteinases, 147
Proteolysis, mechanism of, with chymotrypsin, 82, 83
Proteolytic enzymes, 146–152
  specificity of, 148
  table, 147
Prothorax gland of insects, 357
Prothrombin, 65, 66
Protoheme, 185
Protohemin, 185
Protoporphyrinogen, 178
Provitamin(s), 92, 378
Provitamin A, 251, 378
Provitamin D, 241, 378
Pseudouridine, 117, 124
Pteridine ring, 3
  in folic acid, 108
Pterins, 108
Pteroic acid, 109
Pteroylglutamic acid, 109, 382
Pteroylheptaglutamic acid, 109
Puffing of chromosomes, and hormones, 326

Purification of proteins, 58–59
Purine(s), 3, 116
Purine bases, degradation of, 121–122
Purine nucleotides, biosynthesis of, 120–121
Purine ring, formula of, 116
Putrescine, 154, 155
Pylorus, 385
Pyran, 3
Pyranose, 259
Pyridine, 3
Pyridine 3-carboxylic acid, 94
Pyridine nucleotide(s), 94–98, 113, 381
  light absorption spectra of, 96
  and oxidation, 189
Pyridine nucleotide coenzymes, nomenclature of, 316
Pyridinium salt of nicotinamide, 94
Pyridoxal, 112, 380
Pyridoxal phosphate, 93, 112, 113, 152–154, 379, 380
  formula of, 112
  mechanism of action, 152–153
  Schiff's base of, 112
  and serine, 167
Pyridoxamine, 112, 155, 156
Pyridoxamine phosphate, 152, 382
  formula of, 112
Pyridoxine, 93, 112, 379, 382
Pyridoxinic acid, 382
Pyrimidine(s), 3, 116
Pyrimidine ring, biosynthesis of, 119
  formula of, 116
Pyrocatechol, 349
Pyrophosphatase, 103
Pyrophosphate, 77
  and fatty acid activation, 216
  $\Delta F°$ of hydrolysis, 77
  and phosphatide synthesis, 229, 230
  transfer of, 102–103
Pyrophosphate bond, hydrolysis of, 103
Pyrrole rings, 173, 174, 175
Pyrrolidine, 3
Pyrroline carboxylic acid, 170, 176
Pyruvate, 10
  from cysteine, 166
  formation from alanine, 159, 160
    in glycolysis of, 277
  and neuraminate formation, 267
  oxidative decarboxylation of, 160
  and shikimic acid formation, 291
  stereospecific reduction of, 98
  and transamination, 155
Pyruvate decarboxylase (carboxylase), 87, **279**

## Q

. Q-enzyme, 311
Quantum requirements in photosynthesis, 288
Quantum yield, 288
Quaternary ammonium salt, 5
Quinolate ion, 189
Quinoline, 3
Quinolinic acid, 164, 165
Quinone catalysis, 196
Quinone reductase, 199
Quinones (o- and p-), 189, 197
    and respiratory chain, 194

## R

$R$, the gas constant, 70
$R_f$, 31
Racemate, 18
Rachitis, 379, 380
Radical, 4
Radioactive isotopes, 174
Radioactive substances, dilution of, 322
Raffinose, 298
$\beta$-Rays, 174
Reaction specificity, 69, 77–78
Reaction kinetics of enzyme catalysis, 79–81
Redox chain, microsomal, 327
Redox potential, 190–192, 285
    table, 192
Redox scale, zero point of, 181
Redox systems (half-cells), 190
    ascorbate as, 267
    biochemical, table, 192
    biologic, 191
    and photosynthesis, 285–286
    and quinones, 254
    in respiratory chains, 193–194
Reducing properties of disaccharides, 296
Reducing sugars, 263, 296
Reduction equivalents, 286, 287, 316
    in biosynthesis, 97
Reductones, 263
Reference cell, 190
Relaxin, 336, 350
Relaxing factor, 393
Renin, 355
Rennin, 151
Reproductive organs, hormonal control of, 339–340
Resorcinol, 263, 341, 342

Respiration, regulation in mitochondria, 328–330
Respiratory chain, 192–198, 319
    complete diagram, 194
    and dynamic equilibrium, 74
    and NADH$_2$, 97
    and sequence of redox systems, 193–194
Respiratory chain-linked phosphorylation, 319
Respiratory quotient, definition, 375
    formula of, 375
Resting potential, in nerves, 394–395
Resting state of respiratory chain, 198
Retinene, and visual process, 252
11-cis-Retinene, formula of, 251
all-trans-Retinene, formula of, 251
Reversibility of reactions, 71
Rhamnose, 266
    and sterol glycoside, 242
Rhesus factor, 314
Rhodopsin (visual purple), 251–252
Ribitol, 98
Riboflavin, 93, 98, 379, 381
    formula of, 98
    redox potential of, 192
Riboflavin 5-phosphate, 93, 99
Ribonuclease(s), 43, 55, 68, 142–144
Ribonucleic acid (RNA), 124ff.
    alkaline hydrolysis of, 117
    biosynthesis of, 131–132
    messenger, 124, 131, 132, 133, 134, 135, 138
    molecular weights of, 124, 125
    nuclear, 325–326
    and protein synthesis, 132–135
    ribosomal, 132, 133, 134, 135
    soluble, 117, 124, 132, 133, 134, 135
        amino acid activation, 132–133
    structure of, 124, 126
    transfer, see Ribonucleic acid, soluble
Ribonucleic acid polymerase, 131
Ribonucleoprotein particles, 326, 327
Ribose, 264
    in pyridine nucleotides, 94–95
D-Ribose, formula of, 257
    formula and three-dimensional model, 258
$\beta$-D-Ribose, formula of, 115
Ribose phosphate, 264
Ribose 1-phosphate, 119
Ribose 5-phosphate, 103, 266, 270, 271
    and photosynthesis, 290
    and transketolase, 270
Ribose-5-phosphate isomerase, 271

Ribosomal RNA, 132, 133, 134, 135
Ribosomes, 132, 133, 134, 135, 326–327
    activation by messenger RNA, 133, 134
    electron micrograph, 327
    and protein synthesis, 133, 134
5-Ribosyluracil, 117, 118, *see also* Pseudouridine
Ribulose, 264
Ribulose diphosphate, the $CO_2$ acceptor in
    photosynthesis, 289
    formation of, 289–290
Ribulose 5-phosphate, 272, 289
    formation of, 271
    and photosynthesis, 290
Ribulose-5-phosphate epimerase, 87
Rickets, *see* Rachitis
Rigor mortis, 393
Rings of Ranvier, 394
Ring systems, table of, 3
RNA, *see* Ribonucleic acid
Robison ester, *see* Glucose 6-phosphate
Rotenone
    and $NADH_2$ dehydrogenase, 199
Rubber, natural, 237, 254
Rumen, 308

S

Saccharose, *see* Sucrose
Saffron yellow, 250
Salicylate, 53
Salting out of proteins, 59
Salt regulation in fishes, 360
Saponification, 212–213
Saponins, 241–242
Sarcosine, 24, 25, 167, 168
Sarcosomes, 390
Saturated ring system, 2
Schardinger's enzyme, 121
Schiff's base of pyridoxal phosphate, 112, 152, 153
Scleroproteins, 42
    and X-ray diffraction, 45
Sclerotization, in insects, 204
Scotopsin, 252
Scurvy, 379, 383
Secondary structure of proteins, 45–50
Secretin, 355
Secretory phase, and menstrual cycle, 354
Sedimentation constant, 54
Sedoheptulose, 266
Sedoheptulose diphosphate, 290
Sedoheptulose 7-phosphate, 272
    formation of, 270
    and transaldolase, 269

Seliwanoff's test, 263
Semipermeable membrane, 364, 365
Sequence of bases in messenger RNA as code, 134
Serine, 27, 154, 226
    as active formaldehyde donor, 109–110
    and cephalin, 227
    and cysteine metabolism, 166
    formula of, 21
    key metabolite, 321
    metabolism of, 167, 168
    in phosphorylase, 309
    and sphingosine, 231
L-Serine, 16
Serine cephalins, 227
Serine hydroxymethyltransferase, 86
Serotonin, 154, 165, 356
Serum, 62
Serum proteins, separation of, 58, 62–63
Sex attractants, 358
Shikimic acid, 289–290
Shortening, 215
Sialic acid, 311
Sickle-cell anemia, 44
Sickle-cell hemoglobin, 44
    and genes, 137
Siderophilin, 371
Sitosterol, 339
Skatole, 163
Small intestine, 383
Small pox virus, 140
Snake venom, 226, 229
Snake venom phosphatases, 144
Soaps, 211
Sodium, metabolism of, 370
Solanine, 240
Soluble ribonucleic acids, 117, 124, 132, 133, 134, 135
    and amino acid activation, 132, 133
Solutions, kinds of, table, 57
Somatotropin (growth hormone), 336, 348
    and blood glucose, 352
Specific dynamic effect, 375
Specific rotation, 16
Specificity of enzyme catalysis, 77–79
Spermaceti, 215
Spermatogenesis, 350
Sphingolipids, 231–233
    accumulation of, 232
Sphingomyelins, 226, 232
Spingosine, 231–234
    biosynthesis of, 231
Spingosine phosphatides, 232

Spirographis hemin, 185
Spleen, 372
Spontaneous reactions, 70
Spreading factor, 312
Squalene, 237
Squill, and glycosides, 242
Standard change of free energy ($\Delta F°$), 71
Standard free energy ($F°$), 70
    of hydrolysis, table of energy-rich compounds, 77
Standard potential, 191
Starch, 304–306
    phosphorolysis of, 308–310
Steady concentration of a metabolite, 322
Steady state, 73–74
    and respiratory chain, 197–198
Stearic acid, 213
Sterane, 238, 239
Stercobilin, 182, 183
Stercobilinogen, 182
Stereoisomerism, and fatty acids, 214
Stereospecificity in hydrogen transfer, 97–98
Steric configuration of carbohydrates, 257–258
Steroid hormones, 244–248
    biosynthesis of, 244–248
    inactivation of, 247
    list of, 336
    structure of, 244–250
Steroid hydroxylases, 246–247
Steroid oxygenases, 246–247
Steroids, and hydroxylations, 203
    isomerism in, 238–239
    nomenclature of, 238–239
    stereochemistry of, 238–240
    table of, 240
Sterols, 241
    $\Delta^{5,7}$-unsaturated, 378
    in waxes, 215
Stigmasterol, 241
Storage diseases, 232
Streptomycin, 295, 296
Streptose, 295
Stressful factors, and corticoid production, 349
Strontium, radioactive, and bone, 372
Strophanthin, 242, 266
Structure of cell, diagram of, 324
Submaxillary mucin, 313
Substrate, definition of, 68
Substrate constant ($K_s$), 80
Substrate-linked phosphorylation, 276, 277, 316
Substrate specificity, 69, 78–79

Succinate, 10, 14, 15, 220
    and citrate cycle, 206–208, 210, 211
    redox potential, of, 192
    and respiratory chain, 196
    from valine, 160
Succinate dehydrogenase, 79, 195, 196, 209
    and electron-transport particle, 199
Succinate oxidase complex, 196
Succinoarginine, 169
Succinyl coenzyme A, 221
    and citrate cycle, 206, 208
    formation of, 208
    and porphyrin synthesis, 173, 174
Sucrose, 297
    formation of, 302
    formula of, 298
Sucrose 6-phosphate, 302
Sugar(s), see Mono- and Disaccharide(s)
    see also Glucose, Sucrose, etc.
Sulfate, in agar agar, 306
    and mucopolysaccharides, 311, 312
Sulfate group, transfer of, 104
Sulfatides, 226, 232, 233
Sulfonamides, 108–109, 341
Sulfonylaminoglucose, 312
Sulfuric acid, in sphingolipids, 233
Sweat, 389
Synovial fluid, 311
Synthases, 89
Synthetases, 89

T

Tachysterol, 243
Tartaric acid, 10
    and isomerism, 17
Taurine, 29, 30, 166
    and bile acids, 244, 245
Taurocholate, 244, 245
Taurodeoxycholate, 244, 245
Tautomerism, 8
    in pyrimidines, 116
Teichmann's crystals, 180
Temperature and enzyme activity, 85
Template RNA see Messenger RNA
Terminal amino acid analysis, 35
Terminal catabolic pathway (citrate cycle), 318–319
Terminal oxidase, 197
Terpinolene, 235
Tertiary structure of proteins, 50–53
Testes, 338
    and FSH, 350
    and ICSH, 350

Testosterone, 240, 248, 336, 338, 339
  biosynthesis of, 247–248
  formula of, 248
  and ICSH, 350
Tetrahedral structure, 16
Tetrahydrofolate (THF), 93, 108–109, 203, 382
  and histidine catabolism, 171
  and serine, 167, 168
Tetrahydrofuran, 3
Tetrahydropyran, 3
Tetrahydroxyadipate, 265
Tetraiodothyronine, 342
Tetrapyrrole, 175
Tetroses, 258, 264
Theophylline, 122
Thiamine, 93, 379, 380
  formula of, 111
Thiamine pyrophosphate (TPP), 93, 111, 113, 208, 379, 381
  in oxidative decarboxylation, 160
  and pyruvate decarboxylase, 279
  and transketolase, 270
Thiazol ring, 111
Thioclastic cleavage, 107, 217, 220
Thioctic acid, 379, 380, see also Lipoate
Thiocyanate, 341, 342
Thioester(s), 12, 208
  and coenzyme A, 107
  of fatty acids, 216–217
  and high energy, 201
Thionicotinamide, 98
Thiouracil, 342
Thirst, 362
Three-point attachment by citrate to enzyme, 209
Threonine, 27, 154
  and blood group substances, 313
  catabolism of, 167, 168
  formula of, 21
  and isomerism, 17
D-Threose, formula of, 257
Thrombin, 65, 66
Thrombocyte factor, 65
Thrombocytopenia, 38
Thrombokinase, 65, 66
Thymidine, 117, 118
Thymidine 5'-phosphate, 120
Thymine, 116, 117, 118, 123, 125
Thyroacetate, 342
Thyroglobulin, 340–341
Thyroid activity, diagram of, 342
Thyroid gland, 340
  stimulation of, 348

Thyroid hormones, 340–343
Thyronine, 340
Thyropyruvate, 342
Thyrotoxicosis, 342, 343
Thyrotropic hormone, 340, 348
Thyrotropin, 336, 348
Thyroxine, 336, 340
  biologic effect, 342–343
    and inhibitors of protein synthesis, 343
  biosynthesis of, 340
  and growth and development, 343
  metabolism of, 342
  and metamorphosis, 343
  and oxidative phosphorylation, 343
  and swelling of mitochondria, 343
  and thyrotropin, 348
  and tyrosine, 161, 163
Thyroxine-binding globulin (TBG), 342
Tissue hormones, 355–356
TMV, see Tobacco mosaic virus
Toad poisons, and glycosides, 242
Tobacco mosaic virus (TMV), 139, 140
  model of, 140
  phenol treatment of, 139
  protein of, 44
Tocohydroquinone, 253
Tocopherols, 252–253, 255, 379, 380
α-Tocopherol, formula of, 253, 255
α, γ, δ-Tocopherols, 253
Tocoquinone, 253, 255
Topochemistry of cells, 323ff.
Toxins, 40
TPN, see Nicotinamide-adenine dinucleotide phosphate
Trace elements in food, 376
Transaldolase, 269
Transaminases, 87, 155
Transamination, 292
  of amino acids, 155–156
  role of, 320
Transcellular space (body fluids), 361
Transduction, 129
Transfer of phosphatide group, 231
Transfer RNA, see Ribonucleic acid, soluble
Transferases, partial list, 86–87
Transformation, 129
Transglycosidases, 299, 308
Transglycosidation, 299, 309, 311
Transhydrogenation by estrogens, 339
Transketolase reaction, 269–270
  in photosynthesis, 290
  and thiamine pyrophosphate, 112

Transphosphorylation, and action of ribonuclease, 143
Transport metabolites, 97, 195
Transport phenomena and open systems, 74
Trehalose, 297
    formula of, 296
Trehalose 6-phosphate, 302
Trehalose type, 297
Tricarboxylic acid cycle, see Citrate cycle
Triglyceride, formation of, 224
    formula of, 212
$3\alpha,7\alpha,12\alpha$-Trihydroxycholanic acid, 244
Triiodothyronines, 340–341
Trioses, 264
Triose phosphate isomerase, 264
Tripeptide, 34
Triphosphopyridine nucleotide, see Nicotinamide-adenine dinucleotide phosphate
Trisaccharide, 296
Tropocollagen, 50
Tropomyosin, 391
Trypsin, 55, 87, 147, 149, 151
    activation of, 149, 150
    active site of, 150
    mechanism of action, 150
    specificity of, 148
Trypsinogen, 149
Tryptamine, 154
Tryptic digestion, 43
Tryptophan, 27, 154
    biosynthesis of, 292
    catabolism of, 163–165
    formula of, 21
    and melatonin, 344
    and mutation, 136, 137
    oxidation of, 202
Tryptophan oxidase, 202–203
Tryptophan pyrrolase, 165
Turnover number, 81
Two-electron transfer, 189, 195
Tyndall effect, 55
Tyramine, 154, 356
Tyrosinase, 203, 204
    and melanin formation, 163
Tyrosine, 27, 154
    catabolism of, 161–163
    and epinephrine formation, 343, 344
    formation of, 203
    formula of, 21
    and genetic block, 137
    hydroxylation of, 203, 204
    metabolism of, and ecdysone, 358

    oxidation of, 203
    and thyroxine formation, 340

U

Ubichromenols, 254, 255
Ubihydroquinone and respiratory chain, 196
Ubihydroquinone-cytochrome c reductase, 195, 196
Ubiquinone(s), 199, 252–254, 379, 380
    formula of, 254
    and respiratory chain, 195, 196
    and succinate dehydrogenase, 196
Ultracentrifuge and molecular weights, 54–55
Ultrafiltration, 387, 388
    definition of, 387
    and osmosis, 366
Ultraviolet irradiation, 378
Uncoupling agents, 328
Uracil, 116, 117, 118, 119, 124, 129
    degradation of, 119
Urea, 157, 170
    as denaturing agent, 53
    formation of, 171
    and transamination, 156
    in urine, 388
Urea cycle, 157–159, 320
    and aspartic acid, 169
Urease, 55, 68
Ureidovalerate, 158
Uric acid, 121, 122
Uridine, 117, 118
Uridine diphosphate, 93, 113
    as coenzyme, 105
Uridine diphosphate galactose, 301, 302
Uridine diphosphate glucose, 302, 310
    formation and formula of, 105, 300–301
    oxidation of, 302
Uridine diphosphate glucuronate, 302
Uridine 5′-phosphate, 119
Uridine triphosphate, 119, 301
    formula of, 105
Urine, composition of, 388–389
    concentration, 388
    and kidney, 387–389
    pathologic components of, 389
Urobilin, 182, 183
Urobilinogen, 182, 183
Urocanic acid, 171
Urogastrone, 355
Uronic acids, 267, 311
Uroporphyrin I, 175, 176, 178
Uroporphyrin II, 176
Uroporphyrin III, 175, 176, 178, 179

Uroporphyrin IV, 176
Uroporphyrinogen III, formation of, 177, 178
Uterine mucosa, 340
U–U–U, code word for phenylalanine, 135

**V**

$V_{max}$, 80
Vacuole, 324, 327
Vagus substance, 394
Valine, 25, 292
    catabolism of, 160–161
    formula of, 21
    and β-oxidation, 220
Van Dyke protein, 347
Vasotocin, 38
Vasopressin, 336, 346, 347
    formula of, 38
    and kidneys, 388
    physiological effect, 347
    and water balance, 362
Venom of bee, see Bee venom
Venom of snake, see Snake venom
Verdoglobin, 182, 183
Verdoperoxidases, 185
Vinyl groups, 178
Virilism, 338
Virus(es), 138–142
    alive, 139
    and genes, 138
    and host, 138
    and mutation by nitrous acid, 139
Virus particles, composition of, 139
Visual pigments, 252
Visual process, biochemistry of, 251–252
    diagram of, 252
Visual purple, 251–252
Vitamins, 374ff., 377–383
    biocatalytic role of, 92
    classification, 378
    as coenzymes, 92, 93, 377
    deficiency diseases, 377, 379
    definition, 377
    fat soluble, 378–380
        list of, 379
    and genetic defects, 136
    requirements, list of, 379
    table, 379
    water soluble, 381–383
        list of, 379
Vitamin A, 251–252, 378, 379
    deficiency, 378
    requirement, 379

Vitamin A₁, formula of, 251
Vitamin A₂, formula of, 251
Vitamin A aldehyde, 251, 252
Vitamin B₁, 111, 379, 381
    deficiency, 381
    requirement, 379, 381
Vitamin B₂, 98, 379, 381, 382
    deficiencies, 381–382
    requirements, 379
Vitamin B₆, 112, 379, 382
    requirement, 379
Vitamin B₁₂ (cobalamine), 113–114, 220, 379, 382–383
    analogs, 382–383
    deficiency, 383
    formula of, 114
    mechanism of formation, 175
    requirement, 379
Vitamin C, 267, 379, 383
    deficiency, 383
    requirement, 379, 383
Vitamin D, 242–244, 378, 379
    and calcium absorption, 371
    deficiency, 380
    requirement, 379
Vitamins D₂, D₃, 244
Vitamin E, 253, 379, 380
    deficiency, 380
    requirement, 379
    and respiratory chain, 196
Vitamin F, 214, 379, 380
Vitamin H (biotin), 110, 379, 383
    requirement, 379
Vitamin K, 197, 253–255, 379, 380
    and blood clotting, 66
    deficiency, 380
    requirement, 379
    and respiratory chain, 195, 196
Vitamin K₂, 253
Vitamin Q (ubiquinone), 379, 380
Vitreous humor, 311

**W**

Walden inversion, 308
Warburg-Dickens-Horecker pathway, 271–273
Water, distribution of, 361
    formation of, 188, 194, 319
    of oxidation, 361
    photolysis of, 286–288
    reabsorption in kidneys, 387, 388
    regulation of content, 361–362
    roles of, 360–361
    as solvent, 362–367

Water balance, 360–362
Water content, 360–361
Water formation, 194
    energy released, 192–193
Waxes, 213
Wood-Werkman reaction, 281

## X

Xanthine, 121, 122
Xanthine oxidase, 86, 121
Xanthommatin, 136, 165
Xanthophylls, 249
Xanthopterin, 108
Xanthurenic acid, 164–165, 380
Xerophthalmia, 378, 379
X-ray diffraction analysis, of cellulose, 304
    and secondary structure of proteins, 45
    and tertiary structure of proteins, 51
X-ray radiation and mutation, 128
Xylose, and sterol glycoside, 242

D-Xylose, formula of, 257
Xylulose, 264
Xylulose 5-phosphate, 272, 290
    formula and transketolase, 270

## Y

Yeast press juice, 273
Yellow enzymes, 98, 99, 157, 202, 381

## Z

Zeaxanthine, 249
Zero point on redox scale, 191
Zinc, metabolism of, 373
Z-line, 391, 392
Zoosterol, 238
Zwischenferment, 270
Zwitterions, 22
Zymase, 94
Zymogens, 148
Zymosterol, 241